Addison-Wesley Mathematics

Robert E. Eicholz
Phares G. O'Daffer
Charles R. Fleenor

Randall I. Charles
Sharon Young
Carne S. Barnett

Addison-Wesley Publishing Company

Menlo Park, California • Reading, Massachusetts • New York
Don Mills, Ontario • Wokingham, England • Amsterdam • Bonn
Sydney • Singapore • Tokyo • Madrid • Bogotá • Santiago • San Juan

Illustration Acknowledgments

Frank Ansley 38–39, 228–229, 256, 266–267, 302–303, 322–323, 350–351

Sherry Balestra 18, 47, 85, 86, 104, 155, 157, 160–161, 186, 226–227, 262, 306–307, 313, 338, 342–343, 363, 372–373

Ellen Blonder 2, 16–17, 44, 76–77, 101, 102, 105, 124–125, 154, 184–185, 213, 214, 240–241, 217, 246–247, 260, 287–288, 312, 336–337, 361, 362, 378

Elizabeth Callen 20–21, 30–31, 40, 78, 94–95, 132, 142–143, 156, 234–235, 242, 250, 304–305, 348–349, 358–359, 376–377, 380, 384–391

Maxie Chambliss 4, 24–25, 46, 54–55, 82–83, 116–117, 126, 172–173, 206–207, 216, 222–223, 238, 248–249, 274–275, 290, 310–311, 314, 315, 324–325, 364

Randy Chewning 10–11, 97, 120–121, 146–147, 162–163

Rae Ecklund 73, 90

Barry Geller 36–37, 195, 224–225

Jon Goodell 88, 152, 174–175, 196–197, 296–297

Pat Hoggan 12–13, 112–113, 200–201, 215

Susan Jaekel 60, 74–75, 103, 114–115, 118, 130–131, 138–139, 164–165, 187, 192, 278–279, 291, 298–299, 326–327, 339, 346–347, 352–353, 368

Susan Lexa 56, 72, 91, 98–99, 140–141, 180–181, 190–191, 259, 272–273, 308

Jane McCreary 84

Jim M' Guinness 6–7, 110–111, 210–211

Yoshi Miyake 14, 19, 50–51, 150–151, 168–169, 230–231

Deborah Morse 41, 45, 68, 70, 108–109, 127, 208–209, 220–221, 263, 268–269, 270

Dennis Nolan 26–27, 28–29, 34–35, 52–53, 64–65, 96, 136–137, 148–149, 166–167, 176–177, 202–203, 232–233, 252–253, 261, 272 (upper right), 300–301, 320–321, 332–333, 365

Valerie Randall 3, 15, 67, 89, 122–123, 133, 144, 153, 170–171, 182–183, 204–205, 236–237, 258, 280–281, 282–283, 289, 318–319, 328–329, 334–335, 356–357, 370–371, 399–403

Doug Roy 32–33, 62–63, 92, 134–135, 178, 198–199, 254, 285, 294–295, 330–331, 344–345, 354, 374–375

Pat Traub 8–9, 42–43

Stephen Zinkus 1, 23, 49, 81, 107, 129, 159, 189, 219, 245, 265, 293, 317, 341, 367, 383

Cover Photograph
© **Baron Wolman**

Contents

CHAPTER 9 FRACTIONS, 219

CHAPTER 10 ADDITION AND SUBTRACTION OF FRACTIONS, 245

CHAPTER 11 GEOMETRY AND GRAPHING, 265

CHAPTER 12 MULTIPLICATION: 2-Digit Factors, 293

Maria likes to watch the stars. Her grandfather knows a lot about stars. He shows her groups of stars called constellations. The constellation Orion appears in winter. A row of bright stars makes his belt. A red star is on his shoulder. It is called Betelgeuse. A blue-white star is on his foot. It is called Rigel. Maria saw 7 bright stars in Orion. She saw 8 of the fainter stars. Greek stories tell about Orion. He boasted about being such a good hunter. He was punished by the gods. The Scorpion was sent after him. The Scorpion appears in the summer sky.

Addition Facts

Joan is learning the names of some of her teeth. Her front teeth are made up of 8 incisors and 4 canines. How many front teeth does Joan have?

Since we want the total amount, we add.

$$8 + 4 = 12$$

Addend   Addend   Sum

$$\begin{array}{r} 8 \leftarrow \text{Addend} \\ + 4 \leftarrow \text{Addend} \\ \hline 12 \leftarrow \text{Sum} \end{array}$$

Joan has 12 front teeth.

Warm Up Read each equation aloud and give the sum.

Example We read $9 + 5 = 14$ as **"Nine plus five equals fourteen."**

1. $5 + 9 = n$
2. $8 + 4 = n$
3. $6 + 7 = n$
4. $6 + 5 = n$

5. $2 + 8 = n$
6. $1 + 9 = n$
7. $3 + 6 = n$
8. $8 + 7 = n$

9. $9 + 4 = n$
10. $9 + 7 = n$
11. $7 + 7 = n$
12. $6 + 6 = n$

13. $5 + 3 = n$
14. $7 + 3 = n$
15. $0 + 3 = n$
16. $6 + 4 = n$

17. $6 + 9 = n$
18. $3 + 5 = n$
19. $5 + 7 = n$
20. $4 + 7 = n$

21. $8 + 3 = n$
22. $8 + 6 = n$
23. $5 + 0 = n$
24. $8 + 5 = n$

Practice Add.

1. $5 + 6$
2. $2 + 3$
3. $6 + 8$
4. $6 + 4$
5. $8 + 5$
6. $2 + 0$
7. $4 + 4$

8. $7 + 8$
9. $3 + 6$
10. $5 + 2$
11. $3 + 8$
12. $9 + 8$
13. $5 + 3$
14. $4 + 2$

15. $9 + 3$
16. $0 + 8$
17. $8 + 8$
18. $3 + 7$
19. $9 + 9$
20. $4 + 8$
21. $8 + 2$

22. $3 + 4$
23. $4 + 9$
24. $9 + 7$
25. $9 + 2$
26. $5 + 5$
27. $7 + 4$
28. $6 + 8$

29. $3 + 3$
30. $7 + 2$
31. $7 + 5$
32. $9 + 5$

33. $1 + 6$
34. $6 + 7$
35. $7 + 7$
36. $0 + 7$

37. Find the sum of 9 and 6.

38. Find the sum of 4 and 6.

Mixed Applications

39. Jim's back teeth are made up of 8 bicuspids and 6 molars. How many back teeth does Jim have?

40. **DATA HUNT** Count your upper and lower front teeth. How many of each? How many in all?

41. Write a story problem that you can solve with this equation. $8 + 2 = n$.

THINK

Estimation

Choose the best estimate.

1. About how many oranges are in the full box?

A 40 B 400 C 4,000

2. About how many oranges are in the full truck?

A 40 B 400 C 4,000

MATH

More Practice, page 404, Set A

3

Subtraction Facts

Jack baked 15 large dinner rolls. There were 8 people at the dinner. Each person ate 1 roll.

Take Away

How many rolls were left?

To find how many are left, we subtract.

$$\begin{array}{r} 15 \\ -\ 8 \\ \hline 7 \end{array}$$ $\longleftarrow$ Difference

$$15 - 8 = 7$$

There were 7 rolls left.

Compare

How many more rolls were there than people?

To find how many more (fewer), we subtract.

$$\begin{array}{r} 15 \\ -\ 8 \\ \hline 7 \end{array}$$ $\longleftarrow$ Difference

$$15 - 8 = 7$$

There were 7 more rolls than people.

Warm Up Read each equation aloud and give the difference.

Example We read $12 - 8 = 4$ as **"Twelve minus eight equals four."**

1. $15 - 7 = n$ 2. $10 - 5 = n$ 3. $14 - 9 = n$ 4. $13 - 4 = n$

5. $14 - 7 = n$ 6. $13 - 8 = n$ 7. $12 - 4 = n$ 8. $16 - 9 = n$

9. $8 - 5 = n$ 10. $17 - 8 = n$ 11. $15 - 6 = n$ 12. $6 - 6 = n$

13. $16 - 8 = n$ 14. $7 - 0 = n$ 15. $9 - 7 = n$ 16. $14 - 8 = n$

17. $13 - 7 = n$ 18. $11 - 4 = n$ 19. $11 - 8 = n$ 20. $12 - 9 = n$

21. $15 - 9 = n$ 22. $10 - 7 = n$ 23. $14 - 5 = n$ 24. $12 - 5 = n$

Practice Subtract.

1. 15
 − 8

2. 10
 − 3

3. 13
 − 5

4. 6
 − 0

5. 16
 − 8

6. 11
 − 7

7. 11
 − 5

8. 14
 − 8

9. 15
 − 9

10. 10
 − 4

11. 12
 − 9

12. 9
 − 9

13. 13
 − 6

14. 12
 − 8

15. 17
 − 9

16. 7
 − 5

17. 11
 − 9

18. 15
 − 6

19. 18
 − 9

20. 8
 − 3

21. 13
 − 8

22. 12
 − 5

23. 10
 − 6

24. 9
 − 4

25. 8 − 2

26. 10 − 5

27. 14 − 5

28. 12 − 4

29. 13 − 7

30. 16 − 7

31. 11 − 6

32. 17 − 8

33. Subtract 7 from 15.

34. Subtract 8 from 11.

35. Subtract 2 from 10.

Mixed Applications

36. Janet made 12 cornsticks. Her family ate 9. How many were left?

37. Ted baked 16 muffins and 8 rolls. How many more muffins did he bake?

38. Roberta baked 7 blueberry muffins. She also baked 4 cherry muffins. How many muffins did she bake altogether?

THINK

Logical Reasoning

Study this figure.

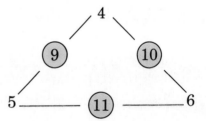

Give the missing addends.

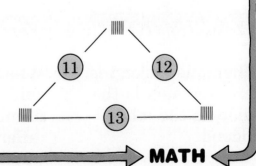

➡ **MATH** ⬅

Addition and Subtraction

Addition and subtraction are related. For two different addends and their sum, there are two addition facts and two subtraction facts.

The fact family helps us see a special property of addition.

Addend	Addend	Sum
8	6	14

Fact Family

$$8 + 6 = 14$$
$$6 + 8 = 14$$
$$14 - 6 = 8$$
$$14 - 8 = 6$$

Order Property +

When the order of the addends is changed, the sum stays the same.

When 0 is an addend, the fact family helps us see some special properties of zero.

Addend	Addend	Sum
7	0	7

Fact Family

$$7 + 0 = 7$$
$$0 + 7 = 7$$
$$7 - 0 = 7$$
$$7 - 7 = 0$$

Zero Property +

When one addend is zero, the sum is the same as the other addend.

Zero Property −

When zero is subtracted from a number, the difference is the number.

Zero Property −

When a number is subtracted from itself, the difference is zero.

Practice Find the sums and differences.

1. 6 + 7
    7 + 6
    13 − 7
    13 − 6

2. 9 + 0
    0 + 9
    9 − 0
    9 − 9

3. 7
  + 7

4. 8
  + 6

5. 5
  + 6

6. 2
  + 0

7. 9
  + 7

8. 3
  + 8

9. 15
  − 9

10. 12
  − 4

11. 18
  − 9

12. 11
  − 3

13. 8
  − 0

14. 6
  − 6

15. 6
  + 0

16. 9
  − 3

17. 12
  − 7

18. 3
  + 4

19. 13
  − 6

20. 11
  − 7

21. 14
  − 6

22. 6
  + 9

23. 0
  + 3

24. 17
  − 8

25. 8
  − 8

26. 5
  + 9

Write four equations for each
set of fact-family numbers.

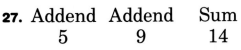

27. Addend   Addend   Sum
       5   9   14

28. Addend   Addend   Sum
       0   8   8

29. Addend   Addend   Sum
       3   4   7

30. Addend   Addend   Sum
       6   1   7

THINK

Guess and Check

Find the hidden addends. Their
difference is 1.

Addend   Addend   Sum

 +  = 15

MATH

7

PROBLEM SOLVING ★ The **5**-Point Checklist

To solve a problem

★ 1. Understand the Question
★ 2. Find the needed Data
★ 3. Plan what to do
★ 4. Find the Answer
★ 5. Check back

Use the 5-Point Checklist to help you solve the following problem.

Jim's family had a garage sale.
They had 14 old books to sell.
Only 8 of them were sold.
How many were not sold?

1. Understand the QUESTION
How many books were left?

2. Find the needed DATA
Had 14 books. Sold 8.

3. PLAN what to do
We want the number of books left.
We should subtract.

4. Find the ANSWER
14 − 8 = 6   6 books were not sold.

5. CHECK back
Read the problem again.
6 seems about right.

Solve. Use the 5-Point Checklist.

1. Paul took $10 to the sale. He spent $6 for books. How much does he have left?

2. Mary sold a lamp for $8 and a doll for $3. How much money did Mary make?

Solve.

1. Mr. Lambert had 4 bow ties and 8 regular ties for sale. How many ties did he have?

2. Mrs. Lambert had 15 glasses to sell. She sold 8 of them. How many were left?

3. Jim put a price of $8 on a ball glove. He put a price of $2 on a small bat. How much more money was the glove than the bat?

4. The sale lasted 3 hours in the morning and 4 hours in the afternoon. How long did the sale last?

5. An old chair was priced at $13. It did not sell in the morning. Mrs. Lambert took $4 off the price. How much was the chair then?

6. Jim had 14 comic books to sell. A friend bought 5 of them. How many were left after the sale?

7. Mr. Lambert sold a radio for $9 and a hand saw for $4. How much did he get for these two sales?

★ 8. Mary sold 5 records for $6. She was paid with a $10 bill. How much change should she return?

9

Practice the Facts

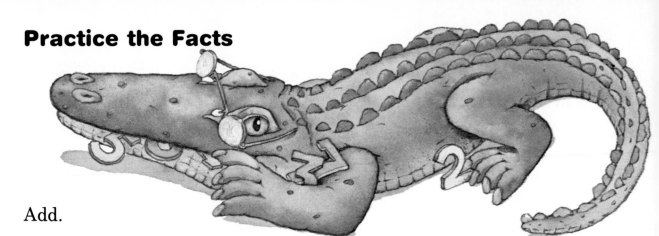

Add.

1. 4
   + 5

2. 7
   + 6

3. 3
   + 5

4. 9
   + 8

5. 6
   + 6

6. 4
   + 6

7. 7
   + 8

8. 6
   + 3

9. 3
   + 7

10. 7
    + 7

11. 5
    + 8

12. 4
    + 7

13. 3
    + 2

14. 4
    + 8

15. 5
    + 9

16. 8
    + 0

17. 9
    + 2

18. 4
    + 3

19. 9
    + 1

20. 8
    + 8

21. 6
    + 5

22. 5
    + 8

23. 7
    + 9

24. 0
    + 6

25. 9
    + 9

26. 8
    + 6

27. 5
    + 5

28. 7
    + 5

Subtract.

29. 14
    − 7

30. 15
    − 7

31. 10
    − 3

32. 12
    − 4

33. 7
    − 0

34. 16
    − 9

35. 11
    − 2

36. 13
    − 6

37. 10
    − 4

38. 17
    − 8

39. 18
    − 9

40. 6
    − 2

41. 12
    − 7

42. 15
    − 6

43. 16
    − 8

44. 12
    − 0

45. 11
    − 6

46. 9
    − 4

47. 10
    − 5

48. 14
    − 5

49. 7
    − 2

50. 13
    − 5

51. 14
    − 8

52. 11
    − 8

53. 8
    − 5

54. 10
    − 3

55. 12
    − 6

56. 10
    − 8

Practice Add or subtract.

1. $\begin{array}{r} 6 \\ + 4 \\ \hline 10 \end{array}$ **2.** $\begin{array}{r} 11 \\ - 3 \\ \hline 8 \end{array}$ **3.** $\begin{array}{r} 15 \\ - 8 \\ \hline 7 \end{array}$ **4.** $\begin{array}{r} 8 \\ + 8 \\ \hline 16 \end{array}$ **5.** $\begin{array}{r} 9 \\ + 7 \\ \hline 16 \end{array}$ **6.** $\begin{array}{r} 12 \\ - 8 \\ \hline 4 \end{array}$

7. $\begin{array}{r} 15 \\ - 8 \\ \hline 7 \end{array}$ **8.** $\begin{array}{r} 13 \\ - 7 \\ \hline 6 \end{array}$ **9.** $\begin{array}{r} 2 \\ + 9 \\ \hline 11 \end{array}$ **10.** $\begin{array}{r} 0 \\ + 7 \\ \hline 7 \end{array}$ **11.** $\begin{array}{r} 11 \\ - 5 \\ \hline 6 \end{array}$ **12.** $\begin{array}{r} 14 \\ - 6 \\ \hline 8 \end{array}$

13. $\begin{array}{r} 5 \\ + 7 \\ \hline 12 \end{array}$ **14.** $\begin{array}{r} 16 \\ - 7 \\ \hline 9 \end{array}$ **15.** $\begin{array}{r} 5 \\ + 4 \\ \hline 9 \end{array}$ **16.** $\begin{array}{r} 16 \\ - 8 \\ \hline 8 \end{array}$ **17.** $\begin{array}{r} 7 \\ + 3 \\ \hline 10 \end{array}$ **18.** $\begin{array}{r} 15 \\ - 9 \\ \hline 6 \end{array}$

19. $\begin{array}{r} 8 \\ + 5 \\ \hline 13 \end{array}$ **20.** $\begin{array}{r} 7 \\ + 7 \\ \hline 14 \end{array}$ **21.** $\begin{array}{r} 12 \\ - 7 \\ \hline 5 \end{array}$ **22.** $\begin{array}{r} 13 \\ - 5 \\ \hline 8 \end{array}$ **23.** $\begin{array}{r} 10 \\ - 7 \\ \hline 3 \end{array}$ **24.** $\begin{array}{r} 11 \\ + 0 \\ \hline 11 \end{array}$

25. $14 - 9$ 5 **26.** $8 + 9$ 17 **27.** $6 + 6$ 12 **28.** $18 - 9$ 9

29. $6 + 0$ 6 **30.** $8 + 1$ 9 **31.** $11 - 8$ 3 **32.** $9 - 2$ 7

33. $14 - 8$ 6 **34.** $5 - 0$ 5 **35.** $15 - 6$ 9 **36.** $6 - 1$ 5

THINK

Patterns

Guess each rule. Then give the missing numbers.

Sara said	José answered
3	11
5	13
7	15
37. 4	|||||
38. |||||	14

José said	Sara answered
10	4
12	6
9	3
39. 7	|||||
40. |||||	9

Sara said	José answered
2	4
4	8
3	6
5	10
41. 8	|||||

MATH

Three Addends

Don planted flowers in a window box. He planted 5 short purple flowers, 3 tall purple flowers, and 6 tall yellow flowers. How many flowers did Don plant?

$$(5 + 3) + 6$$
$$8 + 6 = 14$$

↑ Purple   ↑ Yellow   ↑ In all

$$5 + (3 + 6)$$
$$5 + 9 = 14$$

↑ Short   ↑ Tall   ↑ In all

Don planted 14 flowers.

Grouping Property +

When you add, you can change the grouping and the sum stays the same.

Other Examples

$9 + 3 = 12$

$$(4 + 5) + 3 = 12$$

Adding Down

$$\begin{array}{r} 2 \\ 4 \\ + 5 \\ \hline 11 \end{array}$$

6 and 5 more make 11.

$4 + 8 = 12$

$$4 + (5 + 3) = 12$$

Adding Up

$$\begin{array}{r} 2 \\ 4 \\ + 5 \\ \hline 11 \end{array}$$

9 and 2 more make 11.

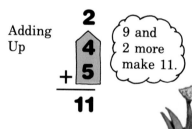

Warm Up Add.

1. $6 + 2 + 3 = n$ 2. $5 + 4 + 1 = n$ 3. $3 + 6 + 3 = n$

4. $\begin{array}{r} 2 \\ 4 \\ + 3 \\ \hline \end{array}$
5. $\begin{array}{r} 5 \\ 5 \\ + 4 \\ \hline \end{array}$
6. $\begin{array}{r} 3 \\ 6 \\ + 2 \\ \hline \end{array}$
7. $\begin{array}{r} 5 \\ 4 \\ + 5 \\ \hline \end{array}$
8. $\begin{array}{r} 6 \\ 2 \\ + 5 \\ \hline \end{array}$
9. $\begin{array}{r} 4 \\ 4 \\ + 6 \\ \hline \end{array}$
10. $\begin{array}{r} 3 \\ 5 \\ + 3 \\ \hline \end{array}$

Practice Add.

1. 2
    3
  + 2

2. 4
    1
  + 3

3. 6
    1
  + 7

4. 4
    5
  + 0

5. 3
    7
  + 2

6. 7
    1
  + 8

7. 6
    2
  + 2

8. 5
    4
  + 3

9. 2
    1
  + 4

10. 6
    4
  + 6

11. 3
    3
  + 3

12. 2
    8
  + 2

Add. Look for tens.

13. 2
    7
  + 3

14. 8
    1
  + 2

15. 6
    4
  + 5

16. 5
    3
  + 5

17. 3
    2
  + 7

18. 9
    1
  + 1

19. 4
    2
  + 6

20. $5 + 2 + 5$

21. $4 + 6 + 3$

22. $2 + 0 + 8$

23. $4 + 2 + 6$

24. $7 + 3 + 3$

25. $4 + 5 + 5$

Mixed Applications

26. Karen planted 6 yellow flowers, 3 blue flowers, and 4 pink flowers. How many flowers did she plant?

27. Danny picked 9 red roses. He gave 3 of them to his sister. How many roses did he keep?

SKILLKEEPER

Add or subtract.

1. 3
  + 5

2. 4
  + 7

3. 13
  − 6

4. 5
  + 2

5. 14
  − 8

6. 17
  − 9

7. 8
  + 8

8. 12
  − 7

9. 15
  − 8

10. 3
  + 4

11. 9
  + 5

12. 10
  − 4

PROBLEM SOLVING
Understanding the Question

To solve any problem, you must **understand the question.** You could ask an addition or a subtraction question about the data on the card.

> DATA CARD
> Amy earned 9 dollars for baby-sitting. She earned 5 dollars for doing dishes.

Addition   How much did Amy earn for both jobs?

Subtraction   How much more did Amy earn for baby-sitting than doing dishes?

Write an addition or a subtraction question for each DATA CARD. Solve your problem.

1.
> DATA CARD
> Larry had 7 dollars. He earned 3 dollars for mowing the lawn.

2.
> DATA CARD
> Molly has 8 dollars in her bank. She has 5 dollars hidden in her desk.

3.
> DATA CARD
> Hank earned 7 dollars for cleaning house. He already had 6 dollars.

4.
> DATA CARD
> Dora spent 6 dollars for a record. She also bought a book for 10 dollars.

PROBLEM SOLVING
Using Data from a Graph

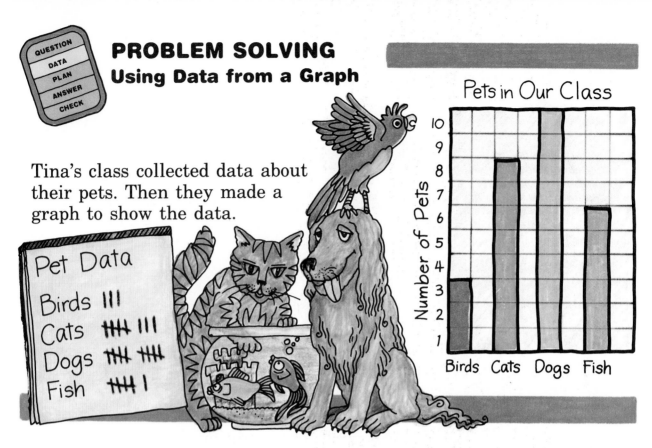

Tina's class collected data about their pets. Then they made a graph to show the data.

Pet Data

Birds III
Cats ₵₵₵ III
Dogs ₵₵₵ ₵₵₵
Fish ₵₵₵ I

Pets in Our Class

1. How many dogs do the students in Tina's class have?

2. How many cats do they have?

3. How many dogs and cats do they have?

4. How many more cats are there than birds?

5. How many cats and fish are there?

6. How many more dogs are there than birds?

7. Three squares are colored for Sue's 3 dogs. How many dogs does the rest of the class have?

8. How many birds, cats, and fish are there?

9. Ben's cat had 4 kittens. How many cats does the class have now?

10. **DATA HUNT** How many pet dogs does your class have? How many pet cats do they have? Find the difference between the number of cats and the number of dogs.

15

PROBLEM-SOLVING STRATEGY
Choose the Operations

QUESTION
DATA
PLAN
ANSWER
CHECK

SOME PROBLEMS CAN BE SOLVED BY USING JUST ONE OPERATION. FOR OTHER PROBLEMS, YOU MAY NEED MORE THAN ONE OPERATION. A STRATEGY THAT CAN HELP YOU IS SHOWN BELOW.

Try This Mary saved $7. She earned $6 more. She spent $4 to fix her bicycle. How much money does Mary have left?

CHOOSE THE OPERATIONS

PUT TOGETHER $\longrightarrow$ Choose addition.

TAKE AWAY $\longrightarrow$ Choose subtraction.

COMPARE $\longrightarrow$ Choose subtraction.

Mary saved $7. She earned $6 more.

I'll add to find how much she has altogether.

$7 + $6 = $13

Now Mary has $13. She spent $4.

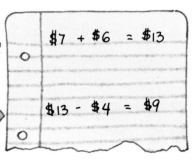

I'll subtract to find how much she has left.

$13 - $4 = $9

Mary has $9 left.

Solve.

1. Steve has saved $11. He bought a record for $5. Then he earned $7 more. How much money does he have now?

2. Jack has $12. Sue has $15. Sue spends $7. Jack does not spend any money. Now how much more money does Jack have than Sue?

Find the sums.

1. 3
+ 6

2. 8
+ 6

3. 7
+ 6

4. 7
+ 5

5. 2
+ 5

6. 7
+ 8

7. 4
+ 2

8. 5
+ 8

9. 5
+ 3

10. 9
+ 0

11. 3
+ 9

12. 3
+ 8

13. 8
+ 9

14. 7
+ 3

Find the differences.

15. 12
− 8

16. 16
− 8

17. 4
− 0

18. 10
− 3

19. 14
− 6

20. 15
− 6

21. 12
− 8

22. 14
− 8

23. 12
− 5

24. 8
− 4

25. 17
− 9

26. 6
− 2

27. 14
− 7

28. 6
− 6

Find the sums.

29. 6
2
+ 4

30. 3
2
+ 3

31. 5
0
+ 1

32. 2
8
+ 2

33. 3
4
+ 3

Solve.

34. Sam sold a skateboard for 6 dollars and a baseball for 3 dollars. How much did he get for both?

35. Debra had 11 comic books to sell. Sheri bought 4 of them. How many comic books does Debra have left?

36. Brian made 8 dollars. Julie made 14 dollars. How much less money did Brian make than Julie?

37. The children in Ken's class have 7 dogs and 9 cats. How many dogs and cats are there in all?

The "doubles" may help you remember the facts.

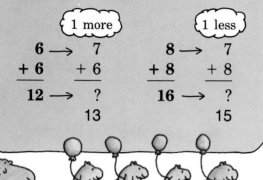

	1 more		1 less
6 →	7	8 →	7
+ 6	+ 6	+ 8	+ 8
12 →	?	16 →	?
	13		15

Thinking of addition may help you with subtraction.

		6			7
13		?	15		?
− 7		+ 7	− 8		+ 8
?		13	?		15
6			7		

5
3
+ 4   5 + 3 = 8
?   and 4 more
12   8 + 4
        make 12.

Find the sums.

1.	8	**2.**	6	**3.**	7
	+ 7		+ 7		+ 3

4.	5	**5.**	9	**6.**	5
	+ 6		+ 8		+ 9

7.	8	**8.**	2	**9.**	8
	+ 6		+ 8		+ 4

Find the differences.

10.	14	**11.**	11	**12.**	13
	− 6		− 6		− 8

13.	12	**14.**	17	**15.**	10
	− 7		− 9		− 3

16.	13	**17.**	14	**18.**	9
	− 4		− 9		− 7

Find the sums.

19.	2	**20.**	8	**21.**	5
	7		1		5
	+ 2		+ 2		+ 5

Logical Reasoning

This game is for two players.

1. Use a figure like the one shown to the right.

2. One player uses the odd digits: 1, 3, 5, 7, and 9. The other player uses the even digits: 0, 2, 4, 6, and 8.

3. The player with odd digits goes first. Players then take turns writing one of their digits in a square. Each digit can be used only once.

4. The winner is the player who can write a digit that gives a sum of 15 for any complete row, column, or diagonal.

Here are some sample games.

You have the even digits and it is your turn. Where can you place a digit to **win**? Try this game with a partner.

You have the odd digits and it is now your turn. Where should you place a digit to **block** the other player?

A calculator can help you solve problems.

Example

A hot-air balloon can lift 200 pounds. Kara weighs 64 pounds, Jason weighs 75 pounds, and Chad weighs 60 pounds. Can the children ride in the balloon at the same time?

Plan the Solution Add the children's weights.

Write Out the Plan 64 + 75 + 60 =

Carry Out the Plan Turn the calculator ON.

Press 6 →Press 4 →Press + →Press 7 →
Press 5 →Press + →Press 6 →Press 0 →Press =

The calculator shows 199.

Check the Answer

$$\begin{array}{r} 64 \\ 75 \\ + 60 \\ \hline 199 \end{array}$$

The children together weigh less than 200 pounds. They can ride in the balloon at the same time.

Remember to press CLEAR c before you begin the next problem.

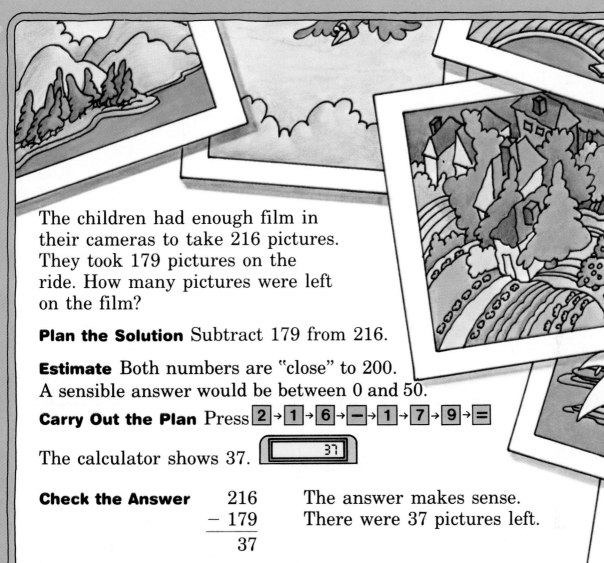

The children had enough film in their cameras to take 216 pictures. They took 179 pictures on the ride. How many pictures were left on the film?

Plan the Solution Subtract 179 from 216.

Estimate Both numbers are "close" to 200. A sensible answer would be between 0 and 50.

Carry Out the Plan Press 2 → 1 → 6 → − → 1 → 7 → 9 → =

The calculator shows 37. `37`

Check the Answer

$$\begin{array}{r} 216 \\ -\ 179 \\ \hline 37 \end{array}$$

The answer makes sense. There were 37 pictures left.

Plan the solution to these problems.
Estimate the answers. Do your estimates make sense?
Use a calculator to help carry out the plan.

1. What is the sum of 392, 4,012, and 573?

2. Subtract 187 from 4,830.

3. Jody had 47 horses. She sold 24. How many were left?

4. Add 28, 999, and 1,407.

5. What is the difference between 592 and 386?

6. Is 100 dollars enough money to buy a coat for 58 dollars and shoes for 52 dollars?

CUMULATIVE REVIEW

Give the letter for the correct answer.

1. $6 + 2 = n$
- **A** 9
- **B** 4
- **C** 8
- **D** not given

2. $5 + 7 = n$
- **A** 12
- **B** 11
- **C** 13
- **D** not given

3. $9 + 0 = n$
- **A** 0
- **B** 9
- **C** 90
- **D** not given

4. $14 - 7 = n$
- **A** 8
- **B** 5
- **C** 6
- **D** not given

5. $8 - 8 = n$
- **A** 16
- **B** 8
- **C** 0
- **D** not given

6. $16 - 7 = n$
- **A** 8
- **B** 9
- **C** 7
- **D** not given

7.
$$\begin{array}{r} 8 \\ + 3 \\ \hline \end{array}$$
- **A** 11
- **B** 5
- **C** 10
- **D** not given

8.
$$\begin{array}{r} 6 \\ + 9 \\ \hline \end{array}$$
- **A** 15
- **B** 16
- **C** 17
- **D** not given

9.
$$\begin{array}{r} 5 \\ + 4 \\ \hline \end{array}$$
- **A** 1
- **B** 9
- **C** 8
- **D** not given

10.
$$\begin{array}{r} 10 \\ - 3 \\ \hline \end{array}$$
- **A** 7
- **B** 8
- **C** 6
- **D** not given

11.
$$\begin{array}{r} 18 \\ - 9 \\ \hline \end{array}$$
- **A** 8
- **B** 9
- **C** 7
- **D** not given

12.
$$\begin{array}{r} 15 \\ - 6 \\ \hline \end{array}$$
- **A** 7
- **B** 8
- **C** 9
- **D** not given

13. Travis sold a game for 2 dollars and a picture for 3 dollars. How much did Travis get for both?
- **A** $1
- **B** $6
- **C** $5
- **D** not given

14. Cheryl had 9 dollars. She bought a basketball for 6 dollars. How much did she have left?
- **A** $17
- **B** $3
- **C** $2
- **D** not given

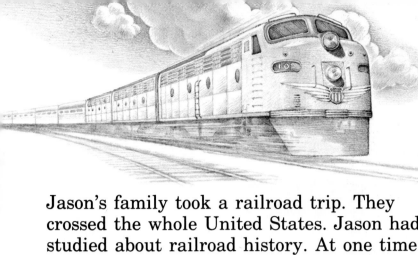

Jason's family took a railroad trip. They crossed the whole United States. Jason had studied about railroad history. At one time eastern rail lines ended in Nebraska. They did not cross the West. America needed a railroad connecting both coasts. Jason learned how this railroad was built. Separate groups laid tracks from either end. Some workers started in California. They crossed the Sierra Nevada Mountains. They laid 1,110 km of track. Other workers started in Nebraska. They crossed the Rocky Mountains. They laid 1,738 km of track. The tracks were joined in Utah in 1869.

Hundreds, Tens, and Ones

These models are used to help you understand numbers.

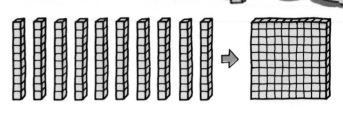

ten ones → one ten (10)   ten tens → one hundred (100)

0, 1, 2, 3, 4, 5, 6, 7, 8, and 9 are called **digits.** We use digits and **place value** to write large numbers.

We see numbers in **standard form.**

243

The model below shows the meaning of 243.

2 hundreds, **4** tens, and **3** ones = **243**
We read, **"two hundred forty-three."**

Warm Up   Read each number. Tell the meaning of the red digit.

Example   456   four hundred fifty-six   The 5 means 5 tens.

1. 362   2. 739   3. 19   4. 402   5. 924

6. 437   7. 806   8. 36   9. 791   10. 91

11. 520   12. 348   13. 143   14. 43   15. 500

16. 677   17. 908   18. 455   19. 380   20. 813

Practice Write the standard number for each picture.

1.

2.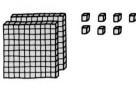

3.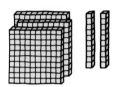

4.

5.

6.

Write the standard number. Be careful!

7. 5 hundreds
6 tens
4 ones

8. 3 tens
7 hundreds
9 ones

9. 6 ones
4 tens

10. 4 hundreds
0 tens
3 ones

11. 7 tens
0 ones
4 hundreds

Write the standard number.

12. two hundred sixty-seven

13. three hundred eighty-four

14. seven hundred three

15. one hundred sixty

16. four hundred ninety-nine

17. five hundred twenty

THINK

Work Backward

1. I have three digits.
2. My hundreds' digit is the sum of my tens' digit and ones' digit.
3. My ones' digit is 3 more than my tens' digit.
4. My tens' digit is 2.

WHO AM I?

MATH

Thousands

The models below may help you understand larger numbers.

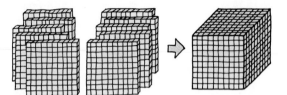

ten hundreds   **one thousand (1,000)**

The Great Wall of China is the longest wall in the world. It is 1,684 miles long.

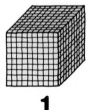 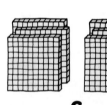 

1	**6**	**8**	**4**
thousand	hundreds	tens	ones

We read, **"one thousand, six hundred eighty-four."**

Warm Up Read each number. Tell the meaning of the red digit.

1. 2,515
2. 4,612
3. 1,704
4. 5,061
5. 3,948

6. 9,323
7. 2,406
8. 6,280
9. 8,729
10. 5,952

11. 4,003
12. 1,691
13. 3,545
14. 2,130
15. 8,017

16. 2,336
17. 5,277
18. 4,094
19. 1,800
20. 3,563

21. 6,008
22. 1,408
23. 2,889
24. 3,070
25. 7,153

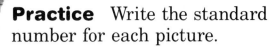

Practice Write the standard number for each picture.

1.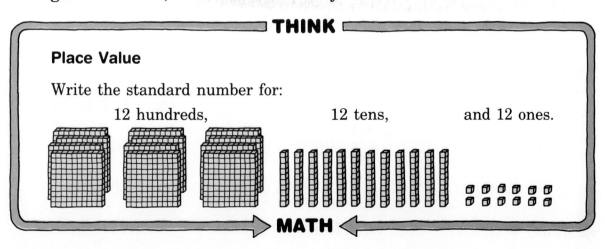

2.

3.

Write the standard number.

4. 3 thousand
2 hundreds
5 tens
9 ones

5. 2 tens
6 hundreds
4 ones
1 thousand

6. 5 hundreds
7 ones
0 tens
4 thousand

7. six thousand, seven hundred eighty-three

8. four thousand, two hundred three

9. eight thousand, five hundred thirty

THINK

Place Value

Write the standard number for:

12 hundreds,   12 tens,   and 12 ones.

MATH

Comparing and Ordering

Mt. Baker and Glacier Peak are volcanoes in Washington State. Mt. Baker is 3,285 m high and Glacier Peak is 3,213 m. Which volcano is higher?

To find which of two numbers is greater, you compare their digits.

Start at the left. Find the first place where the digits are different.	Compare these digits. Which digit is greater?	The numbers compare the same way the digits compare.
3,285 3,213	8 is greater than 1 8 > 1	3,285 is greater than 3,213 3,285 > 3,213

Mt. Baker is higher than Glacier Peak.

Other Examples

Remember: The "arrow" points to the smaller number.

486 is greater than 483   6,275 is less than 6,342
486 > 483   6,275 < 6,342

Warm Up   Write > or < for each ▦.

1. 426 ▦ 430

2. 715 ▦ 695

3. 867 ▦ 864

4. 3,269 ▦ 3,400

5. 5,280 ▦ 5,279

6. 7,563 ▦ 7,463

7. 4,082 ▦ 3,999

8. 3,794 ▦ 4,079

9. 6,280 ▦ 6,267

10. 4,000 ▦ 3,989

11. 3,756 ▦ 3,821

12. 4,987 ▦ 5,000

Practice

Write > or < for each ⬤ .

1. 37 ⬤ 41   **2.** 52 ⬤ 48

3. 327 ⬤ 347   **4.** 138 ⬤ 135

5. 483 ⬤ 476   **6.** 982 ⬤ 892

7. 5,836 ⬤ 5,841   **8.** 7,400 ⬤ 7,398   **9.** 3,279 ⬤ 3,280

10. 4,620 ⬤ 4,618   **11.** 7,000 ⬤ 7,021   **12.** 8,604 ⬤ 7,987

Give the number that is 10 less. Example 8,975 Answer 8,965

13. 3,268   **14.** 1,347   **15.** 8,629   **16.** 4,308   **17.** 7,600

Give the number that is 1,000 more. Example 6,428 Answer 7,428

18. 4,268   **19.** 275   **20.** 3,640   **21.** 7,800   **22.** 6,999

Give the number that is 100 less. Example 3,950 Answer 3,850

23. 3,278   **24.** 4,629   **25.** 3,765   **26.** 8,036   **27.** 7,000

★ **28.** Give these numbers in order from smallest to largest.
5,268, 4,975, 5,187, 5,099, 4,795

Mixed Applications

29. Lassen Peak is 3,187 m high. Mt. Jefferson is 3,199 m. Which volcano is higher?

30. Mt. Hood is 3,424 m high. Mt. Adams is 3,751 m. Which volcano is shorter?

31. **DATA BANK** See page 400. Crater Lake is 2,486 m high. Which volcano is closest in height to Crater Lake?

THINK

Place Value

Use only these four digits. 4 0 8 5

1. Write the largest 4-digit number you can.

2. Write the smallest 4-digit number you can.

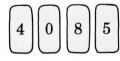

More Practice, page 406, Set A

Rounding

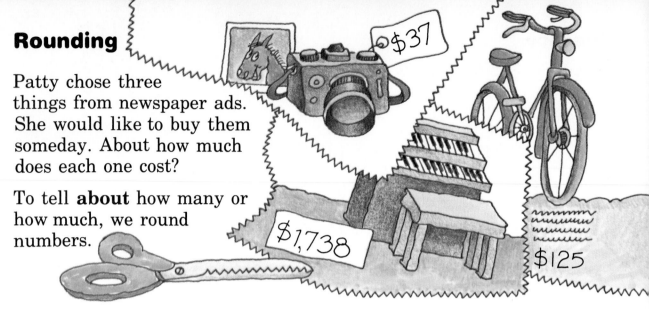

Patty chose three things from newspaper ads. She would like to buy them someday. About how much does each one cost?

To tell **about** how many or how much, we round numbers.

nearest ten	nearest ten	nearest hundred
30 37 40	120 125 130	1,700 1,738 1,800

37 is closer to 40 than to 30.

37 rounded to the nearest ten is 40.

The camera cost about $40.

125 is halfway between 120 and 130. When a number is halfway, round up.

125 rounded to the nearest ten is 130.

The bicycle costs about $130.

1,738 is closer to 1,700 than 1,800.

1,738 rounded to the nearest hundred is 1,700.

The organ costs about $1,700.

Warm Up

Round to the nearest ten.

1. 57   **2.** 33   **3.** 38   **4.** 45   **5.** 92   **6.** 75

Round to the nearest ten.

7. 356   **8.** 482   **9.** 794   **10.** 835   **11.** 279   **12.** 314

Round to the nearest hundred.

13. 2,467   **14.** 382   **15.** 4,625   **16.** 2,850   **17.** 325   **18.** 2,848

Practice Round to the nearest ten.

1. 78
2. 72
3. 26
4. 69
5. 55

6. 43
7. 87
8. 71
9. 48
10. 36

11. 85
12. 64
13. 19
14. 35
15. 93

16. 154
17. 737
18. 382
19. 671
20. 345

21. 289
22. 703
23. 655
24. 277
25. 254

Round to the nearest hundred.

26. 3,271
27. 5,247
28. 466
29. 2,796
30. 3,806

31. 831
32. 5,489
33. 5,726
34. 7,055
35. 7,435

36. 4,463
37. 3,026
38. 385
39. 2,813
40. 2,860

Give the cost to the nearest ten dollars.

41.

42.

More Practice, page 406, Set B

SKILLKEEPER

Add or subtract.

1. 4
   + 3

2. 9
   + 6

3. 8
   − 2

4. 9
   + 9

5. 7
   + 8

6. 14
   − 5

7. 7
   − 7

8. 5
   + 9

9. 17
   − 8

10. 2
    + 4

11. 16
    − 8

12. 7
    + 0

More About Rounding

Newspapers often use rounded numbers in headlines. Actually, there were 8,127 fans at the concert and tickets were $17.95.

nearest thousand

8,000   8,127   9,000

8,127 is closer to 8,000 than to 9,000.

8,127 rounded to the nearest thousand is 8,000.

nearest dollar

$17.00 $17.95 $18.00

$17.95 is closer to $18.00 than to $17.00.

$17.95 rounded to the nearest dollar is $18.00.

Other Examples

nearest thousand	nearest dollar	nearest dollar
6,500 → 7,000	$36.49 → $36.00	$7.50 → $8.00

Warm Up

Round to the nearest thousand.

1. 3,247	**2.** 7,860	**3.** 5,702	**4.** 7,500
5. 1,487	**6.** 8,295	**7.** 9,142	**8.** 6,567
9. 2,600	**10.** 4,288	**11.** 8,167	**12.** 6,503

Round to the nearest dollar.

13. $27.65	**14.** $24.10	**15.** $7.50	**16.** $28.95
17. $15.20	**18.** $16.35	**19.** $28.49	**20.** $37.98
21. $8.56	**22.** $16.89	**23.** $2.49	**24.** $38.16

32

Practice Round to the nearest thousand.

1. 2,426   2. 2,300   3. 5,675   4. 4,500

5. 6,521   6. 5,387   7. 7,162   8. 3,499

9. 8,568   10. 1,600   11. 9,208   12. 4,835

13. 5,162   14. 9,030   15. 8,278   16. 1,630

Round to the nearest dollar.

17. $16.08   18. $6.75   19. $14.49   20. $3.50

21. $78.16   22. $3.18   23. $37.50   24. $2.79

25. $29.88   26. $79.95   27. $5.26   28. $62.38

Write a newspaper headline for each story.
Use rounded numbers.

29. There were 3,918 fans at the game. Tickets were $4.95 each.

★ 30. There were 3,124 fans at Friday's games and 4,897 at Saturday's games. All tickets were $6.90 each.

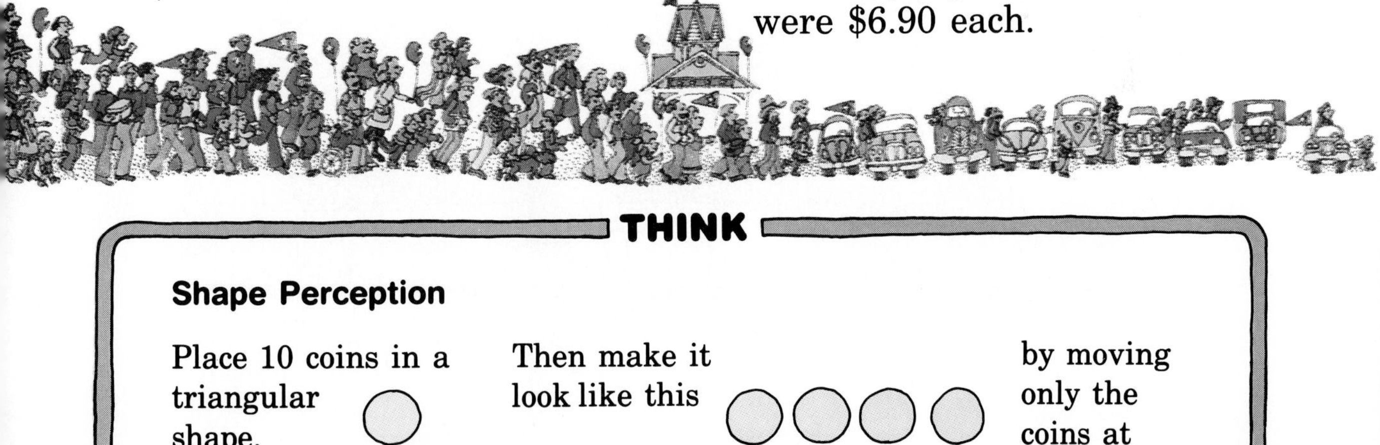

THINK

Shape Perception

Place 10 coins in a triangular shape.

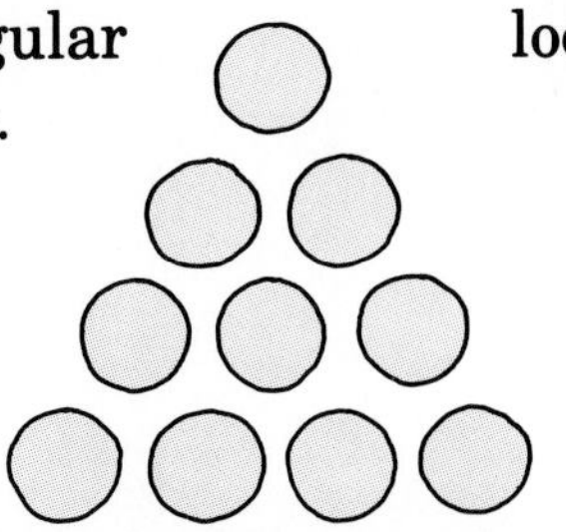

Then make it look like this

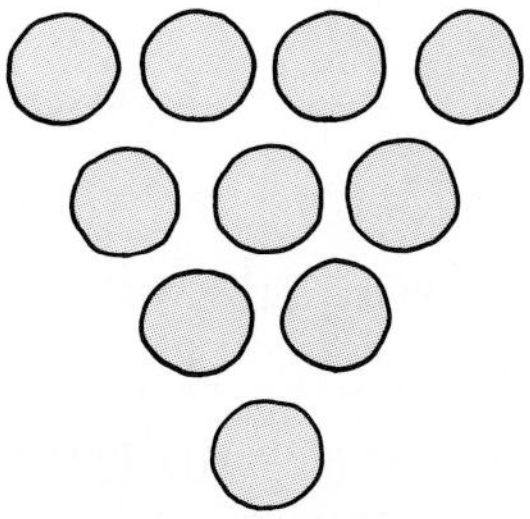

by moving only the coins at the corners.

MATH

Thinking About Large Numbers

Part 1

1. Sit still for a minute. Look at the clock and time yourself. Now, imagine sitting still for an hour. How many minutes would that be?

   - If you sat still for one whole day, that would be more than one thousand minutes! For one year, more than five hundred thousand minutes!

   - If you sat still for two years, that would be more than a million minutes.

In this lesson, you will be thinking about very large numbers.

Part 2

Work with a group.

You will need a ball of string and a pair of scissors.

2. Discuss how far you walk every day. How many steps do you think you take on the way to school? 100? 1,000? More? If you walked 100 steps from where you are now, where do you think you would be? What if you walked 1,000 steps?

3. Work with your group. Use string to show how far 10 steps is. How might you show 1,000 steps?

- Find a way to record your work.

- Will every group have exactly the same results? Why or why not?

4. Talk about how far 10,000 steps would be. Could you cut a string 10,000 steps long? 100,000 steps long? 1,000,000 (one million) steps long?

- A million steps is about 400 miles. Look at a map. Where might you be if you walked 1,000,000 steps?

Part 3

5. Predict how long it would take to walk 1,000,000 steps. Record your predictions.

6. How can you use your strings and a clock to find out?

- Decide on a way to show your results. Compare them with those of other groups.

- What are some reasons your results may be different from those of other groups?

7. Now think again about how far you walk on a school day. Can you make a more reasonable guess?

Comparing Larger Numbers

The table shows the cost of TV ads for different nights. Which costs more, the Thursday night ad or the Saturday night ad?

To find which of two numbers is greater, you compare their digits.

PRICE OF A 30-SECOND TV AD*

MONDAY	$135,000
TUESDAY	95,000
WEDNESDAY	92,000
THURSDAY	115,000
FRIDAY	170,000
SATURDAY	112,000
SUNDAY	175,000

*Estimates for selected programs during prime time in a recent year.

Start at the left. Find the first place where the digits are different.
5 > 2

115,000 > 112,000
↑ Check here. ↑

The Thursday night ad costs more.

Remember
> means "is greater than"
< means "is less than"

Other Examples

32,468 < 32,568
↑ Check here. ↑

172,286 > 96,857

This number has more digits.

Practice Write the sign > or < for each ◫.

1. 32,468 ◫ 31,568
2. 47,286 ◫ 46,286
3. 57,419 ◫ 67,419
4. 95,200 ◫ 85,200
5. 110,215 ◫ 98,215
6. 87,989 ◫ 100,000
7. 86,493 ◫ 386,490
8. 518,379 ◫ 518,380

★ Which costs more,

9. the Friday ad or the Sunday ad?

10. the Thursday ad or the Wednesday ad?

More Practice, page 407, Set B

Roman Numerals

The Romans used letters to write numbers.

$$I = 1 \quad X = 10 \quad C = 100 \quad M = 1{,}000$$
$$V = 5 \quad L = 50 \quad D = 500$$

Some Roman numerals are written by adding.

III	XI	VIII	LX
↓	↓	↓	↓
(1 + 1 + 1)	(10 + 1)	(5 + 3)	(50 + 10)
3	11	8	60

Other numerals are written by subtracting.

IV	IX	XL	XC
↓	↓	↓	↓
(5 − 1)	(10 − 1)	(50 − 10)	(100 − 10)
4	9	40	90

Look at these other examples.

X	III	XL	V	XC	II	M	DC
↓	↓	↓	↓	↓	↓	↓	↓
10	3	40	5	90	2	1,000	600
	13		45		92		1,600

Write the standard number.

1. XII 2. XXIV 3. IV 4. XXXIV

5. LX 6. LIX 7. MD 8. MC

Write the Roman numeral.

9. 7 10. 21 11. 61 12. 35

13. 40 14. 600 15. 1,500 16. 700

Millions

One million is 1,000 thousands.

1,000,000

The chart below will help you read numbers in the millions.

In a recent year, about 44,238,000 passengers used Chicago's O'Hare Airport.

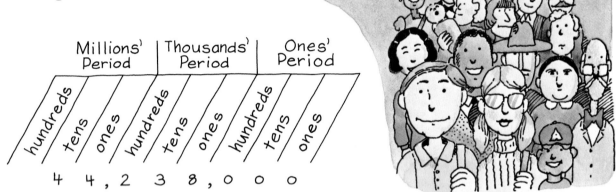

Millions' Period			Thousands' Period			Ones' Period		
hundreds	tens	ones	hundreds	tens	ones	hundreds	tens	ones
4	4,	2	3	8,	0	0	0	

We read, **"forty-four million, two hundred thirty-eight thousand."**

Other Examples

346,285,000   three hundred forty-six million, two hundred eighty-five thousand

7,360,500   seven million, three hundred sixty thousand, five hundred

27,469,000   twenty-seven million, four hundred sixty-nine thousand

Warm Up   Read each number aloud.

1. 75,342,000   2. 8,286,000   3. 216,415,000   4. 345,000,000

5. 124,700,000   6. 86,000,000   7. 7,287,000   8. 240,365,000

9. 36,720,900   10. 500,000,000   11. 18,283,000   12. 768,400,000

Practice Match.

1. 28,375,000 **2.** 28,753,000 **3.** 2,837,000

4. 283,570,000 **5.** 28,573,000 **6.** 283,750,000

A two million, eight hundred thirty-seven thousand

B twenty-eight million, five hundred seventy-three thousand

C twenty-eight million, seven hundred fifty-three thousand

D twenty-eight million, three hundred seventy-five thousand

E two hundred eighty-three million, seven hundred fifty thousand

F two hundred eighty-three million, five hundred seventy thousand

Write the standard number.

7. seven million, three hundred eighteen thousand

8. twenty-nine million, four hundred eighty-four thousand

9. nine hundred sixteen million, three hundred thousand

10. 29 million **11.** 375 million **12.** 8 million

13. Estimate the number of people in the United States.
  A 23,000 **B** 23,000,000 **C** 230,000,000

14. **DATA BANK** See page 403. Which airport served this number of passengers in the given year?

  A 23,190,000

  B 29,977,000

  C 15,087,000

  D 23,775,000

  E 15,281,000

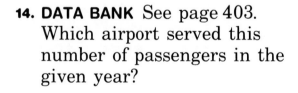

⌐ THINK ⌐

Ordinal Numbers

How many kilometers to the moon?

To find the answer, list the digits below in order from left to right.

fifth—8 third—6
sixth—4 fourth—2
first—3 second—7

➤ **MATH** ◄

Counting Money

We often use skip counting when we count money. How much are the nickels worth?

To count nickels, we can count by fives.

| 5 | 10 | 15 | 20 | 25 | 30 | 35 |

35¢
or
$0.35
35 cents

How much are the dimes worth?

To count dimes, we can count by tens.

| 10 | 20 | 30 | 40 | 50 | 60 |

60¢
or
$0.60
60 cents

Count this money.

| $1.00 | $1.25 | $1.35 | $1.45 | $1.50 | $1.55 | $1.60 |

Warm Up Count the money. Write the total.

1.

2.

Practice   Count the money. Write the total.

1.

2.

3.

4.

5.

6.

SKILLKEEPER

Find the sums.

1. 7		**2.** 2		**3.** 7		**4.** 3		**5.** 5		**6.** 2	
2		3		0		2		4		8	
+ 3		+ 2		+ 1		+ 6		+ 5		+ 2	

7. 6		**8.** 3		**9.** 1		**10.** 0		**11.** 6		**12.** 3	
1		4		8		9		3		4	
+ 8		+ 3		+ 2		+ 1		+ 7		+ 3	

41

Counting Change

A sales clerk must know how to count out the correct change. The example below shows how some clerks count change.

Jack sold a tape for $3.78. The customer paid with a five-dollar bill. This is how Jack counted the change.

Start with the cost.

Count the smaller coins first.

End with the amount given.

Warm Up Look at the money chart. Touch the money you would use as you count the change aloud.

1. You sold   Amount given

$3.89

2. You sold   Amount given

84¢

3. You sold   Amount given

$2.78

4. You sold   Amount given

$8.80

Practice Match each price tag with the change you would give for a five-dollar bill.

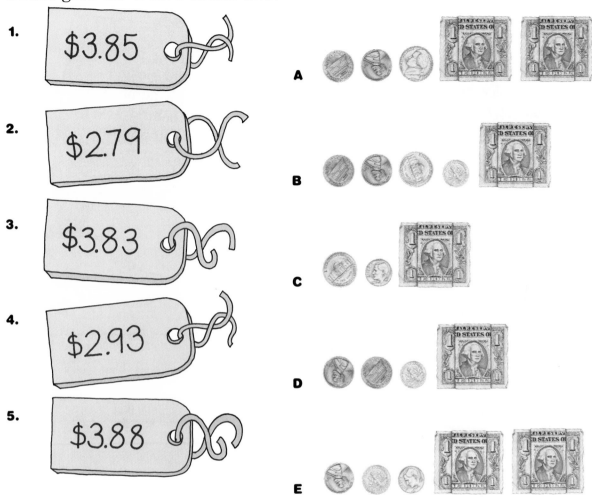

1. $3.85

2. $2.79

3. $3.83

4. $2.93

5. $3.88

A

B

C

D

E

★ Tell what coins and bills you would use to make change for $10.00.

6. $7.78

7. $8.82

THINK

Calendar Puzzle

Joan said, "Today is Friday, December 22." Then she asked, "I wonder what day of the week New Year's Day will be?"

Can you help her? December has 31 days.

MATH

PROBLEM-SOLVING STRATEGY
Draw a Picture

TO SOLVE A PROBLEM LIKE THIS, IT MAY BE HELPFUL TO USE THE STRATEGY SHOWN BELOW.

Try This Four boys are in line for tickets. Bill is ahead of Ted. Don is behind Ted. Bill is behind Sam. Who is first in line?

DRAW A PICTURE

FIRST, I'LL DRAW AND LABEL A LINE.

NOW, I'LL SHOW BILL AHEAD OF TED.

NEXT, I'LL SHOW DON BEHIND TED.

LAST, I'LL SHOW BILL BEHIND SAM.

SAM MUST BE FIRST IN LINE!

BACK   FRONT

BACK   TED BILL   FRONT

BACK   DON TED BILL   FRONT

BACK   DON TED BILL SAM   FRONT

Solve.

1. Terry is shorter than Betty. Fran is taller than Betty. Donna is shorter than Terry. Who is the tallest girl?

2. Sue is younger than Carl. Joan is older than Carl. Ed's age is between Carl's and Joan's. Who is the youngest?

44

Write the standard number.

1. 6 hundreds
4 tens
5 ones

2. 7 tens
0 ones
5 hundreds

3. 2 thousands
9 hundreds
0 tens
4 ones

4. 5 tens
6 ones
7 thousands
0 hundreds

Write > or < for each .

5. 525 ⬤ 540

6. 761 ⬤ 758

7. 6,921 ⬤ 6,879

8. 5,724 ⬤ 5,719

9. 6,834 ⬤ 6,835

10. 4,600 ⬤ 4,599

Round.

nearest ten		nearest ten		nearest hundred	
11. 68	**12.** 74	**13.** 375	**14.** 423	**15.** 2,472	**16.** 3,649

nearest thousand		nearest dollar	
17. 3,379	**18.** 6,500	**19.** $15.69	**20.** $28.25

Write > or < for each ⬤.

21. 121,000 ⬤ 98,000

22. 653,497 ⬤ 653,500

23. 29,887 ⬤ 29,890

Write the standard number. **24.** XII **25.** IV
26. three hundred twelve million, five hundred sixty-seven thousand

Count the money.

27.

28.

29.

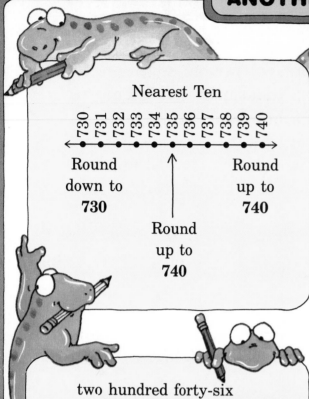

Nearest Ten

730 731 732 733 734 735 736 737 738 739 740

Round down to **730**

Round up to **740**

Round up to **740**

Round to the nearest ten.

1. 48   **2.** 74   **3.** 25

4. 367   **5.** 433   **6.** 755

Round to the nearest hundred.

7. 2,763   **8.** 3,548

Round to the nearest dollar.

9. $37.50   **10.** $24.49

two hundred forty-six thousand, seven hundred fifty-three

Thousands	Ones
2 4 6	7 5 3

Write the standard number.

11. seven hundred eighteen thousand, five hundred thirty-two

12. forty-nine thousand, six hundred seventy-three

1,834 < 1,851

3 < 5

More digits   Fewer digits

2,376 > 729

Give the sign > or < for each ▥.

13. 546 ▥ 564   **14.** 387 ▥ 378

15. 63 ▥ 637   **16.** 480 ▥ 478

17. 6,524 ▥ 6,542

18. 376 ▥ 1,476

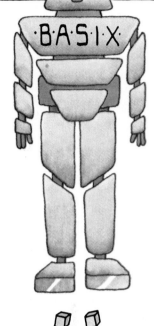

Place Value

Pretend you are on the planet Basix. On Basix, they group by sixes instead of tens for place value.

They use the digits 0, 1, 2, 3, 4, and 5 and place value to write larger numbers.

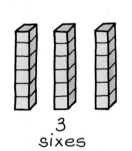

six ones   one six

This model shows the meaning of the Basix numbers. ⟶

So on Basix,
  32 means 3 sixes and 2 ones.

3
sixes

2
ones

The chart below compares Basix counting with Earth counting.

Basix counting	1	2	3	4	5	10	11	12	13	14	15	20	21
Earth counting	1	2	3	4	5	6	7	8	9	10	11	12	13

Write a Basix numeral for the number of objects.

Example

1. 🁢🁢🁢🁢
🁢🁢🁢🁢
🁢🁢🁢🁢
🁢🁢🁢🁢
🁢🁢🁢🁢
🁢🁢🁢

2. 🁢🁢🁢🁢🁢
🁢🁢🁢🁢🁢
🁢🁢🁢🁢🁢
🁢🁢🁢🁢🁢
🁢🁢🁢🁢🁢
🁢🁢🁢🁢

3. 🁢🁢🁢
🁢🁢🁢
🁢🁢🁢
🁢🁢🁢
🁢🁢🁢

Answer 24

4. Write the Basix counting numbers from 1 to 55.

CUMULATIVE REVIEW

Give the letter for the correct answer.

1. $3 + 5 = n$
- **A** 8
- **B** 10
- **C** 9
- **D** not given

2. $8 + 0 = n$
- **A** 0
- **B** 80
- **C** 8
- **D** not given

3. $6 + 7 = n$
- **A** 11
- **B** 12
- **C** 14
- **D** not given

4.
$$\begin{array}{r} 17 \\ -\ 8 \\ \hline \end{array}$$
- **A** 7
- **B** 8
- **C** 9
- **D** not given

5.
$$\begin{array}{r} 14 \\ -\ 9 \\ \hline \end{array}$$
- **A** 6
- **B** 5
- **C** 7
- **D** not given

6.
$$\begin{array}{r} 12 \\ -\ 6 \\ \hline \end{array}$$
- **A** 5
- **B** 8
- **C** 6
- **D** not given

7.
$$\begin{array}{r} 10 \\ -\ 4 \\ \hline \end{array}$$
- **A** 5
- **B** 6
- **C** 7
- **D** not given

8.
$$\begin{array}{r} 2 \\ 4 \\ +\ 5 \\ \hline \end{array}$$
- **A** 11
- **B** 10
- **C** 9
- **D** not given

9.
$$\begin{array}{r} 3 \\ 3 \\ +\ 3 \\ \hline \end{array}$$
- **A** 12
- **B** 11
- **C** 10
- **D** not given

10.
$$\begin{array}{r} 5 \\ 3 \\ +\ 7 \\ \hline \end{array}$$
- **A** 13
- **B** 15
- **C** 14
- **D** not given

11.
$$\begin{array}{r} 1 \\ 2 \\ +\ 7 \\ \hline \end{array}$$
- **A** 12
- **B** 11
- **C** 10
- **D** not given

12.
$$\begin{array}{r} 6 \\ 3 \\ +\ 6 \\ \hline \end{array}$$
- **A** 15
- **B** 16
- **C** 14
- **D** not given

13. Allen had 8 dollars. He spent 7 dollars. How much did Allen have left?
- **A** $15
- **B** $17
- **C** $1
- **D** not given

14. Margo had 8 seashells. She found 5 more seashells. How many seashells does Margo have now?
- **A** 12
- **B** 13
- **C** 3
- **D** not given

ADDITION AND SUBTRACTION

3

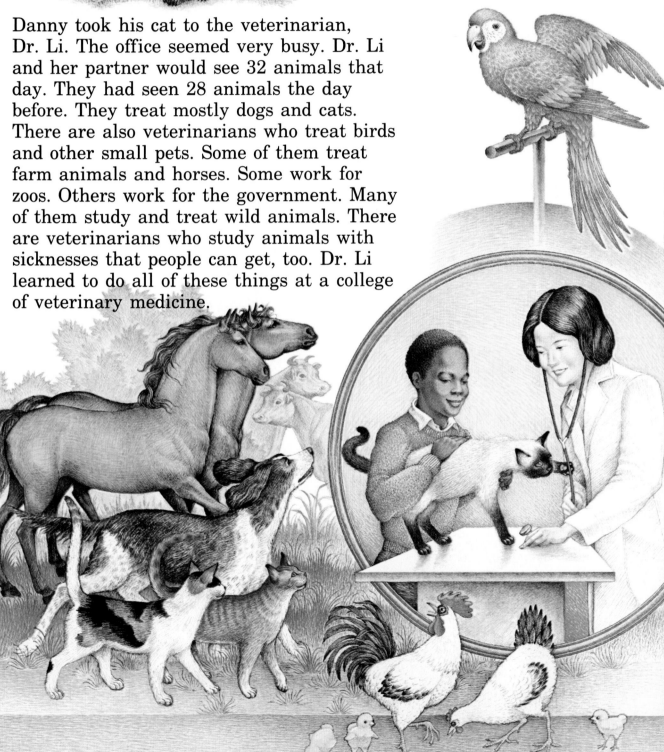

Danny took his cat to the veterinarian, Dr. Li. The office seemed very busy. Dr. Li and her partner would see 32 animals that day. They had seen 28 animals the day before. They treat mostly dogs and cats. There are also veterinarians who treat birds and other small pets. Some of them treat farm animals and horses. Some work for zoos. Others work for the government. Many of them study and treat wild animals. There are veterinarians who study animals with sicknesses that people can get, too. Dr. Li learned to do all of these things at a college of veterinary medicine.

Adding: One Trade

Tara checked her breathing rate after running.
She counted 48 breaths for the first minute.
She counted 27 breaths for the second minute.
How many breaths did Tara take in the two minutes?

Since we want the total, we add.

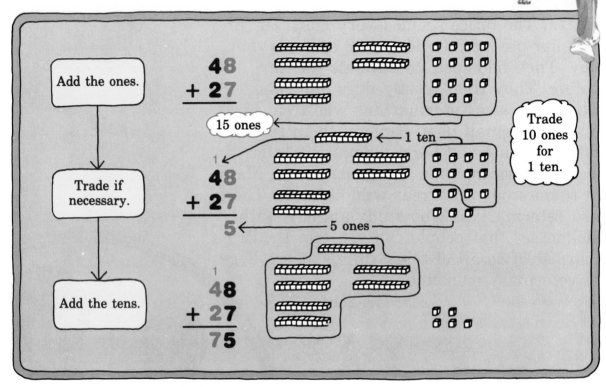

Tara took 75 breaths in the two minutes.

Other Examples

75	54	327	6	482
+ 53	+ 25	+ 146	+ 53	+ 136
128	79	473	59	618

12 tens =
1 hundred
and 2 tens

Warm Up Add.

1. 26
   + 38

2. 95
   + 41

3. 175
  + 281

4. 382
   + 94

5. 654
  + 820

Practice Find the sums.

1. $\begin{array}{r} 39 \\ + 46 \\ \hline \end{array}$
2. $\begin{array}{r} 52 \\ + 83 \\ \hline \end{array}$
3. $\begin{array}{r} 24 \\ + 35 \\ \hline \end{array}$
4. $\begin{array}{r} 76 \\ + 8 \\ \hline \end{array}$
5. $\begin{array}{r} 9 \\ + 24 \\ \hline \end{array}$

6. $\begin{array}{r} 352 \\ + 180 \\ \hline \end{array}$
7. $\begin{array}{r} 216 \\ + 157 \\ \hline \end{array}$
8. $\begin{array}{r} 324 \\ + 912 \\ \hline \end{array}$
9. $\begin{array}{r} 261 \\ + 90 \\ \hline \end{array}$
10. $\begin{array}{r} 365 \\ + 121 \\ \hline \end{array}$

11. $\begin{array}{r} 257 \\ + 13 \\ \hline \end{array}$
12. $\begin{array}{r} 762 \\ + 824 \\ \hline \end{array}$
13. $\begin{array}{r} 325 \\ + 142 \\ \hline \end{array}$
14. $\begin{array}{r} 281 \\ + 346 \\ \hline \end{array}$
15. $\begin{array}{r} 643 \\ + 164 \\ \hline \end{array}$

16. $64 + 82$
17. $75 + 18$
18. $26 + 52$
19. $38 + 9$

20. $356 + 125$
21. $710 + 628$
22. $381 + 125$
23. $275 + 82$

24. Add 27 to 59.
25. Add 917 to 830.
26. Add 261 to 56.

Mixed Applications

27. After swimming, Cindy counted 39 breaths the first minute and 24 the second. How many breaths was this?

28. Kate rode her bicycle 8 miles on Friday, 3 miles on Saturday, and 5 miles on Sunday. How far did she ride?

29. **DATA HUNT** Run for a minute. Then count your breaths for each of the first two minutes. How many breaths did you take in the two minutes?

THINK

Mental Math

Sometimes you can find sums in your head.

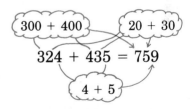

$324 + 435 = 759$

Add. Write only the answers.

1. $231 + 753$
2. $451 + 317$
3. $204 + 594$
4. $635 + 322$
5. $324 + 335$
6. $223 + 264$
7. $532 + 364$
8. $456 + 242$

MATH

Adding: Two or More Trades

Nina and Bert are circus elephants.
One night Nina ate 196 kg of hay and Bert ate 227 kg.
How many kilograms of hay did they eat together?

Since we want the total amount, we add.

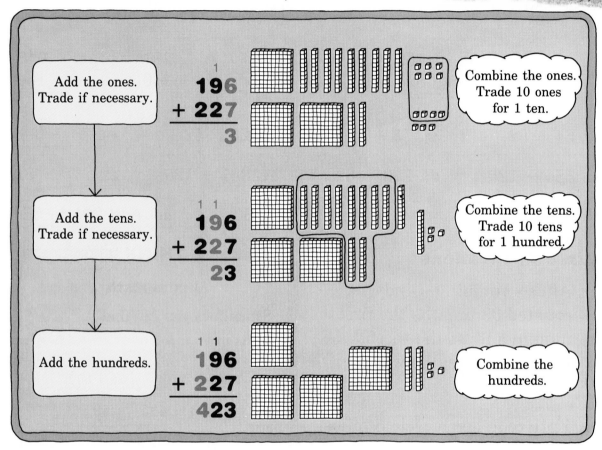

Add the ones. Trade if necessary.

$$\begin{array}{r} \overset{1}{196} \\ + 227 \\ \hline 3 \end{array}$$

Combine the ones. Trade 10 ones for 1 ten.

Add the tens. Trade if necessary.

$$\begin{array}{r} \overset{1\,1}{196} \\ + 227 \\ \hline 23 \end{array}$$

Combine the tens. Trade 10 tens for 1 hundred.

Add the hundreds.

$$\begin{array}{r} \overset{1\,1}{196} \\ + 227 \\ \hline 423 \end{array}$$

Combine the hundreds.

Nina and Bert ate 423 kg of hay that night.

Other Examples

14 hundreds = 1 thousand and 4 hundreds

$$\begin{array}{r} \overset{1}{627} \\ + 845 \\ \hline 1{,}472 \end{array}$$

$$\begin{array}{r} \overset{1\,1}{754} \\ + 489 \\ \hline 1{,}243 \end{array}$$

$$\begin{array}{r} \overset{1\,1}{987} \\ + \ 38 \\ \hline 1{,}025 \end{array}$$

$$\begin{array}{r} \overset{1\,1}{\$6.87} \\ + \ 1.16 \\ \hline \$8.03 \end{array}$$

Warm Up   Add.

1. 368
   + 137

2. 649
   + 824

3. 375
   + 980

4. 695
   + 87

5. $4.75
   + 5.72

52

Practice Find the sums.

1. 728
  + 659

2. 346
  + 188

3. 695
  + 28

4. 764
  + 236

5. 416
  + 807

6. 76
  + 185

7. $2.25
  + 1.50

8. $3.69
  + 1.45

9. $2.98
  + 1.29

10. $6.88
  + 3.90

11. $8.95
  + 3.60

12. $2.95
  + 3.27

13. $3.57
  + 0.88

14. $9.16
  + 7.15

15. $6.75
  + 0.98

16. 836 + 918
17. 296 + 175
18. 67 + 289
19. 315 + 909

20. 675 + 956
21. 374 + 187
22. 737 + 418
23. 89 + 596

24. $1.69 + $2.58
25. $3.88 + $1.75
26. $3.15 + $1.85

Mixed Applications

27. One night Nina drank 188 L of water. Bert drank 232 L of water. How much water did they drink together?

28. Write a question that can be answered using subtraction and the data below. Then solve the problem.

Bert ate 14 bales of hay on Saturday. He ate 6 bales of hay on Sunday.

More Practice, page 408, Set B

THINK

Logical Reasoning

Find the missing digits.

1.   ▮ 2 ▮
  + 5 ▮ 7
  ―――――
    8 7 5

2.   2 ▮ 9
  + 1 8 ▮
  ―――――
    ▮ 5 4

3.   3 ▮ ▮
  + ▮ 4 8
  ―――――
    7 5 3

4.   ▮ 6 2
  + 4 ▮ ▮
  ―――――
  1, 0 7 1

MATH

Adding Larger Numbers

The deepest part of the Atlantic Ocean is 8,385 m. The deepest part of the Pacific Ocean is 2,475 m deeper than the Atlantic. How deep is this?

Since we want 2,475 more than 8,385, we add.

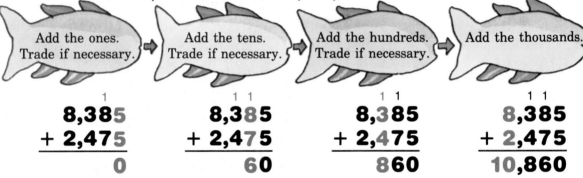

Add the ones. Trade if necessary.	Add the tens. Trade if necessary.	Add the hundreds. Trade if necessary.	Add the thousands.
$\begin{array}{r} 1 \\ 8,385 \\ +\ 2,475 \\ \hline 0 \end{array}$	$\begin{array}{r} 1\ 1 \\ 8,385 \\ +\ 2,475 \\ \hline 60 \end{array}$	$\begin{array}{r} 1\ 1 \\ 8,385 \\ +\ 2,475 \\ \hline 860 \end{array}$	$\begin{array}{r} 1\ 1 \\ 8,385 \\ +\ 2,475 \\ \hline 10,860 \end{array}$

The deepest part of the Pacific Ocean is 10,860 m.

Other Examples

$$\begin{array}{r} 1\ \ 1\ 1 \\ 5,697 \\ +\ 1,843 \\ \hline 7,540 \end{array} \qquad \begin{array}{r} 1\ 1 \\ \$76.92 \\ +\ \ 8.53 \\ \hline \$85.45 \end{array} \qquad \begin{array}{r} 1\ \ 1 \\ 92,463 \\ +\ 43,572 \\ \hline 136,035 \end{array} \qquad \begin{array}{r} 1\ 1\ \ \ 1 \\ 7,659 \\ +\ 86,837 \\ \hline 94,496 \end{array}$$

Warm Up Add.

1. $\begin{array}{r} 3,742 \\ +\ 5,924 \end{array}$
2. $\begin{array}{r} 3,867 \\ +\ 1,549 \end{array}$
3. $\begin{array}{r} \$68.23 \\ +\ 75.91 \end{array}$
4. $\begin{array}{r} 18,296 \\ +\ 24,385 \end{array}$
5. $\begin{array}{r} 17,619 \\ +\ 9,285 \end{array}$

Practice Find the sums.

1.
$$2{,}369 + 1{,}358$$

2.
$$6{,}721 + 8{,}937$$

3.
$$6{,}598 + 276$$

4.
$$3{,}057 + 9{,}386$$

5.
$$2{,}856 + 14{,}728$$

6.
$$26{,}395 + 34{,}120$$

7.
$$78{,}265 + 49{,}141$$

8.
$$65{,}295 + 74{,}968$$

9.
$$\$38.95 + 19.88$$

10.
$$\$57.50 + 4.95$$

11.
$$\$69.95 + 27.50$$

12.
$$\$16.98 + 13.25$$

13. 7,268 + 6,471

14. 2,697 + 583

15. 1,358 + 9,672

16. $26.50 + $17.80

17. $16.95 + $7.75

18. $58.60 + $29.30

19. Add 1,566 to 1,890.

20. Add 379 to 2,658.

21. Add 483 to 1,456.

22. Add $37.45 to $26.98.

23. Add $27.89 to $1.35.

Mixed Applications

24. The deepest part of the Arctic Ocean is 5,334 m. The Indian Ocean is 2,117 m deeper than that. How deep is the Indian Ocean?

25. The deepest part of the Pacific Ocean is about 10 thousand meters. The South China Sea is 5 thousand meters deep. How many thousand meters deeper is the Pacific Ocean?

26. DATA BANK See page 401. The Gulf of Mexico is 3,452 m deeper than the Caribbean Sea. How deep is the Gulf of Mexico?

THINK

Using a Calculator

Show 306,458 on your calculator. By adding just one number, make your calculator read 376,458.

MATH

More Practice, page 409, Set A

Estimating Sums Using Rounding

Sometimes you want an answer that is only close to the exact answer. One way to estimate sums is to round and add.

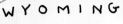

I wonder about how far it is between these two national parks.

$$\begin{array}{r} 541 \\ + 399 \\ \end{array} \quad \boxed{\text{nearest hundred}} \quad \begin{array}{r} 500 \\ + 400 \\ \hline 900 \end{array}$$

It is about 900 miles between these two parks.

WYOMING

Rocky Mountain

541 mi

UTAH

COLORADO

399 mi Canyonlands

Grand Canyon

ARIZONA

NEW MEXICO

Other Examples

nearest ten	nearest hundred	nearest dollar
$\begin{array}{r} 78 \rightarrow 80 \\ + 54 \rightarrow + 50 \\ \hline 130 \end{array}$	$\begin{array}{r} 387 \rightarrow 400 \\ + 129 \rightarrow + 100 \\ \hline 500 \end{array}$	$\begin{array}{r} \$6.75 \rightarrow \$7.00 \\ + 2.29 \rightarrow + 2.00 \\ \hline \$9.00 \end{array}$

Warm Up Estimate by rounding to the nearest ten.

1. $\begin{array}{r} 59 \\ + 32 \end{array}$
2. $\begin{array}{r} 87 \\ + 49 \end{array}$
3. $\begin{array}{r} 52 \\ + 19 \end{array}$
4. $\begin{array}{r} 65 \\ + 34 \end{array}$

Estimate by rounding to the nearest hundred.

5. $\begin{array}{r} 698 \\ + 315 \end{array}$
6. $\begin{array}{r} 427 \\ + 178 \end{array}$
7. $\begin{array}{r} 632 \\ + 778 \end{array}$
8. $\begin{array}{r} 309 \\ + 492 \end{array}$

Estimate by rounding to the nearest dollar.

9. $\begin{array}{r} \$5.65 \\ + 3.25 \end{array}$
10. $\begin{array}{r} \$8.98 \\ + 1.39 \end{array}$
11. $\begin{array}{r} \$4.25 \\ + 5.79 \end{array}$
12. $\begin{array}{r} \$6.95 \\ + 2.17 \end{array}$

Practice Find these special sums.

1. 30
   + 40

2. 60
   + 20

3. 80
   + 70

4. 900
   + 600

5. 300
   + 500

6. 700
   + 900

7. 600
   + 800

8. 700
   + 500

9. $4.00
   + 2.00

10. $7.00
    + 9.00

Estimate by rounding to the nearest ten.

11. 29
   + 42

12. 56
   + 31

13. 88
   + 39

14. 26
   + 53

15. 85
   + 24

Estimate by rounding to the nearest hundred.

16. 395
   + 206

17. 418
   + 276

18. 750
   + 342

19. 867
   + 444

Estimate by rounding to the nearest dollar.

20. $3.75
   + 2.16

21. $4.67
   + 2.39

22. $4.78
   + 3.24

23. $6.95
   + 2.13

Estimate by rounding to the nearest thousand.

24. 6,284
   + 7,869

25. 3,785
   + 6,392

26. 4,195
   + 6,500

Solve.

27. Glacier Park is 370 miles northwest of Yellowstone. Rocky Mountain is 598 miles southeast of Yellowstone. About how far is it from Glacier to Rocky Mountain?

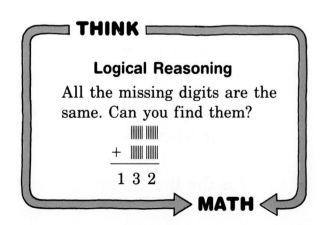

THINK

Logical Reasoning

All the missing digits are the same. Can you find them?

$$\begin{array}{r} \text{▓▓▓} \\ + \text{▓▓▓} \\ \hline 1\,3\,2 \end{array}$$

MATH

PROBLEM SOLVING
Estimation and Mental Math

Yellowstone National Park is the oldest (1872) and largest (9,000 square kilometers) park in the United States.

Solve. Use estimation or mental math. Write only the answers.

1. The average elevation of Yellowstone Park is 2,400 m. Its highest mountain, Electric Peak, is 950 m higher than this. About how high is Electric Peak?

2. Mortar Geyser may erupt water and steam for as long as 15 minutes at a time. After it has erupted for 8 minutes, how long could it continue?

3. Splendid Geyser erupts water at least 29 m high. The highest it erupts is 21 m higher than that. What is the geyser's greatest height of eruption?

4. The limber pine gets as tall as 15 m. The whitebark pine grows to 9 m. How much taller is the limber pine?

5. Yellowstone Lake is at an altitude of 2,356 m. Mt. Sheridan is 783 m higher than the lake. About how high is Mt. Sheridan?

6. Old Faithful Geyser erupts water and steam 52 m high. Grand Geyser erupts 9 m higher than that. How high is that?

7. The main road system is 225 km long. There are 265 km of other roads. About how many kilometers is this in all?

8. *Strategy Practice* The Upper Falls plunges 33 m. The Lower Falls plunges 28 m more than twice the Upper Falls. How far does the Lower Falls plunge? Hint: Choose the operations.

Adding: Mental Math

Sometimes you want to add numbers "in your head" without writing anything down. You may need to find sums like **15 + 7** in your head when you add three or more numbers.

Here are some ways you might think.

15 + 7

> THINK
> 15 + 5 = 20
> and 2 more makes 22

27 + 8

> THINK
> 7 + 8 = 15
> and 20 more makes 35

16 + 16

> THINK
> 20
> 16 + 16 = 32
> 12

Practice Find the sums. Write only the answers.

1. 12 + 9
2. 17 + 5
3. 19 + 6
4. 14 + 7
5. 23 + 9
6. 28 + 9
7. 13 + 9
8. 11 + 7
9. 16 + 8
10. 15 + 9
11. 12 + 8
12. 18 + 7
13. 24 + 8
14. 17 + 6
15. 22 + 9
16. 29 + 4
17. 13 + 8
18. 25 + 6
19. 15 + 8
20. 14 + 8
21. 27 + 7
22. 16 + 7
23. 26 + 9
24. 18 + 8
25. 12 + 12
26. 23 + 12
27. 13 + 13
28. 13 + 23
29. 15 + 15
30. 25 + 15
31. 17 + 17
32. 32 + 43
33. 18 + 18
34. 27 + 17
35. 28 + 18
36. 26 + 16

SKILLKEEPER

Write > or < for each ▥.

1. 540 ▥ 515
2. 781 ▥ 763
3. 385 ▥ 410
4. 6,529 ▥ 5,963
5. 3,570 ▥ 4,699
6. 7,866 ▥ 9,550
7. 6,400 ▥ 7,500
8. 39,656 ▥ 36,447
9. 7,938 ▥ 8,256
10. 180,000 ▥ 165,780
11. 513,265 ▥ 523,345
12. 28,665 ▥ 27,670

Column Addition

Work with a group.

Part 1

1. The sum of the numbers in each row, column, or diagonal of this Magic Square is 34. The sum of the numbers in the shaded part is also 34.

   - In the Magic Square, how many other "squares" of 4 numbers can you find that have a sum of 34?
   - What would happen if you changed one number in the square? Compare your ideas with those of other groups.

16	2	3	13
5	11	10	8
9	7	6	12
4	14	15	1

Part 2

2. In the Magic Addition Sign, the sum of the numbers in each row or column of 4 numbers is the same.

   - Work with your group to fill in the missing numbers.
   - Show your group's numbers to another group.
   - Did all the groups write the same numbers?

	27	10	
7		23	16
	6	15	
		9	

3. Put the missing digits in the boxes.

```
A        □2       B      4 6 7      C         5 8 3     D       □,9 4□
         4 3             □3              2,7□4            4,□6 8
         □8             3 9□           □,7 2□       +       5□6
     +    2□        +      □       +       □8          1 1,1 1 1
        1 7 2            □4 0          7,□5 1
```

   - Compare answers in your group.
   - Which problems have more than one solution?

Part 3

Look at Becky's math paper.

4. You will have two minutes to check Becky's work.

   - Do not work the problems. Use estimation to see if her answers are reasonable.

   - Write down the numbers of the problems you think Becky got wrong.

   - Compare your results with those of others in your group. Talk about the different ways you estimated.

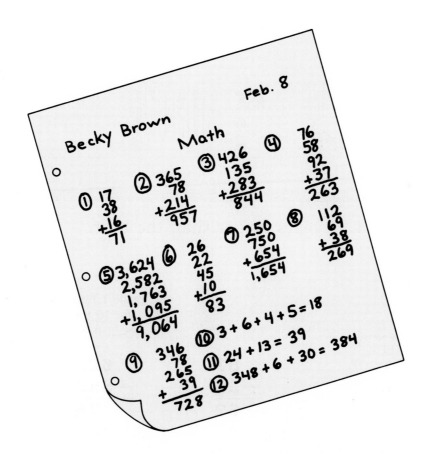

Subtracting: One Trade

A record age for an elephant is 61 years. A record age for a bear is 34 years. How much longer did the elephant live?

Since we want to find how much longer the elephant lived, we subtract.

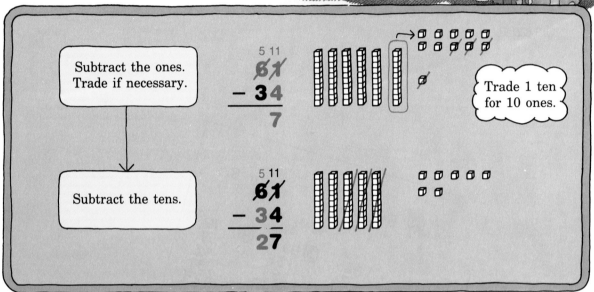

Subtract the ones. Trade if necessary.	$\begin{array}{r} {}^{5\ 11} \\ \cancel{61} \\ -\ 34 \\ \hline 7 \end{array}$	Trade 1 ten for 10 ones.
Subtract the tens.	$\begin{array}{r} {}^{5\ 11} \\ \cancel{61} \\ -\ 34 \\ \hline 27 \end{array}$	

The elephant lived 27 years longer than the bear.

Other Examples

Trade 1 hundred for 10 tens.

$$\begin{array}{r} {}^{6\ 12} \\ \cancel{72} \\ -\ 48 \\ \hline 24 \end{array}$$

CHECK
$$\begin{array}{r} 1 \\ 24 \\ +\ 48 \\ \hline 72 \end{array}$$

$$\begin{array}{r} 87 \\ -\ 25 \\ \hline 62 \end{array}$$

$$\begin{array}{r} {}^{5\ 12} \\ 6\cancel{28} \\ -\ 552 \\ \hline 76 \end{array}$$

$$\begin{array}{r} {}^{6\ 10} \\ \$8.\cancel{70} \\ -\ 1.34 \\ \hline \$7.36 \end{array}$$

Warm Up Subtract. Check by adding.

1. $\begin{array}{r} 84 \\ -\ 29 \\ \hline \end{array}$

2. $\begin{array}{r} 68 \\ -\ 17 \\ \hline \end{array}$

3. $\begin{array}{r} 739 \\ -\ 264 \\ \hline \end{array}$

4. $\begin{array}{r} 138 \\ -\ 83 \\ \hline \end{array}$

5. $\begin{array}{r} \$5.24 \\ -\ 1.30 \\ \hline \end{array}$

Practice Subtract.

1. 72 − 25

2. 54 − 18

3. 67 − 24

4. 98 − 16

5. 70 − 26

6. 529 − 179

7. 615 − 340

8. 136 − 72

9. 148 − 95

10. 390 − 36

11. 482 − 58

12. 627 − 92

13. $5.95 − 1.49

14. $3.65 − 1.90

15. $2.79 − 1.35

16. 73 − 36

17. 97 − 64

18. 729 − 63

19. 994 − 175

20. $1.29 − $0.75

21. $4.76 − $1.39

22. Subtract 58 from 92.

23. Subtract 327 from 475.

24. Subtract 82 from 146.

25. Subtract 284 from 729.

Mixed Applications

26. A record age for a horse is 54 years. A record age for a monkey is 25 years. How much longer did the horse live than the monkey?

27. A zoo had one bear for 18 years. It had another bear for 8 years longer than the first. How long was the second bear at the zoo?

28. **DATA BANK** See page 402. How much longer did the hippopotamus live than the cat?

THINK

▦ **Calculator Patterns**

Discover the pattern. Then find the next 4 numbers. 367, 734, 1,101, 1,468, . . .

MATH

More Practice, page 410, Set B

Subtracting: Two or More Trades

The albatross has a wingspread of about 356 cm.
The condor has a wingspread of about 298 cm.
How much less is the wingspread of the condor?

Since we are comparing the numbers, we subtract.

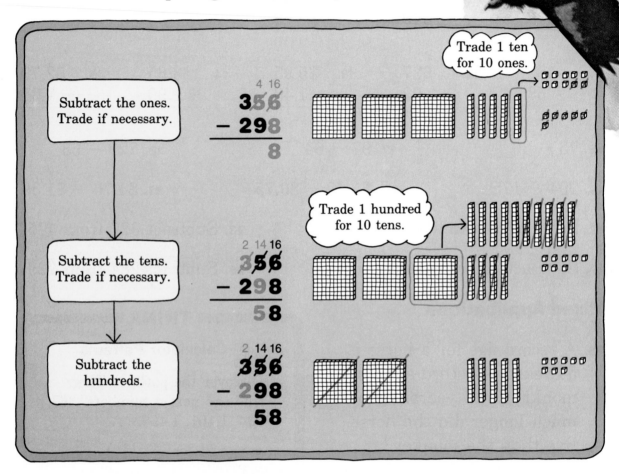

The wingspread of the condor is 58 cm less than the albatross.

Other Examples

$$\begin{array}{r} \overset{5\ 13\ 12}{642} \\ -\ 179 \\ \hline 463 \end{array} \qquad \begin{array}{r} \overset{11\ 14}{124} \\ -\ 78 \\ \hline 46 \end{array} \qquad \begin{array}{r} \overset{5\ 12\ 15}{635} \\ -\ 96 \\ \hline 539 \end{array} \qquad \begin{array}{r} \overset{3\ 15\ 10}{\$4.60} \\ -\ 1.85 \\ \hline \$2.75 \end{array}$$

Warm Up   Subtract. Check by adding.

1. $\begin{array}{r} 726 \\ -\ 149 \\ \hline \end{array}$
2. $\begin{array}{r} 650 \\ -\ 283 \\ \hline \end{array}$
3. $\begin{array}{r} 135 \\ -\ 97 \\ \hline \end{array}$
4. $\begin{array}{r} 726 \\ -\ 58 \\ \hline \end{array}$
5. $\begin{array}{r} \$8.50 \\ -\ 2.98 \\ \hline \end{array}$

64

Practice Subtract.

1. $\begin{array}{r} 632 \\ -365 \\ \hline \end{array}$	2. $\begin{array}{r} 815 \\ -196 \\ \hline \end{array}$	3. $\begin{array}{r} 741 \\ -478 \\ \hline \end{array}$	4. $\begin{array}{r} 930 \\ -156 \\ \hline \end{array}$	5. $\begin{array}{r} 850 \\ -279 \\ \hline \end{array}$
6. $\begin{array}{r} 134 \\ -75 \\ \hline \end{array}$	7. $\begin{array}{r} 156 \\ -98 \\ \hline \end{array}$	8. $\begin{array}{r} 124 \\ -77 \\ \hline \end{array}$	9. $\begin{array}{r} 628 \\ -79 \\ \hline \end{array}$	10. $\begin{array}{r} 526 \\ -89 \\ \hline \end{array}$
11. $\begin{array}{r} 640 \\ -95 \\ \hline \end{array}$	12. $\begin{array}{r} 722 \\ -275 \\ \hline \end{array}$	13. $\begin{array}{r} \$3.56 \\ -0.78 \\ \hline \end{array}$	14. $\begin{array}{r} \$4.50 \\ -1.75 \\ \hline \end{array}$	15. $\begin{array}{r} \$4.25 \\ -1.79 \\ \hline \end{array}$

16. $624 - 278$　　　17. $530 - 142$　　　18. $762 - 95$

19. $124 - 88$　　　20. $\$7.35 - \$1.49$　　　21. $\$6.50 - \$2.77$

22. Find the difference between 620 and 288.

23. Find the difference between 427 and 712.

Mixed Applications

24. The king vulture can have a wingspread of 310 cm. The bald eagle can have a wingspread of 244 cm. How much greater is the wingspread of the king vulture?

25. A baby pelican had a wingspread of 98 cm. When it was grown its wingspread had increased by 176 cm. What was its wingspread then?

26. Write a question that can be answered using the following:

The sandhill crane can have a wingspread of 213 cm. The condor can have a wingspread of about 298 cm.

┌─ **THINK** ─

🖩 **Using a Calculator**

Here is Mrs. Ortega's bill from the supermarket. The cost of the ground meat is marked out. How much was the ground meat?

$\begin{array}{r} \$5.37 \\ 2.49 \\ 3.68 \\ \hline 2.13 \\ +4.59 \\ \hline \$23.60 \end{array}$

ground meat

➤ **MATH** ◄

Mental Math: Compensation

Sometimes you can find sums in your head by adding too much and then subtracting the extra.

$$167 + 100 = 267$$

Add 3 too many. **167 + 97 = 264** Subtract the extra 3.

Practice Find the sums in your head. Write only the answers.

$153 + 100$	$275 + 100$	$476 + 100$	$385 + 100$
1. $153 + 98$	2. $275 + 97$	3. $476 + 99$	4. $385 + 98$
5. $481 + 98$	6. $174 + 99$	7. $346 + 97$	8. $295 + 96$
9. $172 + 97$	10. $368 + 98$	11. $427 + 96$	12. $588 + 96$

Sometimes you can find differences in your head by subtracting too much and then adding back the extra.

$$235 - 100 = 135$$

Subtract 3 too many. **235 - 97 = 138** Add 3 back.

Find the differences in your head. Write only the answers.

$276 - 100$	$137 - 100$	$425 - 100$	$364 - 100$
13. $276 - 98$	14. $137 - 99$	15. $425 - 97$	16. $364 - 98$
17. $291 - 98$	18. $385 - 97$	19. $764 - 99$	20. $216 - 98$
21. $384 - 97$	22. $172 - 98$	23. $655 - 96$	24. $234 - 96$

PROBLEM SOLVING
Using Data from a Table

FAMOUS TOWERS	Height
Leaning Tower of Pisa	54 m
Skylon Tower	156 m
Space Needle	180 m
Stuttgart Tower	211 m
Cairo Tower	225 m
Eiffel Tower	295 m

Use the table to solve.

1. How much higher is the Space Needle than the Skylon Tower?

2. The Moscow Tower is 222 m higher than the Eiffel Tower. How high is the Moscow Tower?

3. What is the difference in the heights of the Space Needle and the Cairo Tower?

4. The Washington Monument is 54 m shorter than the Cairo Tower. How tall is the Washington Monument?

5. The Statue of Liberty in New York is 54 m taller than the Leaning Tower of Pisa. How tall is the Statue of Liberty?

6. What is the difference in the heights of the tallest tower in the table and the shortest tower in the table?

7. How much higher is the Cairo Tower than the Skylon Tower?

8. The Great Pyramid in Egypt is 73 m shorter than the sum of the heights of the Leaning Tower of Pisa and the Skylon Tower. How tall is the Great Pyramid?

9. Which tower in the table is just 9 m shorter than the sum of the heights of the Leaning Tower of Pisa and the Space Needle?

10. *Strategy Practice* Tower A is shorter than Tower B. Tower A is taller than Tower C. The height of Tower D is between Towers A and C. Which tower is the shortest?

Subtracting Across a Middle Zero

Over one hundred years ago there were as many as 60,000,000 buffalo in the United States. A park ranger found a male buffalo that weighed 806 kg. A female buffalo was found that weighed 458 kg. How much more did the male weigh?

Since we are comparing numbers, we subtract.

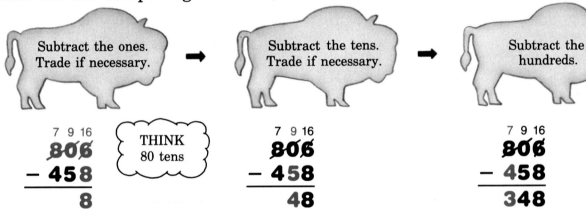

Subtract the ones. Trade if necessary.		Subtract the tens. Trade if necessary.		Subtract the hundreds.

$$\begin{array}{r} {\scriptstyle 7\ \ 9\ \ 16} \\ \cancel{806} \\ -\ 458 \\ \hline 8 \end{array}$$ THINK 80 tens

$$\begin{array}{r} {\scriptstyle 7\ \ 9\ \ 16} \\ \cancel{806} \\ -\ 458 \\ \hline 48 \end{array}$$

$$\begin{array}{r} {\scriptstyle 7\ \ 9\ \ 16} \\ \cancel{806} \\ -\ 458 \\ \hline 348 \end{array}$$

The male buffalo weighed 348 kg more than the female.

Other Examples

${\scriptstyle 8\ \ 10}$	${\scriptstyle 49\ \ 13}$	${\scriptstyle 9\ \ 14}$	${\scriptstyle 79\ \ 10}$	${\scriptstyle 5\ \ 9\ \ 14}$
$\cancel{907}$	$\cancel{503}$	$\cancel{104}$	$\cancel{800}$	$\$\cancel{6.04}$
$-\ 382$	$-\ \ 68$	$-\ \ 67$	$-\ 764$	$-\ 2.59$
525	435	37	36	$\$3.45$

Warm Up   Subtract. Check by adding.

1. 503
  − 147

2. 705
  − 37

3. 900
  − 275

4. 601
  − 529

5. $7.04
  − 2.98

Practice Subtract.

1. 601
  − 259

2. 602
  − 123

3. 400
  − 176

4. 706
  − 324

5. 501
  − 56

6. 803
  − 75

7. 805
  − 726

8. 601
  − 537

9. 900
  − 254

10. 403
  − 231

11. 702
  − 356

12. 902
  − 87

13. $7.05
  − 1.47

14. $9.00
  − 3.34

15. $9.03
  − 7.98

16. 504 − 125

17. 906 − 829

18. 500 − 275

19. 603 − 56

20. $4.00 − $2.98

21. $7.06 − $1.49

22. Subtract 247 from 705.

23. Subtract 124 from 406.

24. Subtract 39 from 604.

25. Subtract 727 from 801.

Mixed Applications

26. A very large male buffalo weighed 900 kg. A very large female buffalo weighed 504 kg. How much more did the male buffalo weigh than the female buffalo?

27. **DATA HUNT** Look up "buffalo" in your encyclopedia. Find the greatest weight of a male buffalo. What is the total weight of this buffalo and the female buffalo in problem 26?

SKILLKEEPER

Add or subtract.

1. 7
  + 2

2. 18
  − 9

3. 8
  + 6

4. 13
  − 8

5. 8
  + 0

6. 6
  − 4

7. 9
  + 3

8. 1
  + 5

9. 15
  − 6

10. 5
  − 4

Subtracting Larger Numbers

While orbiting Earth, a communications satellite was 5,634 km from Earth at its farthest point. It was 956 km from Earth at its closest point in orbit. How much greater is the farthest point than the closest point?

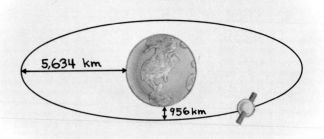

5,634 km

956km

Since we are comparing, we subtract.

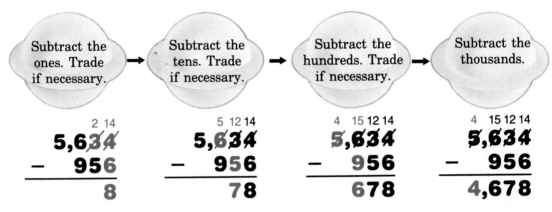

Subtract the ones. Trade if necessary.	Subtract the tens. Trade if necessary.	Subtract the hundreds. Trade if necessary.	Subtract the thousands.

The farthest point was 4,678 km greater than the closest point.

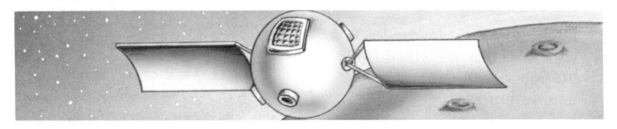

Other Examples

$$
\begin{array}{r} {\scriptstyle 11\ 14\ 13}\\ 1{,}253 \\ -\ \ \ 675 \\ \hline 578 \end{array}
\qquad
\begin{array}{r} {\scriptstyle 599\ \ 12}\\ 6{,}002 \\ -\ 1{,}758 \\ \hline 4{,}244 \end{array}
$$

THINK 600 tens.

$$
\begin{array}{r} {\scriptstyle 5\ 11\ 15\ 6\ 13}\\ 62{,}573 \\ -\ 24{,}728 \\ \hline 37{,}845 \end{array}
\qquad
\begin{array}{r} {\scriptstyle 6\ 11\ 10\ 15}\\ \$72.15 \\ -\ 26.87 \\ \hline \$45.28 \end{array}
$$

Warm Up   Subtract. Check by adding.

1. $\begin{array}{r} 6{,}243 \\ -\ 1{,}768 \end{array}$

2. $\begin{array}{r} 1{,}340 \\ -\ \ \ 856 \end{array}$

3. $\begin{array}{r} 7{,}004 \\ -\ 2{,}836 \end{array}$

4. $\begin{array}{r} 74{,}823 \\ -\ 27{,}365 \end{array}$

5. $\begin{array}{r} \$59.25 \\ -\ 32.68 \end{array}$

Practice Subtract.

1.	6,238 − 2,873	**2.**	5,624 − 1,586	**3.**	1,324 − 786	**4.**	9,640 − 958
5.	5,003 − 1,678	**6.**	8,302 − 3,249	**7.**	6,000 − 2,354	**8.**	7,002 − 683
9.	48,378 − 26,795	**10.**	72,340 − 16,875	**11.**	$76.00 − 24.25	**12.**	$59.25 − 4.98

13. 6,823 − 2,476

14. 7,210 − 3,463

15. 8,001 − 2,675

16. 3,628 − 789

17. 34,286 − 7,529

18. $27.30 − $3.59

19. Subtract 3,726 from 8,002.

20. Subtract 24,365 from 42,831.

21. Subtract $28.75 from $65.20.

Mixed Applications

22. A satellite was 6,023 km from Earth at its farthest point in orbit and 1,756 km at its closest point. What is the difference in these distances?

23. Some information is missing in this problem. Make up the information and find the answer.

Satellite A travels 7,263 km from Earth. How much farther does Satellite A travel from Earth than Satellite B?

THINK

Greatest Sum Game

1. Make this set of cards.

2. Mix the cards facedown.

3. Give each player six cards.

4. Each player makes an addition problem.

Example

```
  8 0 0        9 7 1
+ 7 3 2      + 6 2 1
-------      -------
 1,5 3 2      1,5 9 2
                Winner
```

5. Greatest sum wins.

→ MATH ←

Estimating Differences Using Rounding

Jeff wondered about how much more the boots cost than the hat. To find out, he **rounded** the prices and subtracted.

$$
\begin{array}{r}
\$27.95 \\
-\ \ 6.25 \\
\hline
\end{array}
\quad \boxed{\text{nearest dollar}} \!\!\!> \quad
\begin{array}{r}
\$28.00 \\
-\ \ 6.00 \\
\hline
\$22.00
\end{array}
$$

$\boxed{\text{nearest dollar}}$

The boots were about $22 more than the hat.

Other Examples

$\boxed{\text{nearest ten}}$

$$
\begin{array}{r}
59 \\
-\ 22 \\
\hline
\end{array}
\ \to \
\begin{array}{r}
60 \\
-\ 20 \\
\hline
40
\end{array}
$$

$\boxed{\text{nearest hundred}}$

$$
\begin{array}{r}
812 \\
-\ 289 \\
\hline
\end{array}
\ \to \
\begin{array}{r}
800 \\
-\ 300 \\
\hline
500
\end{array}
$$

$\boxed{\text{nearest dollar}}$

$$
\begin{array}{r}
\$7.89 \\
-\ 5.25 \\
\hline
\end{array}
\ \to \
\begin{array}{r}
\$8.00 \\
-\ 5.00 \\
\hline
\$3.00
\end{array}
$$

Practice

Estimate by rounding to the nearest ten.

1. $\begin{array}{r} 81 \\ -\ 39 \\ \hline \end{array}$
2. $\begin{array}{r} 69 \\ -\ 23 \\ \hline \end{array}$
3. $\begin{array}{r} 81 \\ -\ 49 \\ \hline \end{array}$
4. $\begin{array}{r} 86 \\ -\ 29 \\ \hline \end{array}$
5. $\begin{array}{r} 67 \\ -\ 21 \\ \hline \end{array}$
6. $\begin{array}{r} 73 \\ -\ 48 \\ \hline \end{array}$

Estimate by rounding to the nearest hundred.

7. $\begin{array}{r} 379 \\ -\ 198 \\ \hline \end{array}$
8. $\begin{array}{r} 607 \\ -\ 398 \\ \hline \end{array}$
9. $\begin{array}{r} 615 \\ -\ 299 \\ \hline \end{array}$
10. $\begin{array}{r} 590 \\ -\ 221 \\ \hline \end{array}$
11. $\begin{array}{r} 918 \\ -\ 388 \\ \hline \end{array}$

Estimate by rounding to the nearest dollar.

12. $\begin{array}{r} \$7.95 \\ -\ 1.25 \\ \hline \end{array}$
13. $\begin{array}{r} \$6.15 \\ -\ 3.98 \\ \hline \end{array}$
14. $\begin{array}{r} \$9.08 \\ -\ 3.95 \\ \hline \end{array}$
15. $\begin{array}{r} \$12.89 \\ -\ 8.15 \\ \hline \end{array}$
16. $\begin{array}{r} \$10.17 \\ -\ 2.79 \\ \hline \end{array}$

PROBLEM SOLVING
Using Estimation

QUESTION
DATA
PLAN
ANSWER
CHECK

Use estimation to choose the correct answer.

1. Geri had 400 tiles. She used 187 of them. How many tiles does she have left?
   A 113   **B** 213   **C** 313

2. Geri earned $196 one week. The next week she earned $289. How much did she earn in the two weeks?
   A $385   **B** $485   **C** $585

3. On a vacation, Geri drove 304 miles one day and only 197 miles the next day. How many more miles did she drive the first day?
   A 107   **B** 207   **C** 307

4. Geri weighs 127 pounds, Jean weighs 94 pounds, and Sally weighs 107 pounds. How many pounds do they weigh altogether?
   A 128   **B** 228   **C** 328

5. Geri used a 10-dollar bill to pay for a box of tiles. The total cost was $6.95. What was her change?
   A $5.05   **B** $4.05   **C** $3.05

6. Geri worked 39 hours one week, 44 hours the next, 41 hours the next, and 37 hours the next. How many hours is this for the four weeks?
   A 61   **B** 161   **C** 261

7. Geri had a 20-dollar bill and a 10-dollar bill. She spent $24.88. How much money does she have left?
   A $3.12   **B** $4.12   **C** $5.12

8. *Strategy Practice* Geri is taller than Sue. Lynn is shorter than Sue. Ann is taller than Geri. Who is the shortest?

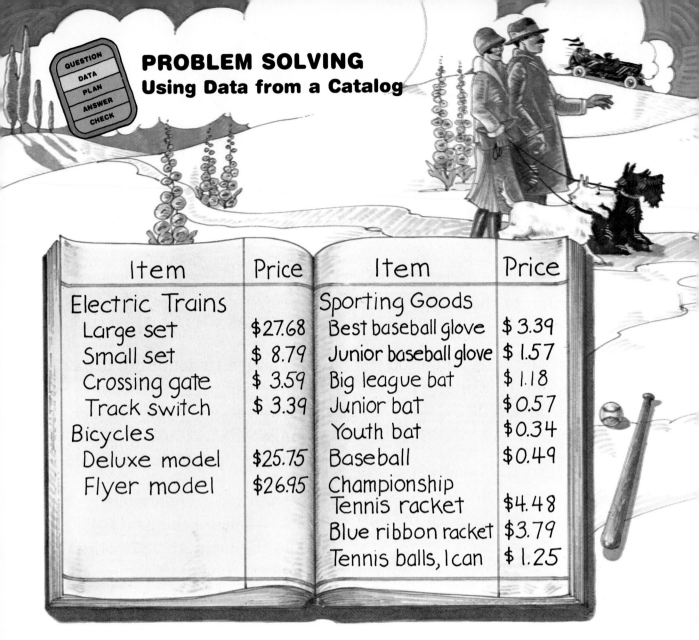

PROBLEM SOLVING
Using Data from a Catalog

Item	Price	Item	Price
Electric Trains		Sporting Goods	
Large set	$27.68	Best baseball glove	$3.39
Small set	$8.79	Junior baseball glove	$1.57
Crossing gate	$3.59	Big league bat	$1.18
Track switch	$3.39	Junior bat	$0.57
Bicycles		Youth bat	$0.34
Deluxe model	$25.75	Baseball	$0.49
Flyer model	$26.95	Championship Tennis racket	$4.48
		Blue ribbon racket	$3.79
		Tennis balls, 1 can	$1.25

Use the 1927 catalog price list above to help
you solve the following problems.

1. How much more was the small train set than the crossing gate?

2. How much less was the small train set than the large train set?

3. How much would it cost to buy a crossing gate and a track switch?

4. How much would you get back from $10.00 if you bought the small train set?

5. How much would you get back from $5.00 if you bought the crossing gate?

6. How much more is the Best baseball glove than the Junior glove?

7. Suppose you bought a Junior glove, a Youth bat, and a baseball. How much would you spend?

8. How much more is the Big League bat than the Junior bat?

9. How much would it cost for a can of tennis balls and a Blue Ribbon racket?

10. If you bought both kinds of bicycles, **estimate** how much you would spend.

11. **Estimate** the cost of a Best baseball glove and a Blue Ribbon racket.

12. You have $10.00. **Estimate** how much money you would get back if you bought a track switch.

13. **DATA HUNT** Choose an item from the catalog. Find the difference between today's price and the catalog price.

14. *Strategy Practice* You have a 10-dollar bill and a 5-dollar bill. You buy a crossing gate, a Best glove, and a Championship racket. How much money will you have left?

PROBLEM-SOLVING STRATEGY
Guess and Check

QUESTION
DATA
PLAN
ANSWER
CHECK

SOME PROBLEMS REQUIRE MORE THAN JUST DECIDING WHETHER TO ADD OR SUBTRACT. TO HELP US SOLVE A PROBLEM SUCH AS THIS, WE CAN USE THE STRATEGY SHOWN BELOW.

Try This Jenny keeps her 12 pet rabbits in two pens, one large and one small. The large pen has 2 more rabbits than the small pen. How many rabbits are in the small pen?

GUESS AND CHECK

I'LL START BY GUESSING 4. THEN THE LARGE PEN WOULD HAVE 6.

THEN I'LL CHECK MY GUESS. IT'S TOO SMALL.

I'LL GUESS AGAIN USING A LARGER NUMBER.

THIS CHECKS. THERE ARE 5 RABBITS IN THE SMALL PEN.

GUESS

Small Pen
4

large Pen
4 + 2
6

CHECK
4 + 6 = 10

GUESS

Small pen
5

large pen
5 + 2
7

CHECK
5 + 7 = 12
It checks.

Solve.

1. Jack had 10 checkers. He made two stacks. One stack had 2 more checkers than the other. How many were in each stack?

2. Diane spent $13 for two books. One book cost $1 more than the other. How much did the higher priced book cost?

76

Add.

1. $\begin{array}{r} 38 \\ +\ 46 \\ \hline \end{array}$	**2.** $\begin{array}{r} 914 \\ +\ 820 \\ \hline \end{array}$	**3.** $\begin{array}{r} \$9.86 \\ +\ 0.58 \\ \hline \end{array}$	**4.** $\begin{array}{r} 3{,}924 \\ +\ 5{,}187 \\ \hline \end{array}$	**5.** $\begin{array}{r} \$17.54 \\ +\ 13.89 \\ \hline \end{array}$	**6.** $\begin{array}{r} 62{,}753 \\ +\ 19{,}628 \\ \hline \end{array}$

Estimate the sums. Round as indicated.

nearest ten	nearest hundred	nearest dollar
7. $\begin{array}{r} 79 \\ +\ 53 \\ \hline \end{array}$	**8.** $\begin{array}{r} 267 \\ +\ 413 \\ \hline \end{array}$	**9.** $\begin{array}{r} \$6.95 \\ +\ 3.25 \\ \hline \end{array}$

Add.

10. $\begin{array}{r} 27 \\ 58 \\ +\ 39 \\ \hline \end{array}$	**11.** $\begin{array}{r} \$1.50 \\ 2.34 \\ +\ 3.76 \\ \hline \end{array}$	**12.** $\begin{array}{r} 326 \\ 58 \\ 39 \\ +\ 125 \\ \hline \end{array}$	**13.** $\begin{array}{r} 623 \\ 5{,}817 \\ +\ 6{,}985 \\ \hline \end{array}$	**14.** $\begin{array}{r} \$\ 2.29 \\ 25.63 \\ +\ 37.14 \\ \hline \end{array}$

Subtract.

15. $\begin{array}{r} 72 \\ -\ 38 \\ \hline \end{array}$	**16.** $\begin{array}{r} \$6.25 \\ -\ 2.98 \\ \hline \end{array}$	**17.** $\begin{array}{r} 604 \\ -\ 179 \\ \hline \end{array}$	**18.** $\begin{array}{r} 3{,}004 \\ -\ 1{,}627 \\ \hline \end{array}$	**19.** $\begin{array}{r} 62{,}375 \\ -\ 14{,}827 \\ \hline \end{array}$

Estimate the differences. Round as indicated.

nearest ten	nearest hundred	nearest dollar
20. $\begin{array}{r} 26 \\ -\ 11 \\ \hline \end{array}$ 	**21.** $\begin{array}{r} 813 \\ -\ 295 \\ \hline \end{array}$ 	**22.** $\begin{array}{r} \$12.13 \\ -\ 4.87 \\ \hline \end{array}$

Solve.

23. How much taller is the Cairo Tower?

Leaning Tower of Pisa	54 m
Cairo Tower	225 m

24. How much for both?

Train Set	$19.56
Ball glove	$ 2.95

ANOTHER LOOK

Trading tens and hundreds
is like trading ones.

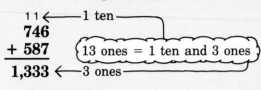

$$11$$
$$746$$
$$+ 587$$
$$\overline{1,333}$$

1 ten → 11
13 ones = 1 ten and 3 ones
3 ones → 3

13 tens = 1 hundred and 3 tens
13 hundreds = 1 thousand and
3 hundreds

70 tens = 69 tens and 10 ones

6 9 14
$$704$$
$$- 278$$
$$\overline{426}$$

THINK
I need more ones.

3
3 **7**
2 **8**
4 9
$$+ 1 7$$
$$\overline{13\ 1}$$

THINK
7 + 8 = 15
15 + 9 = 24
24 + 7 = 31

Add.

1. 275
   + 186

2. 359
   + 175

3. 867
   + 346

4. 407
   + 621

5. 364
   + 542

6. 286
   + 107

7. 2,759
   + 1,678

8. 4,563
   + 9,875

9. 2,864
   + 9,358

Subtract.

10. 342
    − 127

11. 702
    − 169

12. 802
    − 175

13. 7,210
    − 3,651

14. 9,026
    − 3,554

15. 7,000
    − 2,674

Add.

16. 36
    29
   + 15

17. 76
    38
    57
   + 25

18. 462
    375
    468
   + 103

19. 356
    279
   + 135

20. 9,214
    3,652
   + 1,837

21. 4,692
    5,867
   + 2,547

ENRICHMENT

Front-end Estimation

You have learned to estimate by rounding. Another way to estimate is to use the **front-end** numbers.

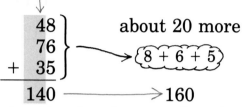

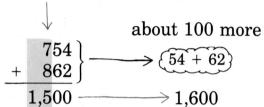

Estimate the sums. Use front-end estimation.

1. 24 33 + 14	**2.** 46 38 + 17	**3.** 61 20 + 52	**4.** 34 44 + 94	**5.** 87 69 + 36	**6.** 79 69 + 99
7. 342 + 461	**8.** 602 + 813	**9.** 784 + 531	**10.** $5.87 + 5.94	**11.** $9.95 + 7.11	**12.** $8.95 + 9.98
13. 630 742 + 253	**14.** 312 403 + 614	**15.** 671 563 + 864	**16.** $5.13 6.83 + 7.00	**17.** $6.49 8.34 + 5.27	**18.** $2.98 3.89 + 1.95

19. Pat bought an animal book for $3.95 and a short story book for $5.98. Estimate how much she spent.

20. Ted bought some socks for $2.89, gloves for $8.95, and earmuffs for $1.15. Estimate how much he spent.

CUMULATIVE REVIEW

Give the letter for the correct answer.

1.
$$\begin{array}{r} 4 \\ 4 \\ +3 \\ \hline \end{array}$$
A 11 **B** 7
C 10 **D** not given

2.
$$\begin{array}{r} 6 \\ 2 \\ +5 \\ \hline \end{array}$$
A 12 **B** 11
C 13 **D** not given

3.
$$\begin{array}{r} 1 \\ 5 \\ +3 \\ \hline \end{array}$$
A 9 **B** 8
C 7 **D** not given

4.
$$\begin{array}{r} 7 \\ 2 \\ +5 \\ \hline \end{array}$$
A 16 **B** 14
C 15 **D** not given

5.
$$\begin{array}{r} 8 \\ 1 \\ +3 \\ \hline \end{array}$$
A 13 **B** 11
C 12 **D** not given

6.
$$\begin{array}{r} 6 \\ 4 \\ +5 \\ \hline \end{array}$$
A 16 **B** 13
C 14 **D** not given

7. 5 hundreds
4 tens
6 ones
A 465
B 546
C 654
D not given

8. 6 tens
0 ones
7 hundreds
A 760
B 607
C 706
D not given

9. 3 thousands
2 hundreds
4 tens
2 ones
A 4,232
B 2,342
C 3,242
D not given

Which statement is correct?

10. **A** 325 > 352
B 352 < 325
C 325 < 352
D not given

11. **A** 1,781 > 1,779
B 1,781 < 1,779
C 1,779 > 1,781
D not given

12. **A** 9,670 > 9,801
B 9,670 < 9,801
C 9,801 < 9,670
D not given

13. Kim had 6 dollars. She earned 8 dollars. How much does Kim have now?
A $13 **B** $15
C $14 **D** not given

14. Gary had 17 marbles. He gave away 9 of the marbles. How many were left?
A 8 **B** 6
C 7 **D** not given

MULTIPLICATION FACTS 4

Alice Liddell lived in England. On July 4, 1862 Alice went on a picnic. That afternoon her friend Charles Dodgson told a story. It was about a 7-year-old girl named Alice. She sees a White Rabbit in a terrible hurry. Alice follows him. She falls into a rabbit hole. Alice Liddell begged Dodgson to write about Alice's adventures underground. He wrote *Alice's Adventures in Wonderland*. Dodgson's pen name was Lewis Carroll. Alice Liddell was 2 times the age of Alice in the story when the book was printed.

Understanding Multiplication

The pet store is having a sale. How many fish are in the 2 bowls?

The bowls have the same number of fish. We **multiply** to find the total number.

2 threes

$$2 \times 3 = 6$$

Factor   Factor   Product

$$\begin{array}{r} 3 \leftarrow \text{Factor} \\ \times\ 2 \leftarrow \text{Factor} \\ \hline 6 \leftarrow \text{Product} \end{array}$$

We read, **"Two times three equals six."**
There are 6 fish in the bowls.

How many birds? Multiply.

1.   4 twos

$$4 \times 2 = n$$

2.   2 fours

$$2 \times 4 = n$$

> You can change the order of the factors and the product will be the same.

3.   3 ones

$$3 \times 1 = n$$

> When 1 is a factor, the product is the other factor.

4.   2 zeros

$$2 \times 0 = n$$

> When 0 is a factor, the product is 0.

Practice Find the products.

1. **5 twos**

5×2

2. **2 fives**

2×5

3. **4 threes**

$$\begin{array}{r} 3 \\ \times\ 4 \\ \hline \end{array}$$

4. **3 fours**

$$\begin{array}{r} 4 \\ \times\ 3 \\ \hline \end{array}$$

5. $\begin{array}{r} 4 \\ \times\ 1 \\ \hline \end{array}$
6. $\begin{array}{r} 1 \\ \times\ 3 \\ \hline \end{array}$
7. $\begin{array}{r} 2 \\ \times\ 0 \\ \hline \end{array}$
8. $\begin{array}{r} 0 \\ \times\ 3 \\ \hline \end{array}$
9. $\begin{array}{r} 2 \\ \times\ 1 \\ \hline \end{array}$
10. $\begin{array}{r} 0 \\ \times\ 4 \\ \hline \end{array}$
11. $\begin{array}{r} 1 \\ \times\ 4 \\ \hline \end{array}$

12. 4×0
13. 1×2

14. 3×1
15. 0×3

16. Multiply 3 by 0.

17. Multiply 1 by 4.

18. Multiply 3 by 1.

19. Find the product of 0 and 2.

20. Find the product of 1 and 3.

⊏ THINK ⊐

Logical Reasoning

Each missing number is the same.

 $\times$  $= 4$

 $+$ $= 4$

Can you find it?

→ **MATH** ←

More Practice, page 413, Set A

Factors of 2, 3, and 4

Thinking about doubles may help you find products when 2, 3, or 4 are factors.

Find the products.

A Factor of 2

1. $2 \times 2 = n$
2 twos

2. $2 \times 3 = n$
2 threes

3. $2 \times 4 = n$
2 fours

4. $2 \times 5 = n$
2 fives

5. $2 \times 6 = n$
2 sixes

6. $2 \times 7 = n$
2 sevens

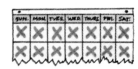

7. $2 \times 8 = n$
2 eights

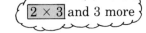

8. $2 \times 9 = n$
2 nines

A Factor of 3

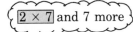 2×6 and 6 more

 2×5 and 5 more

2×3 and 3 more

2×8 and 8 more

9. $3 \times 6 = n$

10. $3 \times 5 = n$

11. $3 \times 3 = n$

12. $3 \times 8 = n$

 2×7 and 7 more

 2×2 and 2 more

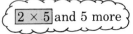 2×9 and 9 more

2×4 and 4 more

13. $3 \times 7 = n$

14. $3 \times 2 = n$

15. $3 \times 9 = n$

16. $3 \times 4 = n$

A Factor of 4

 2×5 plus 2×5

2×3 plus 2×3

2×7 plus 2×7

2×4 plus 2×4

17. $4 \times 5 = n$

18. $4 \times 3 = n$

19. $4 \times 7 = n$

20. $4 \times 4 = n$

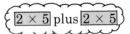 2×9 plus 2×9

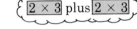 2×2 plus 2×2

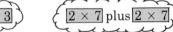 2×6 plus 2×6

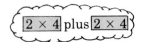 2×8 plus 2×8

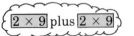

21. $4 \times 9 = n$

22. $4 \times 2 = n$

23. $4 \times 6 = n$

24. $4 \times 8 = n$

Practice Multiply.

THINK
2×6

THINK
4×5

1. 2×6 **2.** 6×2 **3.** 4×5 **4.** 5×4

5. 3×7 **6.** 7×3 **7.** 2×8 **8.** 8×2

9. 4×6 **10.** 6×4 **11.** 3×9 **12.** 9×3

13. $\begin{array}{r} 2 \\ \times\,6 \\ \hline \end{array}$ **14.** $\begin{array}{r} 6 \\ \times\,3 \\ \hline \end{array}$ **15.** $\begin{array}{r} 3 \\ \times\,4 \\ \hline \end{array}$ **16.** $\begin{array}{r} 5 \\ \times\,4 \\ \hline \end{array}$ **17.** $\begin{array}{r} 3 \\ \times\,9 \\ \hline \end{array}$ **18.** $\begin{array}{r} 4 \\ \times\,3 \\ \hline \end{array}$ **19.** $\begin{array}{r} 3 \\ \times\,3 \\ \hline \end{array}$

20. $\begin{array}{r} 3 \\ \times\,2 \\ \hline \end{array}$ **21.** $\begin{array}{r} 7 \\ \times\,4 \\ \hline \end{array}$ **22.** $\begin{array}{r} 2 \\ \times\,2 \\ \hline \end{array}$ **23.** $\begin{array}{r} 2 \\ \times\,7 \\ \hline \end{array}$ **24.** $\begin{array}{r} 7 \\ \times\,3 \\ \hline \end{array}$ **25.** $\begin{array}{r} 2 \\ \times\,4 \\ \hline \end{array}$ **26.** $\begin{array}{r} 4 \\ \times\,0 \\ \hline \end{array}$

27. $\begin{array}{r} 9 \\ \times\,4 \\ \hline \end{array}$ **28.** $\begin{array}{r} 2 \\ \times\,8 \\ \hline \end{array}$ **29.** $\begin{array}{r} 4 \\ \times\,2 \\ \hline \end{array}$ **30.** $\begin{array}{r} 0 \\ \times\,3 \\ \hline \end{array}$ **31.** $\begin{array}{r} 1 \\ \times\,4 \\ \hline \end{array}$ **32.** $\begin{array}{r} 4 \\ \times\,4 \\ \hline \end{array}$ **33.** $\begin{array}{r} 2 \\ \times\,9 \\ \hline \end{array}$

34. $\begin{array}{r} 3 \\ \times\,1 \\ \hline \end{array}$ **35.** $\begin{array}{r} 4 \\ \times\,8 \\ \hline \end{array}$ **36.** $\begin{array}{r} 8 \\ \times\,3 \\ \hline \end{array}$ **37.** $\begin{array}{r} 2 \\ \times\,3 \\ \hline \end{array}$ **38.** $\begin{array}{r} 5 \\ \times\,2 \\ \hline \end{array}$ **39.** $\begin{array}{r} 5 \\ \times\,3 \\ \hline \end{array}$ **40.** $\begin{array}{r} 4 \\ \times\,6 \\ \hline \end{array}$

41. Multiply 4 by 6.   **42.** Multiply 8 by 3.   **43.** Multiply 2 by 7.

Mixed Applications

44. Chico has 6 dollars. Each dollar is worth 4 quarters. How many quarters can Chico get for his dollars?

45. James has 1 quarter, 2 dimes, and 3 nickels. What is the total amount of money he has?

46. Carla has 45 dollars. Each dollar is worth 4 quarters. How many quarters can Carla get for her dollars?

THINK

Logical Reasoning

I'm each of the missing digits below.

‖‖‖ × ‖‖‖ = 20 + ‖‖‖

WHO AM I?

MATH

5 as a Factor

David has 7 nickels. Each nickel is worth 5 pennies. How many pennies can David get for his 7 nickels?

Since each nickel is worth the same number of pennies, we multiply.

 5   10    15   20   25   30   35

7 fives
7 × 5 = 35

David can get 35 pennies for his 7 nickels.

Warm Up

Copy and complete counting the coins. Give the products.

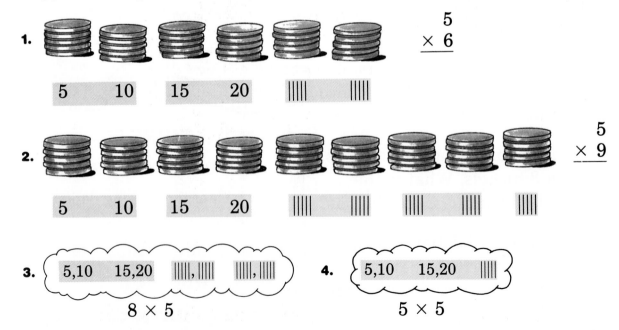

1.
$$\begin{array}{r} 5 \\ \times\ 6 \\ \hline \end{array}$$

5   10   15   20 ||||| |||||

2.
$$\begin{array}{r} 5 \\ \times\ 9 \\ \hline \end{array}$$

5   10   15   20 ||||| ||||| ||||| ||||| |||||

3. (5,10   15,20 |||||,||||| |||||,|||||)

8 × 5

4. (5,10   15,20 |||||)

5 × 5

Practice Multiply.

1. $\begin{array}{r} 3 \\ \times\ 5 \\ \hline \end{array}$
2. $\begin{array}{r} 9 \\ \times\ 4 \\ \hline \end{array}$
3. $\begin{array}{r} 5 \\ \times\ 8 \\ \hline \end{array}$
4. $\begin{array}{r} 1 \\ \times\ 5 \\ \hline \end{array}$
5. $\begin{array}{r} 3 \\ \times\ 3 \\ \hline \end{array}$
6. $\begin{array}{r} 5 \\ \times\ 6 \\ \hline \end{array}$
7. $\begin{array}{r} 9 \\ \times\ 3 \\ \hline \end{array}$

8. $\begin{array}{r} 3 \\ \times\ 8 \\ \hline \end{array}$
9. $\begin{array}{r} 9 \\ \times\ 5 \\ \hline \end{array}$
10. $\begin{array}{r} 7 \\ \times\ 5 \\ \hline \end{array}$
11. $\begin{array}{r} 5 \\ \times\ 0 \\ \hline \end{array}$
12. $\begin{array}{r} 4 \\ \times\ 8 \\ \hline \end{array}$
13. $\begin{array}{r} 8 \\ \times\ 5 \\ \hline \end{array}$
14. $\begin{array}{r} 5 \\ \times\ 5 \\ \hline \end{array}$

15. $\begin{array}{r} 4 \\ \times\ 2 \\ \hline \end{array}$
16. $\begin{array}{r} 5 \\ \times\ 7 \\ \hline \end{array}$
17. $\begin{array}{r} 6 \\ \times\ 4 \\ \hline \end{array}$
18. $\begin{array}{r} 4 \\ \times\ 5 \\ \hline \end{array}$
19. $\begin{array}{r} 5 \\ \times\ 2 \\ \hline \end{array}$
20. $\begin{array}{r} 7 \\ \times\ 3 \\ \hline \end{array}$
21. $\begin{array}{r} 3 \\ \times\ 4 \\ \hline \end{array}$

22. 5×2
23. 1×7
24. 5×5
25. 5×9

26. 3×5
27. 5×8
28. 3×6
29. 7×4

30. 9×2
31. 3×9
32. 5×4
33. 6×5

34. Multiply 5 by 7.

35. Find the product of 8 and 5.

Mixed Applications

36. There are 5 packages of muffins. There are 4 muffins in a package. How many muffins are there in all?

★37. Write a story problem that you can solve using this multiplication equation:

SKILLKEEPER

Add or subtract.

1. $\begin{array}{r} 76 \\ -\ 32 \\ \hline \end{array}$
2. $\begin{array}{r} 275 \\ +\ 383 \\ \hline \end{array}$
3. $\begin{array}{r} 5,935 \\ +\ 784 \\ \hline \end{array}$
4. $\begin{array}{r} \$5.65 \\ -\ 0.48 \\ \hline \end{array}$
5. $\begin{array}{r} 680 \\ -\ 275 \\ \hline \end{array}$

6. $\begin{array}{r} 600 \\ -\ 183 \\ \hline \end{array}$
7. $\begin{array}{r} 53,645 \\ +\ 16,536 \\ \hline \end{array}$
8. $\begin{array}{r} 700 \\ -\ 183 \\ \hline \end{array}$
9. $\begin{array}{r} \$6.25 \\ +\ 2.98 \\ \hline \end{array}$
10. $\begin{array}{r} 4,153 \\ -\ 1,675 \\ \hline \end{array}$

PROBLEM SOLVING
Using Data from a Recipe

Holiday Salad
Serves 6

4 apples
½ cup of raisins
6 small stalks of celery

9 walnuts
2 bananas

Chop and lightly toss the ingredients above. Use 1 cup yogurt with a squeeze of fresh lemon for dressing.

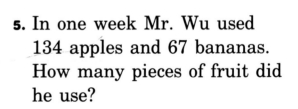

Mr. Wu is a chef. Here is one of his recipes that is a favorite. Solve the following problems. Use data from the recipe as needed.

1. One Friday Mr. Wu served 174 people for lunch and 256 for dinner. How many people did he serve that day?

2. That Friday Mr. Wu made 5 batches of his salad. How many apples did he use?

3. How many walnuts did Mr. Wu use when he made the 5 batches of salad?

4. One Saturday Mr. Wu served 187 people for lunch and 312 for dinner. How many more people did Mr. Wu serve for dinner than for lunch?

5. In one week Mr. Wu used 134 apples and 67 bananas. How many pieces of fruit did he use?

6. How many bananas would Mr. Wu use for 3 batches of salad?

7. **Strategy Practice** Mr. Wu had 11 pieces of fruit (apples and bananas) left. He had 3 more apples than bananas. How many apples did he have? Hint: Use guess and check.

PROBLEM SOLVING
Using Data from a Picture Graph

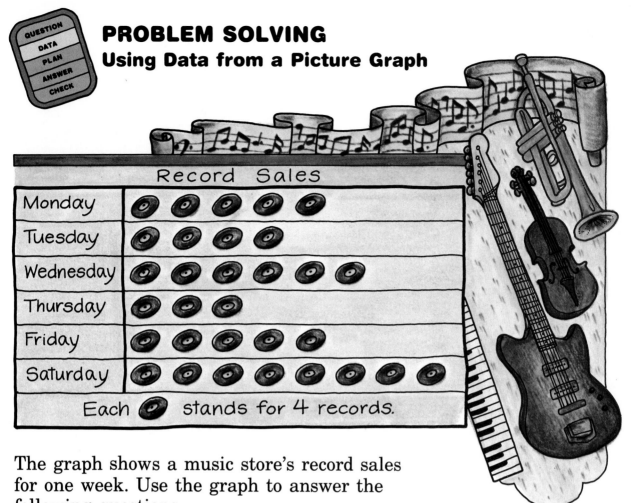

Record Sales

Monday	◎ ◎ ◎ ◎ ◎
Tuesday	◎ ◎ ◎ ◎
Wednesday	◎ ◎ ◎ ◎ ◎ ◎
Thursday	◎ ◎ ◎
Friday	◎ ◎ ◎ ◎ ◎
Saturday	◎ ◎ ◎ ◎ ◎ ◎ ◎ ◎

Each ◎ stands for 4 records.

The graph shows a music store's record sales for one week. Use the graph to answer the following questions.

1. On what day were the most records sold?

2. On what day were the fewest records sold?

3. How many records were sold on Monday?

4. How many records were sold on Saturday?

5. How many more records were sold on Saturday than on Monday?

6. How many records were sold on Wednesday and Thursday altogether?

7. How many fewer records were sold on Tuesday than on Saturday?

8. *Strategy Practice* Another week 14 records were sold on Monday and Tuesday. There were 2 more records sold on Tuesday than on Monday. How many records were sold on Monday?

89

9 as a Factor

At camp, Dee had 7 stacks of 10 dimes each. She put 1 dime from each stack into her piggy bank. How many dimes are in the 7 stacks now?

$7 \times 10 = 70$

7 tens

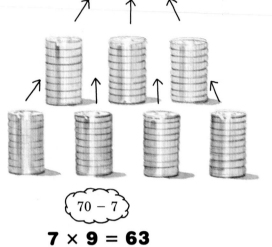

70 − 7

$7 \times 9 = 63$

7 tens − 7

There are 63 dimes in the stacks.

Warm Up Find the products.

THINK
6 tens − 6

1. 6×9

THINK
4 tens − 4

2. 4×9

THINK
8 tens − 8

3. 8×9

THINK
5 tens − 5

4. 5×9

THINK
9 tens − 9

5. 9×9

THINK
7 tens − 7

6. 7×9

THINK
6 × 9

7. 9×6

THINK
8 × 9

8. 9×8

THINK
5 × 9

9. 9×5

10. 9×7

11. 9×4

12. 9×3

Practice Find the products.

1. $\begin{array}{r} 6 \\ \times 5 \\ \hline \end{array}$
2. $\begin{array}{r} 9 \\ \times 7 \\ \hline \end{array}$
3. $\begin{array}{r} 3 \\ \times 9 \\ \hline \end{array}$
4. $\begin{array}{r} 9 \\ \times 0 \\ \hline \end{array}$
5. $\begin{array}{r} 9 \\ \times 8 \\ \hline \end{array}$
6. $\begin{array}{r} 3 \\ \times 5 \\ \hline \end{array}$
7. $\begin{array}{r} 5 \\ \times 6 \\ \hline \end{array}$

8. $\begin{array}{r} 9 \\ \times 6 \\ \hline \end{array}$
9. $\begin{array}{r} 6 \\ \times 4 \\ \hline \end{array}$
10. $\begin{array}{r} 7 \\ \times 1 \\ \hline \end{array}$
11. $\begin{array}{r} 9 \\ \times 9 \\ \hline \end{array}$
12. $\begin{array}{r} 7 \\ \times 9 \\ \hline \end{array}$
13. $\begin{array}{r} 7 \\ \times 0 \\ \hline \end{array}$

14. $\begin{array}{r} 6 \\ \times 4 \\ \hline \end{array}$
15. $\begin{array}{r} 6 \\ \times 9 \\ \hline \end{array}$
16. $\begin{array}{r} 7 \\ \times 9 \\ \hline \end{array}$
17. $\begin{array}{r} 3 \\ \times 7 \\ \hline \end{array}$

18. $\begin{array}{r} 9 \\ \times 1 \\ \hline \end{array}$
19. $\begin{array}{r} 3 \\ \times 6 \\ \hline \end{array}$
20. $\begin{array}{r} 9 \\ \times 9 \\ \hline \end{array}$
21. $\begin{array}{r} 8 \\ \times 5 \\ \hline \end{array}$

22. 9×6
23. 7×9
24. 9×8

25. 9×7
26. 6×4
27. 7×5

Mixed Applications

28. Tom went to camp for 6 weeks. How many days was this?

29. This year there were 18 girls in Dee's cabin. Last year there were 24 girls in her cabin. How many more girls were there last year?

30. Some data is missing from this problem. Make up the data. Then answer the question.

    Jane had craft classes on 3 days each week at camp. How many craft classes did Jane have at camp?

THINK

Logical Reasoning

Each missing digit is the same.

$$\text{▥} \times \text{▥} = 30 + \text{▥}$$

Can you find it?

➤ MATH ◄

The Last Six Facts

Three of the new facts are squares. Find each one. Try to remember them.

6 × 6

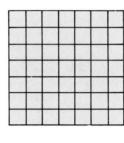
7 × 7

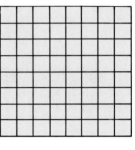
8 × 8

See if you can figure out the other new facts.

6 × 7

6 × 8

7 × 8

Warm Up   Find the products.

THINK
6 × 7

THINK
6 × 8

1. 6×7 2. 7×6 3. 6×8 4. 8×6

5. 7×8 6. 8×7 7. 6×6 8. 6×9

9. 7×7 10. 9×7 11. 8×8 12. 8×9

13. $\begin{array}{r} 7 \\ \times 7 \\ \hline \end{array}$ 14. $\begin{array}{r} 7 \\ \times 6 \\ \hline \end{array}$ 15. $\begin{array}{r} 8 \\ \times 8 \\ \hline \end{array}$ 16. $\begin{array}{r} 8 \\ \times 6 \\ \hline \end{array}$ 17. $\begin{array}{r} 6 \\ \times 6 \\ \hline \end{array}$ 18. $\begin{array}{r} 6 \\ \times 7 \\ \hline \end{array}$ 19. $\begin{array}{r} 7 \\ \times 8 \\ \hline \end{array}$

Practice Find the products.

1. $\begin{array}{r}9\\ \times 4\end{array}$	2. $\begin{array}{r}7\\ \times 8\end{array}$	3. $\begin{array}{r}8\\ \times 3\end{array}$	4. $\begin{array}{r}9\\ \times 6\end{array}$	5. $\begin{array}{r}5\\ \times 9\end{array}$	6. $\begin{array}{r}8\\ \times 8\end{array}$	7. $\begin{array}{r}9\\ \times 3\end{array}$	

8. $\begin{array}{r}8\\ \times 9\end{array}$	9. $\begin{array}{r}6\\ \times 9\end{array}$	10. $\begin{array}{r}9\\ \times 1\end{array}$	11. $\begin{array}{r}8\\ \times 4\end{array}$	12. $\begin{array}{r}8\\ \times 6\end{array}$	13. $\begin{array}{r}9\\ \times 5\end{array}$	14. $\begin{array}{r}9\\ \times 8\end{array}$

15. $\begin{array}{r}7\\ \times 7\end{array}$	16. $\begin{array}{r}8\\ \times 5\end{array}$	17. $\begin{array}{r}8\\ \times 0\end{array}$	18. $\begin{array}{r}9\\ \times 9\end{array}$	19. $\begin{array}{r}5\\ \times 8\end{array}$	20. $\begin{array}{r}6\\ \times 3\end{array}$	21. $\begin{array}{r}9\\ \times 9\end{array}$

22. $\begin{array}{r}2\\ \times 8\end{array}$	23. $\begin{array}{r}6\\ \times 8\end{array}$	24. $\begin{array}{r}9\\ \times 2\end{array}$	25. $\begin{array}{r}7\\ \times 4\end{array}$	26. $\begin{array}{r}8\\ \times 2\end{array}$	27. $\begin{array}{r}9\\ \times 4\end{array}$	28. $\begin{array}{r}8\\ \times 7\end{array}$

29. 8×9 30. 7×8 31. 6×7 32. 5×8 33. 6×8

34. 7×7 35. 0×9 36. 8×7 37. 9×5 38. 8×4

39. Find the product of 8 and 8.   40. Find the product of 7 and 6.

Mixed Applications

41. Gale's team won 17 games last year. They won 9 more games this year. How many games did they win this year?

42. There are 6 baseball teams. Each team has 9 players. How many players is this?

43. This problem has missing data. Make up the data. Then find the answer.

    Each team has 8 players. How many players are there in all?

THINK

Patterns

Study the pattern.
Then copy the equations.
Give the missing numbers.

$1 \times 8 = 10 - 2$
$2 \times 8 = 20 - 4$
$3 \times 8 = 30 - 6$
$4 \times 8 = 40 - 8$
$5 \times 8 = \text{||||} - \text{||||}$
$6 \times 8 = \text{||||} - \text{||||}$
$7 \times 8 = \text{||||} - \text{||||}$
$8 \times 8 = \text{||||} - \text{||||}$

MATH

Multiples

The **multiples** of 5 are the products when 5 is one of the factors.

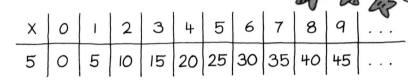

Multiples of 5											
X	0	1	2	3	4	5	6	7	8	9	...
5	0	5	10	15	20	25	30	35	40	45	...

The multiples of 2 are the **even** numbers.
All other whole numbers are **odd** numbers.

Multiples of 2											
X	0	1	2	3	4	5	6	7	8	9	...
2	0	2	4	6	8	10	12	14	16	18	...

The multiples of 9 have some interesting patterns.

0×9	1×9	2×9	3×9	4×9	5×9
0	9	18	27	36	45
		1 + 8	2 + 7	3 + 6	4 + 5

Give the remaining multiples of 9 through 9×9.

Warm Up Give the multiples.

Multiples of 4											
X	0	1	2	3	4	5	6	7	8	9	...
4	0	4	8	12	▓	▓	▓	▓	▓	▓	...

Practice Copy and complete each set of multiples.

1.

Multiples of 3

X	0	1	2	3	4	5	6	7	8	9	...
3	0	3	6	9	▥	▥	▥	▥	▥	▥	...

2.

Multiples of 6

X	0	1	2	3	4	5	6	7	8	9	...
6	0	6	12	18	▥	▥	▥	▥	▥	▥	...

3.

Multiples of 7

X	0	1	2	3	4	5	6	7	8	9	...
7	0	7	14	21	▥	▥	▥	▥	▥	▥	...

4.

Multiples of 8

X	0	1	2	3	4	5	6	7	8	9	...
8	0	8	16	24	▥	▥	▥	▥	▥	▥	...

Find the products.

5. $\begin{array}{r} 7 \\ \times\ 7 \\ \hline \end{array}$ **6.** $\begin{array}{r} 7 \\ \times\ 4 \\ \hline \end{array}$ **7.** $\begin{array}{r} 8 \\ \times\ 9 \\ \hline \end{array}$ **8.** $\begin{array}{r} 5 \\ \times\ 7 \\ \hline \end{array}$

9. $\begin{array}{r} 8 \\ \times\ 5 \\ \hline \end{array}$ **10.** $\begin{array}{r} 8 \\ \times\ 8 \\ \hline \end{array}$ **11.** $\begin{array}{r} 9 \\ \times\ 5 \\ \hline \end{array}$ **12.** $\begin{array}{r} 7 \\ \times\ 8 \\ \hline \end{array}$

THINK

Logical Reasoning

Of the numbers with 2 digits, I'm the smallest with this fate. I'm a multiple of 6 and a multiple of 8.

WHO AM I?

MATH

PROBLEM SOLVING
Identifying Needed Data

The following problems have more data than you need. You will have to find the needed data to solve each problem.

1. The Douglas fir tree can grow as high as 76 m. Its trunk can have a width of between 89 cm and 243 cm. What is the difference in these widths?

2. Giant bamboos can grow as high as 36 m. Sometimes they can grow as fast as 7 m a week. At this rate how much would one grow in 3 weeks?

3. An elephant tree grew to a height of 914 cm. From side to side it was 9 m. The distance around it was about 3 times that. How many meters is it around the tree?

4. The loblolly pine tree grows to 30 m tall and 91 cm across. Its needles usually come in bundles of 3. How many needles would be in 8 such bundles?

5. **DATA BANK** See page 400. How much taller is the Douglas fir tree than the yellow poplar tree?

6. *Strategy Practice* Jesse planted 15 apple and pear trees. He planted 7 more apple trees than pear trees. How many apple trees did he plant?

Practice the Facts

Multiply.

1. 8×6	**2.** 4×7	**3.** 3×5	**4.** 0×5	**5.** 3×6	**6.** 7×8	**7.** 9×2	
8. 1×3	**9.** 6×7	**10.** 5×5	**11.** 3×8	**12.** 9×4	**13.** 7×3	**14.** 6×1	
15. 7×9	**16.** 4×8	**17.** 9×0	**18.** 2×7	**19.** 4×3	**20.** 8×8	**21.** 3×2	

22. 7×7 **23.** 9×8 **24.** 6×6 **25.** 4×5

26. 5×7 **27.** 4×4 **28.** 1×7 **29.** 9×6

30. 0×8 **31.** 8×2 **32.** 3×9 **33.** 8×5

Guess each rule. Then give the missing numbers.

Maria said	Bob answered
3	15
0	0
4	20
34. 6	‖‖‖
35. ‖‖‖	40

Maria said	Bob answered
5	45
3	27
7	63
36. 8	‖‖‖
37. ‖‖‖	18

Maria said	Bob answered
4	28
2	14
9	63
38. 6	‖‖‖
39. ‖‖‖	21

Missing Numbers

Work with a group.

You will need counters, index cards, and calculators.

Part 1

Look at these missing-number equations.

$$\blacklozenge + \blacktriangle = 12$$
$$\blacksquare + \blacksquare = 12$$

1. How are they alike? How are they different?

2. Use counters to help you find all the values of the ▲, ◆, and ■. List them.

3. Compare your lists with those of other groups. Explain why the ◆ and ▲ had a different number of possible values than the ■.

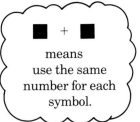

■ + ■

means use the same number for each symbol.

Part 2

With your group, look at these missing-number equations.

4. Without actually finding the values, predict which equations will have more than one solution. Record your predictions.

5. For each equation, find and record some of the values of the ■, ◆, and ▲.

   • Were your predictions accurate?

   • Which equations have many solutions? Only one solution? Explain.

A $\blacktriangle + \blacktriangle + \blacklozenge = 13$

B $\blacksquare - \blacksquare = 0$

C $3 \times \blacktriangle = 12$

D $\blacklozenge + \blacklozenge = 18$

E $5 \times \blacklozenge = \blacktriangle$

F $56 \div \blacktriangle = \blacksquare$

Part 3

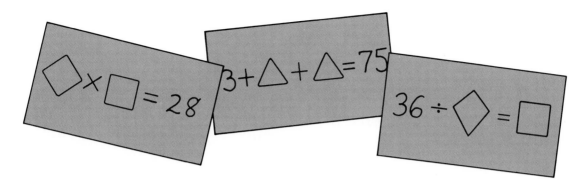

6. Make up some mystery-number equations to share with other groups.

   • Think of some that have only one solution, and some that have many solutions.

   • Write each equation on an index card. Write possible solutions on the back.

7. Trade cards with another group and solve their equations. Then compare your answers with the ones written on the backs of the cards.

8. Discuss the mystery-number equations with the class. Were some more difficult than others? Why? When was a calculator useful?

More Practice, page 414, Set B

Mixed Skills Practice

Computation

Find the answers.

1. $27 + 49$
2. $624 + 813$
3. $\$6.54 + 2.19$
4. $346 + 795$
5. $\$18.95 + 7.69$
6. $36{,}428 + 14{,}347$

7. $75 - 29$
8. $624 - 182$
9. $\$7.24 - 1.67$
10. $804 - 195$
11. $\$36.50 - 29.25$
12. $42{,}368 - 14{,}725$

13. 9×5
14. 7×6
15. 5×8
16. 9×6
17. 8×8
18. 8×7
19. 4×7

20. 6×8
21. 3×7
22. 7×9
23. 7×5
24. 8×4
25. 7×7
26. 8×9

Mental Math

Write only the answers.

27. $33 + 4$
28. $46 + 3$
29. $72 + 6$
30. $41 + 5$

31. $27 + 9$
32. $38 + 9$
33. $256 + 99$
34. $378 + 98$

35. $20 + 40$
36. $70 + 80$
37. $500 + 400$
38. $600 + 700$

Estimation

Estimate.

39. $32 + 49$
40. $58 + 19$
41. $198 + 305$
42. $695 + 198$

43. $72 - 39$
44. $61 - 48$
45. $704 - 296$
46. $712 - 195$

47. $\$1.98 + \$3.89$
48. $\$6.95 - \$4.98$
49. $\$3.11 + \$4.93$
50. $\$9.10 - \$4.98$

APPLIED PROBLEM SOLVING

You want to buy a calculator. You find two kinds of calculators at the store. One kind uses solar cells and costs $9.95. The other uses a small battery and costs $6.75 with the battery included. Which calculator will you buy?

Some Things to Consider

- The solar calculator works with any good light source such as sunlight or electric light.
- The solar calculator should last about 5 years.

- The battery calculator comes with a small battery that lasts one to two years. A new battery costs $2.69.
- You have $12.00, but you would like to buy some other things.

Some Questions to Answer

1. How much more does the solar calculator cost than the battery calculator?

2. If you buy the solar calculator, how much money will you have left to spend on the other things?

3. If you buy the battery calculator, how much money will you have left to spend on the other things?

4. After you have replaced the battery one time, how much will you have spent in all for the battery calculator?

5. How much will you have spent in all when you have bought 2 new batteries?

What Is Your Decision?

Will you buy the solar calculator or the battery calculator?

PROBLEM-SOLVING STRATEGY
Make a List

QUESTION / DATA / PLAN / ANSWER / CHECK

THIS TYPE OF PROBLEM MAY REQUIRE MORE THAN JUST DECIDING TO ADD, SUBTRACT, OR MULTIPLY. A STRATEGY THAT WILL HELP YOU WITH THIS PROBLEM IS GIVEN BELOW.

Try This The bicycle shop had girls' bicycles and boys' bicycles. Both kinds come in three colors, red, blue, and white. The owner said, "Today I sold one of each kind of bicycle that I have." How many did he sell?

MAKE A LIST

IF I WANTED A BOY'S BICYCLE, I COULD GET IT IN 3 COLORS.

IF I WANTED A GIRL'S BICYCLE, I COULD GET IT IN 3 COLORS.

boy's -- red
boy's -- blue
boy's -- white

girl's -- red
girl's -- blue
girl's -- white

The owner sold 6 bicycles.

Solve.

1. When Lori got home from school, her mother said, "You can have an apple or a pear. Also, you can have milk or juice." How many different "snacks" can Lori choose?

2. Ed had 3 kinds of bread— rye, white, and wheat. He found cheese and turkey. How many sandwiches can he make? (One kind of bread and one thing on it.)

Find the products.

1. $\begin{array}{r} 4 \\ \times\, 5 \\ \hline \end{array}$	**2.** $\begin{array}{r} 8 \\ \times\, 6 \\ \hline \end{array}$	**3.** $\begin{array}{r} 7 \\ \times\, 6 \\ \hline \end{array}$	**4.** $\begin{array}{r} 3 \\ \times\, 0 \\ \hline \end{array}$	**5.** $\begin{array}{r} 5 \\ \times\, 7 \\ \hline \end{array}$	**6.** $\begin{array}{r} 9 \\ \times\, 7 \\ \hline \end{array}$	**7.** $\begin{array}{r} 4 \\ \times\, 7 \\ \hline \end{array}$
8. $\begin{array}{r} 7 \\ \times\, 8 \\ \hline \end{array}$	**9.** $\begin{array}{r} 3 \\ \times\, 2 \\ \hline \end{array}$	**10.** $\begin{array}{r} 9 \\ \times\, 9 \\ \hline \end{array}$	**11.** $\begin{array}{r} 4 \\ \times\, 4 \\ \hline \end{array}$	**12.** $\begin{array}{r} 6 \\ \times\, 6 \\ \hline \end{array}$	**13.** $\begin{array}{r} 5 \\ \times\, 6 \\ \hline \end{array}$	**14.** $\begin{array}{r} 7 \\ \times\, 7 \\ \hline \end{array}$
15. $\begin{array}{r} 8 \\ \times\, 8 \\ \hline \end{array}$	**16.** $\begin{array}{r} 5 \\ \times\, 5 \\ \hline \end{array}$	**17.** $\begin{array}{r} 9 \\ \times\, 6 \\ \hline \end{array}$	**18.** $\begin{array}{r} 4 \\ \times\, 6 \\ \hline \end{array}$	**19.** $\begin{array}{r} 8 \\ \times\, 9 \\ \hline \end{array}$	**20.** $\begin{array}{r} 3 \\ \times\, 1 \\ \hline \end{array}$	**21.** $\begin{array}{r} 9 \\ \times\, 3 \\ \hline \end{array}$

22. Give the next 6 multiples of 8.

X	0	1	2	3	4	5	6	7	8	9
8	0	8	16	24						

Find the missing factors.

23. $\text{||||} \times 4 = 12$ **24.** $3 \times \text{||||} = 18$ **25.** $\text{||||} \times 2 = 10$ **26.** $3 \times \text{||||} = 6$

27. $4 \times \text{||||} = 20$ **28.** $\text{||||} \times 6 = 30$ **29.** $8 \times \text{||||} = 24$ **30.** $\text{||||} \times 5 = 15$

Solve.

31.

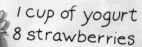

STRAWBERRY SMOOTHIE MIX
1 cup of yogurt
8 strawberries

How many strawberries would it take to make 6 smoothies?

32. Kevin has a plant that is 57 cm tall. Rob's plant is 48 cm tall. How much taller is Kevin's plant than Rob's?

Think 3 sevens → 21
and 3 sevens. → 21

6 × 7 = 42

Think 6 fours → 24
and another 4. → 4

7 × 4 = 28

6 × 2 = 12
6 × 3 = 18
6 × 4 = 24
6 × 5 = 30

6 × ||||| = 30

Find the products.

1. 8 × 5   **2.** 5 × 9   **3.** 7 × 7

4. 6 × 5   **5.** 8 × 4   **6.** 7 × 9

7. 8 × 9   **8.** 7 × 6   **9.** 4 × 9

10. 4 × 6   **11.** 8 × 7   **12.** 9 × 9

Find the missing factors.

13. 5 × ||||| = 20   **14.** ||||| × 4 = 12

15. ||||| × 5 = 10   **16.** 9 × ||||| = 27

17. ||||| × 5 = 10   **18.** ||||| × 6 = 18

19. 2 × ||||| = 6   **20.** 5 × ||||| = 35

Logical Reasoning

Use the drawing to answer the questions.

1. How many ducks are in the shadow?

2. How many ducks are in the pond?

3. How many ducks are inside the fence?

4. How many ducks are inside the fence *and* in the shadow?

5. How many ducks are in the shadow but not in the pond?

6. How many ducks are not in the shadow and not in the pond?

7. How many ducks are in the pond, not in the shadow, and inside the fence?

8. How many ducks are in the pond, not inside the fence, and are in the shadow?

9. Tell where the colored duck is.

CUMULATIVE REVIEW

Give the letter for the correct answer.

1. 53 rounded to the nearest ten

  A 60   **B** 50
  C 30   **D** not given

2. 87 rounded to the nearest ten

  A 70   **B** 80
  C 90   **D** not given

3. 351 rounded to the nearest ten

  A 360   **B** 340
  C 350   **D** not given

4. 246 rounded to the nearest ten

  A 240   **B** 250
  C 260   **D** not given

5. 2,375 rounded to the nearest hundred

  A 2,400   **B** 2,300
  C 2,000   **D** not given

6. 4,435 rounded to the nearest hundred

  A 4,500   **B** 4,400
  C 4,000   **D** not given

7.
$$\begin{array}{r} 26 \\ + 45 \\ \hline \end{array}$$
  A 71   **B** 73
  C 61   **D** not given

8.
$$\begin{array}{r} 63 \\ + 59 \\ \hline \end{array}$$
  A 112   **B** 113
  C 123   **D** not given

9.
$$\begin{array}{r} 256 \\ + 185 \\ \hline \end{array}$$
  A 341   **B** 331
  C 441   **D** not given

10.
$$\begin{array}{r} \$7.76 \\ + 1.35 \\ \hline \end{array}$$
  A \$9.11   **B** \$8.01
  C \$8.11   **D** not given

11.
$$\begin{array}{r} 1,578 \\ + 7,456 \\ \hline \end{array}$$
  A 9,034   **B** 9,924
  C 7,034   **D** not given

12.
$$\begin{array}{r} 556 \\ 428 \\ + 119 \\ \hline \end{array}$$
  A 1,083   **B** 1,104
  C 1,103   **D** not given

13. Greg bought a game for \$15, a ball for \$8, and a book for \$7. How much did he spend?

  A \$30   **B** \$32
  C \$20   **D** not given

14. Carmen bought a radio for \$38. She spent \$9 for tapes and \$12 on posters. How much did she spend?

  A \$49   **B** \$57
  C \$59   **D** not given

Michael Joe and his grandmother arrived at Cedar Pass Campground as the sun was setting. Across the road, Michael Joe could see strangely-shaped rock forms. They stood out against the evening sky. A cool wind was blowing. Michael Joe felt a chill go up his back. No wonder his Indian ancestors had called the place "mako sica." It means "lands bad." Michael Joe and his grandmother spent four days in Badlands National Park. They hunted for fossils. They slept there 3 nights. Michael Joe got only 15 hours of sleep in all. He could not sleep well in this strange and beautiful place.

Understanding Division

Work with a group.
You will need 15 ten strips, about 60 unit squares, and a number cube.

Part 1

1. Try this activity to explore division. Take turns in your group.
   - Build a number by taking from 0 to 15 ten strips and from 0 to 9 unit squares.
   - Roll the number cube. Divide your total number equally into the number of groups that you rolled. Trade ten strips for unit squares if you need to.
   - Count the number in each group and the number left over.
   - Record your work on a chart like this:

Total Number	Number of Groups	Number in Each Group	Number Left Over
53	2	26	1
124	4	31	0

2. Talk about when you needed to trade ten strips for unit squares. Did you ever have a ten strip left over? Why or why not?

3. Suppose the number you rolled is greater than your total number. How would you record this?

Part 2

4. Fold back the Total Number column on your chart. Then trade charts with another group.

Number of Groups	Number in Each Group	Number Left Over
2	26	1
4	31	0

5. Use the number of groups, the number in each group, and the number left over to find the total number. Use your place-value materials if you need to. Record.

6. Then unfold the chart and check your answers. Talk about how you solved for the total number. Can you think of other ways to find the total number?

Part 3

7. Find the missing information in the chart below. Use place-value materials to help.

Total Number	Number of Groups	Number in Each Group	Number Left Over
48		6	0
23		10	
134	5		
77	3		
	2	9	0
	4	13	3
	6	16	2

8. Talk with your group.
  - What information did you need in order to find the number of groups? The number in each group? The total number?
  - Tell how you know when to divide. When to multiply.

9. What if you saw a chart that looked like this?

Total Number	Number of Groups	Number in Each Group	Num Left
15	2		
25		8	

  - How do you know that there must be numbers left over?

  - How can you find what they are?

10. Suppose you know that there are 3 groups and 2 left over. Can you find the total number and the number in each group? Explain.

More Practice, page 414, Set C

Fact Families: Dividing by 4 and 5

$$4 \times 5 = 20$$

If you know one multiplication fact, you know another multiplication fact and two division facts.

Fact Family

$4 \times 5 = 20$
$5 \times 4 = 20$
$20 \div 5 = 4$
$20 \div 4 = 5$

Warm Up Find the products and quotients.

1. $4 \times 3 = n$
   $3 \times 4 = n$
   $12 \div 3 = n$
   $12 \div 4 = n$

2. $5 \times 2 = n$
   $2 \times 5 = n$
   $10 \div 2 = n$
   $10 \div 5 = n$

3. $3 \times 5 = n$
   $5 \times 3 = n$
   $15 \div 5 = n$
   $15 \div 3 = n$

4. $2 \times 4 = n$
   $4 \times 2 = n$
   $8 \div 4 = n$
   $8 \div 2 = n$

You can find quotients by thinking of missing factors.

THINK
$? \times 4 = 24$

5. $24 \div 4 = n$

THINK
$? \times 5 = 35$

6. $35 \div 5 = n$

THINK
$? \times 4 = 36$

7. $36 \div 4 = n$

THINK
$? \times 5 = 40$

8. $40 \div 5 = n$

THINK
$? \times 4 = 32$

9. $32 \div 4 = n$

THINK
$? \times 5 = 45$

10. $45 \div 5 = n$

Practice Divide. Think about fact families or missing factors.

1. $12 \div 4$ **2.** $15 \div 5$ **3.** $14 \div 2$ **4.** $28 \div 4$

5. $20 \div 5$ **6.** $27 \div 3$ **7.** $40 \div 5$ **8.** $18 \div 2$

9. $16 \div 4$ **10.** $36 \div 4$ **11.** $21 \div 3$ **12.** $30 \div 5$

13. $4\overline{)8}$ **14.** $2\overline{)16}$ **15.** $5\overline{)45}$ **16.** $5\overline{)40}$ **17.** $3\overline{)15}$ **18.** $4\overline{)24}$

19. $5\overline{)10}$ **20.** $4\overline{)20}$ **21.** $3\overline{)18}$ **22.** $4\overline{)32}$ **23.** $5\overline{)35}$ **24.** $2\overline{)12}$

25. $5\overline{)20}$ **26.** $2\overline{)10}$ **27.** $4\overline{)36}$ **28.** $3\overline{)24}$ **29.** $4\overline{)28}$ **30.** $5\overline{)25}$

Write a multiplication and a division equation for each picture.

Example

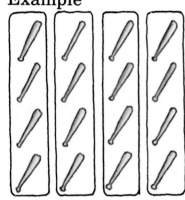

31.

32.

33.

34.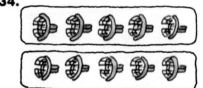

$4 \times 4 = 16$
$16 \div 4 = 4$

SKILLKEEPER

Find the products.

| **1.** $\begin{array}{r} 3 \\ \times 9 \end{array}$ | **2.** $\begin{array}{r} 5 \\ \times 6 \end{array}$ | **3.** $\begin{array}{r} 4 \\ \times 8 \end{array}$ | **4.** $\begin{array}{r} 2 \\ \times 7 \end{array}$ | **5.** $\begin{array}{r} 8 \\ \times 6 \end{array}$ | **6.** $\begin{array}{r} 7 \\ \times 7 \end{array}$ |

| **7.** $\begin{array}{r} 9 \\ \times 8 \end{array}$ | **8.** $\begin{array}{r} 0 \\ \times 9 \end{array}$ | **9.** $\begin{array}{r} 7 \\ \times 8 \end{array}$ | **10.** $\begin{array}{r} 9 \\ \times 9 \end{array}$ | **11.** $\begin{array}{r} 5 \\ \times 5 \end{array}$ | **12.** $\begin{array}{r} 6 \\ \times 7 \end{array}$ |

Division Properties

There are some special 0 and 1 properties for division.

<table>
<tr><td>Examples</td><td>Properties</td></tr>
</table>

$7 \times 1 = 7$
$7 \div 1 = 7$  Any number divided by 1 is that number.

$1 \times 6 = 6$
$6 \div 6 = 1$ Any number (not 0) divided by itself is 1.

$0 \times 4 = 0$
$0 \div 4 = 0$ Zero divided by any number (not 0) is 0.

$n \times 0 = 9$ $n \times 0 = 0$ Remember: We never divide
$9 \div 0 = n$ $0 \div 0 = n$ by 0.

No number works. Any number works.

Practice Find the quotients.

1. $0 \div 8$ 2. $9 \div 1$ 3. $0 \div 2$ 4. $4 \div 1$

5. $8 \div 8$ 6. $28 \div 4$ 7. $0 \div 6$ 8. $30 \div 5$

9. $18 \div 3$ 10. $3 \div 3$ 11. $8 \div 1$ 12. $5 \div 5$

13. $7\overline{)0}$ 14. $4\overline{)24}$ 15. $1\overline{)7}$ 16. $5\overline{)45}$ 17. $4\overline{)4}$ 18. $5\overline{)0}$

19. $9\overline{)9}$ 20. $3\overline{)0}$ 21. $2\overline{)16}$ 22. $1\overline{)3}$ 23. $3\overline{)21}$ 24. $1\overline{)5}$

25. $5\overline{)40}$ 26. $1\overline{)6}$ 27. $4\overline{)20}$ 28. $4\overline{)0}$ 29. $7\overline{)7}$ 30. $5\overline{)35}$

PROBLEM SOLVING
Understanding the Operation

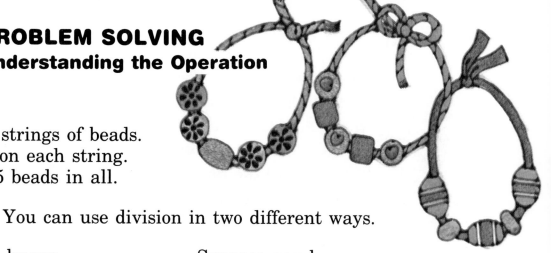

There are 3 strings of beads.
5 beads are on each string.
There are 15 beads in all.

You can use division in two different ways.

Suppose you know:
  15 beads, 5 for each string.

You can **divide** to find **how many strings.**

$$15 \div 5 = 3$$

There are 3 strings.

| Division can tell how many sets. |

Suppose you know:
  15 beads, the same number on each of 3 strings.
You can **divide** to find **how many on each string.**

$$15 \div 3 = 5$$

There are 5 beads on each string.

| Division can tell how many in each set. |

Solve.

1. There are 20 beads. Put the same number on each of 4 strings. How many beads are on each string?

2. Janis has 12 beads. She puts 3 beads on each string. How many strings does she have?

3. There are 16 berries. The berries are shared equally by 4 children. How many berries are there for each child?

4. Alex spent 15 dollars for tickets. Each ticket cost 5 dollars. How many tickets did he buy?

5. Phil bought 7 tickets. He spent 14 dollars. How much was each ticket?

6. *Strategy Practice* Lyn can buy an A ticket, a B ticket, or a C ticket. How many ways can Lyn buy 2 different tickets? Hint: Make a list.

PROBLEM SOLVING ⭐ Using the 5-Point Checklist

To solve a problem

⭐ 1. Understand the Question
⭐ 2. Find the needed Data
⭐ 3. Plan what to do
⭐ 4. Find the Answer
⭐ 5. Check back

QUESTION
DATA
PLAN
ANSWER
CHECK

Made in Denver 1924

Liberty Dime

Large Cent—1851

Use the 5-Point Checklist to help you solve the following problem.

Jasmine has a 1924 penny made in Denver. Robin has an 1851 Large Cent. How many years apart are these dates?

1. Understand the QUESTION
What is the difference in the two dates?

2. Find the needed DATA
Denver penny: 1924   Large Cent: 1851

3. PLAN what to do
Since we want the difference in two numbers, we subtract.

4. Find the ANSWER
$1924 - 1851 = 73$ The dates are 73 years apart.

5. CHECK back
Check by adding 73 to 1851. 73 seems about right.

Indian Head Penny

Solve. Use the 5-Point Checklist.

1. Tod has Denver pennies in his coin book. One page has 5 rows with 4 in each row. How many pennies is this?

2. Lisa has 18 Denver pennies. She will put them in 3 rows in her coin book. How many should she put in each row?

Solve.

1. Sal has a 1901 Indian head penny. He also has a Denver penny made 28 years later. What is the date of his Denver penny?

2. Glen has one page of Lincoln head pennies. It has 6 rows with 5 pennies in each row. How many pennies does he have?

3. Dotty has 20 coins to put in her book. She puts 4 coins in each row. How many rows does she have?

4. Leah has an 1851 Large Cent that is worth $7.95. She has an Indian head penny worth $2.75. How much are both coins worth?

5. Eva put 24 coins in rows of 4 in her book. How many rows does she have?

6. Lou put 12 coins in rows of 4 in his book. How many rows did he make?

7. Jill has 8 Indian head pennies and 12 Lincoln head pennies. She put them into 5 equal rows. How many did she put in each row?

8. Della sold 8 Large Cents for $6 each. She also sold a Liberty dime for $7. How much money did she get?

9. **Strategy Practice** Al has 15 pennies on one page. They are either Indian head or Denver pennies. There are 3 more Indian head pennies than Denver pennies. How many Denver pennies are on the page?

Dividing by 6 and 7

Lynn bought 42 cans of juice. They are packaged in boxes of 6. How many boxes of juice did Lynn buy?

$$42 \div 6 = 7$$

Lynn bought 7 boxes of juice.

Lynn plans to use one can of juice each day. How many weeks will the 42 cans last?

$$42 \div 7 = 6$$

The juice will last 6 weeks.

Warm Up Divide.

> THINK
> $? \times 6 = 30$

1. $30 \div 6 = n$

> THINK
> $? \times 7 = 28$

2. $28 \div 7 = n$

> THINK
> $? \times 6 = 48$

3. $48 \div 6 = n$

> THINK
> $? \times 7 = 63$

4. $63 \div 7 = n$

> THINK
> $? \times 6 = 18$

5. $18 \div 6 = n$

> THINK
> $? \times 6 = 54$

6. $54 \div 6 = n$

7. $6\overline{)30}$ **8.** $7\overline{)35}$ **9.** $7\overline{)28}$ **10.** $6\overline{)48}$ **11.** $7\overline{)56}$

12. $7\overline{)49}$ **13.** $6\overline{)54}$ **14.** $7\overline{)63}$ **15.** $6\overline{)36}$ **16.** $6\overline{)24}$

Practice Find the quotients.

1. $18 \div 6$ **2.** $35 \div 5$

3. $14 \div 2$ **4.** $14 \div 7$

5. $42 \div 6$ **6.** $8 \div 1$

7. $24 \div 3$ **8.** $56 \div 7$ **9.** $54 \div 6$ **10.** $40 \div 5$

11. $12 \div 6$ **12.** $24 \div 4$ **13.** $7 \div 7$ **14.** $49 \div 7$

15. $42 \div 7$ **16.** $32 \div 4$ **17.** $21 \div 3$ **18.** $24 \div 6$

19. $6\overline{)54}$ **20.** $4\overline{)36}$ **21.** $7\overline{)63}$ **22.** $7\overline{)0}$ **23.** $5\overline{)30}$

24. $2\overline{)18}$ **25.** $7\overline{)35}$ **26.** $6\overline{)6}$ **27.** $6\overline{)36}$ **28.** $3\overline{)27}$

29. $6\overline{)48}$ **30.** $5\overline{)45}$ **31.** $7\overline{)21}$ **32.** $6\overline{)42}$ **33.** $4\overline{)28}$

34. $7\overline{)49}$ **35.** $7\overline{)56}$ **36.** $9\overline{)81}$ **37.** $7\overline{)42}$ **38.** $9\overline{)72}$

39. Divide 35 by 7.   **40.** Divide 45 by 9.   **41.** Divide 54 by 6.

42. Divide 30 by 6.   **43.** Divide 63 by 7.   **44.** Divide 56 by 7.

Mixed Applications

45. Karl bought 48 cans of grape juice. They were packed in boxes of 6. How many boxes did he buy?

46. Write a question for this data. Solve your own problem. Justin bought 24 cans of orange juice and 18 cans of grapefruit juice. He uses one of these cans of juice each day.

THINK

Calculator

Rules: You can only press these keys: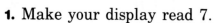

1. Make your display read 7.

2. Make your display read 13.

MATH

Dividing by 8 and 9

There were 72 students going to the picnic. There were 9 station wagons to take them. How many students should ride in each one?

Eight students should ride in each station wagon.

When all 72 students arrived, they divided equally into 8 baseball teams. How many were on each team?

There were 9 students on each team.

$8 \times 9 = 72$

72 ÷ 9 = 8

$9 \times 8 = 72$

72 ÷ 8 = 9

Go Tigers!

Warm Up   Divide.

THINK
? × 8 = 32

1. $32 \div 8 = n$

THINK
? × 9 = 27

2. $27 \div 9 = n$

THINK
? × 8 = 40

3. $40 \div 8 = n$

THINK
? × 9 = 45

4. $45 \div 9 = n$

THINK
? × 8 = 56

5. $56 \div 8 = n$

THINK
? × 9 = 54

6. $54 \div 9 = n$

7. $9\overline{)72}$ **8.** $8\overline{)40}$ **9.** $9\overline{)54}$ **10.** $9\overline{)36}$ **11.** $8\overline{)16}$

12. $8\overline{)64}$ **13.** $9\overline{)81}$ **14.** $8\overline{)72}$ **15.** $9\overline{)63}$ **16.** $9\overline{)18}$

Practice Find the quotients.

1. $40 \div 8$ **2.** $35 \div 7$ **3.** $45 \div 9$ **4.** $48 \div 6$

5. $32 \div 4$ **6.** $81 \div 9$ **7.** $40 \div 5$ **8.** $24 \div 8$

9. $36 \div 9$ **10.** $72 \div 8$ **11.** $49 \div 7$ **12.** $20 \div 4$

13. $35 \div 5$ **14.** $30 \div 6$ **15.** $18 \div 9$ **16.** $64 \div 8$

17. $8 \div 8$ **18.** $63 \div 9$ **19.** $24 \div 4$ **20.** $56 \div 7$

21. $6 \overline{)36}$ **22.** $9 \overline{)9}$ **23.** $8 \overline{)56}$ **24.** $7 \overline{)42}$ **25.** $4 \overline{)28}$

26. $8 \overline{)48}$ **27.** $5 \overline{)25}$ **28.** $6 \overline{)54}$ **29.** $9 \overline{)27}$ **30.** $8 \overline{)32}$

31. $4 \overline{)36}$ **32.** $9 \overline{)54}$ **33.** $7 \overline{)63}$ **34.** $8 \overline{)16}$ **35.** $6 \overline{)42}$

36. Divide 63 by 9.   **37.** Divide 49 by 7.   **38.** Divide 48 by 8.

39. Divide 32 by 8.   **40.** Divide 40 by 8.   **41.** Divide 54 by 9.

Mixed Applications

42. There were 54 students and 9 picnic tables. The same number of students sat at each table. How many were at each table?

43. Eight cars with 6 students in each left early. How many students left early?

★ **44.** There were 72 students at the picnic. After 48 left, the rest divided into 4 equal teams. How many were on each team?

┌─ **THINK** ─────────┐

Logical Reasoning

Find the mystery number.

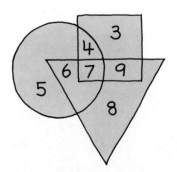

1. It is inside the circle.
2. It is inside the square.
3. It is not inside the triangle.

└────────→ **MATH** ◄─┘

More Practice, page 415, Set C

119

Practice the Facts

Find the quotients.

1. $30 \div 5$ 2. $42 \div 7$ 3. $24 \div 3$ 4. $36 \div 6$

5. $54 \div 9$ 6. $16 \div 2$ 7. $72 \div 8$ 8. $28 \div 4$

9. $21 \div 3$ 10. $40 \div 5$ 11. $10 \div 2$ 12. $56 \div 7$

13. $24 \div 6$ 14. $32 \div 4$ 15. $28 \div 7$ 16. $63 \div 9$

17. $2 \div 2$ 18. $48 \div 6$ 19. $15 \div 3$ 20. $25 \div 5$

21. $4\overline{)24}$ 22. $6\overline{)18}$ 23. $3\overline{)27}$ 24. $6\overline{)54}$ 25. $5\overline{)45}$

26. $7\overline{)63}$ 27. $5\overline{)35}$ 28. $2\overline{)18}$ 29. $4\overline{)0}$ 30. $9\overline{)81}$

31. $8\overline{)48}$ 32. $1\overline{)3}$ 33. $4\overline{)36}$ 34. $5\overline{)20}$ 35. $2\overline{)14}$

36. Divide 35 by 7. 37. Divide 27 by 9. 38. Divide 72 by 9.

39. Divide 56 by 8. 40. Divide 63 by 9. 41. Divide 42 by 6.

Copy and complete each table.

Divide by 7	
42	6
42. 56	||||||
43. 28	||||||
44. 63	||||||
45. 35	||||||
46. 49	||||||

Divide by 8	
32	4
47. 56	||||||
48. 72	||||||
49. 40	||||||
50. 48	||||||
51. 64	||||||

Divide by 9	
45	5
52. 54	||||||
53. 81	||||||
54. 63	||||||
55. 36	||||||
56. 72	||||||

120

Factors

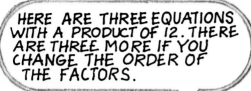

Factor		Factor		Product
1	×	12	=	12
2	×	6	=	12
3	×	4	=	12

Other Examples

$1 × 6 = 6$
$2 × 3 = 6$

The factors of 6
are 1, 2, 3, and 6.

$1 × 4 = 4$
$2 × 2 = 4$

The factors of 4
are 1, 2, and 4.

$1 × 3 = 3$

The factors of 3
are 1 and 3.

Practice Copy and complete the equations.
Then list all the factors of the product.

1. $1 × \text{▓} = 8$
   $2 × \text{▓} = 8$

2. $1 × \text{▓} = 2$

3. $1 × \text{▓} = 9$
   $3 × \text{▓} = 9$

4. $1 × \text{▓} = 5$

5. $1 × \text{▓} = 10$
   $2 × \text{▓} = 10$

6. $1 × \text{▓} = 7$

7. $1 × \text{▓} = 15$
   $3 × \text{▓} = 15$

8. $1 × \text{▓} = 16$
   $2 × \text{▓} = 16$
   $4 × \text{▓} = 16$

9. $1 × \text{▓} = 18$
   $2 × \text{▓} = 18$
   $3 × \text{▓} = 18$

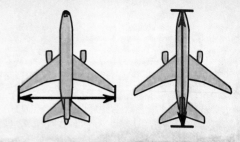

PROBLEM SOLVING
Using Data from a Table

Aircraft	Wingspan*	Length*
DC-9	28	36
DC-10	47	56
L-1011	47	54
727	33	47
747	60	71
767	48	49

* Approximate number of meters

Use the data given in the table to solve these problems.

1. How much longer is the 747 than the DC-9?

2. Charles Lindbergh made the first solo flight across the Atlantic Ocean. It would take 7 of Lindbergh's planes end-to-end to be as long as a DC-10. How long was Lindbergh's plane?

3. The DC-8 has a wingspan that is 17 m greater than the DC-9. What is the wingspan of the DC-8?

4. An early private plane had a length of 7 m. A 737 jet is just 4 times that long. How long is the 737?

5. If you add the length and the wingspan of the DC-9 and divide by 8, you'll have its approximate height. About how high is the DC-9?

★ 6. The Wright brothers built the first plane to achieve true flight. The wingspan of the DC-9 is just 4 times that of one of their gliders. What was the wingspan of the glider?

7. **Strategy Practice** The DC-8 is longer than the A300. The DC-8 is shorter than the Concorde. The A300 is longer than the 757. Which of the planes is longest?

Solve.

1. A 747 carried 529 people from Los Angeles to Honolulu and 487 on the return trip. What was the total number of people?

2. The 747 can seat 550 people. The 767 can seat 289 people. How many more people can the 747 seat?

3. There were 63 crew members working on Friday. 7 of them were on each flight. How many flights was this?

4. A 747 plane has 550 seats. Only 67 seats are empty. How many seats are used?

5. There were 7 flight crews who reported for work on Monday. There were 8 people in each crew. How many people reported for work?

6. One section has 72 seats. Each row has 9 seats. How many rows are there?

7. There were 5 crews with 6 people each and 7 crews with 8 people each. How many people is this?

8. The late flight crews had 29 men and 27 women. There were 8 flights with the same number of crew members on each flight. How many were on each flight?

9. **DATA BANK** See page 403. How many more can an L-1011 seat than a DC-10?

10. *Strategy Practice* There were 13 crew members for two flights. The early flight had 3 more members than the late flight. How many crew members were on each flight?

123

PROBLEM-SOLVING STRATEGY
Make a Table

QUESTION
DATA
PLAN
ANSWER
CHECK

Try This Hiro is riding his bicycle. He rides 2 miles every 10 minutes. At this rate, how far will he go in 60 minutes?

TO SOLVE A PROBLEM SUCH AS THIS, YOU MAY NEED TO DO MORE THAN JUST ADD, SUBTRACT, MULTIPLY, OR DIVIDE. A STRATEGY THAT MIGHT HELP YOU IS GIVEN BELOW.

MAKE A TABLE

FIRST, I'LL MAKE A TABLE AND WRITE WHAT I KNOW.

NOW I'LL FILL IN THE TABLE TO FIND THE ANSWER.

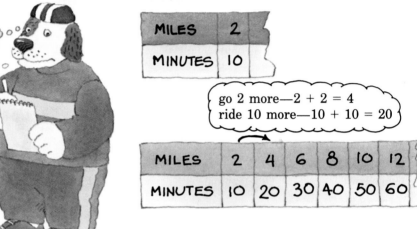

MILES	2
MINUTES	10

go 2 more—2 + 2 = 4
ride 10 more—10 + 10 = 20

MILES	2	4	6	8	10	12
MINUTES	10	20	30	40	50	60

When the number reaches 60 minutes, you will have the number of miles in your table.

Hiro will ride 12 miles in 60 minutes.

Solve.

1. A recipe calls for 3 eggs and 4 cups of flour. A baker used 24 eggs. How many cups of flour did he use? Copy and complete the table.

EGGS	3	6	9
FLOUR	4	8	12

2. Cups are $3 and saucers are $2. How much will you have to spend for saucers if you spend $27 for cups? Copy and complete the table.

CUPS	$3	$6	$9	$12
SAUCERS	$2	$4	$6	$8

CHAPTER REVIEW/TEST

Find the quotients.

1. $32 \div 4$ **2.** $63 \div 9$ **3.** $30 \div 5$ **4.** $42 \div 7$

5. $56 \div 8$ **6.** $0 \div 2$ **7.** $30 \div 6$ **8.** $35 \div 5$

9. $21 \div 3$ **10.** $48 \div 6$ **11.** $36 \div 4$ **12.** $28 \div 7$

13. $7\overline{)35}$ **14.** $3\overline{)27}$ **15.** $5\overline{)45}$ **16.** $6\overline{)18}$ **17.** $4\overline{)28}$

18. $9\overline{)45}$ **19.** $6\overline{)6}$ **20.** $8\overline{)64}$ **21.** $9\overline{)36}$ **22.** $2\overline{)16}$

23. $9\overline{)54}$ **24.** $6\overline{)36}$ **25.** $8\overline{)48}$ **26.** $9\overline{)72}$ **27.** $4\overline{)24}$

28. $7\overline{)49}$ **29.** $5\overline{)40}$ **30.** $1\overline{)7}$ **31.** $4\overline{)36}$ **32.** $7\overline{)28}$

33. $3\overline{)24}$ **34.** $8\overline{)32}$ **35.** $2\overline{)14}$ **36.** $6\overline{)42}$ **37.** $5\overline{)25}$

38. List all the factors of 15.   **39.** List all the factors of 17.

$$1 \times 15 = 15$$
$$3 \times \ \ 5 = 15$$

$$1 \times 17 = 17$$

Solve.

40. Linda has 48 Lincoln pennies to put in her book. Each row of the book holds 6 pennies. How many rows can she fill?

41. There were 8 planes leaving in the next hour. Each one had a crew of 7. How many crew members is this in all?

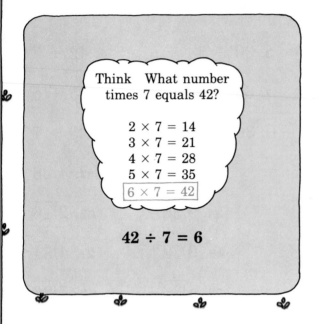

Think   What number times 7 equals 42?

$2 \times 7 = 14$
$3 \times 7 = 21$
$4 \times 7 = 28$
$5 \times 7 = 35$
$6 \times 7 = 42$

$42 \div 7 = 6$

Find the quotients.

1. $45 \div 5$ **2.** $35 \div 7$

3. $12 \div 2$ **4.** $24 \div 6$

5. $72 \div 9$ **6.** $8 \div 8$

7. $32 \div 8$ **8.** $27 \div 3$

9. $36 \div 4$ **10.** $21 \div 7$

11. $28 \div 4$ **12.** $81 \div 9$

13. $16 \div 8$ **14.** $63 \div 9$

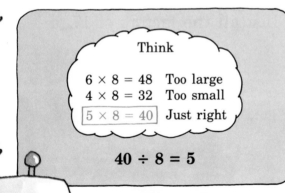

Think

$6 \times 8 = 48$ Too large
$4 \times 8 = 32$ Too small
$5 \times 8 = 40$ Just right

$40 \div 8 = 5$

15. $6\overline{)30}$ **16.** $2\overline{)14}$ **17.** $9\overline{)63}$

18. $9\overline{)81}$ **19.** $7\overline{)42}$ **20.** $5\overline{)40}$

21. $4\overline{)24}$ **22.** $6\overline{)0}$ **23.** $6\overline{)12}$

24. $8\overline{)40}$ **25.** $5\overline{)30}$ **26.** $1\overline{)7}$

27. $2\overline{)18}$ **28.** $6\overline{)18}$ **29.** $3\overline{)18}$

Prime Numbers

When a number has just two **different** factors, itself and 1, the number is a **PRIME NUMBER.**

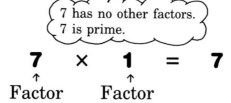

7 has no other factors.
7 is prime.

$$7 \quad \times \quad 1 \quad = \quad 7$$

↑ Factor   ↑ Factor

Other Examples

3 is prime.

$$3 \times 1 = 3$$

15 is not prime.

$$15 \times 1 = 15$$
$$5 \times 3 = 15$$

17 is prime.

$$17 \times 1 = 17$$

1. Is 9 prime?

$9 \times 1 = 9$
$3 \times 3 = 9$

2. Is 5 prime?

$5 \times 1 = 5$

3. Is 13 prime?

$13 \times 1 = 13$

4. Is 2 prime?

$2 \times 1 = 2$

5. Is 21 prime?

$21 \times 1 = 21$
$7 \times 3 = 21$

6. Is 25 prime?

$25 \times 1 = 25$
$5 \times 5 = 25$

7. Which of these four numbers are prime?

A

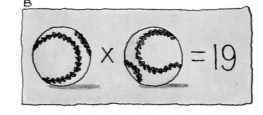

B

C

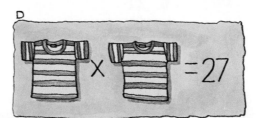

D

Give the letter for the correct answer.

1. $\begin{array}{r} 2 \\ + 4 \\ \hline \end{array}$ **A** 5   **B** 6
    C 8   **D** not given

2. $\begin{array}{r} 6 \\ + 8 \\ \hline \end{array}$ **A** 14   **B** 13
    C 12   **D** not given

3. $\begin{array}{r} 3 \\ + 9 \\ \hline \end{array}$ **A** 11   **B** 13
    C 12   **D** not given

4. $\begin{array}{r} 5 \\ + 7 \\ \hline \end{array}$ **A** 13   **B** 12
    C 15   **D** not given

5. $\begin{array}{r} 10 \\ - 5 \\ \hline \end{array}$ **A** 5
    B 4
    C 6
    D not given

6. $\begin{array}{r} 15 \\ - 7 \\ \hline \end{array}$ **A** 9
    B 7
    C 8
    D not given

7. $\begin{array}{r} 12 \\ - 8 \\ \hline \end{array}$ **A** 2
    B 4
    C 3
    D not given

8. $\begin{array}{r} 88 \\ - 69 \\ \hline \end{array}$ **A** 29
    B 21
    C 19
    D not given

9. $\begin{array}{r} 782 \\ - 367 \\ \hline \end{array}$ **A** 315
    B 425
    C 415
    D not given

10. $\begin{array}{r} 560 \\ - 58 \\ \hline \end{array}$ **A** 502
    B 518
    C 512
    D not given

11. $\begin{array}{r} \$7.52 \\ - 3.75 \\ \hline \end{array}$ **A** $3.77
    B $4.23
    C $4.87
    D not given

12. $\begin{array}{r} \$4.76 \\ - 3.78 \\ \hline \end{array}$ **A** $1.08
    B $1.98
    C $1.02
    D not given

13. A paint set costs $9.50. Ann has $5.75. How much more will she need to buy the paint set?
    A $3.75   **B** $4.25
    C $4.85   **D** not given

14. Curtis has 282 stamps. Todd has 321 stamps. How many more stamps does Todd have?
    A 161   **B** 49
    C 39   **D** not given

MEASUREMENT: Metric Units

The gym clock read 4:25. They had been playing for 1 hour. There were 5 seconds left in the fourth quarter. The score was 44 to 43. The other team was ahead. Tyler held the ball tightly. He had made baskets from this far away before. But it was not an easy angle. At his old school Tyler had been one of the best players. Making this basket would show the new coach how good he was. Tyler saw that a teammate near the basket was open. The coach was always talking about how important teamwork was. Four seconds left . . .

Telling Time

Alan was supposed to be home by 6 o'clock.
He looked at his watch when he walked
in the door. Did he make it?

Alan did make it.
He was 10 minutes
early!

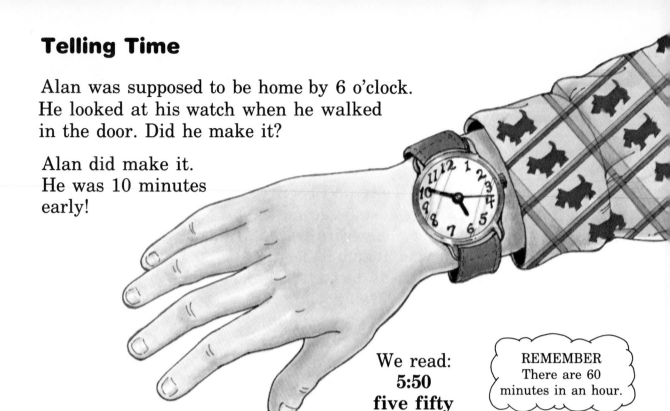

We read:
5:50
five fifty
10 minutes to 6

REMEMBER
There are 60
minutes in an hour.

Other Examples

We read:
10:15
ten fifteen
15 minutes past 10
quarter past 10

We read:
two forty-five
15 minutes to 3
quarter to 3

We read:
3:30
three thirty
half past 3

Warm Up   Give each time.

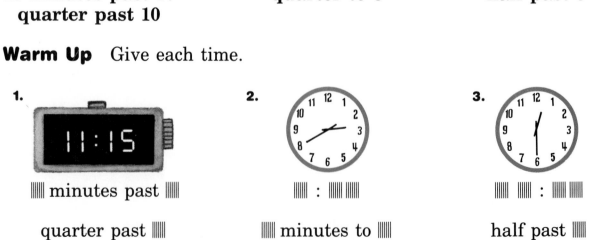

1.

▯▯▯▯▯ minutes past ▯▯▯▯▯

quarter past ▯▯▯▯▯

2.

▯▯▯▯▯ : ▯▯▯▯▯ ▯▯▯▯▯

▯▯▯▯▯ minutes to ▯▯▯▯▯

3.

▯▯▯▯▯ ▯▯▯▯▯ : ▯▯▯▯▯ ▯▯▯▯▯

half past ▯▯▯▯▯

130

Practice Write each time.

1. 

____ minutes past ____

quarter past ____

2. 

____ : ____ ____

____ minutes to ____

3. 

____ ____ : ____ ____

half past ____

4. 

____ minutes past ____

quarter past ____

5. 

____ minutes to ____

quarter to ____

6. 

____ minutes to ____

____ minutes past ____

7. 

____ : ____ ____

____ minutes to ____

★ 8. 

____ ____ : ____ ____

____ minutes past ____

★ 9. 

____ : ____ ____

____ minutes to ____

Match.

10. 6:05 — A 20 minutes to 3

11. 3:20 — B quarter past 10

12. 10:15 — C 5 minutes to 6

13. 2:40 — D quarter to 10

14. 5:55 — E 5 minutes past 6

15. 9:45 — F 20 minutes past 3

THINK MATH

Estimating Time

The minute hand has fallen off these clocks. Estimate the times.

a.m. and p.m.

The hour hand goes around twice each day, once for the a.m. hours and once for the p.m. hours.

The minute hand goes around once each hour.

The hours between midnight and noon are the a.m. hours.

The hours between noon and midnight are the p.m. hours.

MIDNIGHT   8:05 a.m.   NOON   8:05 p.m.   MIDNIGHT

Write each time as a.m. or p.m.

1. Lois got up early and ate breakfast at 7:00 ▦ .

2. Guy was out of school and roller-skating by 3:15 ▦ .

3. Carol had an early lunch at 11:30 ▦ .

4. On Saturday Dean likes to sleep until 8:00 ▦ .

5. One afternoon May rode her bicycle until 5:00 ▦ .

6. Kirk fished all day until 6:00 ▦ .

7. One night the late show wasn't over until 1:45 ▦ .

8. Kay's family has dinner at 6:30 ▦ .

9. Paco's school starts at 8:45 ▦ .

10. Peg's has afternoon recess at 2:10 ▦ .

132

PROBLEM SOLVING
Using Data from a Table

Use the data in the table to solve the following problems.

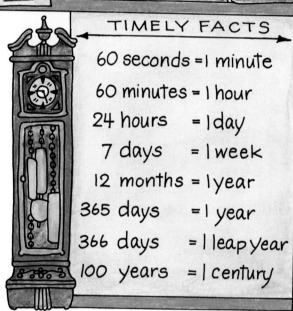

TIMELY FACTS

60 seconds	= 1 minute
60 minutes	= 1 hour
24 hours	= 1 day
7 days	= 1 week
12 months	= 1 year
365 days	= 1 year
366 days	= 1 leap year
100 years	= 1 century

1. Mike's school is open 180 days each year. How many days is his school closed in a leap year?

2. Helen sleeps 9 hours each night. How many hours is Helen awake each day?

3. School is divided into 6-week periods. How many days are in 6 weeks?

4. Summer vacation lasted for 63 days. How many weeks was this?

5. Cathy swam underwater for 27 seconds. How much less than 1 minute was this?

6. Gregory went to school for 180 days and summer school for 38 days. During a regular year, how many days was he not in school?

★ 7. Brian jogged for 37 minutes. Then for 26 minutes he walked to cool off. Did his jogging and walking take more or less than 1 hour?

8. **Strategy Practice** Mr. Hill gives piano lessons to 3 boys and 4 girls every day except Sunday. When he has taught 18 boys, how many girls has he taught? Hint: Complete the table.

boys	3	6	9
girls	4	8	12

133

More About Time

Dina gets out of school for lunch at 11:30 a.m. She has 45 minutes. What time should she be back to school?

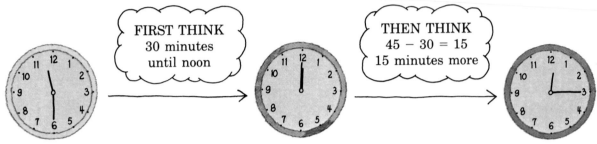

FIRST THINK
30 minutes
until noon

THEN THINK
45 − 30 = 15
15 minutes more

Dina should be back to school by 12:15 p.m.

Other Examples

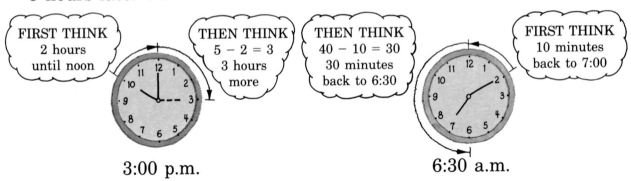

5 hours later than 10:00 a.m.

FIRST THINK
2 hours
until noon

THEN THINK
5 − 2 = 3
3 hours
more

3:00 p.m.

40 minutes before 7:10 a.m.

THEN THINK
40 − 10 = 30
30 minutes
back to 6:30

FIRST THINK
10 minutes
back to 7:00

6:30 a.m.

Give the times.

1. What time was it 5 hours before 2:00 p.m.?

2. What time will it be 25 minutes after 8:50 a.m.?

3. What time was it 45 minutes before 4:55 p.m.?

4. What time will it be 8 hours after 9:00 a.m.?

Mixed Applications

1. Jane Ruel goes to work at 8:00 a.m. She is at the office for 8 hours. What time does she leave work?

2. Frank Winters owns a paint store. He opens at 9:00 a.m. and stays open for 9 hours. What time does he close?

3. School starts at 8:10 a.m. Amy needs 20 minutes to get there. What time should she leave for school?

4. Roger Woo needs 50 minutes to drive to work. He must be there at 8:30 a.m. What time should he leave for work?

5. Adam James is a guard. He starts work at 10:00 p.m. and works for 8 hours. What time does he get off?

6. Gail takes 45 minutes to get ready for school. What time should she get up if she wants to leave home at 7:30 a.m.?

7. Lena works 2 hours each day. She starts at 3:30 p.m. What time does she get off from work?

8. Ron gets paid by the hour for baby-sitting. One night he started at 7:30 p.m. and quit at 12:30 a.m. How many hours did he baby-sit?

★ **9.** Ruth Fine starts work at 8:45 a.m. She works 7 hours and 30 minutes. What time does she get off from work?

Reading the Calendar

Use the calendar art to help you answer the following questions. The months are shown in order from top to bottom beginning with the first month, January.

1. What is the seventh month?

2. The first Wednesday in December is December 2. What is the date of the fourth Wednesday?

3. The Camera Club meets on the second Tuesday of each month. On what date will they meet in December?

4. The Stamp Club usually meets on the fourth Friday. In December, they met 5 days late. When did they meet?

5. How many days is it from the second Thursday to the third Monday?

6. Jo gave her birth date like this: 6/24/77. This means the 6th month, the 24th day of 1977. Write your birth date that way.

7. Write today's date like Jo would.

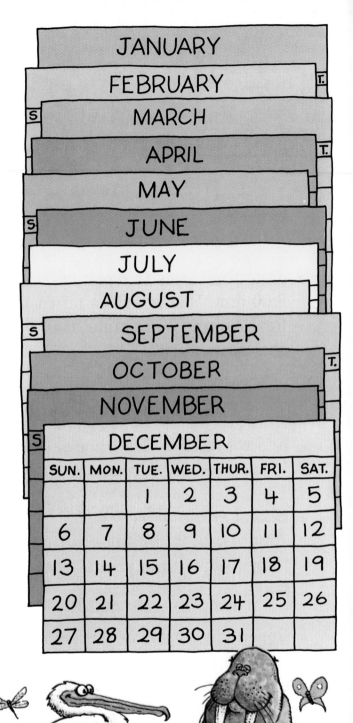

| JANUARY |
| FEBRUARY |
| MARCH |
| APRIL |
| MAY |
| JUNE |
| JULY |
| AUGUST |
| SEPTEMBER |
| OCTOBER |
| NOVEMBER |

DECEMBER

SUN.	MON.	TUE.	WED.	THUR.	FRI.	SAT.
		1	2	3	4	5
6	7	8	9	10	11	12
13	14	15	16	17	18	19
20	21	22	23	24	25	26
27	28	29	30	31		

Time Zones

The time-zone map shows times in different parts of the United States when it is 12:00 noon in the Central zone.

Use the map to answer the following questions.

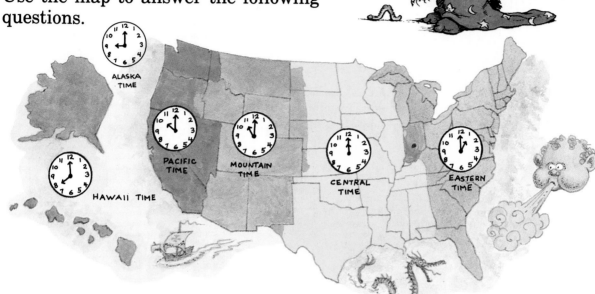

1. What is the Eastern Time?

2. What is the Mountain Time?

3. What is the Alaska Time?

4. How many hours' difference is there between Eastern Time and Pacific Time?

5. How many hours' difference is there between Central Time and Hawaii Time?

6. When it is 12:00 noon Pacific Time, what time is it in the Eastern Time zone?

7. When it is 12:00 midnight Eastern Time, what is the Hawaii Time?

★ 8. Suppose you leave Chicago (Central Time) at 9:00 a.m. on a nonstop flight to Hawaii. You arrive in Hawaii at 2:00 p.m. How long was your flight?

9. **DATA HUNT** Look up world time zones. Plan a phone call to London. Find out what time you should call so that it will be 10:00 a.m. in London.

Measuring with Centimeter Units

Sara is making a small planter box. She cut the board below for one of the end pieces. What is the length of the board to the nearest centimeter?

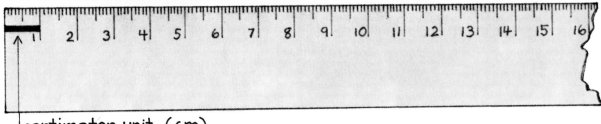

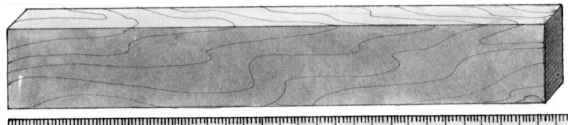

centimeter unit (cm)

The length of the board to the nearest centimeter is 15 cm.

Warm Up

Sara used different size nails for the planter box. Give the length to the nearest centimeter.

1.   2.   3.

Sara cut these sticks for signs. Give the length to the nearest centimeter.

4.

5.

Sara kept a record of how corn, peppers, and beans grew for a three-week period. Write the height of each plant to the nearest centimeter.

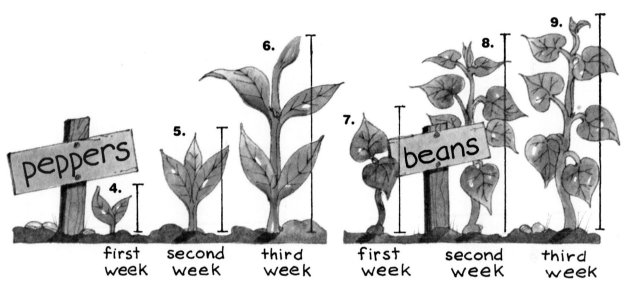

10. Which plant was tallest the first week?

11. Which plant was tallest the second week?

12. Which plant grew the least in the three weeks?

Find a box in your classroom.

13. How tall is the box?

14. How long is the box?

15. How wide is the box?

┌─ **THINK** ─┐

Estimation

Suppose this is the unit. ▭
(Length 1)

Estimate each of these lengths.

1. ▭

2. ▭

Find a way to check your estimate.

MATH

Meters and Kilometers

The **meter** is a large metric unit used to measure length or distance.

1 meter (m) = 100 centimeters

Trudy found that a meter stick came up to the underside of her arm.

The **kilometer** is a still larger unit used to measure distance.

1 kilometer (km) = 1,000 meters

You might walk 1 km in about 10 minutes.

Warm Up   Choose a unit so the statement seems reasonable.

1. The distance across town is 7 __?__.

2. The tree is 10 __?__ tall.

3. Jane ran in the 400 __?__ race.

4. The jet is flying 8 __?__ high.

5. Copy and complete the table to show how far you could walk in different amounts of time.

km	1	2	3	|||||	|||||	|||||
minutes	10	20	30	|||||	|||||	60

6. If it takes you 20 minutes to walk to school, about how far is it?

7. **DATA HUNT**   Time yourself as you walk 6 km. How much more or less than 60 minutes did it take?

Practice Choose a unit so the statement seems reasonable.

1. The pool is 40 __?__ long.
2. The pencil is 14 __?__ long.
3. The bus traveled 80 __?__ in an hour.
4. The door is 2 __?__ high.
5. The plant is 5 __?__ high.
6. The lake is 5 __?__ long.

Mixed Applications

7. Suppose you ride your bicycle 3 km in 10 minutes. Copy and complete the table to show how far you could ride in different amounts of time.

km	3	6	9	▥	▥	▥
minutes	10	20	30	▥	▥	60

8. If it takes you 40 minutes to ride to the park, about how far is it?

9. About how far can you ride in an hour?

10. Suppose you can drive a car 15 km in 10 minutes. Copy and complete the table to show how far you can drive in different amounts of time.

km	15	30	45	▥	▥	▥
minutes	10	20	30	▥	▥	60

11. If it takes 50 minutes to drive to the lake, about how far is the lake?

12. About how far can you drive in an hour?

SKILLKEEPER

Divide.

1. $4\overline{)36}$
2. $5\overline{)35}$
3. $7\overline{)56}$
4. $9\overline{)81}$
5. $8\overline{)72}$

6. $6\overline{)54}$
7. $3\overline{)27}$
8. $8\overline{)64}$
9. $5\overline{)20}$
10. $6\overline{)36}$

Perimeter

Casey drew a plan for a pen for his dog. He wanted to know how much fence he would need to go all the way around.

The distance around a figure is its **perimeter.**

To find the perimeter, we add the lengths of the sides.

$$\begin{array}{r} \overset{2}{1}9 \\ 14 \\ 19 \\ + \ 14 \\ \hline 66 \end{array}$$

The perimeter of the pen is 66 m.

Casey will need 66 m of fence.

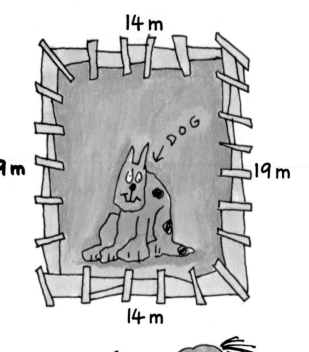

Warm Up Find the perimeter.

1.

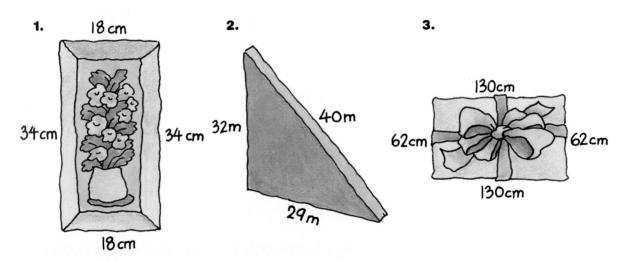

18 cm

34 cm   34 cm

18 cm

2.

32m   40m

29m

3.

130cm

62cm   62cm

130cm

142

Practice Find the perimeter.

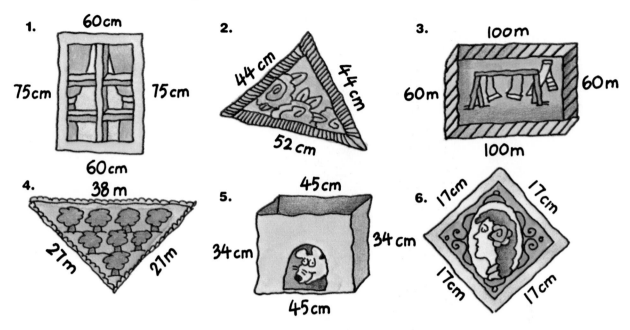

1.
60cm
75cm   75cm
60cm

2.
44 cm   44 cm
52 cm

3.
100m
60m   60m
100m

4.
38 m
21m   21m

5.
45cm
34 cm   34 cm
45cm

6.
17cm   17cm
17cm   17cm

Use your centimeter ruler to measure the
sides. Then find the perimeter of each figure.

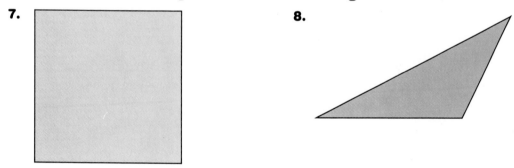

7.

8.

9. Find the perimeter of a picture or
   drawing in your classroom.

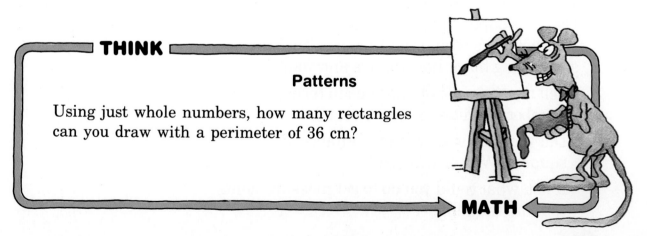

THINK

Patterns

Using just whole numbers, how many rectangles
can you draw with a perimeter of 36 cm?

MATH

Area

Work with your group to explore the area of a figure.

You will need plain paper, graph paper, several kinds of flat objects, and scissors.

Part 1

1. Experiment to find how many units it takes to cover a piece of paper. Try using counters, tiles, paper clips, and so on.

2. Talk about what you find. Which objects are easier to use for measuring? Why?

3. Share your ideas with the class.

Part 2

4. On a sheet of plain paper, draw a closed figure. Cut out enough same-sized paper squares to cover your design.

5. Trade designs with a partner in your group. Use your paper squares to measure the area of your partner's design. Your partner does the same using his or her squares and your design.

   • Tell the areas of both designs in terms of number of squares (square units).

   • Did you each say the same number of squares? Why or why not?

   • If not, what could you do to get measurements that are the same?

6. Talk with your group about finding area.

   - What problems did you have finding the area of your design with paper squares?

   - Which kinds of designs were more difficult to work with? Why?

   - What ways did you discover to help you measure areas of difficult designs?

Part 3

7. Use graph paper. Draw rectangles that have these areas: 8 square units, 11 square units, 13 square units, and 24 square units. Can you draw more than one rectangle for each area?

8. Use your drawings to complete a chart like this.

Area	Width	Length

9. Write some areas on a piece of paper. Exchange papers with a partner in your group.

   - Draw rectangles that have the areas your partner wrote.

   - Use these drawings to add to your chart.

10. Look at the charts your group made. Describe any patterns that might help you find the area of a rectangle.

11. Test your ideas. One person gives the length and width of a rectangle. Another person uses the group's pattern to find the area. Check by drawing the rectangle on graph paper and finding the number of square units.

Volume

Work with a group.
You will need unit cubes.

Part 1

1. Each person in the group takes the same number of unit cubes (5 or more) and builds a different-shaped solid figure.
   - Compare your figures. How are they alike? How are they different?
   - Can you make any other shapes?
   - How many cubes are in each figure?

   The number of **cubic units** in a figure is the **volume** of the figure.

2. Repeat the activity several times. Use a different number of cubes each time.
   - Can you use the same number of cubes to make figures that have different shapes *and* different volumes?
   - What can you say about how volume and shape relate to each other?

Part 2

Now work with your group to explore the volume of a box figure.

3. Each person builds a box figure using the same number of unit cubes.
   - Compare your box figures. How are they the same? How are they different?
   - Compare the volume of your box to that of the other boxes.
   - Are there any other box figures you can build with that number of cubes?

4. Repeat the activity several times, using a different number of cubes each time.
   - Are there some numbers of unit cubes with which you can make only one box shape? Explain.

Part 3

5. With your group, use unit cubes to build Box 1. Make a group chart to record its length, width, height, and volume.

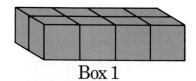

Box 1

Length	Width	Height	Volume
4	2	1	8

6. Add another layer to Box 1.

- What is the new volume?
- What if you added more layers? Talk about how the volume would change.
- Use unit cubes to add layers. Record the data on the chart.

7. Now use unit cubes to build Box 2. What is the volume? How do you know?

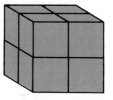

Box 2

- Predict how the volume would change as you added layers to Box 2. Try it.
- Record your work on another chart.

8. Look at your charts.

- Discuss the patterns you see.
- How can the patterns help you find the volume of a box figure without counting unit cubes?

9. Build a box figure with cubes.

- Use what you have learned to predict what the volume would be if you added 1 layer of cubes, then 2 layers.
- Use cubes to test your predictions.
- Write your method for predicting and testing, and share it with other groups.

Estimating Capacity

Lee saw this sign at a supermarket. He decided to learn as much as he could about the **liter.** He made the poster below.

SAVE
Buy Orange Juice
in the large
1 LITER SIZE

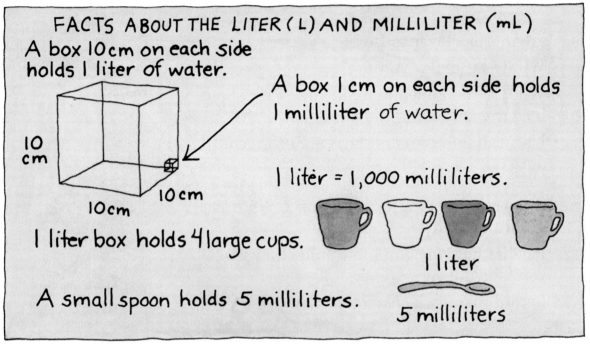

FACTS ABOUT THE LITER (L) AND MILLILITER (mL)

A box 10 cm on each side holds 1 liter of water.

10 cm

10 cm

10 cm

A box 1 cm on each side holds 1 milliliter of water.

1 liter = 1,000 milliliters.

1 liter box holds 4 large cups.

1 liter

A small spoon holds 5 milliliters.

5 milliliters

Warm Up Choose the better estimate of capacity.

1. A sink

A more than
1 liter

B less than
1 liter

2. One raindrop

A more than
1 milliliter

B less than
1 milliliter

3. A paper cup

A more than
1 liter

B less than
1 liter

Practice Choose the better estimate of capacity.

1.

 A 4 L B 4 mL

2.

 A 1 L B 1 mL

3.

 A 200 L B 200 mL

4.

 A 25 L B 25 mL

5.

 A 175 L B 175 mL

6.

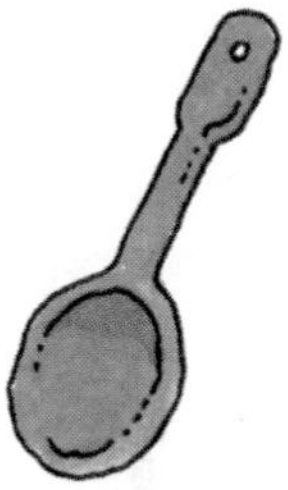

 A 15 L B 15 mL

7.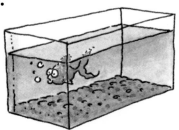

 A 30 L B 30 mL

8.

 A 100 L B 100 mL

9.

 A 8 L B 8 mL

SKILLKEEPER

Add or subtract.

1.   76
     + 43

2.   56
     − 13

3.   165
     + 751

4. $7.15
     − 0.32

5.   983
     + 378

6.   26
     10
     + 45

7.   148
     − 73

8.   627
     + 445

9.   740
     − 283

10. $58.26
     − 32.67

Estimating Weight

Sandy read that 1 liter of water weighs 1 **kilogram** (kg). She checked this by putting a liter of water in a plastic bag and weighing it.

Sandy also found out that 1 milliliter of water weighs 1 **gram** (1 g).

> 1 kilogram = 1,000 grams

Other Examples

pencil

large book

about 5 grams   about 1 kilogram

Give the better estimate of weight.

1.

A 1 g   B 1 kg

2.

A 1 g   B 1 kg

3.

A 20 g   B 20 kg

4.

A 16 g   B 16 kg

5.

A 6 g   B 6 kg

6.

A 240 g   B 240 kg

7.

A 35 g   B 35 kg

8.

A 200 g   B 200 kg

9.

A 5 g   B 5 kg

Estimating Temperature

Becky's mother said, "You have to wear your sweater this morning. The temperature outside is 10 degrees."

Becky's mother was giving the temperature in degrees **Celsius** (°C). The thermometer shows different Celsius temperatures.

Choose the better estimate of temperature.

1.

Hot cocoa

A 75°C   **B** 35°C

2.

Ice tea

A 20°C   **B** 2°C

3.

Warm bread

A 65°C   **B** 25°C

4.

Frozen yogurt

A 20°C   **B** ⁻5°C

5.

Warm bath

A 50°C   **B** 80°C

6.

Hot day

A 10°C   **B** 30°C

°C

115 —
— 110
105 —
— 100
95 —
— 90
85 —
75 —
— 70
65 —
— 60
55 —
— 50
45 —
— 40
35 —
— 30
25 —
— 20
15 —
— 10
5 —
— 0
⁻5 —
— ⁻10
⁻15

Boiling point of water

Hot soup

Normal body temperature

Room temperature

Freezing point of water

Cold day

PROBLEM SOLVING
Using Estimation

Use estimation to decide which answer is most reasonable.

1. In a year with 365 days, Al Gunn worked 248 days. How many days did he not work?

   A 17 days **B** 117 days **C** 217 days

2. Julio swam for 27 minutes. He jogged for 39 minutes. How long did he exercise?

   A 46 min **B** 66 min **C** 86 min

3. Vida planted a tree that was 87 cm tall. In 5 years the tree was 316 cm tall. How much had it grown in the 5 years?

   A 229 cm **B** 129 cm **C** 329 cm

4. Lori Chu drove 289 km, ate lunch, then drove 315 km. How far did she drive that day?

   A 404 km **B** 504 km **C** 604 km

5. Ana Ruiz had a rectangular fence built. Two sides were 98 m and two sides 105 m. How much fence was this?

   A 406 m **B** 203 m **C** 304 m

6. Ian has a square bulletin board. Each side is 96 cm. What is the perimeter of the bulletin board?

   A 192 cm **B** 288 cm **C** 384 cm

7. Trisha has 750 mL of juice. She used 397 mL. How much juice does Trisha have left?

   A 353 mL **B** 313 mL **C** 403 mL

8. *Strategy Practice* There are two roads, Crest and Pine, from Reed to Troy. There are three roads, Wolfe, Mills, and Birch, from Troy to Upland. How many ways can you get from Reed to Upland going through Troy?

PROBLEM SOLVING
Mixed Practice

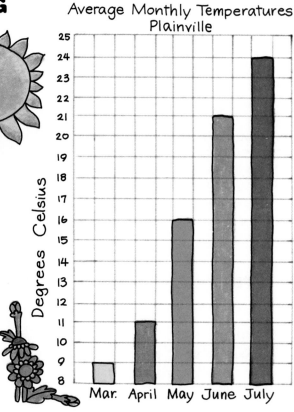

Average Monthly Temperatures
Plainville

Degrees Celsius

Mar. April May June July

The bar graph shows average monthly temperatures in degrees Celsius. Use the graph for problems 1, 2, and 3.

1. How much higher was the average temperature in July than it was in April?

2. The average temperature in August was three times what it was in March. What was the average temperature in August?

3. The average temperature for January was 17°C less than it was in June. What was the average temperature in January?

4. Bev had a pet calf that weighed 287 kg in February. By July it weighed 423 kg. How much weight had Bev's calf gained?

5. During a 3-day storm, 15 cm of rain fell on Plainville. If it rained the same amount each day, how much rain fell on the first day?

6. The Whites used 567 liters of oil to heat their home in January. They used 485 liters in February. How many liters of oil did they use in two months?

7. **DATA HUNT** Find your weight in kilograms. Find the weight of a friend. How much more or less do you weigh than your friend?

8. *Strategy Practice* One year in Plainville, July had more rain than August. May had less rain than August. Also, May had more rain than June. Which month had the most rain?

153

PROBLEM-SOLVING STRATEGY
Find a Pattern

QUESTION
DATA
PLAN
ANSWER
CHECK

YOU MAY NEED TO DO MORE THAN JUST ADD, SUBTRACT, MULTIPLY, OR DIVIDE TO SOLVE THIS PROBLEM. A STRATEGY THAT MAY HELP YOU IS GIVEN BELOW.

FIND A PATTERN

I'LL MAKE A TABLE AND LOOK FOR A PATTERN.

I SEE THE PATTERN. THERE ARE 4 MORE TILES IN EACH ROW. I'LL COMPLETE THE TABLE TO ROW 8.

Try This Julia put 3 tiles in row one, 7 tiles in row two, 11 tiles in row three, 15 tiles in row four, and so on.

ROW1
ROW2
ROW3
ROW4

How many tiles will she put in row eight?

ROW NUMBER	1	2	3	4
TILES	3	7	11	15

ROW NUMBER	1	2	3	4	5	6	7	8
TILES	3	7	11	15	19	23	27	31

Julia will put 31 tiles in row 8.

Solve.

1. Bruce did 3 push-ups every day the first week, 6 push-ups every day the second week, 9 the third, and so on. How many push-ups did he do each day the tenth week?

2. In a video game, the first goal is worth 1 point, the second 2 points, the third 4 points, the fourth 8 points, and so on. How many points is the eighth goal worth?

Write each time as a.m. or p.m.

1. Marcia left for school each morning at _____.

2. She returned home in the afternoon at _____.

Use a centimeter ruler. Find the length to the nearest centimeter.

3.

4.

Write the missing unit—cm, m, or km.

5. Jerry's mother drove 8 _____ to the park.

6. Rosa's brother is 2 _____ tall.

7. Find the perimeter.
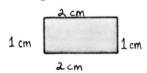

8. Find the area in square units.

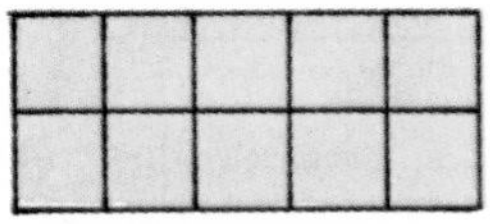

9. Find the volume.

10. Choose the better estimate.

A 250 mL   **B** 250 L

11. Choose the better weight for a bag of potatoes.

A 5 g   **B** 5 kg

12. Choose the better temperature for boiling water.

A 10°C   **B** 100°C

Solve.

13. Amelia practices the clarinet 30 minutes each day. In 6 days how many hours will she practice?
Hint: 60 minutes = 1 hour

14. Mr. Fitch built a fence around his garden. Two sides were 53 m and two sides were 48 m. How much fence was this? Choose the best estimate.

A 100 m   **B** 200 m   **C** 150 m

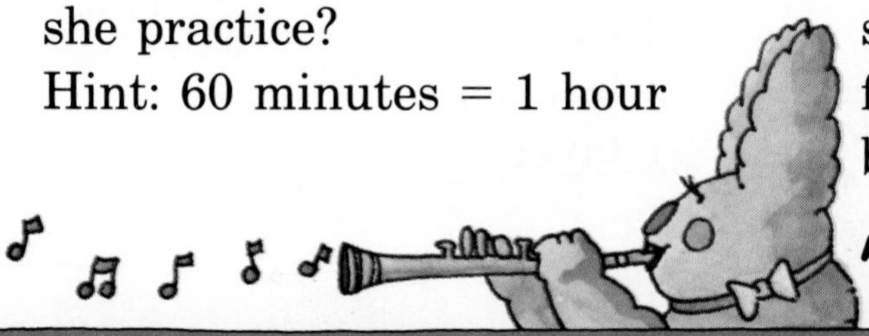

ANOTHER LOOK

What is the time
45 minutes before 4:15 p.m.?

45 − 15 = 30   15 minutes
30 minutes   back to
more back   4:00
to 3:30

15 minutes back to 4:00

Write each time.

1. What time was it 3 hours before 1 p.m.?

2. What time will it be 30 minutes after 7:50 a.m.?

3. What time was it 20 minutes before 3:05 p.m.?

Find the perimeter and area.

8

7   7

8

Perimeter
7 + 8 + 7 + 8 = **30** units

Area
7 × 8 = **56** square units

4. Find the perimeter and area.

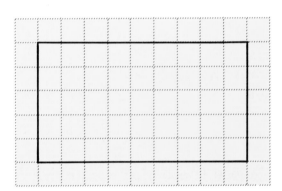

Find the volume.

2 rows
3 in each
2 layers

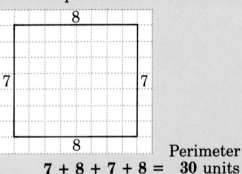

2 × 3 × 2 = **12** cubes

Find the volume.

5.

3 rows
4 in each
1 layer

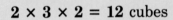

156

Space Perception

Each face of a cube is 1 square unit. You are going to paint as much of the cubes as you can without moving them. For each position tell how many square units you could paint.

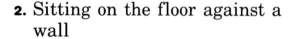

1 SQUARE UNIT

1. Standing on one corner

2. Sitting on the floor against a wall

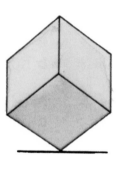

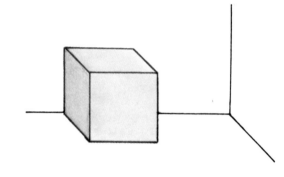

Hint: How many faces can you not see?

Hint: How many faces are against the wall or floor?

3. Sitting in a corner

4. Count carefully.

CUMULATIVE REVIEW

Give the letter for the correct answer.

Round to the nearest thousand.

1. 3,500
- **A** 3,000
- **B** 4,000
- **C** 5,000
- **D** not given

2. 6,489
- **A** 6,000
- **B** 7,000
- **C** 6,500
- **D** not given

Round to the nearest dollar.

3. $25.98
- **A** $25
- **B** $26
- **C** $24
- **D** not given

4. $16.35
- **A** $17
- **B** $15
- **C** $16
- **D** not given

What is the standard number?

5. thirteen thousand, five hundred twenty
- **A** 15,282
- **B** 13,520
- **C** 13,250
- **D** not given

6. twenty-seven thousand, forty-six
- **A** 27,426
- **B** 28,536
- **C** 27,036
- **D** not given

7. five hundred thirty thousand, four hundred fifty-nine
- **A** 53,459
- **B** 530,459
- **C** 534,590
- **D** not given

8. two hundred fifteen million, five hundred thirteen thousand
- **A** 215,513,000
- **B** 215,513
- **C** 250,513,000
- **D** not given

9. $\begin{array}{r} 3 \\ \times\ 6 \\ \hline \end{array}$
- **A** 12
- **B** 24
- **C** 18
- **D** not given

10. $\begin{array}{r} 4 \\ \times\ 0 \\ \hline \end{array}$
- **A** 4
- **B** 40
- **C** 0
- **D** not given

11. $\begin{array}{r} 7 \\ \times\ 8 \\ \hline \end{array}$
- **A** 48
- **B** 56
- **C** 63
- **D** not given

12. $\begin{array}{r} 6 \\ \times\ 9 \\ \hline \end{array}$
- **A** 54
- **B** 72
- **C** 81
- **D** not given

13. Matt planted 8 rows of corn. He planted 8 seeds in each row. How many seeds did Matt plant?
- **A** 6
- **B** 48
- **C** 64
- **D** not given

14. Mona's bicycle is 22 inches long. Randy's bicycle is 26 inches long. How much longer is Randy's bicycle than Mona's?
- **A** 4 inches
- **B** 3 inches
- **C** 2 inches
- **D** not given

MULTIPLICATION: 1-Digit Factors

Ekwa's class was studying animals that may become extinct. They prepared special reports. Some children drew pictures. Others talked about plans to save the animals. They made a movie of their reports. Ekwa's mother taught them to use a video camera. They learned to move it very slowly. They used a special lens for close-ups. They taped their show two times. Between tapings they decided which parts to cut out. Their first taping was 2 times as long as the second. The second taping was 26 minutes long. They showed it on the school television. Other classes were invited to watch.

Special Products: Mental Math

Kristy and Gerald played a game. Kristy had to pay the rent on Hawaii Avenue 4 times. Gerald had to pay the rent on Alaska Avenue 4 times. How much rent did each person pay in all?

Since we want the totals for equal amounts, we multiply.

Kristy's rent

> 4 × 3 tens = 12 tens

4 × 30 = 120

Gerald's rent

> 4 × 3 hundreds = 12 hundreds

4 × 300 = 1,200

Kristy paid $120 rent and Gerald paid $1,200 rent.

Other Examples

6 × 10 = 60   **5 × 3,000 = 15,000**   **4 × 500 = 2,000**

> 20 hundreds = 2 thousand

Warm Up   Give each product aloud.

1. 5 × 10	**2.** 4 × 20	**3.** 7 × 30
4. 1 × 80	**5.** 9 × 40	**6.** 3 × 50
7. 8 × 500	**8.** 3 × 900	**9.** 4 × 600
10. 7 × 400	**11.** 3 × 300	**12.** 5 × 500
13. 9 × 1,000	**14.** 7 × 2,000	**15.** 4 × 8,000
16. 2 × 3,000	**17.** 4 × 4,000	**18.** 3 × 7,000

Practice Find the products. Write answers only.

1. 7×10 2. 6×30 3. 2×90

4. 3×80 5. 5×20 6. 4×50

7. 9×100 8. 6×200 9. 8×400

10. 5×300 11. 2×700 12. 3×200

13. $6 \times 1,000$ 14. $2 \times 8,000$ 15. $9 \times 6,000$

16. $3 \times 6,000$ 17. $4 \times 9,000$ 18. $8 \times 5,000$

19. 2×400 20. $8 \times 1,000$ 21. 7×60

22. Multiply 7 and 1,000.   23. Multiply 2 and 8,000.

Mixed Applications

24. The rent on Montana Avenue is $40. Claire paid the rent 7 times. How much rent did she pay in all?

25. You land on another player's property and owe $65. You give the player a $100 bill. How much change do you get?

★ 26. You land on Lindsey Place. The rent is 10 times the sum of the numbers on the cubes. What is the rent? $120

> **THINK**
>
> **Logical Reasoning**
>
> At what times during a day does a digital clock read the same forward and backward?
>
> Example
>
> 12:21
>
> **MATH**

Multiplying Three Numbers: Mental Math

Kent and Sandra work in a supply room. They want to know how many envelopes they have. There are 2 boxes of envelopes. Each box holds 4 packages and each package holds 100 envelopes.

Kent and Sandra got the same answer but they used different groupings when they multiplied.

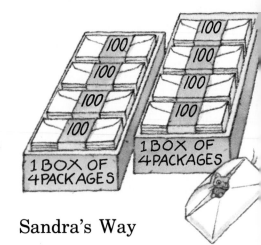

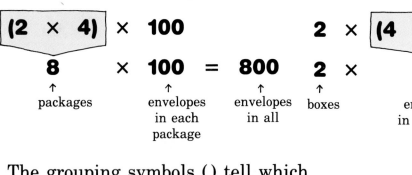

Kent's Way	Sandra's Way
$(2 \times 4) \times 100$	$2 \times (4 \times 100)$

Kent's Way:
$8 \times 100 = 800$
↑ packages   ↑ envelopes in each package   ↑ envelopes in all

Sandra's Way:
$2 \times 400 = 800$
↑ boxes   ↑ envelopes in each box   ↑ envelopes in all

The grouping symbols ( ) tell which multiplication to do first. When you multiply, you get the same product even if you change the groupings.

Find these products. Use the grouping shown.

1. $(3 \times 2) \times 100$

2. $3 \times (2 \times 100)$

3. $(4 \times 1) \times 10$

4. $4 \times (1 \times 10)$

5. $(3 \times 3) \times 1,000$

6. $3 \times (3 \times 1,000)$

Find these products. Use any grouping you want.

7. $2 \times 3 \times 100$

8. $6 \times 1 \times 10$

9. $2 \times 4 \times 1,000$

10. $3 \times 3 \times 100$

11. $7 \times 1 \times 10$

12. $1 \times 8 \times 1,000$

More Practice, page 416, Set A

Practice the Facts

Find the products.

1. 4 × 3

2. 2 × 2

3. 5 × 2

4. 3 × 6

5. 5 × 3

6. 5 × 5

7. 3 × 8

8. 3 × 2

9. 8 × 4

10. 5 × 6

11. 4 × 4

12. 4 × 6

13. 3 × 7

14. 4 × 2

15. 5 × 4

16. 8 × 3

17. 5 × 1

18. 3 × 4

19. 4 × 1

20. 0 × 5

21. 4 × 7

22. 3 × 5

23. 3 × 9

24. 2 × 1

25. 6 × 5

26. 4 × 5

27. 7 × 3

28. 0 × 4

29. 6 × 9

30. 7 × 7

31. 5 × 9

32. 7 × 8

33. 9 × 7

34. 7 × 6

35. 9 × 8

36. 9 × 4

37. 6 × 6

38. 7 × 5

39. 9 × 9

40. 8 × 6

41. 8 × 8

42. 9 × 6

43. 9 × 5

44. 8 × 9

45. 4 × 9

46. 6 × 7

47. 8 × 7

48. 8 × 5

49. 6 × 8

50. 7 × 7

51. 5 × 8

52. 7 × 9

53. 5 × 7

54. 9 × 4

55. 9 × 9

56. 5 × 9

Multiplying and Adding: Mental Math

Alvaro and Dennis are playing a card game.

> *Rules:* Multiply each number on the yellow ones' card and the red tens' card by the number on the times card. Add the products.

Alvaro's cards

What is Alvaro's score?

1. Multiply ones. ——→ **4 × 6 = 24**
2. Multiply tens. ——→ **4 × 30 = 120**
3. Add the products. ————————→ **144**

Alvaro's score is 144.

Give the total score for each turn below.

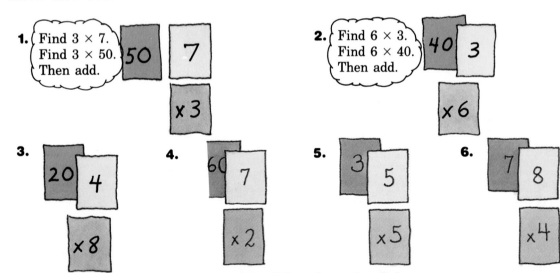

1. (Find 3 × 7. Find 3 × 50. Then add.) 50 7 × 3

2. (Find 6 × 3. Find 6 × 40. Then add.) 40 3 × 6

3. 20 4 × 8

4. 60 7 × 2

5. 3 5 × 5

6. 7 8 × 4

The boys played a game using blue hundreds' cards. Give the total score for each turn.

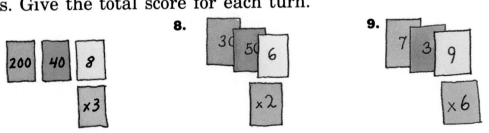

7. 200 40 8 × 3

8. 300 50 6 × 2

9. 7 3 9 × 6

Multiply and Then Add: Mental Math

Portia bought 3 tickets for children and 1 for an adult for admission into the fair. How much did she pay for tickets?

Portia paid $9 for tickets.

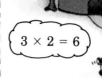

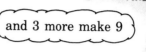

$3 \times 2 = 6$

and 3 more make 9

Practice Multiply and then add 2. Write answers only.

1. 6×2	**2.** 7×5	**3.** 4×9	**4.** 8×0
5. 2×3	**6.** 4×1	**7.** 6×6	**8.** 3×8

Multiply and then add 3. Write answers only.

9. 3×4	**10.** 4×8	**11.** 2×0	**12.** 5×1
13. 7×2	**14.** 9×9	**15.** 6×4	**16.** 8×3

Multiply and then add 4. Write answers only.

17. 2×5	**18.** 6×7	**19.** 3×2	**20.** 7×4
21. 8×1	**22.** 5×5	**23.** 4×0	**24.** 9×2

Multiply and then add 5. Write answers only.

25. 5×2	**26.** 4×7	**27.** 3×3	**28.** 5×0
29. 2×9	**30.** 8×6	**31.** 6×3	**32.** 7×3

Multiply and then add 6. Write answers only.

33. 9×3	**34.** 4×6	**35.** 6×8	**36.** 5×7
37. 2×9	**38.** 3×0	**39.** 7×7	**40.** 8×2

Multiply and then add 7. Write answers only.

41. 3×5	**42.** 6×9	**43.** 2×7	**44.** 9×4
45. 7×0	**46.** 4×4	**47.** 5×9	**48.** 8×4

Multiplying: Trading Ones

A trout swims 24 km/h (kilometers per hour). A flying fish can swim 3 times as fast as a trout. How many kilometers per hour can a flying fish swim?

Since we want the total for equal amounts, we multiply.

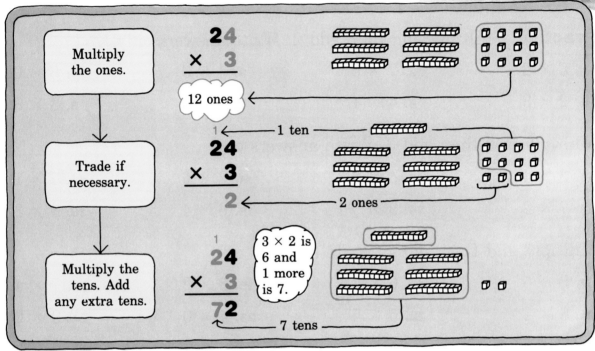

Multiply the ones.	24 × 3

12 ones

1 ← 1 ten

Trade if necessary.	24 × 3 2

2 ones

Multiply the tens. Add any extra tens.	1 24 × 3 72

3 × 2 is 6 and 1 more is 7.

7 tens

A flying fish can swim 72 km/h.

Other Examples

$$\begin{array}{r} 23 \\ \times\ 3 \\ \hline 69 \end{array}$$
NO TRADE NECESSARY

$$\begin{array}{r} {}^{2} \\ 17 \\ \times\ 4 \\ \hline 68 \end{array}$$

$$\begin{array}{r} 20 \\ \times\ 4 \\ \hline 80 \end{array}$$
NO TRADE NECESSARY

$$\begin{array}{r} {}^{3} \\ 15 \\ \times\ 6 \\ \hline 90 \end{array}$$

Warm Up Multiply.

1. $\begin{array}{r} 21 \\ \times\ 3 \end{array}$

2. $\begin{array}{r} 37 \\ \times\ 2 \end{array}$

3. $\begin{array}{r} 12 \\ \times\ 3 \end{array}$

4. $\begin{array}{r} 18 \\ \times\ 4 \end{array}$

5. $\begin{array}{r} 19 \\ \times\ 5 \end{array}$

6. $\begin{array}{r} 25 \\ \times\ 2 \end{array}$

Practice Find the products.

1. $\begin{array}{r} 23 \\ \times\ 4 \\ \hline \end{array}$
2. $\begin{array}{r} 34 \\ \times\ 2 \\ \hline \end{array}$
3. $\begin{array}{r} 14 \\ \times\ 6 \\ \hline \end{array}$
4. $\begin{array}{r} 32 \\ \times\ 3 \\ \hline \end{array}$
5. $\begin{array}{r} 15 \\ \times\ 4 \\ \hline \end{array}$

6. $\begin{array}{r} 14 \\ \times\ 5 \\ \hline \end{array}$
7. $\begin{array}{r} 25 \\ \times\ 3 \\ \hline \end{array}$
8. $\begin{array}{r} 20 \\ \times\ 4 \\ \hline \end{array}$
9. $\begin{array}{r} 12 \\ \times\ 8 \\ \hline \end{array}$
10. $\begin{array}{r} 46 \\ \times\ 2 \\ \hline \end{array}$

11. $\begin{array}{r} 16 \\ \times\ 6 \\ \hline \end{array}$
12. $\begin{array}{r} 33 \\ \times\ 3 \\ \hline \end{array}$
13. $\begin{array}{r} 24 \\ \times\ 3 \\ \hline \end{array}$
14. $\begin{array}{r} 12 \\ \times\ 4 \\ \hline \end{array}$
15. $\begin{array}{r} 29 \\ \times\ 2 \\ \hline \end{array}$

16. 4×19
17. 2×33
18. 3×31

19. 5×18
20. 3×30
21. 2×27

22. Multiply 17 by 3.
23. Multiply 13 by 6.
24. Multiply 21 by 4.

25. Multiply 48 by 2.
26. Multiply 16 by 5.
27. Multiply 15 by 5.

Mixed Applications

28. A penguin swims 14 km/h. A dolphin swims 4 times as fast as a penguin. How many kilometers per hour can a dolphin swim?

29. Write a question for this story and then solve the problem.

    Salmon can swim 36 km/h. Tuna can swim twice as fast as salmon.

30. A person swam 665 meters in 5 minutes. How far did this person swim each minute if she swam the same distance each minute?

THINK

Logical Reasoning

The missing digits are all the same. There are 2 different answers. Find them.

MATH

Multiplying: Trading Ones and Tens

Jeffrey hopes to skate in the Winter Olympics someday. He trained 4 hours a day on each of the 31 days in March. How many hours did he train in March?

Since we want the total for equal amounts of time, we multiply.

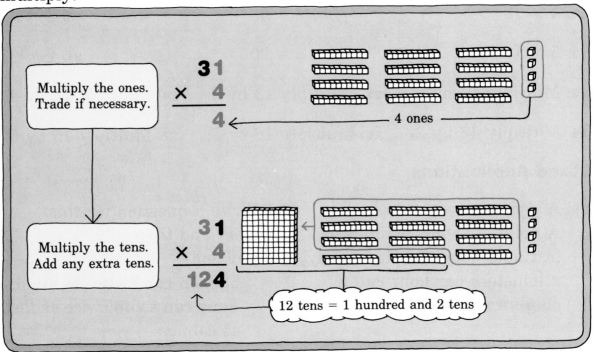

Multiply the ones. Trade if necessary.

$$\begin{array}{r} 3\mathbf{1} \\ \times\ 4 \\ \hline 4 \end{array}$$ ← 4 ones

Multiply the tens. Add any extra tens.

$$\begin{array}{r} 31 \\ \times\ 4 \\ \hline 124 \end{array}$$

12 tens = 1 hundred and 2 tens

Jeffrey trained for 124 hours in March.

Other Examples

$$\begin{array}{r} 52 \\ \times\ 3 \\ \hline 156 \end{array} \qquad \begin{array}{r} {}^{1}\ \\ 43 \\ \times\ 6 \\ \hline 258 \end{array} \qquad \begin{array}{r} {}^{2}\ \\ 35 \\ \times\ 5 \\ \hline 175 \end{array} \qquad \begin{array}{r} {}^{2}\ \\ 75 \\ \times\ 4 \\ \hline 300 \end{array}$$

Warm Up   Multiply.

1. $\begin{array}{r} 63 \\ \times\ 2 \end{array}$
2. $\begin{array}{r} 31 \\ \times\ 8 \end{array}$
3. $\begin{array}{r} 54 \\ \times\ 3 \end{array}$
4. $\begin{array}{r} 29 \\ \times\ 4 \end{array}$
5. $\begin{array}{r} 78 \\ \times\ 5 \end{array}$
6. $\begin{array}{r} 34 \\ \times\ 9 \end{array}$

Practice Find the products.

1. 62
    × 3

2. 42
    × 6

3. 43
    × 5

4. 41
    × 7

5. 23
    × 4

6. 99
    × 2

7. 53
    × 9

8. 37
    × 3

9. 78
    × 8

10. 80
    × 5

11. 67
    × 6

12. 78
    × 4

13. 47
    × 2

14. 96
    × 9

15. 75
    × 7

16. 6 × 35

17. 8 × 16

18. 4 × 26

19. 7 × 16

20. 3 × 96

21. 2 × 84

22. Give the product of 7 and 58.

23. Give the product of 5 and 62.

24. Give the product of 8 and 67.

25. Give the product of 6 and 84.

Mixed Applications

26. Jeffrey trained 28 days in April. He trained 3 hours on each of those days. How many hours did he train in April?

27. An ice skater practices 6 hours each day during the week and 10 hours on the weekend. How many hours does this skater practice in 1 week?

SKILLKEEPER

Write each time.

Multiplying Larger Numbers: One Trade

Washington State Ferryboats

Number of autos each ferryboat carries	
Super ferryboats	162
Yakima	
Hyak	
Kaleetan	
Jumbo ferryboats	206
Walla Walla	
Spokane	

How many autos could the 3 super ferryboats carry if they were full?

Since we want the total for equal numbers of autos, we multiply.

Multiply the ones. Trade if necessary.	→	Multiply the tens. Add any extra tens. Trade if necessary.	→	Multiply the hundreds. Add any extra hundreds.

$$\begin{array}{r} 162 \\ \times\quad 3 \\ \hline 6 \end{array}$$

$$\begin{array}{r} ^1\ \\ 162 \\ \times\quad 3 \\ \hline 86 \end{array}$$

18 tens = 1 hundred and 8 tens

$$\begin{array}{r} ^1\ \\ 162 \\ \times\quad 3 \\ \hline 486 \end{array}$$

The 3 super ferryboats could carry 486 autos.

Other Examples

trading ones
$$\begin{array}{r} ^2\ \\ 216 \\ \times\quad 4 \\ \hline 864 \end{array}$$

trading tens
$$\begin{array}{r} ^1\ \\ 380 \\ \times\quad 2 \\ \hline 760 \end{array}$$

trading hundreds
$$\begin{array}{r} 301 \\ \times\quad 5 \\ \hline 1{,}505 \end{array}$$

15 hundreds = 1 thousand and 5 hundreds

Warm Up Multiply.

1. $\begin{array}{r} 241 \\ \times\ 3 \end{array}$
2. $\begin{array}{r} 435 \\ \times\ 2 \end{array}$
3. $\begin{array}{r} 322 \\ \times\ 4 \end{array}$
4. $\begin{array}{r} 302 \\ \times\ 3 \end{array}$
5. $\begin{array}{r} 120 \\ \times\ 5 \end{array}$

Practice Find the products.

1. $\begin{array}{r} 227 \\ \times\ 3 \\ \hline \end{array}$
2. $\begin{array}{r} 161 \\ \times\ 6 \\ \hline \end{array}$
3. $\begin{array}{r} 421 \\ \times\ 4 \\ \hline \end{array}$
4. $\begin{array}{r} 306 \\ \times\ 2 \\ \hline \end{array}$
5. $\begin{array}{r} 171 \\ \times\ 5 \\ \hline \end{array}$

6. $\begin{array}{r} 411 \\ \times\ 7 \\ \hline \end{array}$
7. $\begin{array}{r} 219 \\ \times\ 4 \\ \hline \end{array}$
8. $\begin{array}{r} 912 \\ \times\ 4 \\ \hline \end{array}$
9. $\begin{array}{r} 232 \\ \times\ 3 \\ \hline \end{array}$
10. $\begin{array}{r} 109 \\ \times\ 9 \\ \hline \end{array}$

11. $\begin{array}{r} 294 \\ \times\ 2 \\ \hline \end{array}$
12. $\begin{array}{r} 510 \\ \times\ 6 \\ \hline \end{array}$
13. $\begin{array}{r} 71 \\ \times\ 8 \\ \hline \end{array}$
14. $\begin{array}{r} 401 \\ \times\ 5 \\ \hline \end{array}$
15. $\begin{array}{r} 283 \\ \times\ 3 \\ \hline \end{array}$

16. 4×621
17. 5×181
18. 2×523

19. 3×129
20. 2×49
21. 6×812

22. Multiply 3 times 703.
23. Multiply 2 times 182.

24. Multiply 5 times 115.
25. Multiply 9 times 181.

Mixed Applications

26. How many autos could the 2 jumbo ferryboats carry if they were full?

27. The Hyak ferryboat is 45 m long. The Walla Walla is 135 m long. How much longer is the Walla Walla ferryboat than the Hyak ferryboat?

28. **DATA BANK** See page 401. Find the number of autos the ferryboat Columbia can carry. If there were 3 people in each auto how many people could go on the ferryboat?

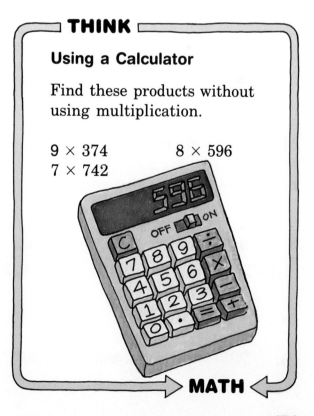

THINK

Using a Calculator

Find these products without using multiplication.

9×374 8×596
7×742

MATH

Multiplying Larger Numbers: Two or More Trades

Mr. Rowe's class wants to make 6 batches of modeling clay. How many milliliters of cornstarch do they need?

Since we want the total for 6 equal amounts, we multiply.

Recipe for Modeling Clay
250 mL Baking Soda
125 mL Cornstarch
165 mL Warm Water
This recipe makes one batch.

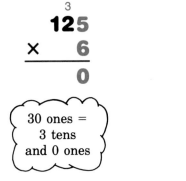

Multiply the ones. Trade if necessary. → Multiply the tens. Add any extra tens. Trade if necessary. → Multiply the hundreds. Add any extra hundreds.

$$
\begin{array}{r}
3 \\
125 \\
\times \quad 6 \\
\hline
0
\end{array}
\qquad
\begin{array}{r}
1\ 3 \\
125 \\
\times \quad 6 \\
\hline
50
\end{array}
\qquad
\begin{array}{r}
1\ 3 \\
125 \\
\times \quad 6 \\
\hline
750
\end{array}
$$

30 ones = 3 tens and 0 ones

15 tens = 1 hundred and 5 tens

Mr. Rowe's class needs 750 mL of cornstarch.

Other Examples

$$
\begin{array}{r}
3 \\
318 \\
\times \ 4 \\
\hline
1{,}272
\end{array}
\quad
\begin{array}{r}
1\ 2 \\
237 \\
\times \ 3 \\
\hline
711
\end{array}
\quad
\begin{array}{r}
3 \\
871 \\
\times \ 5 \\
\hline
4{,}355
\end{array}
\quad
\begin{array}{r}
1 \\
706 \\
\times \ 2 \\
\hline
1{,}412
\end{array}
\quad
\begin{array}{r}
2\ 4 \\
625 \\
\times \ 8 \\
\hline
5{,}000
\end{array}
$$

Warm Up   Multiply.

1. $\begin{array}{r} 237 \\ \times\ 4 \end{array}$
2. $\begin{array}{r} 453 \\ \times\ 3 \end{array}$
3. $\begin{array}{r} 807 \\ \times\ 2 \end{array}$
4. $\begin{array}{r} 744 \\ \times\ 7 \end{array}$
5. $\begin{array}{r} 735 \\ \times\ 6 \end{array}$

Practice Find the products.

1. 342
   × 5

2. 468
   × 2

3. 591
   × 4

4. 412
   × 8

5. 154
   × 6

6. 807
   × 3

7. 59
   × 9

8. 360
   × 3

9. 903
   × 5

10. 623
    × 9

11. 79
    × 4

12. 649
    × 2

13. 764
    × 5

14. 650
    × 7

15. 135
    × 8

16. 3 × 276

17. 2 × 971

18. 4 × 704

19. 9 × 841

20. 8 × 825

21. 6 × 243

22. Find the product of 184 and 3.

23. Find the product of 521 and 7.

24. Find the product of 230 and 5.

25. Find the product of 375 and 2.

Mixed Applications

26. Look at the recipe on page 172. How many milliliters of baking soda does Mr. Rowe's class need to make 6 batches of modeling clay?

27. Write a question for this data and solve the problem.
    A box of cornstarch weighs 454 g. Leo bought 3 boxes.

28. **DATA BANK** See page 399. How much more water is needed to make 1 batch of finger paint than is needed to make 1 batch of modeling clay?

THINK

Logical Reasoning

Find missing digits for this problem.

Example: 444
         × 1
         ‾‾‾‾‾
         444

There are 3 more ways.

MATH

More Practice, page 418, Set A

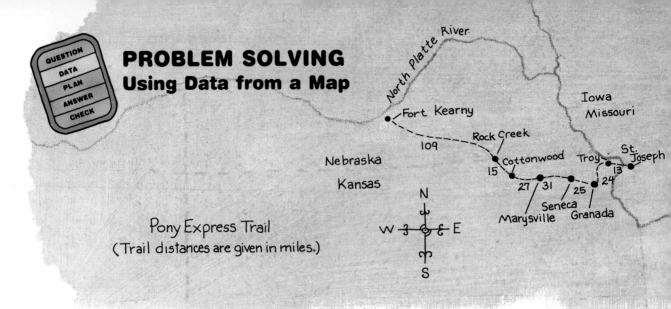

PROBLEM SOLVING
Using Data from a Map

This map shows some of the stations along the Pony Express Trail.

Find each distance.

1. Fort Kearny to Rock Creek
2. Rock Creek to Cottonwood
3. Granada to Troy

4. St. Joseph to Troy
5. Seneca to Rock Creek
6. Troy to Cottonwood

Find the total round-trip distance for problems 7–12.

7. between Rock Creek and Fort Kearny
8. between Marysville and Cottonwood
9. between Marysville and Seneca

10. between Cottonwood and Fort Kearny
11. between Rock Creek and Marysville
12. between Cottonwood and Seneca

Use the data from the map to solve the following problems.

13. A rider made 4 round trips a week between Cottonwood and Marysville. How many miles did he travel each week?

14. A rider made 4 round trips a month between Fort Kearny and Rock Creek. How many miles did he travel each month?

Solve.

15. Pony Express riders were paid $125 a month. How much money did a rider earn in 6 months?

16. Each station needed 2 men to take care of the horses and supplies. How many stations could be cared for by 14 men?

17. There were 198 Pony Express stations. If each station had 3 horses, how many horses did the Pony Express have in all?

18. The Pony Express traveled from St. Joseph to Salt Lake City in 124 hours. It took 116 more hours to get to San Francisco. How many hours did it take to get from St. Joseph to San Francisco?

19. The first Pony Express mail that left San Francisco on April 3, 1860 carried a total of 85 letters. The charge for each letter was $5. How much money was collected for this first mail?

20. In good weather one rider traveled 10 miles each hour. At this rate how many miles did he travel in 8 hours?

21. **Strategy Practice** Strawberry station was east of Moss station. Lakeside was east of Strawberry station. Sportsman Hall station was west of Moss but east of Placerville station. Which of these stations was the farthest west?

Estimating Products Using Rounding

A black-footed penguin eats 475 g of fish in 1 day. **About** how much fish would a penguin eat in 1 week (7 days)?

Since you want an answer that is only **close** to the exact answer, you **estimate** by rounding and then multiplying in your head.

Think of the problem. $\longrightarrow$

Round and multiply. $\longrightarrow$ **7 × 500 = 3,500**

A black-footed penguin eats **about** 3,500 g of fish in 1 week.

Other Examples

nearest ten	nearest hundred	nearest dollar
3 × 48	**6 × 612**	**8 × $3.78**
3 × 50 = 150	6 × 600 = 3,600	8 × $4 = $32
About 150	About 3,600	About $32

Warm Up   Estimate by rounding to the nearest ten.

1. 4 × 58   2. 3 × 65   3. 7 × 84

Estimate by rounding to the nearest hundred.

4. 3 × 205   5. 7 × 894   6. 2 × 913

Estimate by rounding to the nearest dollar.

7. 8 × $7.45   8. 9 × $2.50   9. 6 × $5.91

176

Practice Estimate the products. Write estimated answers only. Estimate by rounding to the nearest ten.

1. 4×21 **2.** 3×38 **3.** 6×53 **4.** 7×25

5. 5×13 **6.** 2×79 **7.** 4×61 **8.** 9×36

Estimate by rounding to the nearest hundred.

9. 6×310 **10.** 8×185 **11.** 2×99 **12.** 9×506

13. 3×665 **14.** 4×783 **15.** 7×450 **16.** 8×275

Estimate by rounding to the nearest dollar.

17. $8 \times \$2.03$ **18.** $3 \times \$5.88$ **19.** $5 \times \$3.23$ **20.** $2 \times \$9.13$

21. $4 \times \$2.82$ **22.** $7 \times \$5.18$ **23.** $6 \times \$1.43$ **24.** $3 \times \$1.50$

Mixed Applications

25. A rock-hopper penguin is 38 cm tall. An emperor penguin is 3 times as tall as a rock-hopper penguin. About how tall is an emperor penguin?

penguin?

26. Tell what information is not needed in this story. Then answer the question.

A zoo has 10 male penguins and 14 female penguins. The zoo pays $6.75 each day for penguin food. How many penguins does the zoo have?

SKILLKEEPER

Multiply.

1. $\begin{array}{r} 7 \\ \times\, 3 \\ \hline \end{array}$ **2.** $\begin{array}{r} 2 \\ \times\, 8 \\ \hline \end{array}$ **3.** $\begin{array}{r} 9 \\ \times\, 4 \\ \hline \end{array}$ **4.** $\begin{array}{r} 5 \\ \times\, 6 \\ \hline \end{array}$ **5.** $\begin{array}{r} 1 \\ \times\, 5 \\ \hline \end{array}$ **6.** $\begin{array}{r} 6 \\ \times\, 8 \\ \hline \end{array}$

7. $\begin{array}{r} 7 \\ \times\, 9 \\ \hline \end{array}$ **8.** $\begin{array}{r} 6 \\ \times\, 9 \\ \hline \end{array}$ **9.** $\begin{array}{r} 8 \\ \times\, 5 \\ \hline \end{array}$ **10.** $\begin{array}{r} 4 \\ \times\, 7 \\ \hline \end{array}$ **11.** $\begin{array}{r} 9 \\ \times\, 0 \\ \hline \end{array}$ **12.** $\begin{array}{r} 8 \\ \times\, 7 \\ \hline \end{array}$

Multiplying Larger Numbers: All Trades

In the story, *Gulliver's Travels*, the tiny people of Lilliput had to give Gulliver 1,728 times as much food and water as 1 Lilliputian. If a Lilliputian ate 7 loaves of bread in 1 week, how many loaves would they give Gulliver?

Since we want the total for equal amounts, we multiply.

Multiply the ones. Trade if necessary.	Multiply the tens. Add any extra tens. Trade if necessary.	Multiply the hundreds. Add any extra hundreds. Trade if necessary.	Multiply the thousands Add any extra thousands.
5	1 5	5 1 5	5 1 5
1,728	1,728	1,728	1,728
× 7	× 7	× 7	× 7
6	96	096	12,096

Gulliver would get 12,096 loaves of bread each week.

Other Examples

$$\begin{array}{r} {}^{1\ \ 1\ 3} \\ 3,428 \\ \times\quad 4 \\ \hline 13,712 \end{array} \qquad \begin{array}{r} {}^{3\quad 3} \\ 2,505 \\ \times\quad 6 \\ \hline 15,030 \end{array} \qquad \begin{array}{r} {}^{4\ 8} \\ 1,049 \\ \times\quad 9 \\ \hline 9,441 \end{array} \qquad \begin{array}{r} {}^{1} \\ 7,006 \\ \times\quad 3 \\ \hline 21,018 \end{array}$$

Warm Up Find the products.

	1.	2.	3.	4.	5.
	3,458	5,389	4,703	5,072	8,003
	× 2	× 6	× 4	× 7	× 5

Practice Find the products.

1. 3,172
   × 3

2. 6,314
   × 8

3. 6,956
   × 4

4. 3,205
   × 9

5. 7,095
   × 2

6. 4,009
   × 7

7. 3,418
   × 5

8. 868
   × 6

9. 9,538
   × 3

10. 9,087
    × 9

11. 5,279
    × 8

12. 208
    × 4

13. 9,837
    × 2

14. 3,990
    × 6

15. 7,148
    × 8

16. 5 × 7,926

17. 9 × 6,041

18. 3 × 4,086

19. 4 × 3,519

20. 7 × 1,386

21. 8 × 3,007

22. Find the product of 2,691 and 2.

23. Find the product of 1,274 and 6.

24. Find the product of 5,240 and 5.

25. Find the product of 3,807 and 9.

Mixed Applications

26. If a person in Lilliput eats 4 fish each week, how many fish would Gulliver get? (Remember, Gulliver gets 1,728 times as much as a person in Lilliput.)

27. Gulliver ate 3,456 sandwiches on Saturday. On Sunday he ate 5,184 sandwiches. How many fewer sandwiches did Gulliver eat on Saturday than on Sunday?

THINK
Greatest Product Game

1. Number a cube 1 through 6. Each player draws a grid.

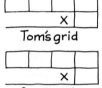

2. Take turns tossing the cube. After each toss, write the number in one of the boxes. Do this 5 times.

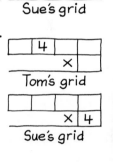

3. Find your product. The winner is the player with the greatest product.

Who won?

MATH

Multiplying with Money

MENU

#1. Taco, beans, rice $2.35

#2. Burrito, beans, rice $2.79

#3. Enchilada, beans, rice $2.85

#4. Taco, Enchilada, beans, rice $3.25

The Wilson family went out to dinner. They wanted 5 orders of the number 4 dinner. How much did the Wilsons pay for the food?

Since we want the total for 5 dinners of the same price, we multiply.

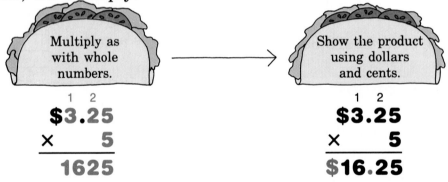

Multiply as with whole numbers.

$$
\begin{array}{r}
{}^{1}\ {}^{2}\ \\
\$3.25 \\
\times\ \ \ \ 5 \\
\hline
1625
\end{array}
$$

Show the product using dollars and cents.

$$
\begin{array}{r}
{}^{1}\ {}^{2}\ \\
\$3.25 \\
\times\ \ \ \ 5 \\
\hline
\$16.25
\end{array}
$$

The Wilsons paid $16.25 for the food.

Other Examples

$$
\begin{array}{r}
{}^{5}\ {}^{2}\ {}^{5}\ \\
\$27.38 \\
\times\ \ \ \ \ \ 7 \\
\hline
\$191.66
\end{array}
\qquad
\begin{array}{r}
{}^{2}\ \\
\$30.04 \\
\times\ \ \ \ \ \ 6 \\
\hline
\$180.24
\end{array}
\qquad
\begin{array}{r}
{}^{2}\ {}^{4}\ \\
\$6.25 \\
\times\ \ \ \ 8 \\
\hline
\$50.00
\end{array}
\qquad
\begin{array}{r}
{}^{3}\ \\
\$0.79 \\
\times\ \ \ \ 4 \\
\hline
\$3.16
\end{array}
$$

Warm Up Multiply. Write the answers with dollars and cents.

1.	2.	3.	4.	5.
$34.27	$6.98	$20.05	$75.75	$0.35
× 7	× 3	× 4	× 8	× 6

Practice Multiply. Write the amounts with dollars and cents.

1. $19.43
   × 2

2. $13.59
   × 5

3. $10.72
   × 9

4. $0.87
   × 4

5. $6.82
   × 5

6. $83.70
   × 6

7. $14.08
   × 8

8. $0.93
   × 7

9. $23.74
   × 3

10. $57.62
    × 2

11. $9.85
    × 9

12. $0.23
    × 8

13. $36.19
    × 4

14. $70.04
    × 5

15. $51.60
    × 7

16. 6 × $41.26

17. 3 × $5.01

18. 5 × $0.75

19. 2 × $80.98

20. 9 × $34.66

21. 4 × $40.80

22. 8 at $49.60 each

23. 3 at $0.89 each

24. 7 at $8.95 each

Mixed Applications

25. Estimate, then find the cost of 6 dinners at $7.95 each.

26. How much would 6 orders of the number 2 dinner cost? Use the menu on page 180.

27. The cook buys tomatoes and beans by the box. Tomatoes cost $12.75 a box and beans cost $9.35 a box. What does it cost to buy 1 box of tomatoes and 2 boxes of beans?

28. **DATA HUNT** Get a menu from a place where you like to eat. Pick something you would want to order. How much would it cost for 7 orders?

THINK

🖩 **Using a Calculator**

How many books did Dr. Thomas buy?

Books $17.45 each

Book Store
$ 17.45
× IIII
Total $122.15

MATH

PROBLEM SOLVING
Using Data from an Order Form

Marian Miller owns the Costume Shop in San Francisco. She is ordering some costumes to sell in her store. She has filled out the order form to show how many of each item she wants.

COSTUME FACTORY
New York, New York

Name __The Costume Shop__
Address __1234 Market St.__
__San Francisco, California__

Item	Catalog Number	Quantity	PRICE EACH		TOTAL PRICE	
			Dollars	Cents	Dollars	Cents
1. Clown wig	21-281	8	$ 7.	45	$ 59.	60
2. Clown suit	23-281	5	17.	98		
3. Rabbit suit	25-116	—	19.	98		
4. Superman suit	25-118	1	19.	98		
5. Wonder Woman suit	27-118	—	22.	49		
6. Pirate suit	25-114	3	21.	99		
7. Witch hat	27-356	6	5.	98		
8. Witch suit	23-545	6	18.	75		

TOTAL FOR ORDER [   ]

Use the order form to answer these questions.

1. How much do 5 clown suits cost?

2. What is the cost of 1 clown wig and 1 clown suit?

3. How much more does a Wonder Woman suit cost than a Superman suit?

QUESTION
DATA
PLAN
ANSWER
CHECK

PROBLEM SOLVING
Choosing a Calculation Method

Your choice!
Pencil- Paper • Mental Math
Estimation • Calculator

You may use any of these methods to solve the problems, but use each method at least once.

Each problem refers to the order form on page 182.

1. Marian is ordering 3 pirate suits. How much will they cost in all?

2. How much does it cost to order 1 witch hat and 1 witch suit?

3. How much will Marian pay for the witch suits she wants to order?

4. Which suits cost more than the Superman suit?

5. Will 5 rabbit suits cost more or less than $100?

6. How much more will 3 pirate suits cost than 1 Superman suit?

7. How much will 6 witch outfits cost? (A witch outfit is hat and suit together.)

8. *Strategy Practice* A space suit and hat cost $30. The suit costs $8 more than the hat. How much is the space suit?

183

PROBLEM-SOLVING STRATEGY
Work Backward

QUESTION
DATA
PLAN
ANSWER
CHECK

TO SOLVE THIS PROBLEM, YOU NEED TO DO MORE THAN JUST QUICKLY DECIDE TO ADD, SUBTRACT, MULTIPLY OR DIVIDE. A STRATEGY THAT MIGHT BE HELPFUL TO YOU IS GIVEN BELOW.

Try This Farmer Jones decided to stop raising hogs. He sold 17. He divided the rest equally among his 6 children. Each child got 8 hogs. How many hogs did Farmer Jones start with?

WORK BACKWARD

SINCE EACH OF THE 6 CHILDREN GOT 8 HOGS, I'LL MULTIPLY TO FIND THE NUMBER THAT WERE DIVIDED EQUALLY.

SINCE 17 WERE SOLD, I'LL "ADD BACK" THAT NUMBER TO SEE HOW MANY THERE WERE TO START.

$$8 \times 6 = 48$$
hogs children number
divided equally

$$48 + 17 = 65$$
number   number   number
shared   sold   at the start

Farmer Jones started with 65 hogs.

Solve.

1. Andrew bought 6 books. Each book cost $3. Then he spent $7 for a tape. How much money did Andrew start with if he had no money left?

2. Loni had some cards. She gave 6 friends 5 cards each. She gave another friend 7. Loni kept 9 cards. How many cards did she start with?

CHAPTER REVIEW/TEST

Multiply.

1. 3×50 **2.** 9×40 **3.** 7×400 **4.** $4 \times 8,000$

5. $2 \times 2 \times 100$ **6.** $6 \times 1 \times 10$ **7.** $2 \times 4 \times 1,000$

| **8.** $\begin{array}{r} 63 \\ \times\ 9 \\ \hline \end{array}$ | **9.** $\begin{array}{r} 78 \\ \times\ 3 \\ \hline \end{array}$ | **10.** $\begin{array}{r} 34 \\ \times\ 5 \\ \hline \end{array}$ | **11.** $\begin{array}{r} 612 \\ \times\ 4 \\ \hline \end{array}$ | **12.** $\begin{array}{r} 105 \\ \times\ 7 \\ \hline \end{array}$ |

| **13.** $\begin{array}{r} 243 \\ \times\ 3 \\ \hline \end{array}$ | **14.** $\begin{array}{r} 116 \\ \times\ 6 \\ \hline \end{array}$ | **15.** $\begin{array}{r} 386 \\ \times\ 2 \\ \hline \end{array}$ | **16.** $\begin{array}{r} 637 \\ \times\ 5 \\ \hline \end{array}$ | **17.** $\begin{array}{r} 436 \\ \times\ 9 \\ \hline \end{array}$ |

Estimate. Round as indicated.

18. nearest ten

4×83

19. nearest hundred

7×315

20. nearest dollar

$6 \times \$8.79$

Multiply.

| **21.** $\begin{array}{r} 6,351 \\ \times\ 3 \\ \hline \end{array}$ | **22.** $\begin{array}{r} 4,036 \\ \times\ 8 \\ \hline \end{array}$ | **23.** $\begin{array}{r} 8,607 \\ \times\ 6 \\ \hline \end{array}$ | **24.** $\begin{array}{r} 7,050 \\ \times\ 4 \\ \hline \end{array}$ | **25.** $\begin{array}{r} 5,812 \\ \times\ 7 \\ \hline \end{array}$ |

| **26.** $\begin{array}{r} \$0.13 \\ \times\ 5 \\ \hline \end{array}$ | **27.** $\begin{array}{r} \$0.46 \\ \times\ 7 \\ \hline \end{array}$ | **28.** $\begin{array}{r} \$1.08 \\ \times\ 8 \\ \hline \end{array}$ | **29.** $\begin{array}{r} \$6.87 \\ \times\ 6 \\ \hline \end{array}$ | **30.** $\begin{array}{r} \$84.28 \\ \times\ 9 \\ \hline \end{array}$ |

Solve.

31. How much do 5 witch hats cost?

32. How much more does the witch suit cost than the witch hat?

ITEM	PRICE EACH	
	DOLLARS	CENTS
1.WITCH HAT	5.	98
2. WITCH SUIT	18.	75

ANOTHER LOOK

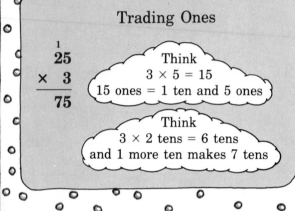

Trading Ones

$$\begin{array}{r} \overset{1}{25} \\ \times\ 3 \\ \hline 75 \end{array}$$

Think
$3 \times 5 = 15$
15 ones = 1 ten and 5 ones

Think
3×2 tens = 6 tens
and 1 more ten makes 7 tens

Trading Tens

$$\begin{array}{r} \overset{2}{68} \\ \times\ 3 \\ \hline 204 \end{array}$$

← 2 tens

24 ones = 2 tens and 4 ones

20 tens = 2 hundreds and 0 tens

Trading Hundreds

$$\begin{array}{r} \overset{3\,3}{879} \\ \times\ 4 \\ \hline 3516 \end{array}$$

36 ones = 3 tens and 6 ones

31 tens = 3 hundreds and 1 ten

35 hundreds =
3 thousands and 5 hundreds

Multiply.

1. $\begin{array}{r}17\\ \times\ 4\\ \hline\end{array}$	**2.** $\begin{array}{r}16\\ \times\ 5\\ \hline\end{array}$	**3.** $\begin{array}{r}26\\ \times\ 3\\ \hline\end{array}$
4. $\begin{array}{r}48\\ \times\ 2\\ \hline\end{array}$	**5.** $\begin{array}{r}13\\ \times\ 6\\ \hline\end{array}$	**6.** $\begin{array}{r}23\\ \times\ 4\\ \hline\end{array}$
7. $\begin{array}{r}19\\ \times\ 3\\ \hline\end{array}$	**8.** $\begin{array}{r}37\\ \times\ 2\\ \hline\end{array}$	**9.** $\begin{array}{r}17\\ \times\ 5\\ \hline\end{array}$
10. $\begin{array}{r}67\\ \times\ 4\\ \hline\end{array}$	**11.** $\begin{array}{r}73\\ \times\ 6\\ \hline\end{array}$	**12.** $\begin{array}{r}49\\ \times\ 3\\ \hline\end{array}$
13. $\begin{array}{r}78\\ \times\ 2\\ \hline\end{array}$	**14.** $\begin{array}{r}51\\ \times\ 5\\ \hline\end{array}$	**15.** $\begin{array}{r}65\\ \times\ 8\\ \hline\end{array}$
16. $\begin{array}{r}33\\ \times\ 7\\ \hline\end{array}$	**17.** $\begin{array}{r}83\\ \times\ 3\\ \hline\end{array}$	**18.** $\begin{array}{r}75\\ \times\ 9\\ \hline\end{array}$
19. $\begin{array}{r}576\\ \times\ 2\\ \hline\end{array}$	**20.** $\begin{array}{r}607\\ \times\ 3\\ \hline\end{array}$	**21.** $\begin{array}{r}765\\ \times\ 4\\ \hline\end{array}$
22. $\begin{array}{r}437\\ \times\ 4\\ \hline\end{array}$	**23.** $\begin{array}{r}852\\ \times\ 5\\ \hline\end{array}$	**24.** $\begin{array}{r}386\\ \times\ 7\\ \hline\end{array}$
25. $\begin{array}{r}650\\ \times\ 8\\ \hline\end{array}$	**26.** $\begin{array}{r}432\\ \times\ 6\\ \hline\end{array}$	**27.** $\begin{array}{r}906\\ \times\ 4\\ \hline\end{array}$

Using a Calculator

The multiplication table below has some factors and products missing. Copy the table and use your calculator to find the missing numbers. To help you, the factors are shaded red and the products are shaded blue.

REMEMBER:

1. Missing products are found by multiplying.

2. Missing factors are found by dividing.

✕	37	Hint 4,088 ÷ 73		19
	1,406			
Hint 3,293 ÷ 37	3,293			
67			5,226	Hint 67 × 19
73		4,088		

187

CUMULATIVE REVIEW

Give the letter for the correct answer.

Estimate by rounding to the nearest ten.

1. $\begin{array}{r} 62 \\ + 27 \end{array}$ **A** 10   **B** 80   **C** 90   **D** not given

2. $\begin{array}{r} 86 \\ - 25 \end{array}$ **A** 40   **B** 60   **C** 50   **D** not given

Estimate by rounding to the nearest hundred.

3. $\begin{array}{r} 412 \\ + 350 \end{array}$ **A** 700   **B** 900   **C** 800   **D** not given

4. $\begin{array}{r} 675 \\ - 349 \end{array}$ **A** 300   **B** 400   **C** 200   **D** not given

Estimate by rounding to the nearest dollar.

5. $\begin{array}{r} \$7.28 \\ + 3.62 \end{array}$ **A** $11   **B** $10   **C** $12   **D** not given

6. $\begin{array}{r} \$5.50 \\ - 3.29 \end{array}$ **A** $2   **B** $3   **C** $4   **D** not given

Which answer is correct?

7. $42 \div 6$
   A 9   **B** 8
   C 7   **D** not given

8. $36 \div 4$
   A 9   **B** 8
   C 7   **D** not given

9. $0 \div 7$
   A 0   **B** 7
   C 1   **D** not given

10. $81 \div 9$
   A 7   **B** 8
   C 9   **D** not given

11. $48 \div 8$
   A 5   **B** 6
   C 2   **D** not given

12. $4 \div 4$
   A 0   **B** 1
   C 2   **D** not given

13. Al planted 12 pumpkins. There were 6 pumpkins in each row. How many rows of pumpkins did Al plant?
   A 6   **B** 2
   C 3   **D** not given

14. Laura picked 16 apples. She divided them equally among 4 friends. How many apples did each friend get?
   A 3   **B** 5
   C 4   **D** not given

DIVISION: 1-Digit Divisors

8

Because Katie was blind, she always jogged with a friend. Katie needed some running shoes. Proper shoes would protect her body from the hard pounding when she ran. The shoe store had 64 different kinds of shoes. The clerk said her store had 4 times as many kinds of shoes as there were in the whole world in 1967. She pointed out the thick, flexible sole on the bottom of the shoe. She said there should be enough room for the toes, and the heel should not slip. Katie tried out several pairs of shoes. Then she made her choice.

Using Division Facts: Mental Math

Ms. Benson gives tennis lessons. She needs to buy 120 tennis balls. There are 3 balls in each can. How many cans does she need to order?

Since each can has the same number of balls, we divide.

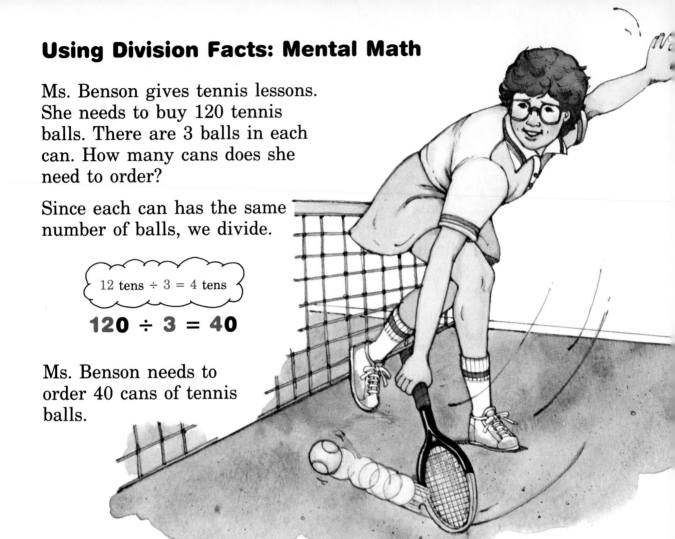

12 tens ÷ 3 = 4 tens

120 ÷ 3 = 40

Ms. Benson needs to order 40 cans of tennis balls.

Other Examples

80 ÷ 4 = 20   **90 ÷ 9 = 10**   **420 ÷ 6 = 70**   **300 ÷ 6 = 50**

Warm Up Give the quotients aloud.

1. 80 ÷ 4	**2.** 50 ÷ 5	**3.** 80 ÷ 2	**4.** 90 ÷ 3
5. 60 ÷ 2	**6.** 70 ÷ 7	**7.** 40 ÷ 2	**8.** 60 ÷ 6
9. 120 ÷ 2	**10.** 150 ÷ 3	**11.** 180 ÷ 6	**12.** 240 ÷ 8
13. 490 ÷ 7	**14.** 350 ÷ 5	**15.** 320 ÷ 4	**16.** 450 ÷ 9
17. 200 ÷ 4	**18.** 400 ÷ 5	**19.** 300 ÷ 5	**20.** 100 ÷ 5
21. 180 ÷ 2	**22.** 270 ÷ 3	**23.** 160 ÷ 8	**24.** 250 ÷ 5

190

Practice Find the quotients. Write answers only.

1. $40 \div 4$
2. $60 \div 3$
3. $80 \div 2$
4. $90 \div 3$

5. $80 \div 4$
6. $80 \div 8$
7. $60 \div 2$
8. $40 \div 2$

9. $80 \div 2$
10. $70 \div 7$
11. $50 \div 5$
12. $60 \div 6$

13. $160 \div 4$
14. $120 \div 3$
15. $150 \div 5$
16. $240 \div 6$

17. $210 \div 7$
18. $320 \div 8$
19. $270 \div 9$
20. $160 \div 2$

21. $20 \div 2$
22. $360 \div 6$
23. $210 \div 3$
24. $450 \div 9$

25. $360 \div 4$
26. $560 \div 8$
27. $60 \div 3$
28. $720 \div 8$

29. $180 \div 9$
30. $200 \div 4$
31. $90 \div 3$
32. $480 \div 6$

33. Divide 280 by 4.
34. Divide 240 by 3.
35. Divide 560 by 7.

Mixed Applications

36. Mr. Cox gives golf lessons. He needs to buy 60 golf balls. There are 3 balls to a box. How many boxes of balls does he need to order?

37. Write a question for this story and then answer it.
Ms. Benson ordered 300 ping-pong balls. There are 6 balls in each box.

38. A certain factory packs 24 cans of tennis balls in a case. If each can holds 3 tennis balls, how many balls would be in 25 cases of tennis balls?

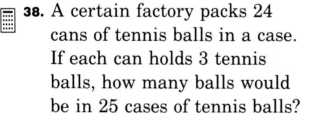

THINK

Logical Reasoning

Find numbers that fit this equation.

 $\div$ $= 20$

Example: $120 \div 6 = 20$

 MATH

Finding Quotients and Remainders

Work with a group.

You will need counters.

Part 1

A local carnival is giving 20 entrance tickets as prizes to the winners of the school cleanup campaign. Each winner will receive the same number of tickets. You do not yet know the number of winners.

1. Discuss how many tickets each winner will receive if there is just 1 winner. If there are 2 winners. 3 winners. Use counters to check your predictions.

2. Choose other numbers of winners. Use your counters to show how to share the prizes equally.

3. As you work, record your findings on a chart like this.

Number of Winners	Number of Tickets for Each Winner	Number of Tickets Left Over
1		
2		
3		

4. Discuss with your group how what you know about multiplication can help you with division. Explain why sometimes there are tickets left over and sometimes there are not.

5. Suppose the carnival was giving the school 24 tickets.
   - Use what you know to predict when there would be leftover tickets.
   - Tell how you could check your predictions.

Part 2

6. Suppose you did not know how many tickets the carnival was giving. With your group, complete the following table.

Number of Leftover Tickets

Number of Winners	Number of Tickets Given							
	20	21	22	23	24	25	26	...
1								
2								
3								
4								
5								
6								
7								

7. Discuss the following questions with another group.
   - What patterns do you see in your table?
   - How many remaining tickets might there be with 8 winners? With 12 winners?

8. When you have a division problem, how do you know when a remainder is reasonable?
   - Write an explanation and share it with another group.

2-Digit Quotients

A chess game has 32 pieces. There are 2 players. How many pieces does each player get?

Since the pieces are shared equally, we divide.

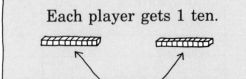

Start with 32.

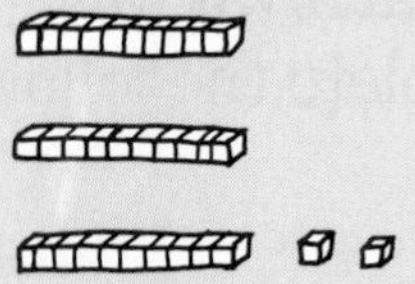

Dividing Tens
- Divide
- Multiply
- Subtract
- Compare

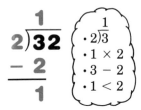

$$2\overline{)32}$$

- $2\overline{)3}$ → 1
- 1×2
- $3 - 2$
- $1 < 2$

Each player gets 1 ten.

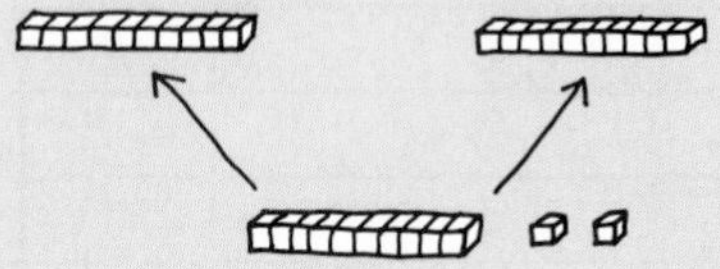

Dividing Ones
- Bring down the ones next to the tens.

$$\begin{array}{r} 1 \\ 2\overline{)32} \\ -2 \\ \hline 12 \end{array}$$

Trade the 1 ten for 10 ones.

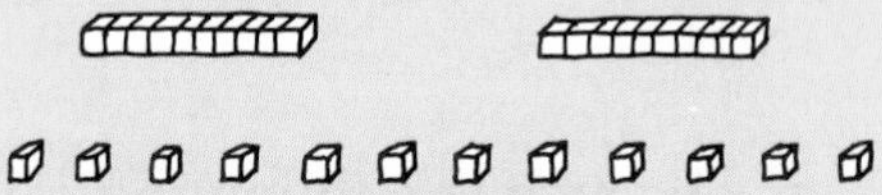

12 ones

- Divide

$$\begin{array}{r} 16 \\ 2\overline{)32} \\ -2 \end{array}$$

- $2\overline{)12}$ → 6

Divide the ones. Each player gets 6 ones.

- Multiply
- Subtract

$$\begin{array}{r} 12 \\ -12 \\ \hline 0 \end{array}$$

- $6 \times 2 = 12$
- $12 - 12 = 0$

- Compare
- $0 < 2$

Each player gets 16 pieces.

Other Examples

$$\begin{array}{r} 16\ \text{R1} \\ 4\overline{)65} \\ -4 \\ \hline 25 \\ -24 \\ \hline 1 \end{array} \qquad \begin{array}{r} 30 \\ 3\overline{)90} \\ -9 \\ \hline 00 \\ -0 \\ \hline 0 \end{array} \qquad \begin{array}{r} 15\ \text{R4} \\ 6\overline{)94} \\ -6 \\ \hline 34 \\ -30 \\ \hline 4 \end{array} \qquad \begin{array}{r} 10\ \text{R2} \\ 7\overline{)72} \\ -7 \\ \hline 02 \\ -0 \\ \hline 2 \end{array}$$

Warm Up Find the quotients and remainders.

1. $3\overline{)42}$ 2. $4\overline{)61}$ 3. $6\overline{)63}$ 4. $2\overline{)80}$ 5. $8\overline{)85}$

Practice Find the quotients and remainders.

1. $4\overline{)52}$ 2. $2\overline{)75}$ 3. $5\overline{)57}$ 4. $8\overline{)97}$ 5. $3\overline{)59}$

6. $2\overline{)60}$ 7. $4\overline{)19}$ 8. $7\overline{)89}$ 9. $6\overline{)80}$ 10. $5\overline{)53}$

11. $3\overline{)67}$ 12. $9\overline{)99}$ 13. $8\overline{)81}$ 14. $3\overline{)96}$ 15. $5\overline{)39}$

16. $4\overline{)71}$ 17. $7\overline{)37}$ 18. $2\overline{)36}$ 19. $5\overline{)83}$ 20. $4\overline{)86}$

21. $94 \div 3$ 22. $71 \div 6$ 23. $42 \div 4$

24. $80 \div 7$ 25. $57 \div 2$ 26. $64 \div 5$

27. Divide 93 by 8.   28. Divide 76 by 6.

29. Divide 76 by 4.   30. Divide 96 by 9.

Mixed Applications

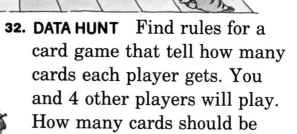

31. Four children played a game with 48 cards. They divided the cards equally among them. How many cards did each player get?

32. **DATA HUNT** Find rules for a card game that tell how many cards each player gets. You and 4 other players will play. How many cards should be dealt?

SKILLKEEPER

Multiply.

1. $\begin{array}{r} 20 \\ \times\ 4 \\ \hline \end{array}$	2. $\begin{array}{r} 12 \\ \times\ 8 \\ \hline \end{array}$	3. $\begin{array}{r} 46 \\ \times\ 2 \\ \hline \end{array}$	4. $\begin{array}{r} 33 \\ \times\ 3 \\ \hline \end{array}$	5. $\begin{array}{r} 31 \\ \times\ 9 \\ \hline \end{array}$
6. $\begin{array}{r} 75 \\ \times\ 7 \\ \hline \end{array}$	7. $\begin{array}{r} 60 \\ \times\ 5 \\ \hline \end{array}$	8. $\begin{array}{r} 302 \\ \times\ 3 \\ \hline \end{array}$	9. $\begin{array}{r} 410 \\ \times\ 6 \\ \hline \end{array}$	10. $\begin{array}{r} 649 \\ \times\ 2 \\ \hline \end{array}$

Checking Division

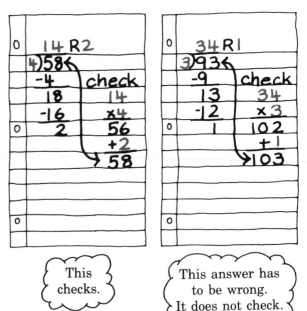

This checks.

This answer has to be wrong. It does not check.

Tracey checked two of her division problems using this method. She multiplied the quotient by the divisor and then added the remainder. If the total is the same as the number she divided, the problem checks.

Can you find Tracey's mistake?

Write the check for each problem and tell whether the problem is correct.

1. 2)35 17 R1

2. 6)75 10 R5

3. 3)62 20

4. 5)39 7 R4

5. 4)92 20 R2

Practice Divide and then check your answers.

6. 3)52

7. 2)67

8. 4)23

9. 6)87

10. 5)72

11. 4)50

12. 6)58

13. 2)71

14. 3)78

15. 7)82

16. 3)20

17. 8)99

18. 3)92

19. 8)47

20. 2)98

21. 66 ÷ 4

22. 44 ÷ 3

23. 40 ÷ 7

24. 90 ÷ 6

25. 59 ÷ 5

26. 91 ÷ 8

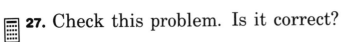 **27.** Check this problem. Is it correct?

532 R5
9)4673

PROBLEM SOLVING
Multi-step Problems

Solve.

1. One library shelf was 94 cm long. Mrs. Abbot put 17 new books on the shelf. Each one was 4 cm thick. How much space was left on the shelf?

2. The library has 56 books about desert animals and 85 books about jungle animals. The student checked out 28 of these books. How many were left in the library?

3. The library has 87 books on water animals. Mrs. Abbot ordered 9 more. The average cost of all of these books is $9 each. How much did they cost altogether?

4. George returned a library book that was 6 days overdue. He paid his fine with 2 quarters and 4 dimes. What was the fine for each day?

5. Mrs. Abbot has $75 to buy new books for the library. Each book costs $9. How many books can she buy? How much money will be left?

6. There are 23 history books on each of 4 shelves and 18 history books on a fifth shelf. How many history books are there?

7. There are 56 old chairs and 24 new chairs in the library. Mrs. Abbot wants to put 6 chairs at each table. At how many tables can she put 6 chairs?

8. **Strategy Practice** Mrs. Abbot took all of the books out of the bookcase. She put 28 books on one table. Then she put the rest on another table in 7 stacks of 8. How many books were in the bookcase when she started? Hint: Work backward.

3-Digit Quotients

Ms. Collins paid $756 for 3 airplane tickets. The tickets were the same price. How much did she pay for each ticket?

Since each ticket costs the same, we divide.

Dividing Hundreds	Dividing Tens	Dividing Ones
• Divide • Multiply • Subtract • Compare	• Bring down • Divide • Multiply • Subtract • Compare	• Bring down • Divide • Multiply • Subtract • Compare

```
      2              25             252
  3)756          3)756          3)756
  - 6            - 6            - 6
  ———            ———            ———
    1              15             15
                 - 15           - 15
                 ———            ———
                   0             06
                                - 6
                                ———
                                  0
```

Check
```
  252
×   3
————
  756
```

Ms. Collins paid $252 for each ticket.

Other Examples

```
   143 R3              181 R2              342 R1
 4)575               5)907               2)685
 - 4                 - 5                 - 6
 ———                 ———                 ———
   17                  40                  08
 - 16                - 40                - 8
 ———                 ———                 ———
   15                  07                  05
 - 12                - 5                 - 4
 ———                 ———                 ———
    3                   2                   1
```

Check
```
  143
×   4
————
  572
+   3
————
  575
```

Check
```
  181
×   5
————
  905
+   2
————
  907
```

Check
```
  342
×   2
————
  684
+   1
————
  685
```

Warm Up   Divide and check.

1. 3)417   2. 4)725   3. 6)705   4. 5)580   5. 4)448

Practice Divide and check.

1. $2\overline{)356}$
2. $4\overline{)635}$
3. $3\overline{)456}$
4. $6\overline{)675}$
5. $7\overline{)807}$

6. $4\overline{)700}$
7. $3\overline{)639}$
8. $2\overline{)937}$
9. $8\overline{)931}$
10. $5\overline{)781}$

11. $4\overline{)924}$
12. $8\overline{)894}$
13. $2\overline{)246}$
14. $3\overline{)805}$
15. $6\overline{)935}$

16. $5\overline{)575}$
17. $6\overline{)790}$
18. $5\overline{)630}$
19. $7\overline{)815}$
20. $3\overline{)364}$

21. $663 \div 4$
22. $500 \div 3$
23. $939 \div 8$

24. $573 \div 2$
25. $817 \div 6$
26. $333 \div 3$

27. What is 836 divided by 2?

28. What is 777 divided by 6?

29. What is 591 divided by 4?

30. What is 609 divided by 5?

Mixed Applications

31. The travel agent sold 5 airline tickets for $670. The tickets are all the same price. What is the price of each ticket?

★ 32. Mr. Kingston bought 3 tickets that cost $15 each. How much was his change if he gave the clerk 3 twenty-dollar bills?

33. Write a story and question for this equation.

$$\$465 \div 3 = \$155$$

THINK

Using a Calculator

Start with 184.
Now guess how many times you can subtract 8 to reach 0.

Try it.

$$
\begin{array}{r}
184 \\
1 \text{ time} \quad - \quad 8 \\
\hline
176 \\
2 \text{ times} - \quad 8 \\
\hline
168 \\
\end{array}
$$
Keep subtracting!

Was your guess too large, too small, or just right?

MATH

Deciding Where to Start

It takes 8 diamonds to make each star in this quilt. Sylvia has cut out 186 diamonds. How many stars can she make with these diamonds?

Since each star takes the same number of diamonds, we divide.

Decide Where to Start Dividing.	Dividing Tens	Dividing Ones
	• Divide • Multiply • Subtract • Compare	• Bring down • Divide • Multiply • Subtract • Compare

$$8 \overline{)186}$$

8 > 1 not enough hundreds
8 < 18 Divide the tens.

$$\begin{array}{r} 2 \\ 8\overline{)186} \\ -16 \\ \hline 2 \end{array}$$

less than 8

$$\begin{array}{r} 23 \text{ R2} \\ 8\overline{)186} \\ -16\downarrow \\ \hline 26 \\ -24 \\ \hline 2 \end{array}$$

less than 8

Sylvia has enough diamonds to make 23 stars. She will have 2 extra diamonds.

Other Examples

$$\begin{array}{r} 33 \text{ R3} \\ 4\overline{)135} \\ -12 \\ \hline 15 \\ -12 \\ \hline 3 \end{array} \qquad \begin{array}{r} 71 \text{ R1} \\ 8\overline{)569} \\ -56 \\ \hline 09 \\ -8 \\ \hline 1 \end{array} \qquad \begin{array}{r} 68 \\ 3\overline{)204} \\ -18 \\ \hline 24 \\ -24 \\ \hline 0 \end{array} \qquad \begin{array}{r} 134 \text{ R3} \\ 5\overline{)673} \\ -5 \\ \hline 17 \\ -15 \\ \hline 23 \\ -20 \\ \hline 3 \end{array}$$

Warm Up Divide and check.

1. $8\overline{)167}$ **2.** $5\overline{)275}$ **3.** $4\overline{)125}$ **4.** $7\overline{)308}$ **5.** $6\overline{)825}$

Practice Divide and check.

1. $2\overline{)156}$ 2. $3\overline{)185}$ 3. $6\overline{)409}$ 4. $8\overline{)340}$ 5. $7\overline{)234}$

6. $6\overline{)309}$ 7. $4\overline{)456}$ 8. $3\overline{)250}$ 9. $8\overline{)283}$ 10. $6\overline{)379}$

11. $5\overline{)893}$ 12. $8\overline{)489}$ 13. $2\overline{)109}$ 14. $9\overline{)378}$ 15. $7\overline{)300}$

16. $5\overline{)355}$ 17. $3\overline{)704}$ 18. $4\overline{)356}$ 19. $2\overline{)835}$ 20. $7\overline{)569}$

21. $430 \div 9$ 22. $170 \div 5$ 23. $200 \div 3$

24. $147 \div 2$ 25. $910 \div 8$ 26. $324 \div 4$

27. $321 \div 9$ 28. $773 \div 8$

29. $219 \div 4$ 30. $463 \div 7$

31. $896 \div 6$ 32. $547 \div 3$

33. Divide 601 by 5.   34. Divide 437 by 9.

35. Divide 292 by 3.   36. Divide 209 by 5.

37. Divide 521 by 6.   38. Divide 168 by 8.

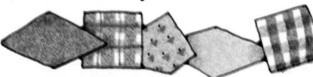

Mixed Applications

39. Each square in the quilt takes 4 dark triangles. Sylvia has 104 triangles. How many squares can she make?

40. A star-shaped design in a quilt has 8 triangles. How many star-shaped designs can be made with 284 triangles?

41. A scarf can be made using 7 squares. How many squares are needed to make 14 scarfs?

42. Mr. Orr is making a quilt that takes 252 triangles. He needs the same number of red, green, and yellow triangles. How many of each color should he cut?

Zero in the Quotient

The Great Pyramid in Egypt has a perimeter of 920 m around the base. The pyramid has a square base. What is the length of each side of the base?

Since we want to know the number of meters for each of the sides, we divide.

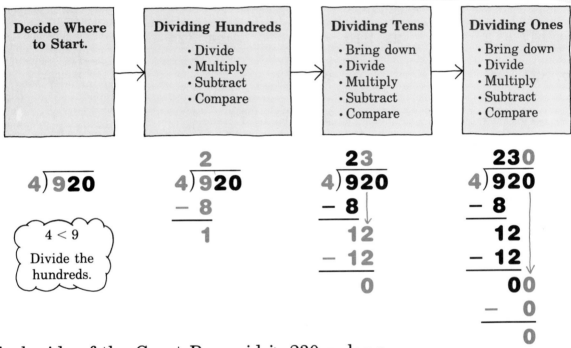

Decide Where to Start.	Dividing Hundreds	Dividing Tens	Dividing Ones
	• Divide • Multiply • Subtract • Compare	• Bring down • Divide • Multiply • Subtract • Compare	• Bring down • Divide • Multiply • Subtract • Compare

$4\overline{)920}$

4 < 9
Divide the hundreds.

```
      2
4)920
 - 8
   1
```

```
     23
4)920
 - 8
  12
- 12
   0
```

```
    230
4)920
 - 8
  12
- 12
  00
 - 0
   0
```

Each side of the Great Pyramid is 230 m long.

Other Examples

```
  10 R5
6)65
- 6
  05
- 0
   5
```

```
  406 R1
2)813
- 8
  01
- 0
  13
- 12
   1
```

```
  200 R2
3)602
- 6
  00
- 0
  02
- 0
   2
```

```
   40
8)320
- 32
  00
- 0
   0
```

Warm Up Divide.

1. $3\overline{)31}$ 2. $4\overline{)837}$ 3. $6\overline{)844}$ 4. $5\overline{)504}$ 5. $9\overline{)456}$

Practice Divide.

1. $2\overline{)61}$
2. $3\overline{)928}$
3. $4\overline{)563}$
4. $7\overline{)735}$
5. $5\overline{)350}$

6. $3\overline{)632}$
7. $6\overline{)485}$
8. $7\overline{)73}$
9. $5\overline{)543}$
10. $8\overline{)806}$

11. $2\overline{)741}$
12. $8\overline{)812}$
13. $7\overline{)703}$
14. $5\overline{)53}$
15. $2\overline{)121}$

16. $650 \div 6$
17. $993 \div 9$
18. $902 \div 3$

19. $321 \div 4$
20. $60 \div 6$
21. $801 \div 4$

22. What is 212 divided by 3?
23. What is 83 divided by 4?

24. What is 418 divided by 2?
25. What is 846 divided by 7?

Mixed Applications

26. The Third Pyramid has a perimeter of 436 m around its square base. How long is each side of the base?

27. **DATA BANK** See page 400. What is the difference between the perimeters of the Pyramid of Maidum and the South Stone Pyramid?

SKILLKEEPER

Divide.

1. $9\overline{)27}$
2. $5\overline{)25}$
3. $7\overline{)63}$
4. $6\overline{)42}$
5. $4\overline{)32}$

6. $9\overline{)81}$
7. $7\overline{)28}$
8. $6\overline{)24}$
9. $8\overline{)40}$
10. $3\overline{)27}$

More Practice, page 421, Set B

Dividing with Money

Ira bought a subscription to a science magazine for children. It cost $6.00 for 8 magazines. How much did each magazine cost?

Since we want the cost of each magazine, we divide.

| Divide as with whole numbers. | → | Show dollars and cents in the quotient. |

```
        75                          $0.75      If there are
    8)$6.00  ← 600¢            8)$6.00       no dollars,
      - 5 6                       - 5 6        write a zero.
        40                          40
      - 40                        - 40
         0                           0
```

Each magazine cost 75 cents.

Other Examples

```
     $0.91          $1.04          $0.05      If there are
   5)$4.55        8)$8.32        9)$0.45       no dimes,
    - 4 5          - 8            - 45         write a zero.
       05            0 3             0
     -  5          -  0
        0            32
                   - 32
                      0
```

Warm Up   Divide. Show dollars and cents.

1. 2)$7.30   2. 4)$8.20   3. 6)$1.50   4. 3)$0.48   5. 5)$0.20

Practice Divide. Show dollars and cents.

1. $5)\overline{\$9.15}$ 2. $6)\overline{\$7.86}$ 3. $7)\overline{\$3.50}$ 4. $4)\overline{\$0.84}$ 5. $2)\overline{\$0.10}$

6. $7)\overline{\$7.00}$ 7. $8)\overline{\$4.24}$ 8. $3)\overline{\$0.90}$ 9. $6)\overline{\$8.94}$ 10. $4)\overline{\$0.24}$

11. $3)\overline{\$2.55}$ 12. $7)\overline{\$7.91}$ 13. $3)\overline{\$0.15}$ 14. $2)\overline{\$6.08}$ 15. $8)\overline{\$0.96}$

16. $4)\overline{\$8.76}$ 17. $2)\overline{\$0.56}$ 18. $8)\overline{\$9.60}$ 19. $6)\overline{\$0.36}$ 20. $5)\overline{\$4.00}$

21. $\$1.40 \div 2$ 22. $\$9.00 \div 3$ 23. $\$0.32 \div 8$

24. $\$0.80 \div 4$ 25. $\$5.46 \div 3$

26. $\$0.78 \div 6$ 27. Divide $3.68 by 4.

28. Divide $0.63 by 7.

Mixed Applications

29. Jamie bought a subscription that cost $9.60. There were 6 magazines. How much did each magazine cost?

30. The daily cost of a newspaper is $0.35. What is the weekly cost of this newspaper if a paper is delivered every day except Sunday?

31. The subscription price for the Sunday newspaper for one year is $28.60. If there are 52 Sundays in the year, what is the price for each paper?

THINK

Logical Reasoning

Find the missing subscription price for 8 magazines.

MAGAZINES 8 for ?

$$\begin{array}{r} \$1.23 \\ 8)\overline{} \\ -8 \\ \hline 18 \\ -16 \\ \hline 24 \\ -24 \\ \hline 0 \end{array}$$

MATH

Finding Averages

Tico, Josh, and Mary Lou went fishing. They put all their fish together and shared them equally. The number of fish each got is the average number of fish caught by each child. What is the average?

Since we want to find the average of 3 numbers, we add the numbers and divide the sum by 3.

Find the sum of all of the numbers. → Divide by the number of addends. → The quotient is the average of the numbers.

$$
\begin{array}{r}
13 \\
12 \\
+ 17 \\
\hline
42
\end{array}
$$

fish caught by Tico, Josh, and Mary Lou

$$
\begin{array}{r}
14 \\
3\overline{)42} \\
-3 \\
\hline
12 \\
-12 \\
\hline
0
\end{array}
$$

14

The average number of fish caught by each child was 14.

Other Example

Distance

21 miles   17 miles   13 miles   13 miles

The average distance is 16 miles.

$$
\begin{array}{r}
21 \\
17 \\
13 \\
+ 13 \\
\hline
64
\end{array}
\qquad
\begin{array}{r}
16 \\
4\overline{)64} \\
-4 \\
\hline
24 \\
-24 \\
\hline
0
\end{array}
$$

Practice Find the averages of these numbers.

1. 16, 15, 22, 31

2. 14, 18, 19

3. 23, 19, 20, 22

4. 39, 47, 85

5. 16, 9, 15, 7, 13

6. 125, 138, 115, 126

More Practice, page 422, Set B

PROBLEM SOLVING
Using Data from a Table

The third, fourth, and fifth grade classes had an aluminum can drive to earn money for soccer equipment.

ALUMINUM CAN DRIVE	First Week	Second Week	Third Week	Fourth Week
MS. TEO Grade 3	73	56	68	87
Mr. JOHNSON Grade 3	59	48	76	81
MRS. RIVERA Grade 4	102	87	53	62
MS. HANSON Grade 4	82	85	89	84
MR. MONROE Grade 5	78	66	67	105
MRS. WHITE Grade 5	66	72	83	75

Use the data in the table to answer these questions.

1. How many cans did Ms. Teo's class collect during the four weeks?

2. What is the average number of cans collected each week by Ms. Teo's class?

3. How many cans did Mrs. Rivera's class collect during the four weeks?

4. What is the average number of cans collected each week by Mrs. Rivera's class?

5. Which fifth grade class collected the most cans?

6. How many cans were collected by all classes during the second week?

7. What is the average number of cans collected by each class during the second week?

8. What is the average number of cans collected each week by Mr. Johnson's class?

9. **Strategy Practice** If 17 children brought in 5 cans each, and the rest of the children brought in 49 cans, what would be the total number of cans?

Estimating Quotients Using Rounding

In 4 hours a hot-air balloon traveled 116 km. If the balloon traveled the same distance each hour, about how many kilometers did it travel each hour?

Since you want an answer that is only **close** to the exact answer, **estimate** by rounding and dividing in your head.

Think of the problem. $\longrightarrow$ $116 \div 4$

Round and divide. $\longrightarrow$ **$120 \div 4 = 30$**

The hot-air balloon traveled about 30 km each hour.

Other Examples

nearest ten	nearest ten	nearest dollar
$87 \div 3$	**$475 \div 8$**	**$\$41.98 \div 6$**
$90 \div 3 = 30$	$480 \div 8 = 60$	$\$42 \div 6 = \$7$
About 30	About 60	About $7

Warm Up Estimate by rounding to the nearest ten.

1. $32 \div 3$ 2. $78 \div 4$ 3. $41 \div 2$ 4. $57 \div 3$

5. $119 \div 3$ 6. $238 \div 6$ 7. $153 \div 5$ 8. $346 \div 7$

Estimate by rounding to the nearest dollar.

9. $\$7.98 \div 2$ 10. $\$6.25 \div 3$ 11. $\$23.95 \div 6$ 12. $\$19.85 \div 4$

Practice Estimate the quotients. Write estimated answers only. Estimate by rounding to the nearest ten.

1. $91 \div 3$
2. $75 \div 4$
3. $58 \div 2$
4. $49 \div 5$

5. $252 \div 5$
6. $423 \div 7$
7. $357 \div 9$
8. $182 \div 3$

9. $4\overline{)83}$
10. $7\overline{)74}$
11. $3\overline{)92}$
12. $2\overline{)58}$

13. $5\overline{)451}$
14. $6\overline{)535}$
15. $7\overline{)142}$
16. $3\overline{)213}$

Estimate by rounding to the nearest dollar.

17. $\$5.95 \div 2$
18. $\$3.89 \div 2$
19. $\$8.25 \div 4$
20. $\$8.98 \div 3$

21. $\$32.19 \div 4$
22. $\$12.10 \div 3$
23. $\$47.95 \div 8$
24. $\$24.95 \div 5$

25. $3\overline{)\$9.15}$
26. $4\overline{)\$7.95}$
27. $6\overline{)\$6.25}$
28. $2\overline{)\$4.05}$

29. $5\overline{)\$24.98}$
30. $9\overline{)\$45.25}$
31. $3\overline{)\$11.75}$
32. $5\overline{)\$9.98}$

Mixed Applications

33. A hot-air balloon traveled 86 km in 3 hours. If the balloon traveled the same distance each hour, about how many kilometers did it travel each hour?

34. It costs $6.85 for each person to ride in a hot-air balloon. About how much would it cost altogether for 8 people to ride in a hot-air balloon?

THINK

Estimation

Estimate by rounding to the nearest ten. Which of these answers are about 600?

A $3 \times 22 = n$ B $47 + 12 = n$ C $995 - 411 = n$

D $190 \div 3 = n$ E $6 \times 9 = n$ F $378 + 213 = n$

MATH

PROBLEM SOLVING
Interpreting the Remainder

Sometimes division does not give you the answer you want. You have to understand how to use the remainder.

There are 82 campers who want to be on rowing teams. Each team has 7 people. How many teams can they make?

$$\begin{array}{r} 11 \text{ R5} \\ 7\overline{)82} \\ -\ 7 \\ \hline 12 \\ -\ 7 \\ \hline 5 \end{array}$$

11 teams can be made.

> The 5 remaining campers are not enough for another team.

Vans took 130 campers to visit the local caves. Each van held 9 campers. How many vans were needed?

$$\begin{array}{r} 14 \text{ R4} \\ 9\overline{)130} \\ -\ 9 \\ \hline 40 \\ -\ 36 \\ \hline 4 \end{array}$$

15 vans were needed.

> There were 14 full vans, but a fifteenth van was needed for the 4 remaining campers.

Lindy had $20 to spend. She bought T-shirts that cost $6 each. How much money did Lindy have after she bought the T-shirts?

$$\begin{array}{r} 3 \text{ R2} \\ 6\overline{)20} \\ -\ 18 \\ \hline 2 \end{array}$$

Lindy had $2 left.

> She bought 3 T-shirts, but the question asks how much she has left. It does not ask how many T-shirts she bought.

Solve. Answer these problems carefully.

1. Each cabin holds 8 campers. How many cabins are needed for 235 campers?

2. Camp pictures cost $4 each. How many pictures can Lou buy with $15?

210

Answer each problem carefully.

1. A roll of film costs $3. Joyce had $11. She used the money to buy film. How much money was left?

2. The cook needs 250 glasses of juice for breakfast. A can of juice fills 7 glasses. How many cans should the cook open?

3. The campers needed 2 sheets for each bed. How many beds could they make if they used 471 sheets?

4. Some campers went to a cave. Each tour group had 5 campers. How many tour groups were needed for 87 campers?

5. The cook had 38 eggs. He used 4 eggs for each cake. He made as many cakes as he could. How many eggs were left?

6. About 129 campers went to a swim class every day. There were 9 campers in each class. How many classes were there?

7. The cook bought 432 rolls. Each package held 8 rolls. How many packages did the cook buy?

★ 8. There are 6 campers on a volleyball team. It takes 2 teams to play a game. How many games can be played at the same time with 54 campers?

9. **Strategy Practice** The cook asked for 1 boy and 1 girl to help him. 3 boys, Ned, Tim, and Ray, and 3 girls, Liz, Jeri, and Pat, wanted to help. How many ways could the cook choose?

Mixed Skills Practice

Computation

Find the answers.

1. $\begin{array}{r} 38 \\ + 29 \\ \hline \end{array}$
2. $\begin{array}{r} 285 \\ + 167 \\ \hline \end{array}$
3. $\begin{array}{r} \$3.45 \\ + 2.75 \\ \hline \end{array}$
4. $\begin{array}{r} 765 \\ + 839 \\ \hline \end{array}$
5. $\begin{array}{r} \$37.95 \\ + \$18.05 \\ \hline \end{array}$
6. $\begin{array}{r} 26,848 \\ + 30,427 \\ \hline \end{array}$

7. $\begin{array}{r} 83 \\ - 19 \\ \hline \end{array}$
8. $\begin{array}{r} 620 \\ - 137 \\ \hline \end{array}$
9. $\begin{array}{r} \$7.00 \\ - 1.89 \\ \hline \end{array}$
10. $\begin{array}{r} 605 \\ - 347 \\ \hline \end{array}$
11. $\begin{array}{r} \$82.65 \\ - 21.95 \\ \hline \end{array}$
12. $\begin{array}{r} 32,678 \\ - 16,293 \\ \hline \end{array}$

13. $\begin{array}{r} 24 \\ \times 6 \\ \hline \end{array}$
14. $\begin{array}{r} 75 \\ \times 4 \\ \hline \end{array}$
15. $\begin{array}{r} 234 \\ \times 7 \\ \hline \end{array}$
16. $\begin{array}{r} 628 \\ \times 5 \\ \hline \end{array}$
17. $\begin{array}{r} 562 \\ \times 8 \\ \hline \end{array}$
18. $\begin{array}{r} 493 \\ \times 9 \\ \hline \end{array}$

19. $4\overline{)39}$ 20. $6\overline{)97}$ 21. $7\overline{)245}$ 22. $3\overline{)\$2.40}$ 23. $5\overline{)\$7.80}$ 24. $6\overline{)\$10.74}$

Mental Math

Write only the answers.

25. $20 + 30$
26. $70 - 25$
27. $400 + 300$
28. $800 - 600$

29. 5×90
30. 7×10
31. 8×100
32. 6×100

33. 3×40
34. 6×30
35. 7×500
36. 3×900

Estimation

Estimate.

37. $29 + 43$
38. $68 - 39$
39. $796 - 212$
40. $589 + 124$

41. 4×95
42. 6×198
43. $3 \times \$1.95$
44. $4 \times \$4.98$

45. $88 \div 3$
46. $238 \div 6$
47. $\$5.95 \div 2$
48. $\$9.98 \div 5$

APPLIED PROBLEM SOLVING

Your neighbor wants you to take care of her pets for 7 days while she is gone. She will pay you for your time and for the pet food you buy. You need to decide how much to charge her for the week.

Some Things to Consider

- Your neighbor has 2 cats and 1 dog.
- The pets must be fed twice a day and be given fresh water every day.
- You must buy the pet food.

- Each cat eats 1 small can of cat food a day and the dog eats 1 large can of dog food a day.
- A small can of cat food costs 43¢ and a large can of dog food costs 86¢.

Some Questions to Answer

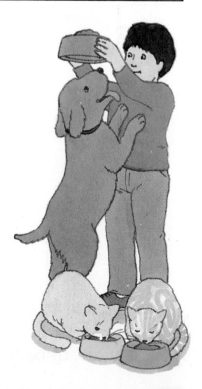

1. How much will it cost you to feed 1 cat for the week?

2. How much for both cats?

3. How much will it cost to feed the dog?

4. How much time do you think you will spend each day caring for the pets?

5. What is your time worth per hour?

What Is Your Decision?

How much will you charge for the week, including your time and the cost of the food?

213

PROBLEM-SOLVING STRATEGY: Use Logical Reasoning

SOME PROBLEMS REQUIRE MORE THAN DECIDING WHETHER TO ADD, SUBTRACT, MULTIPLY, OR DIVIDE. TO SOLVE A PROBLEM LIKE THIS, YOU MIGHT USE THE STRATEGY GIVEN BELOW.

Try This The Seals club had 9 members who won ribbons at the swim meet. 7 of them won one blue ribbon. 6 of them won one red ribbon. How many of the Seals won both a blue and a red ribbon?

USE LOGICAL REASONING

7 BLUE RIBBONS WERE WON. 6 RED RIBBONS WERE WON. SO, 13 RIBBONS WERE WON IN ALL.

ONLY 9 OF THE SEALS WON RIBBONS.

THERE ARE 4 MORE RIBBONS THAN SEALS.

The Seals won 13 ribbons.

9 of the Seals won ribbons.

4 of the Seals must have won both a red and a blue ribbon.

Solve.

1. There are 24 children in Dan's class. 15 of them are in the music club and 18 of them are in the art club. Everyone is in one of the clubs. How many are in both clubs?

2. Everyone in the room is in one of the clubs. There are 10 in the room. There are 8 in the science club and 6 in the math club. How many are in both clubs?

CHAPTER REVIEW/TEST

Find the quotients and remainders.

1. $3\overline{)28}$ 2. $5\overline{)42}$ 3. $6\overline{)51}$ 4. $8\overline{)77}$ 5. $9\overline{)75}$

6. $7\overline{)86}$ 7. $4\overline{)91}$ 8. $2\overline{)54}$ 9. $5\overline{)66}$ 10. $8\overline{)93}$

11. $3\overline{)845}$ 12. $8\overline{)934}$ 13. $4\overline{)709}$ 14. $3\overline{)937}$ 15. $6\overline{)692}$

16. $3\overline{)280}$ 17. $2\overline{)623}$ 18. $3\overline{)818}$ 19. $5\overline{)592}$ 20. $6\overline{)715}$

21. $2\overline{)81}$ 22. $5\overline{)531}$ 23. $8\overline{)967}$ 24. $8\overline{)\$6.00}$ 25. $2\overline{)\$7.50}$

Find the averages of these numbers.

26. 89, 42, 16   27. 22, 16, 10, 12   28. 116, 147, 109, 124

Estimate by rounding to the nearest ten or dollar.

29. $92 \div 3$ 30. $158 \div 4$ 31. $356 \div 4$ 32. $\$3.95 \div 2$

Solve.

33. The cook made corn bread. Each pan of corn bread served 8 campers. How many pans of corn bread were needed to serve 208 campers?

34. There are 7 shelves of science books in the library. Each shelf holds 28 books. How many science books are there in the library?

ANOTHER LOOK

Find the right quotient.

$$3\overline{)26}$$

7 is too small.
$$\begin{array}{r} 7 \\ 3\overline{)26} \\ -21 \\ \hline 5 \end{array}$$

9 is too large.
$$\begin{array}{r} 9 \\ 3\overline{)26} \\ 27 \end{array}$$

8 is just right.
$$\begin{array}{r} 8 \\ 3\overline{)26} \\ -24 \\ \hline 2 \end{array}$$

Find the quotients and remainders.

1. $2\overline{)15}$ 2. $3\overline{)26}$ 3. $4\overline{)31}$

4. $5\overline{)36}$ 5. $6\overline{)53}$ 6. $7\overline{)48}$

7. $8\overline{)51}$ 8. $9\overline{)57}$ 9. $4\overline{)26}$

10. $2\overline{)59}$ 11. $3\overline{)85}$ 12. $4\overline{)70}$

Decide where to start.

Put an X to show where to start.

$$\begin{array}{c} X \\ 3\overline{)784} \end{array}$$ (3 < 7 so divide hundreds.)

$$\begin{array}{c} X \\ 5\overline{)362} \end{array}$$ (5 > 3 so divide tens.)

$$\begin{array}{c} X \\ 7\overline{)483} \end{array}$$ (7 > 4 so divide tens.)

$$\begin{array}{c} X \\ 4\overline{)539} \end{array}$$ (4 < 5 so divide hundreds.)

Put an X to show where to start.

13. $4\overline{)632}$ 14. $7\overline{)551}$

15. $8\overline{)813}$ 16. $6\overline{)235}$

Find the quotients and remainders.

17. $4\overline{)273}$ 18. $3\overline{)418}$

19. $2\overline{)934}$ 20. $6\overline{)325}$

216

Square Numbers

You can use colored chips to show odd numbers. Put the chips in the pattern shown below.

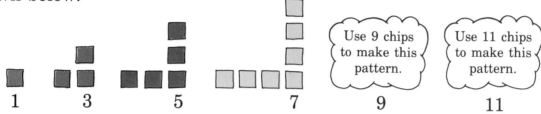

| 1 | 3 | 5 | 7 | 9 | 11 |

Use 9 chips to make this pattern.

Use 11 chips to make this pattern.

Now add the first two odd numbers. Show this with chips.

$$1 + 3 = 4$$

This new pattern is a square. Numbers with this pattern are **square numbers.** So 4 is a square number. There are two chips on each side. You used the first two odd numbers. So 4 is the square number for 2.

Now add the third odd number. There are three chips on each side. You used the first three odd numbers. Notice that 9 makes a square pattern. So 9 is the square number for 3.

$$1 + 3 + 5 = 9$$

What will the square numbers be for the first four odd numbers? the first five? the first six?

CUMULATIVE REVIEW

Choose the letter for the correct answer.

1. $\begin{array}{r} 2 \\ \times 5 \end{array}$ **A** 7   **B** 8   **C** 10   **D** not given

2. $\begin{array}{r} 9 \\ \times 3 \end{array}$ **A** 18   **B** 27   **C** 24   **D** not given

3. $\begin{array}{r} 5 \\ \times 6 \end{array}$ **A** 40   **B** 20   **C** 36   **D** not given

4. $\begin{array}{r} 9 \\ \times 1 \end{array}$ **A** 0   **B** 1   **C** 9   **D** not given

Give the missing factor.

5. $8 \times \text{▥} = 56$
   - **A** 9
   - **B** 7
   - **C** 8
   - **D** not given

6. $\text{▥} \times 3 = 18$
   - **A** 5
   - **B** 6
   - **C** 4
   - **D** not given

7. $\text{▥} \times 8 = 32$
   - **A** 4
   - **B** 3
   - **C** 5
   - **D** not given

Give each time.

8. `2:55`
   - **A** 5 minutes to 1
   - **B** 5 minutes to 2
   - **C** 5 minutes to 3
   - **D** not given

9. `1:45`
   - **A** quarter to 12
   - **B** quarter to 1
   - **C** quarter to 2
   - **D** not given

10. (clock)
   - **A** 6:35
   - **B** 6:25
   - **C** 5:30
   - **D** not given

11. (clock)
   - **A** 12:38
   - **B** 8:00
   - **C** 12:22
   - **D** not given

12. (clock)
   - **A** 20 minutes past 10
   - **B** 20 minutes past 9
   - **C** 40 minutes past 9
   - **D** not given

13. Mia's classroom has 7 rows of desks. 4 desks are in each row. How many desks are in Mia's classroom?
   - **A** 32   **B** 24
   - **C** 28   **D** not given

14. William fills his dog's water dish 2 times a day. How many times does William fill the water dish in 7 days?
   - **A** 9   **B** 14
   - **C** 10   **D** not given

FRACTIONS

9

Terry and Juan had an idea. They wanted to make their own instruments. Then they would start a "jug" band. They put up a sign about it at school. There were 12 interested people in all. There were 6 boys and 6 girls. First they made instruments from things around the house. They made gut buckets and shoe-box guitars. They also made some drums. Juan could read music. He helped the group play some simple songs. Then they started writing songs of their own. Sometime soon they hope to play for a group of people.

Fractions and Regions

The field is divided into 3 equal parts. What part is planted?

Since **2** of the **3** equal parts are planted, we use a fraction to answer the question.

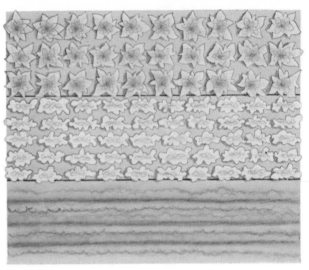

Numerator ⟶ **2**
Number of parts planted

3 ⟵ **Denominator**
Number of equal parts in all

We read the fraction as **"two thirds."** $\frac{2}{3}$ of the field is planted.

Other Examples

$\frac{1}{2}$ is shaded.

One half is shaded.

$\frac{3}{8}$ is shaded.

Three eighths is shaded.

$\frac{5}{5}$ is shaded.

Five fifths is shaded.

Warm Up   Write a fraction to tell what part is shaded. Read the fraction aloud.

1.
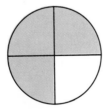

2.
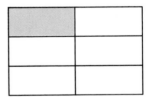

3.
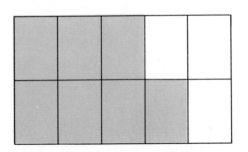

4.
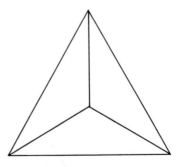

Practice Write a fraction to tell what part is shaded.

1.
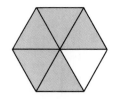

2.

3.
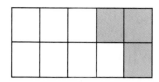

4.
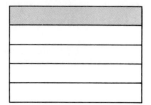

5.
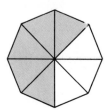

6.

7.
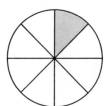

8.
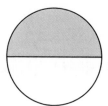

9.
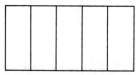

10.

11.
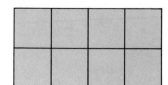

12.
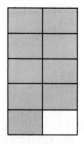

13. What fraction of this garden has been planted?

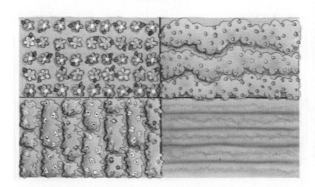

THINK

Guess and Check

Find the mystery fraction.

1. The sum of the numerator and denominator is 13.

2. The denominator is 3 more than the numerator.

MATH

221

Fractions and Sets

The bulletin board is covered with papers from reading class. What fraction of the set of papers are yellow?

5 of the **8** papers are yellow.

$\frac{5}{8}$ of the papers are yellow.

Other Examples

What fraction of the papers are yellow?

$\frac{2}{5}$ of the papers are yellow.

What fraction of the books are red?

$\frac{3}{4}$ of the books are red.

What fraction of the set are pencils?

$\frac{1}{6}$ of the set are pencils.

Warm Up

1. What fraction of the papers are green?

2. What fraction of the books are blue?

3. What fraction of the set are pencils?

Practice Write the fraction for each ▦.

1.

▦ of the papers are yellow.

2.

▦ of the papers are green.

3.

▦ of the books are blue.

4.

▦ of the books are open.

5.

▦ of the pencils are yellow.

6.

▦ of the set are pencils.

7.

▦ of the crayons are green.

8.

▦ of the crayons are missing.

━━ **THINK** ━━

Logical Reasoning

Give the fraction for each ▦.

▦ of the beach balls have **some** blue.

▦ of the beach balls have **no** blue.

▦ of the beach balls have **all** blue.

MATH

223

Equivalent Fractions

Part 1

Work with a group.
Make a set of fraction circles like these.

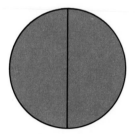 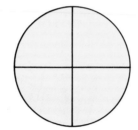 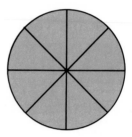

1. Discuss how the fraction circles are alike.
   How are they different? Label each piece
   with a fraction.

   • How many pieces of the yellow circle fit on
     1 piece of the red circle? Try it.

   • How many pieces of the orange circle fit on
     2 pieces of the yellow circle? On 2 pieces of
     the red circle? Try it.

2. Different fractions that name the same
   amount are **equivalent fractions**. Write
   equivalent fractions to show the
   relationships above.

$$\frac{2}{8} = \frac{1}{4}$$

Part 2

Work with your group to make a set of these fraction circles. Label each fraction piece.

3. Place the colored fraction pieces from this new set in the center of the table. Take turns at this activity.

   • One person holds up 2 fraction pieces of the same color. Another person finds pieces of a different color that make an equivalent fraction.

   • List the equivalent fractions you make.

4. Now repeat the activity, using all seven colors of fraction pieces.

   • What other equivalent fractions can you write?

   • Discuss the equivalent fractions on your list. What patterns do you see?

5. Share your group's findings with the rest of your class.

More About Equivalent Fractions

Work with a group.
You will need egg cartons, scissors, and graph
paper.

Part 1

1. Find all the ways you can cut an egg carton into
   different equal parts.

   • Draw a picture of each way.

   • Label each part with the fraction that names
     its part of the whole.

   • Did your group find all of the ways? How do
     you know?

2. What fraction parts could your group cut?

3. Show some ways you can use
   equal parts to make 1 whole
   carton.

   • Record each way you find.

   • Talk about any patterns
     you see.

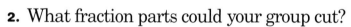

$\frac{12}{12}$ **(1 whole)** $= \frac{2}{2}$

4. Show some ways you can use
   equal parts to make $\frac{1}{2}$ carton.

   • Record each way you find.

   • Talk about any patterns
     you see.

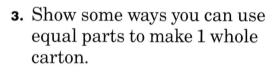

$\frac{1}{2} = \frac{2}{4}$

5. Use your egg-carton fractions
   to make other equivalent
   fractions. Record your results.

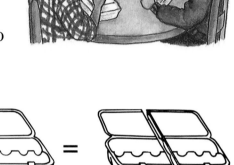

$\frac{1}{3} = \frac{4}{12}$

Part 2

6. Draw each of these rectangles on graph paper.

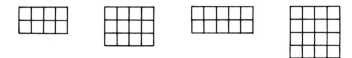

7. Talk about the rectangles with your group.
   - How many squares are in each rectangle?

8. Color one half of each rectangle.
   - How many squares did you color?
   - What fraction of the whole rectangle is this?
   - Show your results in a chart like this:

Rectangle	Number Colored	Total in Whole	Fraction
	4	8	$\frac{4}{8}$

9. Look at the fractions in your chart.
   - How are they different? How are they alike?
   - Talk about any patterns that you see.
   - Share your ideas with the class.

Lowest-Terms Fractions

The store had only 24 tennis balls left. Letta bought 15 of them. What fraction of the tennis balls did Letta buy?

Letta bought $\frac{15}{24}$ of the tennis balls.

Letta bought 5 of the 8 cans. She bought $\frac{5}{8}$ of the tennis balls.

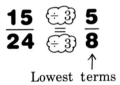

$$\frac{15}{24} \overset{\div 3}{\underset{\div 3}{=}} \frac{5}{8}$$

↑
Lowest terms

You can use division to "reduce" a fraction to an equivalent fraction in **lowest terms**.

> To reduce a fraction, divide both the numerator and the denominator by a whole number greater than 1.

> A fraction is in **lowest terms** when it cannot be reduced.

Other Examples

$$\frac{6}{12} \overset{\div 2}{\underset{\div 2}{=}} \frac{3}{6} \overset{\div 3}{\underset{\div 3}{=}} \frac{1}{2}$$

↑ Lowest terms

$$\frac{8}{12} \overset{\div 4}{\underset{\div 4}{=}} \frac{2}{3}$$

↑ Lowest terms

$$\frac{6}{10} \overset{\div 2}{\underset{\div 2}{=}} \frac{3}{5}$$

↑ Lowest terms

Warm Up Reduce each fraction to lowest terms.

1. $\frac{6}{8} \overset{\div 2}{\underset{\div 2}{=}} \ \blacksquare\!\!\!\!\!\blacksquare$

2. $\frac{6}{15} \overset{\div 3}{\underset{\div 3}{=}} \ \blacksquare\!\!\!\!\!\blacksquare$

3. $\frac{12}{16} \overset{\div 4}{\underset{\div 4}{=}} \ \blacksquare\!\!\!\!\!\blacksquare$

4. $\frac{4}{6}$

5. $\frac{2}{10}$

6. $\frac{10}{16}$

7. $\frac{9}{12}$

8. $\frac{3}{9}$

9. $\frac{8}{20}$

10. $\frac{4}{16}$

Practice Is the fraction in lowest terms? Answer yes or no.

1. $\frac{6}{8}$ 2. $\frac{1}{2}$ 3. $\frac{10}{12}$ 4. $\frac{10}{15}$ 5. $\frac{3}{8}$ 6. $\frac{5}{6}$

7. $\frac{2}{4}$ 8. $\frac{7}{10}$ 9. $\frac{4}{6}$ 10. $\frac{6}{10}$ 11. $\frac{1}{4}$ 12. $\frac{8}{12}$

If possible, reduce to lowest terms.

13. $\frac{3}{9}$ 14. $\frac{2}{10}$ 15. $\frac{10}{16}$ 16. $\frac{3}{30}$ 17. $\frac{9}{10}$ 18. $\frac{8}{20}$

19. $\frac{4}{16}$ 20. $\frac{20}{32}$ 21. $\frac{15}{24}$ 22. $\frac{8}{12}$ 23. $\frac{4}{8}$ 24. $\frac{2}{16}$

25. $\frac{5}{40}$ 26. $\frac{5}{8}$ 27. $\frac{15}{20}$ 28. $\frac{10}{15}$ 29. $\frac{18}{24}$ 30. $\frac{5}{25}$

Write each fraction in lowest terms.

31. Jay played tennis for $\frac{12}{60}$ of an hour.

32. On a weekend, Pam spends $\frac{3}{24}$ of a full day playing tennis.

33. Bill used $\frac{4}{12}$ of his new tennis balls.

THINK

Shape Perception

The rubber band divides the yellow part of the geoboard into halves.

Can you find 4 other ways to place the rubber band so that it divides the yellow part into halves?

Show your ways on dot paper.

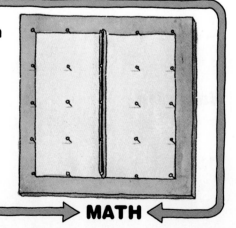

MATH

Comparing Fractions

Emma lives $\frac{9}{10}$ of a mile from school. Ian lives $\frac{7}{10}$ of a mile from school. Who lives farther from school?

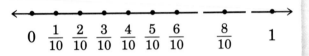

$$0 \quad \frac{1}{10} \quad \frac{2}{10} \quad \frac{3}{10} \quad \frac{4}{10} \quad \frac{5}{10} \quad \frac{6}{10} \quad \frac{8}{10} \quad 1$$

so

Emma lives farther from school than Ian.

When the denominators are different, find equivalent fractions that have the same denominator.

Example: Compare $\frac{1}{2}$ and $\frac{3}{8}$.

Look at the denominators.	Write equivalent fractions with the same denominators.	Compare the numerators.	The fractions compare the same way the numerators compare.
$\frac{1}{2}$ $\frac{3}{8}$	$\frac{1}{2} = \frac{4}{8}$ $\frac{3}{8} = \frac{3}{8}$	$4 > 3$	$\frac{4}{8} > \frac{3}{8}$ so $\frac{1}{2} > \frac{3}{8}$ or $\frac{3}{8} < \frac{1}{2}$

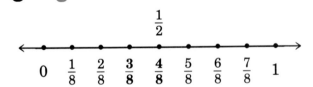

$$0 \quad \frac{1}{8} \quad \frac{2}{8} \quad \frac{3}{8} \quad \frac{4}{8} \quad \frac{5}{8} \quad \frac{6}{8} \quad \frac{7}{8} \quad 1$$

Warm Up Write $>$, $<$, or $=$, for each . The equivalent-fraction table on page 231 may help you.

1. $\frac{1}{2} = \frac{3}{6}$
   $\frac{1}{3} = \frac{2}{6}$ $\frac{1}{2} \circ \frac{1}{3}$

2. $\frac{1}{5} = \frac{4}{20}$
   $\frac{1}{4} = \frac{5}{20}$ $\frac{1}{5} \circ \frac{1}{4}$

3. $\frac{1}{2} = \frac{4}{8}$
   $\frac{5}{8} = \frac{5}{8}$ $\frac{1}{2} \circ \frac{5}{8}$

Practice Write $>$, $<$, or $=$, for each .

1. $\dfrac{3}{10} = \dfrac{3}{10}$
   $\dfrac{2}{5} = \dfrac{4}{10}$
   $\dfrac{3}{10}$ ⬤ $\dfrac{2}{5}$

2. $\dfrac{2}{3} = \dfrac{10}{15}$
   $\dfrac{3}{5} = \dfrac{9}{15}$
   $\dfrac{2}{3}$ ⬤ $\dfrac{3}{5}$

3. $\dfrac{1}{4} = \dfrac{3}{12}$
   $\dfrac{1}{3} = \dfrac{4}{12}$
   $\dfrac{1}{4}$ ⬤ $\dfrac{1}{3}$

4. $\dfrac{1}{8} = \dfrac{1}{8}$
   $\dfrac{1}{2} = \dfrac{4}{8}$
   $\dfrac{1}{8}$ ⬤ $\dfrac{1}{2}$

5. $\dfrac{1}{4} = \dfrac{5}{20}$
   $\dfrac{3}{10} = \dfrac{6}{20}$
   $\dfrac{1}{4}$ ⬤ $\dfrac{3}{10}$

6. $\dfrac{2}{5} = \dfrac{4}{10}$
   $\dfrac{1}{2} = \dfrac{5}{10}$
   $\dfrac{2}{5}$ ⬤ $\dfrac{1}{2}$

7. $\dfrac{1}{8}$ ⬤ $\dfrac{1}{10}$

8. $\dfrac{2}{3}$ ⬤ $\dfrac{3}{4}$

9. $\dfrac{1}{2}$ ⬤ $\dfrac{1}{8}$

10. $\dfrac{5}{8}$ ⬤ $\dfrac{3}{4}$

11. $\dfrac{1}{5}$ ⬤ $\dfrac{1}{3}$

12. $\dfrac{1}{2}$ ⬤ $\dfrac{2}{3}$

EQUIVALENT-FRACTION TABLE					
$\frac{1}{2}$ =	$\frac{2}{4}$ =	$\frac{3}{6}$ =	$\frac{4}{8}$ =	$\frac{5}{10}$ =	$\frac{6}{12}$
$\frac{1}{3}$ =	$\frac{2}{6}$ =	$\frac{3}{9}$ =	$\frac{4}{12}$ =	$\frac{5}{15}$ =	$\frac{6}{18}$
$\frac{2}{3}$ =	$\frac{4}{6}$ =	$\frac{6}{9}$ =	$\frac{8}{12}$ =	$\frac{10}{15}$ =	$\frac{12}{18}$
$\frac{1}{4}$ =	$\frac{2}{8}$ =	$\frac{3}{12}$ =	$\frac{4}{16}$ =	$\frac{5}{20}$ =	$\frac{6}{24}$
$\frac{3}{4}$ =	$\frac{6}{8}$ =	$\frac{9}{12}$ =	$\frac{12}{16}$ =	$\frac{15}{20}$ =	$\frac{18}{24}$
$\frac{1}{5}$ =	$\frac{2}{10}$ =	$\frac{3}{15}$ =	$\frac{4}{20}$ =	$\frac{5}{25}$ =	$\frac{6}{30}$
$\frac{2}{5}$ =	$\frac{4}{10}$ =	$\frac{6}{15}$ =	$\frac{8}{20}$ =	$\frac{10}{25}$ =	$\frac{12}{30}$
$\frac{1}{8}$ =	$\frac{2}{16}$ =	$\frac{3}{24}$ =	$\frac{4}{32}$ =	$\frac{5}{40}$ =	$\frac{6}{48}$
$\frac{5}{8}$ =	$\frac{10}{16}$ =	$\frac{15}{24}$ =	$\frac{20}{32}$ =	$\frac{25}{40}$ =	$\frac{30}{48}$
$\frac{1}{10}$ =	$\frac{2}{20}$ =	$\frac{3}{30}$ =	$\frac{4}{40}$ =	$\frac{5}{50}$ =	$\frac{6}{60}$
$\frac{3}{10}$ =	$\frac{6}{20}$ =	$\frac{9}{30}$ =	$\frac{12}{40}$ =	$\frac{15}{50}$ =	$\frac{18}{60}$

Solve.

13. Roberto walked $\frac{1}{2}$ of a mile to the store. Erika rode her sister's bicycle $\frac{3}{10}$ of a mile to the store. Who traveled farther?

THINK

Estimation

Choose the fraction that best tells how full each container is.

1.
   $\dfrac{3}{4}$ $\dfrac{1}{2}$ $\dfrac{1}{3}$

2.
   $\dfrac{7}{8}$ $\dfrac{2}{3}$ $\dfrac{1}{3}$

3.
   $\dfrac{3}{4}$ $\dfrac{1}{2}$ $\dfrac{2}{5}$

4.
   $\dfrac{3}{5}$ $\dfrac{1}{2}$ $\dfrac{1}{4}$

MATH

Fractions of a Number

Ellen gathered 8 shells at the beach. $\frac{1}{2}$ of the shells are yellow. How many of Ellen's shells are yellow?

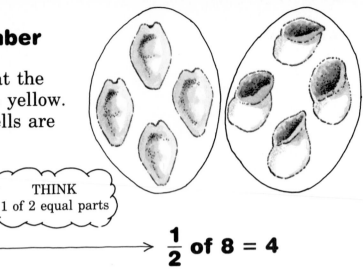

THINK
1 of 2 equal parts

$\frac{1}{2}$ of 8 ⟶ $\frac{1}{2}$ of 8 = 4

To find $\frac{1}{2}$ of a number, **divide by 2.**

4 of Ellen's shells are yellow.

Other Examples

THINK
1 of 3 equal parts

$\frac{1}{3}$ of 12 $\frac{1}{3}$ of 12 = 4

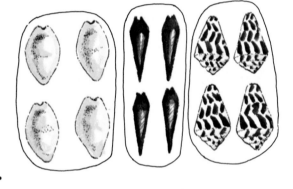

To find $\frac{1}{3}$ of a number, **divide by 3.**

THINK
1 of 4 equal parts

$\frac{1}{4}$ of 8 $\frac{1}{4}$ of 8 = 2

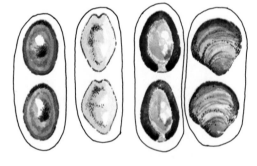

To find $\frac{1}{4}$ of a number, **divide by 4.**

Warm Up   Find the missing number.

1.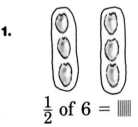

$\frac{1}{2}$ of 6 = ▦

2.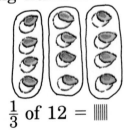

$\frac{1}{3}$ of 12 = ▦

3.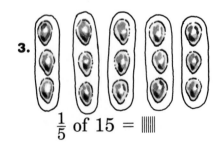

$\frac{1}{5}$ of 15 = ▦

232

Practice Find the missing number.

1.

$\frac{1}{2}$ of 4

2.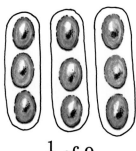

$\frac{1}{3}$ of 9

3.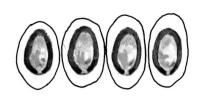

$\frac{1}{4}$ of 4

4.

$\frac{1}{5}$ of 10

5.

$\frac{1}{2}$ of 10

6.

$\frac{1}{3}$ of 15

7. $\frac{1}{2}$ of 12

8. $\frac{1}{3}$ of 6

9. $\frac{1}{4}$ of 20

10. $\frac{1}{5}$ of 30

11. $\frac{1}{4}$ of 16

12. $\frac{1}{2}$ of 18

13. $\frac{1}{3}$ of 18

14. $\frac{1}{8}$ of 24

15. $\frac{1}{3}$ of 24

16. $\frac{1}{2}$ of 16

17. $\frac{1}{5}$ of 20

18. $\frac{1}{2}$ of 14

Mixed Applications

19. Ben collected 15 shells. $\frac{1}{3}$ of Ben's shells are white. How many of Ben's shells are white?

★20. Ross collected 12 large and 15 small shells. He gave away $\frac{1}{3}$ of his shells and kept the rest. How many shells did Ross keep?

THINK

Fraction Puzzle

A store has 18 toy cars. $\frac{1}{2}$ of them are yellow. $\frac{1}{3}$ of them are blue. The others are red. How many are red?

MATH

More Practice, page 424, Set A

Fractions of a Number: Mental Math

Miranda brought 12 pieces of fruit to the party. $\frac{1}{3}$ of the pieces were oranges. $\frac{2}{3}$ of the pieces were apples. How many oranges and how many apples did Miranda bring to the party?

$\frac{1}{3}$ **of 12** → (1 of 3 equal parts / Divide by 3.) → $\frac{1}{3}$ **of 12 = 4**

Miranda brought 4 oranges.

$\frac{2}{3}$ **of 12** → (2 of 3 equal parts / Divide by 3. / Multiply by 2.) → $\frac{2}{3}$ **of 12 = 8**

Miranda brought 8 apples.

Other Examples

$\frac{3}{4}$ **of 8** → (3 of 4 equal parts / Divide by 4. / Multiply by 3.) → $\frac{3}{4}$ **of 8 = 6**

$\frac{4}{5}$ **of 15** → (4 of 5 equal parts / Divide by 5. / Multiply by 4.) → $\frac{4}{5}$ **of 15 = 12**

Warm Up   Find the missing number.

1. $\frac{2}{3}$ of 9 = ▓▓

2. $\frac{3}{4}$ of 12 = ▓▓

3. $\frac{2}{5}$ of 10 = ▓▓

Practice Find the missing numbers.

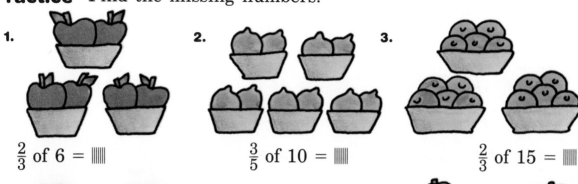

1. $\frac{2}{3}$ of 6 = ||||

2. $\frac{3}{5}$ of 10 = ||||

3. $\frac{2}{3}$ of 15 = ||||

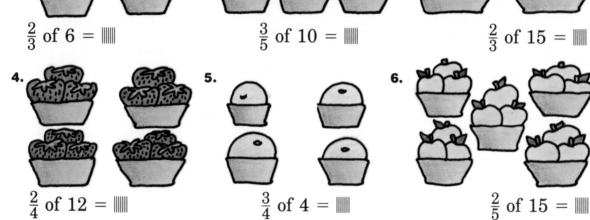

4. $\frac{2}{4}$ of 12 = ||||

5. $\frac{3}{4}$ of 4 = ||||

6. $\frac{2}{5}$ of 15 = ||||

7. $\frac{2}{3}$ of 18

8. $\frac{3}{4}$ of 16

9. $\frac{4}{5}$ of 20

10. $\frac{3}{8}$ of 16

11. $\frac{2}{4}$ of 24

12. $\frac{5}{8}$ of 24

13. $\frac{2}{3}$ of 21

14. $\frac{3}{4}$ of 20

15. $\frac{2}{5}$ of 25

Mixed Applications

16. Felix brought 15 cans of juice to the party. $\frac{2}{5}$ of the cans were grape juice. How many cans of grape juice did Felix bring to the party?

★ 17. Daryl brought 36 sandwich rolls. $\frac{1}{4}$ of them were for hot dogs. The rest were for hamburgers. How many hamburger rolls did Daryl bring?

THINK

Logical Reasoning

The party bus left at 6:50 a.m. The trip takes 35 minutes. Because of rain the trip took an extra 7 minutes. What time did the bus arrive?

MATH

More Practice, page 424, Set B

PROBLEM SOLVING
Using Data from a Graph

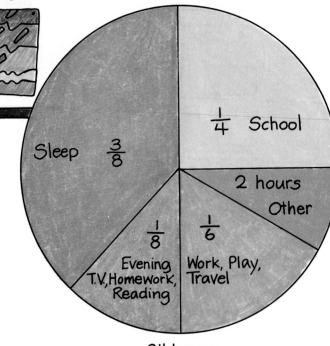

Sleep $\frac{3}{8}$

$\frac{1}{4}$ School

2 hours Other

$\frac{1}{8}$ Evening T.V., Homework, Reading

$\frac{1}{6}$ Work, Play, Travel

24 hours
How Jaime spends his day

The full circle stands for 24 hours (1 day). The parts of the circle show the fraction of the day used for different things. Use the circle graph to solve the problems below.

1. Jaime is in school $\frac{1}{4}$ of the 24 hours. How many hours does Jaime spend in school?

2. How much time does Jaime have in the evening?

3. One evening Jaime took 35 minutes to eat and 45 minutes for homework. How much time did he take for these two things?

4. Jaime takes $\frac{1}{5}$ of an hour to take a bath. An hour has 60 minutes. How many minutes does it take Jaime to bathe?

5. How much time does Jaime take for work, play, and travel?

6. One Saturday, Jaime took 7 trips on his bicycle to deliver groceries. Each trip took about 25 minutes. How long did the 7 trips take?

7. **Strategy Practice** Ruben started painting at 12:00 noon. Jaime joined him later. Ruben quit at 4:00. Jaime worked until 6:00. Jaime worked 5 hours. How long did they work together? Hint: Use logical reasoning.

PROBLEM SOLVING
Mixed Practice

Many people collect stamps as a hobby. Different stamps, new or old and local or foreign, may have interest and value to the stamp collector.

Solve.

1. Michele started her stamp collection with a package of 24 stamps. $\frac{1}{3}$ of them were from France. How many of Michele's stamps were from France?

2. Rich bought a package of 36 stamps. $\frac{1}{4}$ of his stamps were from England. How many of Rich's stamps were from England?

3. Michele paid $2.98 for her stamps. Rich paid $4.25. How much more did Rich pay than Michele?

4. Kathy has a book of stamps. $\frac{1}{5}$ of them are from Mexico and $\frac{1}{4}$ of them are from Canada. Are there more from Mexico or Canada?

5. Susan has 6 full pages of stamps in her book. Each page has 24 stamps. How many stamps does Susan have on these 6 pages?

6. Candy had 84 stamps. She sold $\frac{1}{3}$ of them. How many stamps did Candy sell? 28

7. Connie has a collection of 96 stamps. $\frac{1}{2}$ of them are from Europe. How many stamps does Connie have from Europe?

8. *Strategy Practice* Ted put 12 stamps on one page of his stamp book and 15 on another. He put the rest on 3 pages of 8 each. How many stamps are in the package? Hint: Work backward.

Mixed Numbers

There were 9 people who wanted the breakfast special. How many grapefruit does the restaurant need for them?

$\frac{9}{2}$ (nine halves) is the same amount as $4\frac{1}{2}$ (four and one half).

$$\frac{9}{2} = 4\frac{1}{2}$$

↑ fraction greater than 1

↑ mixed number (whole number and fraction)

You can use division to write a mixed number for a fraction greater than 1.

When the numerator is greater than the denominator, the fraction is greater than 1.

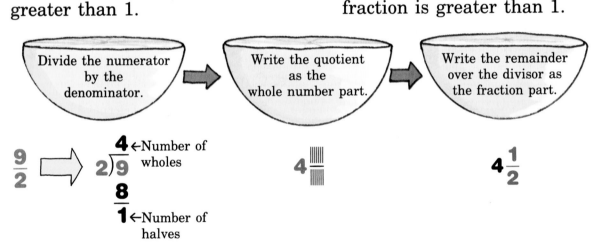

Divide the numerator by the denominator.

Write the quotient as the whole number part.

Write the remainder over the divisor as the fraction part.

$\frac{9}{2}$ ⟹ $2)\overline{9}$ **4** ←Number of wholes

8

1 ←Number of halves

$4\frac{1}{2}$

Other Example

$\frac{18}{3}$ ⟹ $3)\overline{18}$ **6** ← Number of wholes

18

0 ← Number of thirds

⟹ $\frac{18}{3} = 6$

Warm Up Write a mixed number for each fraction.

1. $\frac{7}{2}$ 2. $\frac{20}{4}$ 3. $\frac{27}{4}$ 4. $\frac{25}{3}$ 5. $\frac{12}{3}$ 6. $\frac{23}{5}$

Practice Write as a whole number.

1. $\dfrac{15}{3}$ 2. $\dfrac{16}{2}$ 3. $\dfrac{40}{5}$ 4. $\dfrac{24}{3}$ 5. $\dfrac{14}{2}$ 6. $\dfrac{36}{4}$

7. $\dfrac{16}{8}$ 8. $\dfrac{3}{3}$ 9. $\dfrac{18}{2}$ 10. $\dfrac{5}{5}$ 11. $\dfrac{42}{6}$ 12. $\dfrac{21}{3}$

Write as a mixed number.

13. $\dfrac{11}{2}$ 14. $\dfrac{37}{5}$ 15. $\dfrac{11}{3}$ 16. $\dfrac{19}{2}$ 17. $\dfrac{23}{6}$ 18. $\dfrac{35}{4}$

19. $\dfrac{22}{3}$ 20. $\dfrac{71}{8}$ 21. $\dfrac{9}{4}$ 22. $\dfrac{29}{3}$ 23. $\dfrac{17}{2}$ 24. $\dfrac{51}{8}$

Write as a whole number or mixed number.
Reduce all fraction parts to lowest terms.

25. $\dfrac{10}{4}$ 26. $\dfrac{14}{6}$ 27. $\dfrac{35}{5}$ 28. $\dfrac{19}{3}$ 29. $\dfrac{38}{8}$ 30. $\dfrac{14}{4}$

31. $\dfrac{10}{8}$ 32. $\dfrac{34}{6}$ 33. $\dfrac{21}{5}$ 34. $\dfrac{28}{4}$ 35. $\dfrac{18}{8}$ 36. $\dfrac{56}{6}$

Mixed Applications

37. A restaurant worker cuts pies into eighths. How many pies will be used if 45 pieces are served?

38. Another restaurant worker cuts pies into sixths. How many pies will be used if 45 pieces are served?

THINK

Shape Perception

Which two triangles are marked the same?

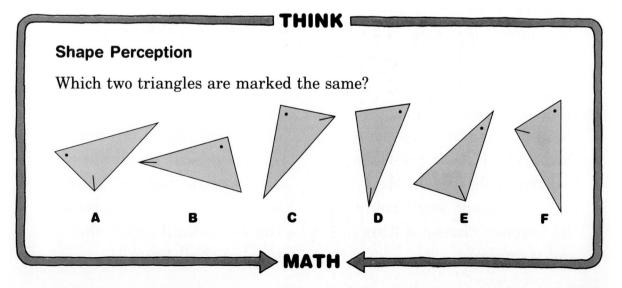

A   B   C   D   E   F

MATH

PROBLEM SOLVING
Using the Strategies

Use one or more of the strategies listed to solve each problem below.

1. Jolene took a math test. There were 20 problems on the test. Jolene got 10 more right answers than wrong answers. How many answers did Jolene get right?

2. The school play was about a king and a queen. Four boys, Nick, Preston, Robbie, and Donald, wanted to be king. Two girls, Hilary and Tess, wanted to be queen. How many different ways could the teacher choose a king and a queen?

3. The tallest girl on the team is the center. Peggy is taller than Linell. Ginny is shorter than Linell. Nancy is taller than Peggy. Edie is shorter than Peggy. Who is the center?

4. The basketball team and baseball team have a total of 24 players. There are 12 basketball players and 18 baseball players. How many players are on both the basketball team *and* the baseball team?

Write a fraction to tell what part is shaded.

1.
2.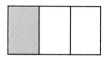
3.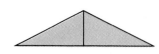

Write a fraction for the ▥.   Find equivalent fractions.

4. ▥ of the cards are red.

5. $\frac{2}{5}$ ▥

6. $\frac{1}{2}$ ▥

Reduce to lowest terms.

7. $\frac{6}{8}$ **8.** $\frac{12}{20}$ **9.** $\frac{10}{15}$ **10.** $\frac{6}{15}$ **11.** $\frac{10}{16}$

Give the correct sign, $>$, $<$, or $=$, for each ▦.

12. $\frac{1}{3}$ ▦ $\frac{1}{2}$ **13.** $\frac{5}{8}$ ▦ $\frac{3}{4}$ **14.** $\frac{3}{4}$ ▦ $\frac{2}{3}$ **15.** $\frac{3}{6}$ ▦ $\frac{1}{2}$ **16.** $\frac{3}{8}$ ▦ $\frac{1}{4}$

Find the missing number.

17. $\frac{1}{2}$ of 14   **18.** $\frac{1}{3}$ of 12   **19.** $\frac{3}{4}$ of 20   **20.** $\frac{2}{5}$ of 15

Write as a whole number or a mixed number.

21. $\frac{15}{2}$ **22.** $\frac{24}{3}$ **23.** $\frac{27}{4}$ **24.** $\frac{10}{5}$ **25.** $\frac{31}{8}$

Solve.

26. Virginia bought a package of 48 stamps. $\frac{1}{6}$ of her stamps are from Germany. How many of Virginia's stamps are from Germany?

27. Roger has 7 full pages of stamps in his book. Each page has 20 stamps. How many stamps does Roger have on these 7 pages?

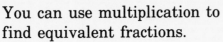

You can use multiplication to find equivalent fractions.

$$\frac{2}{3} = \underset{2\times 2}{\frac{4}{6}} = \underset{3\times 2}{\frac{6}{9}} = \underset{4\times 2}{\frac{8}{12}}$$

$$\frac{4}{5} = \underset{2\times 4}{\frac{8}{10}} = \underset{3\times 4}{\frac{12}{15}} = \underset{4\times 4}{\frac{16}{20}}$$

$$\frac{1}{4} \text{ of } 20 = 5 \qquad (20 \div 4)$$

1 of 4 equal parts

$$\frac{1}{5} \text{ of } 20 = 4 \qquad (20 \div 5)$$

1 of 5 equal parts

You can use division to reduce fractions.

$$\frac{8}{20} = \underset{20\div 2}{\frac{4}{10}} = \underset{10\div 2}{\frac{2}{5}}$$

$$\frac{8}{20} = \frac{2}{5} \qquad \frac{8\div 4}{20\div 4}$$

Multiply the numerator and denominator by 2, 3, and 4 to find a set of equivalent fractions.

1. $\frac{3}{4} = \rule{0.6cm}{0.01cm} = \rule{0.6cm}{0.01cm} = \rule{0.6cm}{0.01cm}$

2. $\frac{3}{8} = \rule{0.6cm}{0.01cm} = \rule{0.6cm}{0.01cm} = \rule{0.6cm}{0.01cm}$

3. $\frac{2}{5} = \rule{0.6cm}{0.01cm} = \rule{0.6cm}{0.01cm} = \rule{0.6cm}{0.01cm}$

Find the missing number.

4. $\frac{1}{2}$ of $10 = $ ||||| **5.** $\frac{1}{2}$ of $16 = $ |||||

6. $\frac{1}{3}$ of $21 = $ ||||| **7.** $\frac{1}{5}$ of $25 = $ |||||

8. $\frac{1}{4}$ of $24 = $ ||||| **9.** $\frac{1}{3}$ of $24 = $ |||||

10. $\frac{1}{8}$ of $40 = $ ||||| **11.** $\frac{1}{4}$ of $36 = $ |||||

Reduce to lowest terms.

12. $\frac{2}{10}$ **13.** $\frac{4}{32}$ **14.** $\frac{3}{15}$

15. $\frac{9}{12}$ **16.** $\frac{10}{16}$ **17.** $\frac{4}{6}$

18. $\frac{4}{12}$ **19.** $\frac{12}{16}$ **20.** $\frac{8}{12}$

Shape Perception

This figure is $\frac{1}{4}$ of a square.

Four of them can be put together to make a square.

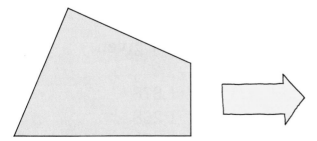

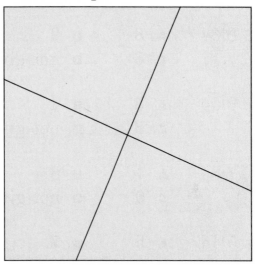

Each figure below is exactly $\frac{1}{4}$ of a square. Choose one and make four copies. Put them together to form a square.

1.

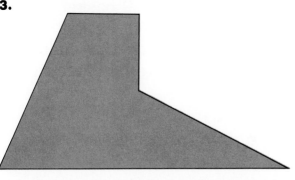

2.

3.

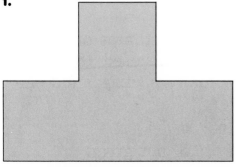

4.

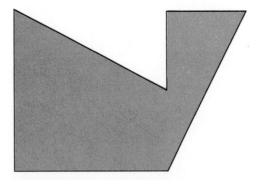

CUMULATIVE REVIEW

Give the letter for the correct answer.

1. $4\overline{)24}$ A 7   B 6
                      C 5   D not given

2. $8\overline{)64}$ A 8   B 9
                      C 6   D not given

3. $9\overline{)54}$ A 5   B 4
                      C 6   D not given

4. $1\overline{)8}$ A 1   B 8
                      C 0   D not given

5. $5\overline{)45}$ A 5   B 7
                      C 9   D not given

6. $7\overline{)7}$ A 0   B 1
                      C 7   D not given

7. $6\overline{)48}$ A 5   B 7
                      C 6   D not given

8. $\begin{array}{r} 22 \\ \times\ 4 \\ \hline \end{array}$ A 88
                      B 28
                      C 26
                      D not given

9. $\begin{array}{r} 36 \\ \times\ 2 \\ \hline \end{array}$ A 62
                      B 38
                      C 72
                      D not given

10. $\begin{array}{r} 64 \\ \times\ 9 \\ \hline \end{array}$ A 546
                      B 576
                      C 572
                      D not given

11. $\begin{array}{r} 213 \\ \times\ 6 \\ \hline \end{array}$ A 1,278
                      B 1,268
                      C 1,276
                      D not given

12. $\begin{array}{r} 207 \\ \times\ 7 \\ \hline \end{array}$ A 1,449
                      B 1,517
                      C 1,409
                      D not given

13. Gina put 3 stamps on each package. She used 18 stamps. How many packages did she have?
    A 15   B 54
    C 6   D not given

14. Travis made 10 baskets in the game. Each basket was worth 2 points. How many points did Travis make in the game?
    A 12   B 20
    C 5   D not given

ADDITION AND SUBTRACTION OF FRACTIONS

Diana remembered her trip to the art museum. The man in the painting by Rembrandt had looked so real. He seemed to be staring right at her. Picasso was her favorite painter. Sometimes people in Picasso's paintings looked like puzzle pieces. The pieces had seemed to fit together as she looked at them. There had been an interesting painting by Frank Stella. It took up $\frac{1}{3}$ of a wall. Stella had carefully measured and painted geometric shapes. Diana had spent a long time looking at it. After her trip, she decided to make her own painting.

Adding Fractions

Your group baked 3 pies to sell at the school fair.
You cut the pies into the number of slices shown.

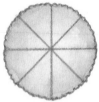
Blueberry

Cherry

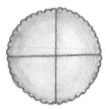
Apple

Work with a group.
Use fraction circles to show the slices of pie.

Part 1

1. Each member of your group takes 3 pieces of pie to represent what he or she sold during the first hour of the fair.

   - Write fractions to show how much of each kind of pie you sold.

   - How much apple pie did your group sell in the first hour? How much blueberry pie? Cherry pie? Write addition sentences to show how you found the amounts your group sold.

Blueberry

Me Jon Cho Sue

$\frac{1}{8} + \frac{1}{8} + \frac{2}{8} + \frac{1}{8} = \frac{5}{8}$

Apple

Part 2

Look at this table showing the slices of pie some students sold. Then read the statements on the next page.

Student	Apple	Blueberry	Cherry
Jordan		1	3
Christa	2		1
Bob		2	1
Soani	2	2	

Statements

- Christa said, "I sold 3 pieces of pie, and Jordan sold 4. Jordan sold more pie than I did."
- Jordan said, "If I sell one more piece of blueberry pie, I will have sold the same amount of pie as Soani."
- Bob said, "Since the blueberry pie is cut into 8 pieces and the cherry pie into 6, cherry would be the better choice for someone who isn't very hungry."

2. Talk about whether the statements are reasonable or unreasonable. Explain why or why not. Use your fraction pieces to help you.

Part 3

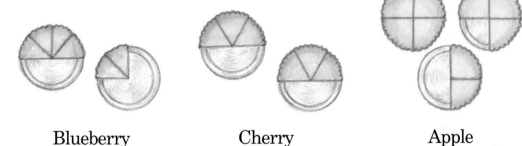

Blueberry   Cherry   Apple

3. With your group, use fraction circles to answer the questions below. Write an addition sentence to show each answer.

- Which type of pie has total slices left that would fill one pie pan? More than one pie pan? Less than one pie pan?
- Use what you know about equivalent fractions. What is the least number of pie pans needed to hold all of the leftover slices of pie?
- Use the pictures above to make up some addition problems of your own. Share the problems with your group. Discuss the solutions together.

Subtracting Fractions

Work with a group.
You will need fraction circles, a fraction mat,
and 8 index cards.

Part 1

With your group, play a game with
fraction cards and circles.

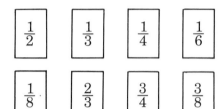

1. Make this set of fraction cards.
   Turn the cards face down and
   mix them up.

2. Use a fraction mat like this one.
   Make "pies" by putting fraction
   pieces on the circles, as shown.

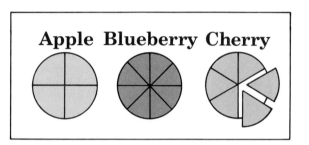

3. Take turns picking a fraction
   card. Take that fraction from
   one of the pies. Talk about the
   ways you can play.

Example: You pick $\boxed{\frac{1}{4}}$.

You can take $\frac{1}{4}$
from the apple pie.

$$\frac{4}{4} - \frac{1}{4} = \frac{3}{4}$$

Or, you can take $\frac{1}{4}$
from the blueberry
pie.

$$\frac{8}{8} - \frac{1}{4} = \frac{6}{8}$$

$$\left(\frac{8}{8} - \frac{2}{8} = \frac{6}{8}\right)$$

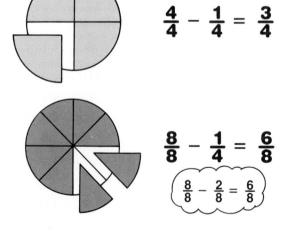

If you cannot play, you must pass. The
game ends when fewer than 6 fraction
pieces are left on the mat.

4. Record a number sentence for each turn you can play. After each round, compare the pies left on the mat.

  • Which pie has the smallest amount left?

  • Which pie has the largest amount left?

5. At the end of the game, compare the pie pieces each of you took.

  • Who has the greatest number of pieces?

  • Who has the largest amount of pie?

Part 2

Put the pieces back to make whole pies again.

6. Talk about the different ways you could take $\frac{1}{2}$.

  • Which way would give you the most pieces?

  • Which way would give you the fewest pieces?

  • If your group wanted to end the game in the fewest possible turns, which would be the best way to take $\frac{1}{2}$? Why?

7. What if your pies had the following pieces left?

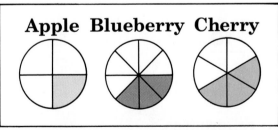

  • Look at the fraction cards. Which ones could you draw to end the game?

  • Can you find all the possible ways?

8. Play the game again. This time try writing each number sentence in more than one way.

Adding and Subtracting: Mixed Numbers

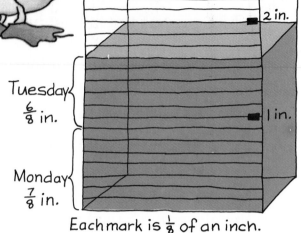

Maria has a rain gauge. The gauge measures amounts of rainfall. On Monday it rained $\frac{7}{8}$ of an inch. On Tuesday it rained another $\frac{6}{8}$ of an inch. How much did it rain in the two days?

Since we want the total amount, we should add.

Each mark is $\frac{1}{8}$ of an inch.

Tuesday $\frac{6}{8}$ in.

Monday $\frac{7}{8}$ in.

Look at the denominators.	→	Add the numerators.	→	Write the sum over the denominator.

$$\frac{7}{8} + \frac{6}{8} \qquad 7 + 6 = 13 \qquad \frac{7}{8} + \frac{6}{8} = \frac{13}{8} = 1\frac{5}{8}$$

It rained $\frac{13}{8}$ or $1\frac{5}{8}$ inches in the two days.

Other Examples

$$\begin{array}{r} 2\frac{1}{4} \\ + 3\frac{2}{4} \\ \hline 5\frac{3}{4} \end{array} \qquad \begin{array}{r} 6\frac{7}{8} \\ - 2\frac{4}{8} \\ \hline 4\frac{3}{8} \end{array} \qquad \begin{array}{r} 7\frac{9}{10} \\ - 5\frac{4}{10} \\ \hline 2\frac{5}{10} = 2\frac{1}{2} \end{array} \qquad \begin{array}{r} 3\frac{1}{2} \\ + 1\frac{1}{2} \\ \hline 4\frac{2}{2} = 5 \end{array}$$

Warm Up Find the sums and differences.

1. $\frac{7}{8} + \frac{2}{8}$
2. $\frac{3}{4} + \frac{3}{4}$
3. $\frac{5}{6} + \frac{3}{6}$
4. $\frac{7}{10} + \frac{8}{10}$

5. $\begin{array}{r} 4\frac{3}{8} \\ + 2\frac{4}{8} \\ \hline \end{array}$
6. $\begin{array}{r} 5\frac{5}{6} \\ - 1\frac{4}{6} \\ \hline \end{array}$
7. $\begin{array}{r} 7\frac{6}{10} \\ - 3\frac{5}{10} \\ \hline \end{array}$
8. $\begin{array}{r} 6\frac{1}{2} \\ + 5\frac{1}{2} \\ \hline \end{array}$
9. $\begin{array}{r} 9\frac{7}{10} \\ - 3\frac{4}{10} \\ \hline \end{array}$
10. $\begin{array}{r} 6\frac{2}{3} \\ - 4\frac{2}{3} \\ \hline \end{array}$

Practice Find the sums and differences.

1. $\frac{6}{10} + \frac{5}{10}$ 2. $\frac{2}{3} + \frac{2}{3}$ 3. $\frac{4}{8} + \frac{7}{8}$ 4. $\frac{3}{4} + \frac{3}{4}$

5. $\frac{5}{6} + \frac{3}{6}$ 6. $\frac{1}{8} + \frac{7}{8}$ 7. $\frac{9}{10} + \frac{9}{10}$ 8. $\frac{1}{2} + \frac{1}{2}$

9. $\begin{array}{r} 7\frac{7}{8} \\ - 4\frac{2}{8} \\ \hline \end{array}$ 10. $\begin{array}{r} 3\frac{1}{4} \\ + 6\frac{1}{4} \\ \hline \end{array}$ 11. $\begin{array}{r} 8\frac{5}{6} \\ - 2\frac{4}{6} \\ \hline \end{array}$ 12. $\begin{array}{r} 9\frac{3}{4} \\ - 3\frac{2}{4} \\ \hline \end{array}$ 13. $\begin{array}{r} 3\frac{1}{2} \\ + 2\frac{1}{2} \\ \hline \end{array}$ 14. $\begin{array}{r} 6\frac{8}{10} \\ - 1\frac{5}{10} \\ \hline \end{array}$

15. $\begin{array}{r} 7\frac{5}{10} \\ + 1\frac{2}{10} \\ \hline \end{array}$ 16. $\begin{array}{r} 12\frac{3}{4} \\ - 4\frac{1}{4} \\ \hline \end{array}$ 17. $\begin{array}{r} 6\frac{2}{4} \\ + 1\frac{1}{4} \\ \hline \end{array}$ 18. $\begin{array}{r} 15\frac{5}{6} \\ - 9\frac{2}{6} \\ \hline \end{array}$ 19. $\begin{array}{r} 14\frac{6}{8} \\ - 7\frac{4}{8} \\ \hline \end{array}$ 20. $\begin{array}{r} 6\frac{5}{8} \\ + 1\frac{2}{8} \\ \hline \end{array}$

21. $\begin{array}{r} 12\frac{5}{10} \\ - 8\frac{1}{10} \\ \hline \end{array}$ 22. $\begin{array}{r} 6\frac{1}{4} \\ + 7\frac{2}{4} \\ \hline \end{array}$ 23. $\begin{array}{r} 10\frac{7}{8} \\ - 3\frac{5}{8} \\ \hline \end{array}$ 24. $\begin{array}{r} 8\frac{3}{8} \\ + 9\frac{1}{8} \\ \hline \end{array}$ 25. $\begin{array}{r} 11\frac{1}{2} \\ - 6\frac{1}{2} \\ \hline \end{array}$ 26. $\begin{array}{r} 17\frac{5}{8} \\ - 8\frac{1}{8} \\ \hline \end{array}$

Mixed Applications

27. On Saturday it rained $\frac{3}{8}$ inch. On Sunday it rained $\frac{7}{8}$ inch. How much did it rain in the 2 days?

28. **DATA BANK** See page 400. How much less rain is there for 1 hour of light rain than there is for 1 hour of moderate rain?

SKILLKEEPER

Find equivalent fractions.

1. $\frac{1}{4} \begin{smallmatrix} (\times 2) \\ \\ (\times 2) \end{smallmatrix} = \frac{\text{▩}}{\text{▩}}$ 2. $\frac{1}{4} \begin{smallmatrix} (\times 3) \\ \\ (\times 3) \end{smallmatrix} = \frac{\text{▩}}{\text{▩}}$ 3. $\frac{4}{5} \begin{smallmatrix} (\times 2) \\ \\ (\times 2) \end{smallmatrix} = \frac{\text{▩}}{\text{▩}}$

4. $\frac{4}{5} \begin{smallmatrix} (\times 3) \\ \\ (\times 3) \end{smallmatrix} = \frac{\text{▩}}{\text{▩}}$ 5. $\frac{2}{3} \begin{smallmatrix} (\times 2) \\ \\ (\times 2) \end{smallmatrix} = \frac{\text{▩}}{\text{▩}}$ 6. $\frac{2}{3} \begin{smallmatrix} (\times 4) \\ \\ (\times 4) \end{smallmatrix} = \frac{\text{▩}}{\text{▩}}$

Reduce the fractions to the lowest terms.

7. $\frac{2}{10}$ 8. $\frac{4}{16}$ 9. $\frac{9}{12}$ 10. $\frac{8}{20}$ 11. $\frac{6}{15}$

PROBLEM SOLVING
Mixed Practice

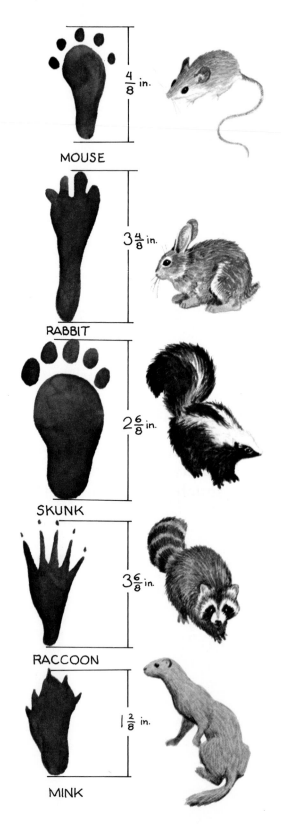

MOUSE — $\frac{4}{8}$ in.

RABBIT — $3\frac{4}{8}$ in.

SKUNK — $2\frac{6}{8}$ in.

RACCOON — $3\frac{6}{8}$ in.

MINK — $1\frac{2}{8}$ in.

The pictures show the tracks of the hind feet of different animals. The lengths given are average for adults. All fractional parts are given in eighths. Use the pictures to help you solve the following problems.

1. How much longer is the raccoon track than the mink track?

2. How much shorter is the quail track than the skunk track?

3. The skunk takes steps that are about 18 inches long. How many inches would it travel in 6 steps?

4. The front print of the weasel is $\frac{2}{8}$ inch long. How long are the front and hind prints end to end?

5. How much longer is the black bear print than the rabbit print?

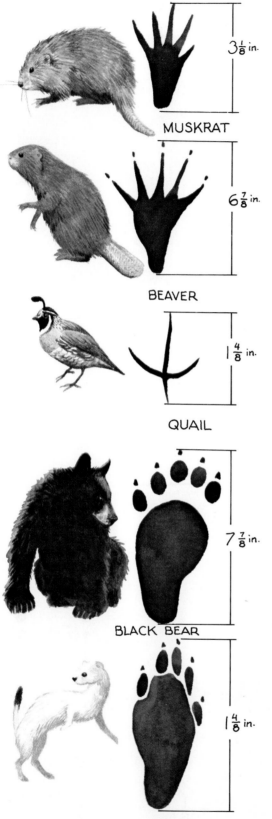

MUSKRAT $3\frac{1}{8}$ in.

BEAVER $6\frac{7}{8}$ in.

QUAIL $1\frac{4}{8}$ in.

BLACK BEAR $7\frac{7}{8}$ in.

WEASEL $1\frac{4}{8}$ in.

6. The muskrat takes steps that are 8 inches long. How many steps would it have to take to go 216 inches?

7. How much longer is the raccoon track than the mouse track?

8. The front footprint of the muskrat is $\frac{7}{8}$ inch long. How long are the front and hind prints end to end?

9. The beaver takes steps that are 18 inches long. How many inches will the beaver travel in 9 steps?

10. How much shorter is the beaver print than the black bear print?

11. The front footprint of the beaver is 3 inches long. How long are the front and hind prints end to end?

12. The rabbit may take steps about 7 inches long. How many steps will it take to travel 245 inches?

13. *Strategy Practice* There were 8 quail and rabbits in the meadow. There were 20 footprints. How many of each were in the meadow?

Adding Fractions: Unlike Denominators

Owen is building a house. The plans call for a floor to have plywood that is $\frac{5}{8}$ inch thick and a layer of concrete that is $\frac{3}{4}$ inch thick. How thick is the floor?

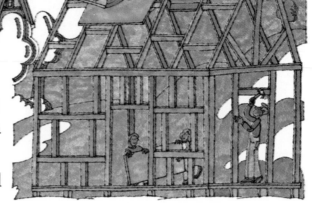

Since we want to know the total thickness, we add.

Look at the denominators	Find equivalent fractions with the same denominator.	Add the fractions.

$$\frac{3}{4} \overset{unlike}{\longleftarrow}$$
$$+\frac{5}{8}$$

$$\frac{3}{4} \overset{(\times 2)}{\underset{(\times 2)}{=}} \frac{6}{8}$$
$$+\frac{5}{8} = \frac{5}{8}$$

$$\frac{6}{8}$$
$$+\frac{5}{8}$$
$$\frac{11}{8} = 1\frac{3}{8}$$

The floor is $1\frac{3}{8}$ inches thick.

Other Examples

$$\frac{1}{2} \overset{(\times 2)}{\underset{(\times 2)}{=}} \frac{2}{4}$$
$$+\frac{1}{4} = +\frac{1}{4}$$
$$\frac{3}{4}$$

$$\frac{5}{9} = \frac{5}{9}$$
$$+\frac{2}{3} \overset{(\times 3)}{\underset{(\times 3)}{=}} +\frac{6}{9}$$
$$\frac{11}{9} = 1\frac{2}{9}$$

$$\frac{1}{6} = \frac{1}{6}$$
$$+\frac{1}{3} \overset{(\times 2)}{\underset{(\times 2)}{=}} +\frac{2}{6}$$
$$\frac{3}{6} = \frac{1}{2}$$

Warm Up Find the sums.

1. $\frac{1}{8}$
   $+\frac{1}{4}$

2. $\frac{2}{3}$
   $+\frac{1}{6}$

3. $\frac{3}{5}$
   $+\frac{1}{10}$

4. $\frac{1}{2}$
   $+\frac{1}{6}$

5. $\frac{3}{8}$
   $+\frac{1}{2}$

6. $\frac{1}{9}$
   $+\frac{2}{3}$

Practice Find the sums.

1. $\dfrac{1}{4} \overset{\times 2}{=} \dfrac{\ \ \ }{\ \ \ }$
$+\ \dfrac{3}{8} = \dfrac{\ \ \ }{\ \ \ }$

2. $\dfrac{1}{6} = \dfrac{\ \ \ }{\ \ \ }$
$+\ \dfrac{1}{3} \overset{\times 2}{=} \dfrac{\ \ \ }{\ \ \ }$

3. $\dfrac{3}{10} = \dfrac{\ \ \ }{\ \ \ }$
$+\ \dfrac{1}{5} \overset{\times 2}{=} \dfrac{\ \ \ }{\ \ \ }$

4. $\dfrac{5}{6} = \dfrac{\ \ \ }{\ \ \ }$
$+\ \dfrac{1}{2} \overset{\times 3}{=} \dfrac{\ \ \ }{\ \ \ }$

5. $\dfrac{3}{4} \overset{\times 2}{=} \dfrac{\ \ \ }{\ \ \ }$
$+\ \dfrac{1}{8} = \dfrac{\ \ \ }{\ \ \ }$

6. $\dfrac{3}{4} = \dfrac{\ \ \ }{\ \ \ }$
$+\ \dfrac{1}{2} \overset{\times 2}{=} \dfrac{\ \ \ }{\ \ \ }$

7. $\dfrac{5}{8}$
$+\ \dfrac{1}{4}$

8. $\dfrac{1}{2}$
$+\ \dfrac{7}{8}$

9. $\dfrac{5}{6}$
$+\ \dfrac{1}{3}$

10. $\dfrac{1}{2}$
$+\ \dfrac{7}{10}$

11. $\dfrac{4}{10}$
$+\ \dfrac{1}{5}$

12. $\dfrac{3}{8}$
$+\ \dfrac{3}{4}$

13. $\dfrac{1}{4}$
$+\ \dfrac{1}{2}$

14. $\dfrac{7}{10}$
$+\ \dfrac{1}{5}$

15. $\dfrac{2}{5}$
$+\ \dfrac{1}{10}$

16. $\dfrac{3}{10}$
$+\ \dfrac{3}{5}$

Mixed Applications

17. A house plan calls for floors with $\frac{3}{4}$-inch plywood and $\frac{7}{8}$-inch concrete. How thick is the floor?

18. A builder put tile that was $\frac{1}{4}$-inch thick on top of $\frac{3}{4}$-inch plywood. How much thicker was the plywood than the tile?

19. This problem does not have enough data. Make up the missing data and solve.
A builder put hardwood flooring on top of $\frac{1}{2}$-inch plywood. How thick were these floors?

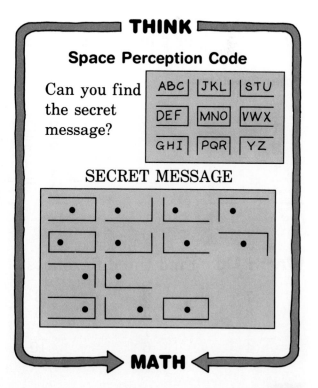

THINK

Space Perception Code

Can you find the secret message?

ABC	JKL	STU
DEF	MNO	VWX
GHI	PQR	YZ

SECRET MESSAGE

MATH

Subtracting Fractions: Unlike Denominators

Anita lives $\frac{9}{10}$ mile from school. After she walks $\frac{1}{2}$ mile, how far does she still have to go?

Since we want to compare, we subtract.

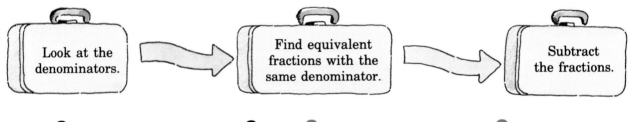

| Look at the denominators. | Find equivalent fractions with the same denominator. | Subtract the fractions. |

$$\begin{array}{c} \dfrac{9}{10} \\ -\dfrac{1}{2} \end{array} \text{ unlike}$$

$$\begin{array}{cc} \dfrac{9}{10} = & \dfrac{9}{10} \\ -\dfrac{1}{2} \overset{\times 5}{\underset{\times 5}{=}} & \dfrac{5}{10} \end{array}$$

$$\begin{array}{c} \dfrac{9}{10} \\ -\dfrac{5}{10} \\ \hline \dfrac{4}{10} = \dfrac{2}{5} \end{array}$$

Anita has $\frac{4}{10}$ or $\frac{2}{5}$ mile to go.

Other Examples

$$\begin{array}{cc} \dfrac{1}{2} \overset{\times 2}{\underset{\times 2}{=}} & \dfrac{2}{4} \\ -\dfrac{1}{4} = & -\dfrac{1}{4} \\ \hline & \dfrac{1}{4} \end{array}$$

$$\begin{array}{cc} \dfrac{2}{3} \overset{\times 3}{\underset{\times 3}{=}} & \dfrac{6}{9} \\ -\dfrac{1}{9} = & -\dfrac{1}{9} \\ \hline & \dfrac{5}{9} \end{array}$$

$$\begin{array}{cc} \dfrac{2}{3} \overset{\times 2}{\underset{\times 2}{=}} & \dfrac{4}{6} \\ -\dfrac{1}{6} = & -\dfrac{1}{6} \\ \hline & \dfrac{3}{6} = \dfrac{1}{2} \end{array}$$

Warm Up   Find the differences.

1. $\begin{array}{c} \frac{7}{8} \\ -\frac{1}{4} \end{array}$

2. $\begin{array}{c} \frac{2}{3} \\ -\frac{1}{6} \end{array}$

3. $\begin{array}{c} \frac{3}{5} \\ -\frac{1}{10} \end{array}$

4. $\begin{array}{c} \frac{1}{2} \\ -\frac{1}{6} \end{array}$

5. $\begin{array}{c} \frac{5}{8} \\ -\frac{1}{2} \end{array}$

6. $\begin{array}{c} \frac{1}{2} \\ -\frac{1}{4} \end{array}$

Practice Find the differences.

1. $\dfrac{3}{8} = \dfrac{\text{\tiny||||||}}{\text{\tiny||||||}}$

   $-\dfrac{1}{4}\overset{\times 2}{\underset{\times 2}{=}} \dfrac{\text{\tiny||||||}}{\text{\tiny||||||}}$

2. $\dfrac{1}{3}\overset{\times 2}{\underset{\times 2}{}} \dfrac{\text{\tiny||||||}}{\text{\tiny||||||}}$

   $-\dfrac{1}{6} = \dfrac{\text{\tiny||||||}}{\text{\tiny||||||}}$

3. $\dfrac{3}{10} = \dfrac{\text{\tiny||||||}}{\text{\tiny||||||}}$

   $-\dfrac{1}{5}\overset{\times 2}{\underset{\times 2}{=}} \dfrac{\text{\tiny||||||}}{\text{\tiny||||||}}$

4. $\dfrac{5}{6} = \dfrac{\text{\tiny||||||}}{\text{\tiny||||||}}$

   $-\dfrac{1}{2}\overset{\times 3}{\underset{\times 3}{=}} \dfrac{\text{\tiny||||||}}{\text{\tiny||||||}}$

5. $\dfrac{2}{3}\overset{\times 2}{\underset{\times 2}{}} \dfrac{\text{\tiny||||||}}{\text{\tiny||||||}}$

   $-\dfrac{1}{6} = \dfrac{\text{\tiny||||||}}{\text{\tiny||||||}}$

6. $\dfrac{3}{4}\overset{\times 2}{\underset{\times 2}{}} \dfrac{\text{\tiny||||||}}{\text{\tiny||||||}}$

   $-\dfrac{1}{8} = \dfrac{\text{\tiny||||||}}{\text{\tiny||||||}}$

7. $\dfrac{5}{8}$
   $-\dfrac{1}{4}$

8. $\dfrac{7}{8}$
   $-\dfrac{1}{2}$

9. $\dfrac{5}{6}$
   $-\dfrac{1}{3}$

10. $\dfrac{7}{10}$
    $-\dfrac{1}{2}$

11. $\dfrac{1}{2}$
    $-\dfrac{1}{4}$

12. $\dfrac{3}{4}$
    $-\dfrac{3}{8}$

13. $\dfrac{2}{3}$
    $-\dfrac{1}{9}$

14. $\dfrac{7}{10}$
    $-\dfrac{1}{5}$

15. $\dfrac{2}{5}$
    $-\dfrac{1}{10}$

16. $\dfrac{3}{5}$
    $-\dfrac{3}{10}$

Mixed Applications

17. Jess lives $\frac{3}{4}$ mile from school. How far does he have to go after he has walked $\frac{1}{2}$ mile?

★ 18. Noell's house is $\frac{7}{8}$ miles from school. How far does she walk each day to school and home?

THINK

Mental Math

Easy Sums

$\frac{1}{2} + \frac{1}{2} = 1$	$\frac{1}{4} + \frac{3}{4} = 1$	$\frac{1}{3} + \frac{2}{3} = 1$

Use easy sums to help you find these mentally.

1. $\frac{1}{2} + \frac{5}{6} + \frac{1}{2}$

2. $\frac{1}{4} + \frac{2}{3} + \frac{3}{4}$

3. $2\frac{1}{2} + 3\frac{1}{2} + 4\frac{2}{3}$

4. $3\frac{1}{3} + 1\frac{5}{8} + 2\frac{2}{3}$

5. $3\frac{1}{4} + 1\frac{3}{5} + 2\frac{3}{4}$

6. $5\frac{2}{3} + 2\frac{7}{8} + \frac{1}{3}$

MATH

PROBLEM SOLVING
Using Data from a Circle Graph

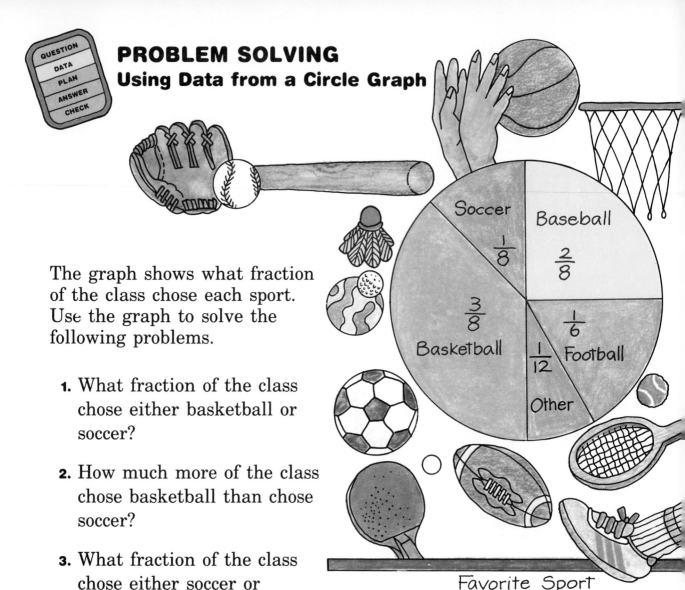

Favorite Sport
Room 38

The graph shows what fraction of the class chose each sport. Use the graph to solve the following problems.

1. What fraction of the class chose either basketball or soccer?

2. How much more of the class chose basketball than chose soccer?

3. What fraction of the class chose either soccer or baseball?

4. How much more of the class chose basketball than baseball?

5. What fraction of the class chose either basketball or baseball?

6. There were 24 children in the class. How many of them chose football?

★ **7.** Of the 24 children in the class, how many of them chose basketball?

★ **8.** How many more of the children chose baseball than football?

9. *Strategy Practice* Tickets are $2 and $3. Nancy sold 7 for $18. How many of each did she sell?

PROBLEM SOLVING
Mixed
Practice

QUESTION
DATA
PLAN
ANSWER
CHECK

The May family drove
to the beach for a picnic.

Solve.

1. There are 6 people in the May family. If $\frac{1}{2}$ of them went swimming, how many people went swimming?

2. If $\frac{1}{3}$ of the May family looked for shells, how many people looked for shells?

3. The May family decided to cook 8 hamburgers at the picnic. The children ate $\frac{1}{2}$ of them. How many hamburgers did the children eat?

4. Simon ate $\frac{2}{4}$ of a melon. Vi ate $\frac{1}{4}$ of the melon. What part of the melon was this?

★5. Mr. May drove $21\frac{5}{10}$ miles to the beach. When he drove home, he took a shortcut that was $19\frac{3}{10}$ miles. Estimate how far he drove. What is the difference between your estimate and the exact number?

★6. A trip from the May home to the park is $38\frac{9}{10}$ miles. Estimate how much farther this is than the $19\frac{3}{10}$–mile shortcut. What is the difference between your estimate and the exact number?

7. *Strategy Practice* The May family took wheat bread and rye bread to the picnic. They had ham, cheese, peanut butter, and turkey for sandwiches. How many kinds of sandwiches could they make if they put just one thing on one kind of bread?

259

PROBLEM SOLVING
Using the Strategies

Use one or more of the strategies listed to solve each problem below.

PROBLEM-SOLVING STRATEGIES

CHOOSE THE OPERATIONS
DRAW A PICTURE
GUESS AND CHECK
MAKE A LIST
MAKE A TABLE
FIND A PATTERN
WORK BACKWARD
USE LOGICAL REASONING

1. Pretend a pet shop sold 3 fish on the first day of the month, 6 fish on the second day, 9 fish on the third day and so on. On what day of the month were 42 fish sold?

2. There are 13 people who work at the pet shop on weekends. 9 of them work on Saturday and 8 work on Sunday. How many work on both Saturday and Sunday?

3. Brenda bought her canary at the pet shop the twelfth day of the month, a Thursday. On what day of the week was the first day of the month?

4. Each time the pet shop orders 8 boxes of birdseed, 3 bird feeders are also ordered. How many bird feeders are ordered at the same time that 48 boxes of birdseed are ordered? Complete the table.

BIRDSEED	8	16	24
BIRDFEEDERS	3	6	9

Find the sums and differences.

1. $\frac{2}{5}$
    $+\ \frac{1}{5}$

2. $\frac{4}{8}$
    $+\ \frac{2}{8}$

3. $\frac{1}{10}$
    $+\ \frac{4}{10}$

4. $\frac{3}{4}$
    $-\ \frac{2}{4}$

5. $\frac{5}{6}$
    $-\ \frac{2}{6}$

6. $\frac{7}{8}$
    $-\ \frac{1}{8}$

7. $6\frac{1}{6}$
    $+\ 2\frac{4}{6}$

8. $3\frac{1}{3}$
    $+\ 4\frac{1}{3}$

9. $5\frac{4}{5}$
    $-\ 2\frac{1}{5}$

10. $8\frac{7}{10}$
    $-\ 1\frac{6}{10}$

11. $\frac{7}{10}$
    $+\ \frac{1}{5}$

12. $\frac{1}{6}$
    $+\ \frac{2}{3}$

13. $\frac{3}{8}$
    $+\ \frac{1}{2}$

14. $\frac{1}{4}$
    $+\ \frac{1}{8}$

15. $\frac{1}{2}$
    $+\ \frac{1}{4}$

16. $\frac{5}{6}$
    $-\ \frac{1}{3}$

17. $\frac{9}{10}$
    $-\ \frac{1}{5}$

18. $\frac{3}{8}$
    $-\ \frac{1}{4}$

19. $\frac{7}{10}$
    $-\ \frac{1}{5}$

20. $\frac{5}{8}$
    $-\ \frac{1}{2}$

Solve.

21. A beaver footprint is $6\frac{7}{8}$ inches. A muskrat footprint is $3\frac{1}{8}$ inches. How much longer is the beaver print than the muskrat print?

22. Judi and Paul shared an apple. Judi ate $\frac{1}{2}$ of the apple and Paul ate $\frac{1}{2}$ of the apple. How much apple did they eat altogether?

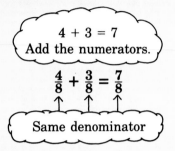

4 + 3 = 7
Add the numerators.

$$\frac{4}{8} + \frac{3}{8} = \frac{7}{8}$$

Same denominator

Find the sums and differences.

1. $\frac{5}{10} + \frac{4}{10}$ **2.** $\frac{3}{8} + \frac{1}{8}$

3. $\frac{1}{6} + \frac{2}{6}$ **4.** $\frac{1}{4} + \frac{1}{4}$

5. $\frac{3}{5}$ **6.** $\frac{7}{10}$ **7.** $\frac{2}{8}$
$+ \frac{1}{5}$ $+ \frac{1}{10}$ $+ \frac{1}{8}$

9 − 6 = 3
Subtract the numerators.

$$\frac{9}{10} - \frac{6}{10} = \frac{3}{10}$$

Same denominator

8. $\frac{7}{10} - \frac{2}{10}$ **9.** $\frac{5}{6} - \frac{4}{6}$

10. $\frac{3}{8} - \frac{1}{8}$ **11.** $\frac{3}{4} - \frac{2}{4}$

12. $\frac{5}{8}$ **13.** $\frac{7}{10}$ **14.** $\frac{4}{6}$
$- \frac{1}{8}$ $- \frac{6}{10}$ $- \frac{1}{6}$

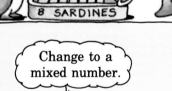

Change to a mixed number.

$$\frac{7}{8} + \frac{5}{8} = \frac{12}{8} = 1\frac{4}{8} = 1\frac{1}{2}$$

Change to lowest terms.

15. $\frac{5}{8} + \frac{4}{8}$ **16.** $\frac{7}{10} + \frac{6}{10}$

17. $\frac{5}{6} + \frac{4}{6}$ **18.** $\frac{3}{8} + \frac{7}{8}$

19. $6\frac{5}{8}$ **20.** $7\frac{6}{10}$ **21.** $2\frac{5}{6}$
$- 4\frac{2}{8}$ $- 3\frac{1}{10}$ $+ 3\frac{2}{6}$

Probability and Prediction

There are 12 marbles in the box. 3 of the marbles are red and 9 are blue. If you pick up a marble without looking, would you be more likely to get a blue marble or a red marble?

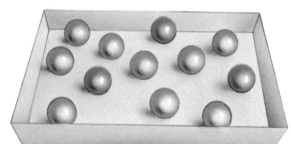

You have 3 chances in 12 of getting a red marble. The **probability** of getting a red marble is $\frac{3}{12}$.

You have 9 chances in 12 of getting a blue marble. The **probability** of getting a blue marble is $\frac{9}{12}$.

1. If you pick up a marble without looking, would you be more likely to get a green or an orange marble?

2. What is the probability of getting a green marble?

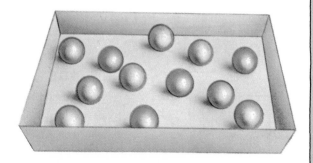

3. What is the probability of getting an orange marble?

4. Get a box and 12 marbles. Be sure there are 8 marbles of a dark color and 4 marbles of a light color. Take out a marble without looking. Check the color. Put it back. Do this 48 times. Keep a record of the marbles you take out. Check to see if you take out a light-colored marble about $\frac{4}{12}$ or $\frac{1}{3}$ of the time.

CUMULATIVE REVIEW

Give the letter for the correct answer.

Measure each length to the nearest centimeter.

1. |————————|

    A 3 cm   **B** 5 cm
    C 4 cm   **D** not given

2. |——————————|

    A 4 cm   **B** 5 cm
    C 6 cm   **D** not given

3. Give the perimeter.

2 cm □ 2 cm

    A 2 cm **B** 4 cm
    C 8 cm **D** not given

4. Give the area.

    A 10 square units
    B 6 square units
    C 3 square units
    D not given

5. Give the volume.

    A 4 cubic units
    B 12 cubic units
    C 8 cubic units
    D not given

Choose the best measure.

6.

    A 1 mL **B** 10 mL
    C 1 L   **D** not given

7.
    A 1 kg **B** 1 g
    C 10 kg **D** not given

8.
    A ⁻10°C **B** 10°C
    C 100°C **D** not given

← Boiling Water

Divide.

9. $6\overline{)52}$ **A** 9 R2 **B** 8 R4
          C 8 R6 **D** not given

10. $5\overline{)44}$ **A** 9 R1 **B** 9 R4
          C 8 R2 **D** not given

11. $3\overline{)215}$ **A** 71 R2 **B** 61 R2
          C 71 R3 **D** not given

12. $5\overline{)457}$ **A** 91 R5 **B** 9 R7
          C 91 R2 **D** not given

13. An apple pie serves 8 people. How many pies are needed to serve 21 people?

    A 2   **B** 3
    C 13   **D** not given

14. Jorgé needs 4 eggs to make a cake. How many cakes can he make with 15 eggs?

    A 3   **B** 5
    C 4   **D** not given

GEOMETRY AND GRAPHING 11

Alyssa saw a movie about Egypt. She liked the pyramids. They were built thousands of years ago. The Great Pyramid is at the city of Giza. It was built for a king named Khufu. Over 2 million blocks of stone were used to build it. Near it sits the Great Sphinx. It was carved of solid rock. Alyssa also liked the tall obelisks. There were hieroglyphics (picture writing) on them. They had been cut from a single piece of stone. Then they were dragged to the Nile River. They were floated on barges to different cities in Egypt.

Space Figures

Objects from the world around you suggest **space figures**.

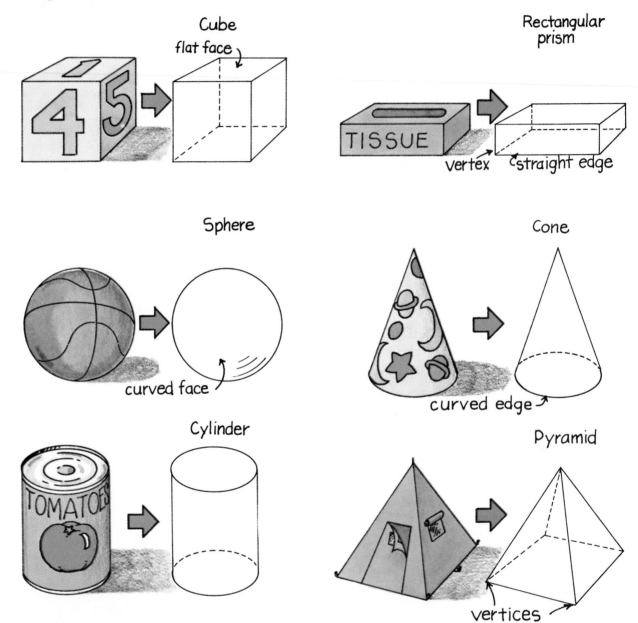

Cube

flat face

Rectangular prism

vertex   straight edge

Sphere

curved face

Cone

curved edge

Cylinder

Pyramid

vertices

Warm Up   Tell what space figure each object suggests.

1.

2.

3.

Practice Tell what space figure each object suggests.

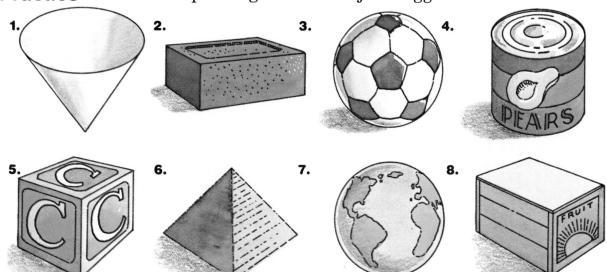

1. 2. 3. 4.

5. 6. 7. 8.

Copy and complete the table.

Name	Number of Flat Faces	Number of Vertices	Number of Straight Edges	Number of Curved Edges	Number of Curved Faces
Cube	6			0	0
Rectangular Prism					0
Sphere	0	0	0	0	
Cone	1	1			
Cylinder			0		
Pyramid				0	

Plane Figures

Objects from the world around you suggest
plane figures. Plane figures lie on a flat
surface.

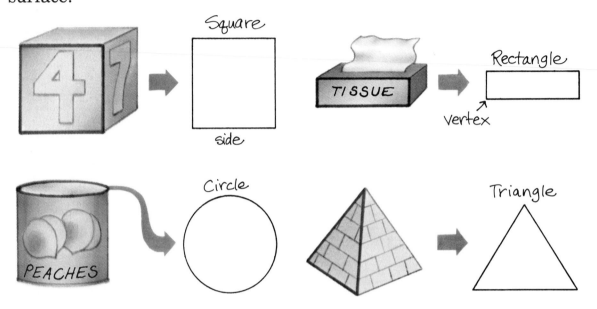

Some other plane figures are shown below.

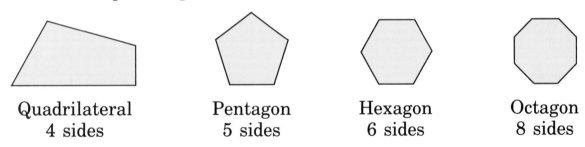

| Quadrilateral | Pentagon | Hexagon | Octagon |
| 4 sides | 5 sides | 6 sides | 8 sides |

Polygons are plane figures that have
all straight sides. Each pair of
sides meet at a vertex.

Warm Up   Which of the figures below are polygons?
Name the polygon.

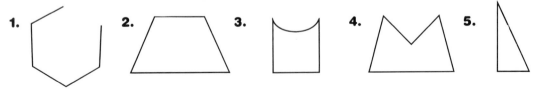

Practice Name the plane figure suggested by each object.

1.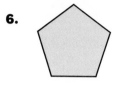
2.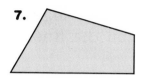
3.
4.

Name each of these polygons.

5.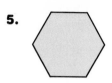
6.
7.
8.

9. How many sides does a hexagon have?

10. How many vertices does a pentagon have?

11. How many vertices does a hexagon have?

12. Draw a quadrilateral. How many sides does it have?

13. How many sides does a pentagon have?

14. Draw an octagon. How many vertices does it have?

THINK

Logical Reasoning

Which figure does not belong?

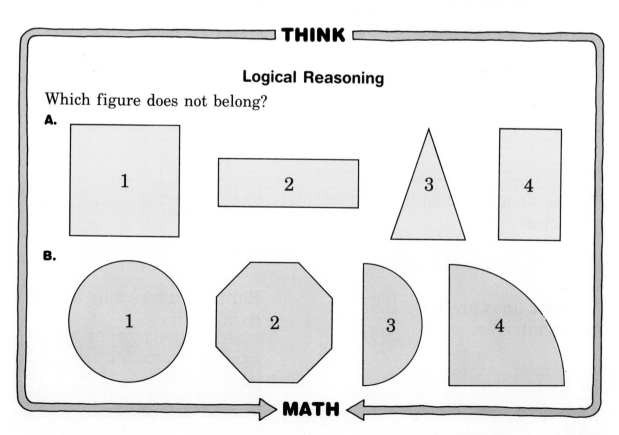

A.
1
2
3
4

B.
1
2
3
4

MATH

Points, Lines, and Segments

A long, straight road in the desert suggests the idea of a **line**.

A line is endless in both directions. A distant car on the road suggests the idea of a **point** on the line.

Points are named with capital letters. A distant crossroad suggests the idea of **intersecting** lines.

The two lines intersect at a point Q. A line is named by any two points on the line.

We write: $\overleftrightarrow{PQ}$ or $\overleftrightarrow{QP}$

The part of the road from the car to the intersection suggests a **segment**.

Segments are named by their endpoints.

We write: $\overline{PQ}$ or $\overline{QP}$

Parallel lines are lines that never intersect.

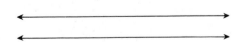

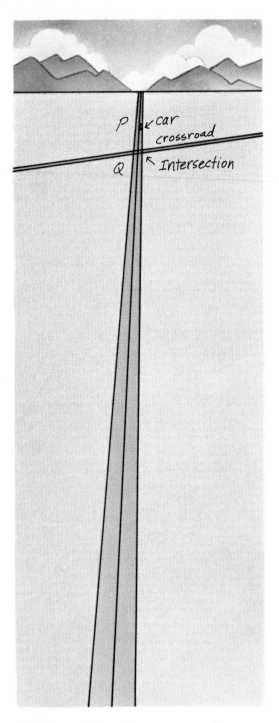

Railroad tracks suggest parallel lines.

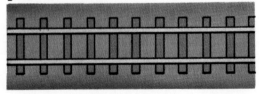

Write the name for each figure.

Example

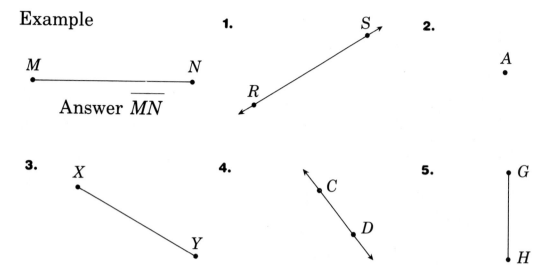

1.

2.

Answer $\overline{MN}$

3.

4.

5.

Pretend you are looking through a telescope
at some far-off lines. Tell whether they are
parallel or intersecting lines.

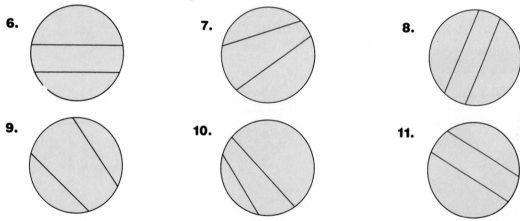

6.

7.

8.

9.

10.

11.

Draw and label a figure for each name.

12. $\overleftrightarrow{RS}$ 13. T 14. $\overline{YZ}$ 15. $\overleftrightarrow{BA}$

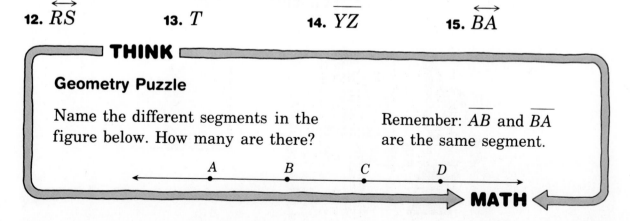

THINK

Geometry Puzzle

Name the different segments in the
figure below. How many are there?

Remember: $\overline{AB}$ and $\overline{BA}$
are the same segment.

A   B   C   D

MATH

Rays and Angles

A rocket fired on a straight path into space suggests the idea of a **ray**.

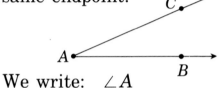

A ray is part of a line. Ray AB has endpoint A and continues through B without end.

We write: $\overrightarrow{AB}$ $\overrightarrow{DC}$

An **angle** is two rays with the same endpoint.

We write: $\angle A$

Polygons have angles at each of their vertices.

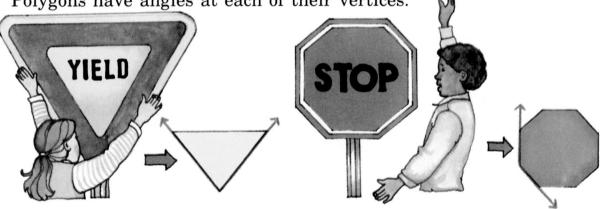

An angle at a "square corner" is a **right angle**.

272

Practice Name each ray.

1.

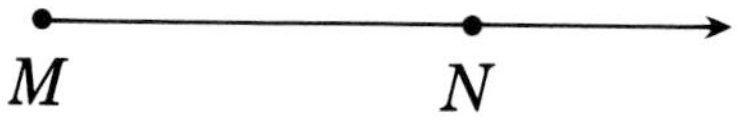

M •————————•————————→ N

2.

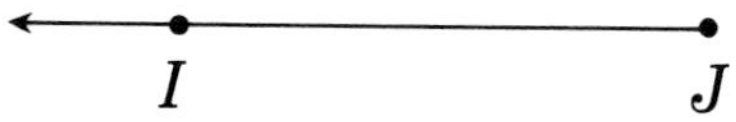

←————————•————————•
I ⟵ J

Name each angle.

3.

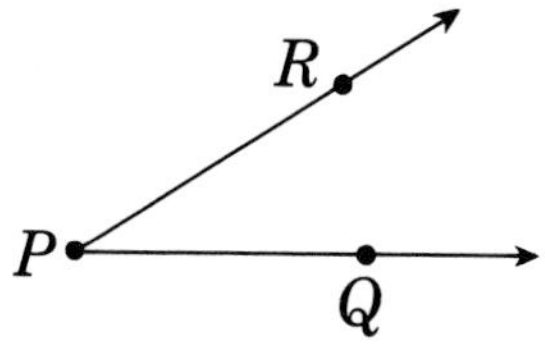

R

P •————•————→
Q

4.

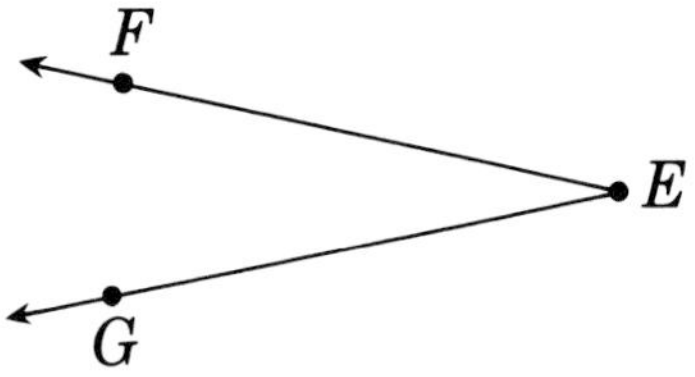

F

E

G

Tell whether the angle shown is a right angle. Write yes or no.

5.

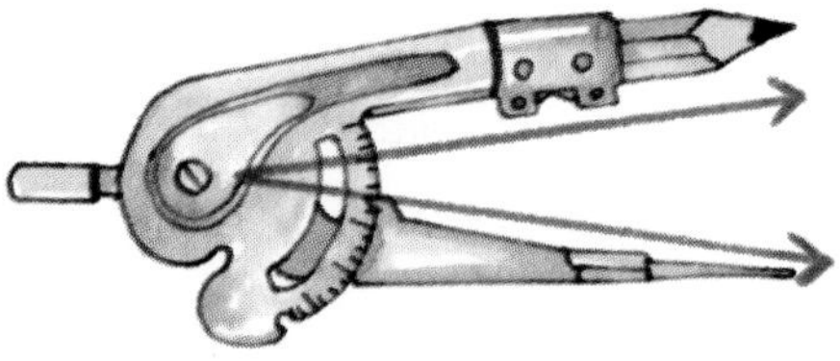

6.

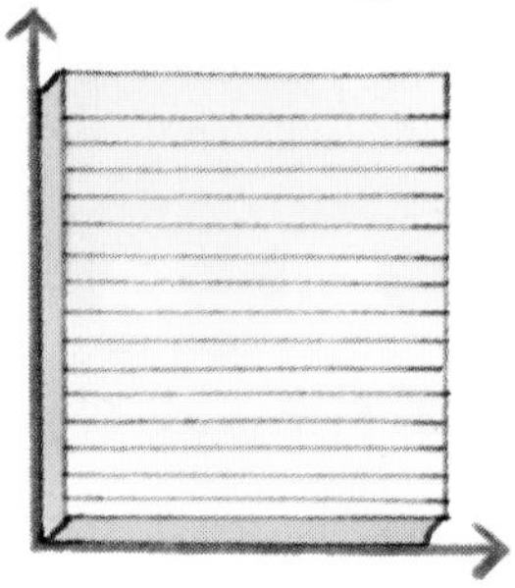

7.

8.

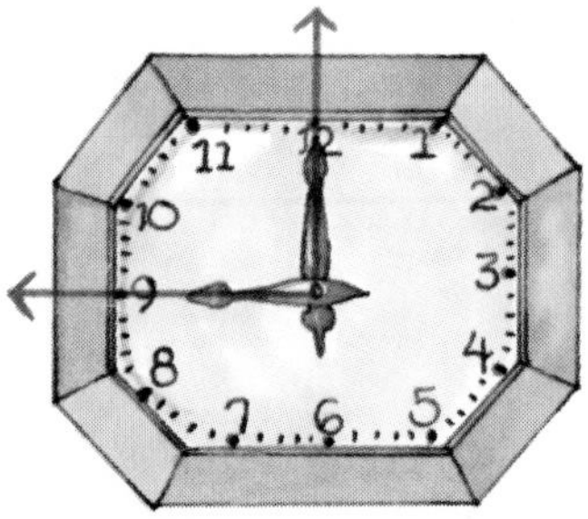

9.

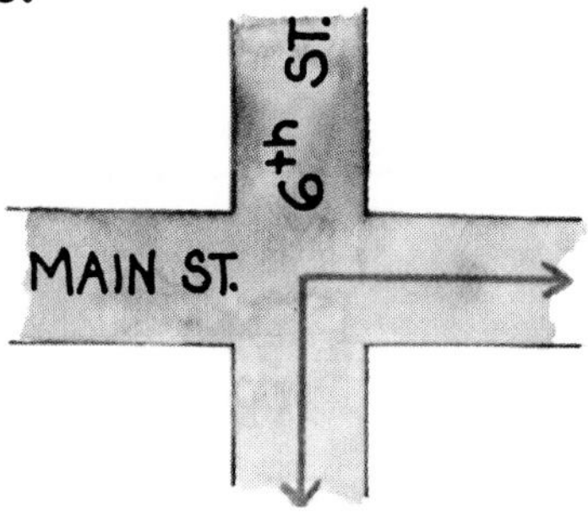

10.

How many right angles does each polygon have?

11.

12.

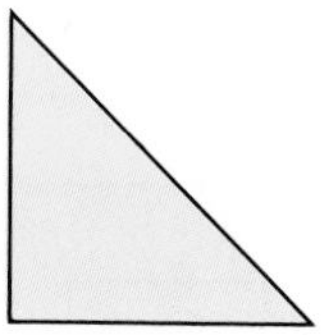

13.

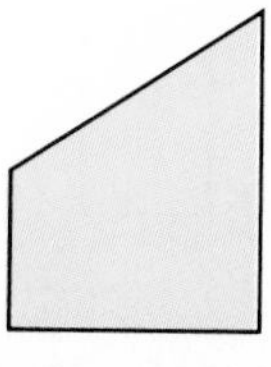

14.

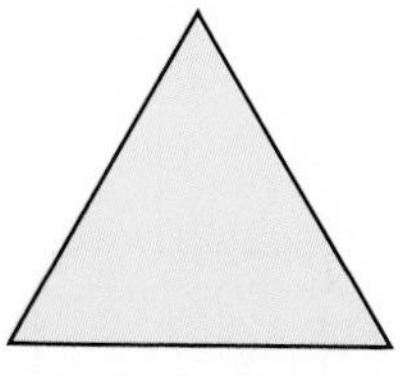

━━ **THINK** ━━

Space Perception

Use graph paper to draw your own space figure.

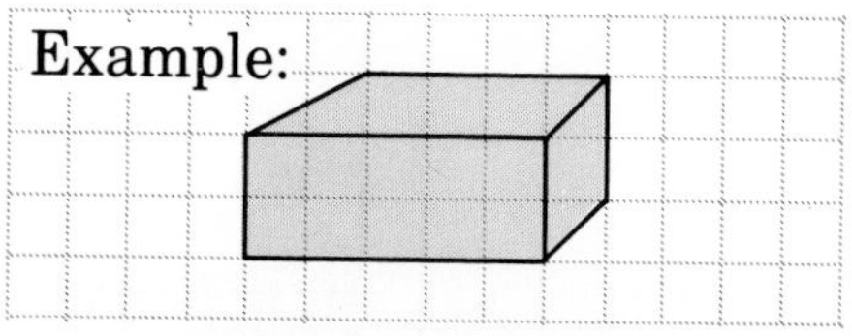

Example:

→ **MATH** ←

273

Congruent Figures

Fred is making copies of a geometric figure. The copy machine turns out figures that are the same size and shape. The figures are all congruent to each other.

You can also make congruent figures by tracing.

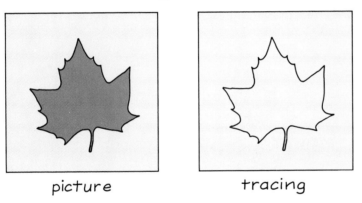

picture   tracing

Warm Up If you need help, make a tracing to decide whether the figures on the two papers are congruent to each other.

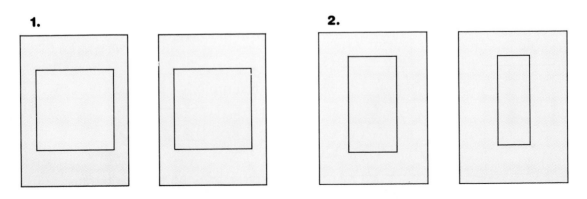

1.

2.

Practice If you need help, make a tracing to decide whether the two figures are congruent. You may need to turn or flip your tracing to see if it fits.

1.

2.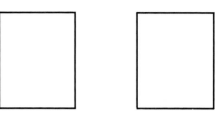

3.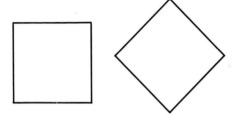

4.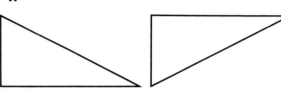

5.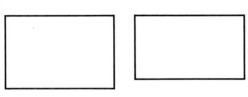

6.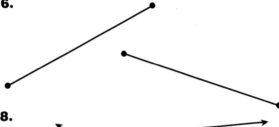

7.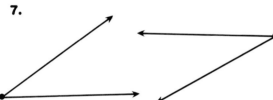

8.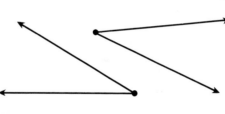

SKILLKEEPER

Find the sums and differences.

1. $\dfrac{3}{10}$
$+ \dfrac{6}{10}$

2. $\dfrac{5}{8}$
$- \dfrac{2}{8}$

3. $\dfrac{1}{3}$
$+ \dfrac{1}{3}$

4. $\dfrac{5}{6}$
$- \dfrac{4}{6}$

5. $\dfrac{2}{5}$
$+ \dfrac{2}{5}$

6. $\dfrac{5}{8}$
$+ \dfrac{4}{8}$

7. $5\dfrac{3}{4}$
$- 2\dfrac{2}{4}$

8. $\dfrac{2}{3}$
$+ \dfrac{2}{3}$

9. $7\dfrac{6}{10}$
$- 2\dfrac{4}{10}$

10. $\dfrac{5}{6}$
$+ \dfrac{3}{6}$

275

Similar Figures

Some copy machines will make larger or smaller copies of an original. Norma is making smaller copies of a geometric figure. The smaller figures are the same shape as the original.

Figures that have the same shape are **similar** to each other. Each small figure is similar to the original.

Warm Up You can use different size graph paper to help you decide if two figures are similar. Write similar or not similar for each pair of figures.

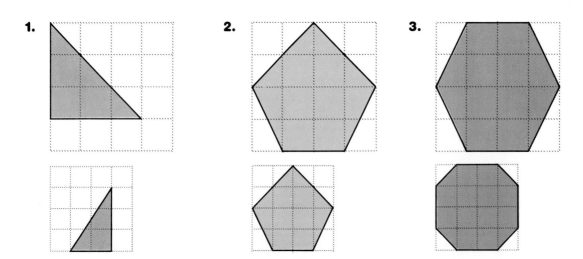

1.

2.

3.

Practice Which figure in each row is similar to the first?

1.

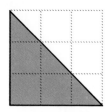
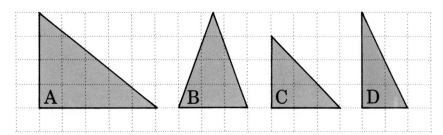

2.

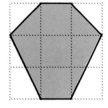
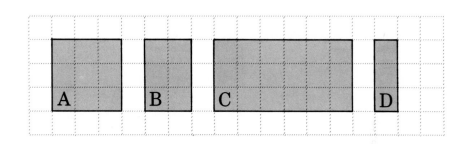

3.

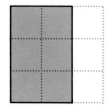
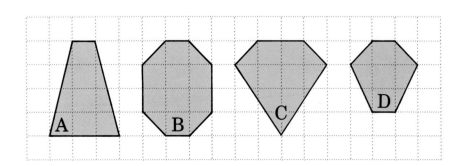

★ Write T (true) or F (false) for each statement.

4. Any two squares are similar to each other.

5. Any two octagons are similar to each other.

6. Any two circles are similar to each other.

THINK

Shape Perception

Trace the figure below. Cut out 4 copies of the figure. Put them together to make a figure that is larger than, but similar to this figure.

MATH

Symmetric Figures

A figure has a **line of symmetry** if it can be folded so that the two parts fit exactly (are congruent). The fold is the line of symmetry. A figure that has a line of symmetry is a **symmetric figure**.

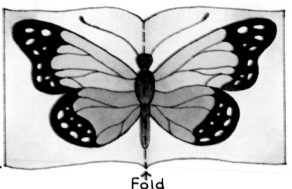

Fold

Here is a way you can make a symmetric figure.

Fold a piece of paper.

Make a cut that starts and ends on the fold.

Unfold the piece you cut out.

Warm Up Tell what the symmetric figure will be when cut out and unfolded.

1.
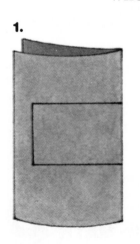

2.

3.
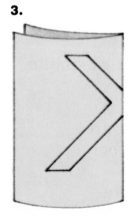

4.
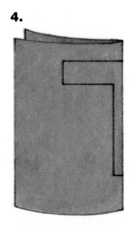

278

Practice Which of these drawings of objects from nature come "close" to being symmetrical?
Write yes or no.

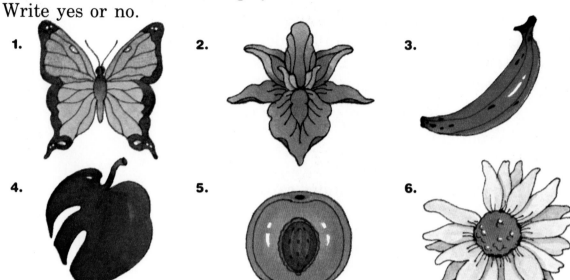

1.

2.

3.

4.

5.

6.

Does the dashed line appear to be a line of symmetry?

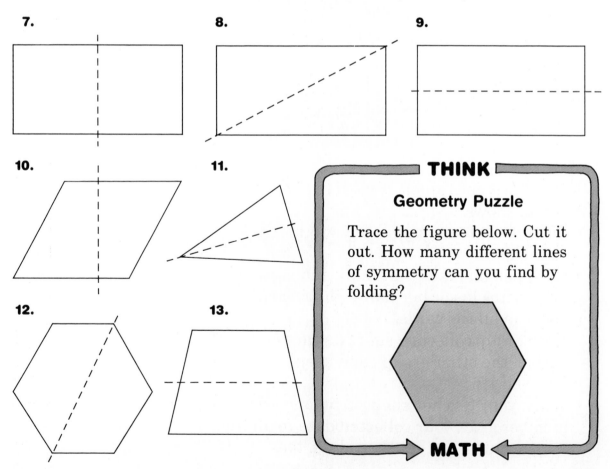

7.

8.

9.

10.

11.

12.

13.

THINK

Geometry Puzzle

Trace the figure below. Cut it out. How many different lines of symmetry can you find by folding?

MATH

279

Using Graphs

The students in Mrs. Brown's class were discussing television shows. Some students mostly watch adventure shows. Others like comedy shows better.

What are the favorite television shows of the students in your class?

Work with a group.
You will need chart paper and index cards.

Part 1

1. Make a list of television shows that your group likes.

2. Organize the list into categories according to the type of show, for example: comedy, movie, cartoon, sports, news, baseball. Some shows may fit into more than one category, and your group will have to decide which category would be best.

3. Using your list, predict which types of shows are the most popular with the whole class.

Part 2

4. Now collect data about each person's favorite shows.
   - First check to see how many groups are in your class.
   - Each person takes that many index cards and writes his or her name and favorite show on all the cards.
   - Each group collects a set of its cards for each of the other groups and keeps a set for itself.
   - When your teacher suggests it, one group member gives your collected data to all the other groups. You get their data, too.

5. With your group, organize the collected data into categories, as you did in Part 1.
- How did the data from the class compare with your group's predictions of the most popular types of shows?
- Did you need to change or add to your categories?

Part 3

6. On a large sheet of paper, make a graph to show how your group organized the data. You may use one of the kinds of graphs shown or create one of your own.

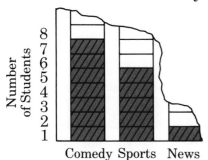

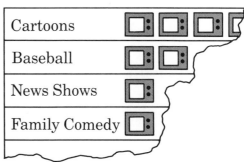

7. Discuss your graph with your group. Below the graph, write one true sentence about the information it illustrates.

8. Compare graphs with other groups.
- How are they the same? How are they different?
- Do some graphs give more information than others?
- Are some easier to read than others?

9. How might the information on the graphs be useful?

10. Could you use the information on the graphs to predict what shows your parents might watch? To predict what a national survey might show?

11. Write a short news story about your class's television viewing, based on your group's graph.

Picture Graphs

Tom Brown owns a TV store. The **picture graph** below shows how many TVs he sold in each of the first 6 months of the year. Each picture means 10 TVs sold. So Tom sold **5 × 10**, or **50**, TVs in January.

BROWN'S TV SALES

January	▢ ▢ ▢ ▢ ▢
February	▢ ▢ ▢ ▢
March	▢ ▢ ▢ ▢ ▢ ▢ ▢ ▢
April	▢ ▢ ▢ ▢ ▢ ▢ ◺
May	▢ ▢ ▢ ▢ ▢
June	▢ ▢ ▢ ◺

Each ▢ means 10 TVs sold.

Warm Up

1. How many TVs did Tom Brown sell in February?

2. In what month were 60 TVs sold?

3. In what month were the most TVs sold? How many were sold?

4. Estimate how many TVs were sold in April.

5. Estimate the number of TVs sold in June.

Practice Use the radio graph to answer questions 1–5.

1. How many radios were sold in March?

2. In what two months were the same number of radios sold?

3. Estimate the number of radios sold in June.

4. In what month were the fewest radios sold? Estimate how many were sold.

5. About how many radios were sold in May?

Use the stereo graph to answer questions 6–8.

6. How many stereos were sold in January?

7. In what two months were about the same number of stereos sold?

8. Estimate the number of stereos sold in June.

★ 9. Make your own picture graph for this data.
    TVs sold:
    July—12, August—18, and September—15. Let each picture mean 3 TVs.

BROWN'S RADIO SALES

January
February
March
April
May
June

Each 📻 means 6 radios.

BROWN'S STEREO SALES

January
February
March
April
May
June

Each 📼 means 4 stereos.

283

Number Pairs

The half-time shows at football games often have marching bands that make patterns on the field. Suppose your group has been asked to plan a half-time show. How would you decide where the band members will stand?

Work with a group of five or six. You will need masking tape, graph paper, geoboards, and geobands.

Look at this grid.

We use **number pairs** to describe points on a grid.

The drummer is standing on point (2,5). Discuss why this point is called (2,5).

- Who is located at (5,2)?
- Use number pairs to tell the locations of some other band members.

Notice that when we read or write a number pair, we always give the number **across** first, and then the number **up**. Talk about why this is important.

Part 1

With masking tape, make a 6-by-6 grid on the floor. Label the lines.

1. Take turns being the band director.
   - Have your group members stand on the grid to make a simple design.
   - Using number pairs, make a list of their places.
   - Use the list to plot the design on graph paper.

   Discuss each group member's design. How can you be sure the number pairs are correct?

2. Work with your group to design a pattern for about 10 people. Draw it on graph paper. Make a list of the number pairs.

- Choose a director to use the number pairs to tell classmates where to stand on the grid.
- Use your graph-paper grid to check the formation.

3. Suppose the high school has hired a new band director. With your group, write an explanation that will help her plan a design and give directions to the band members.

Part 2

On your geoboard, use one geoband to make a design that touches many pegs.

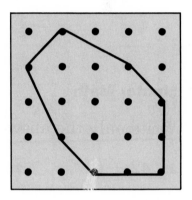

4. Use what you have learned about number pairs to name each peg your geoband touches.

- Draw a picture of your design on graph paper.
- Label the number pairs on your drawing.

5. Write your number pairs on another paper and exchange papers with a partner in your group.

- Have your partner use the number pairs to make the design on a geoboard.
- Compare your picture to the design your partner made. Does one of you have to make changes? Why or why not?

6. On the same geoboard, use another geoband to make the same design on different pegs.

- Add this design to your graph-paper picture.
- Label the number pairs.

Do this several times. Discuss what you notice about the new figures and their number pairs.

Mixed Skills Practice

Computation

Find the answers.

1. $78 + 86$
2. $328 + 195$
3. $\$46.28 + 31.45$
4. $93 - 28$
5. $604 - 258$
6. $\$39.15 - 16.78$

7. 43×6
8. 75×4
9. 86×5
10. 433×5
11. 327×4
12. 689×3

13. $4\overline{)92}$
14. $7\overline{)84}$
15. $6\overline{)83}$
16. $8\overline{)930}$
17. $3\overline{)815}$
18. $5\overline{)541}$

19. $\frac{1}{4} + \frac{2}{4}$
20. $\frac{6}{8} - \frac{3}{8}$
21. $\frac{3}{5} + \frac{1}{5}$
22. $2\frac{1}{2} + 3\frac{1}{4}$
23. $\frac{7}{8} - \frac{1}{8}$
24. $5\frac{1}{2} - 1\frac{1}{4}$

Mental Math

Write only the answers.

25. $42 + 6$
26. $36 + 3$
27. $20 + 60$
28. $300 + 500$

29. $38 - 5$
30. $79 - 6$
31. $90 - 70$
32. $700 - 400$

33. 4×30
34. 6×50
35. 7×200
36. 8×400

Estimation

Estimate.

37. $38 + 23$
38. $62 + 79$
39. $84 + 28$
40. $59 + 97$

41. $72 - 58$
42. $81 - 47$
43. $198 - 59$
44. $295 - 112$

45. $\$1.98 + \$3.95$
46. $\$6.95 + \$9.89$

47. $\$16.95 - \$8.98$
48. $\$10.98 - \$3.95$

APPLIED PROBLEM SOLVING

You and your friends are planning to rent horses for a trail ride. You decide to take the special rate for a 3-hour ride. Will you take the trail to Lookout Point, Window Rock, or Sunset Lake?

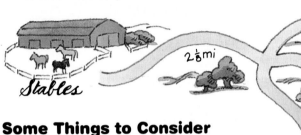

$2\frac{1}{8}$ mi
$2\frac{7}{8}$ mi
4 mi
$3\frac{3}{8}$ mi

Some Things to Consider

- You are not allowed to run the horses.
- In 3 hours the horses can cover up to 12 miles.
- You can see for many miles at Lookout Point.

- You can usually see deer and other wildlife around Window Rock.
- There are ducks and swans at Sunset Lake.
- If you stay out over 3 hours, you will be charged double.

Some Questions to Answer

1. How far is it to Lookout Point? How far is it to Lookout Point and back to the stables?

2. How far is it to Window Rock and back to the stables?

3. How far is it to Sunset Lake and back to the stables?

4. Do you have time to go to Lookout Point and back? To Window Rock and back? To Sunset Lake and back?

What Is Your Decision?

Will you take the trail to Lookout Point, Window Rock, or Sunset Lake? Why?

PROBLEM SOLVING
Using the Strategies

Use one or more of the strategies listed to solve each problem.

1. The bus left the downtown station and traveled 2 hours before stopping. The rest stop lasted 20 minutes. The bus then traveled an hour and a half before arriving in Middletown at 4:30 p.m. What time did the bus leave for Middletown?

2. There were 20 people left on the bus when it got to Middletown. There were 2 more men than women. How many men were on the bus?

3. On the trip, the bus passed through 5 towns. Bern was before Aden. Aden was before Dale. Eaton was after Dale. Center was between Bern and Aden. Which town did the bus leave last?

4. When the bus loaded to return, there were 3 empty seats—one in front, one in back, and one in the middle. The bus stopped at Bern and picked up a man and a woman. How many ways could they sit down?

Tell what space figure each object suggests

1.

2.

Name each polygon.

3.

4.

Are the lines parallel?

5.

6.

Are the angles right angles?

7.

8.

9. Which figure is congruent to the first?

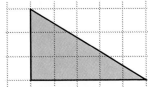 **A**  **B** 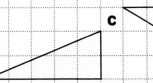 **C**

10. Which figure is similar to the first?

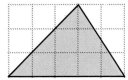 **A**   **B**

11. Which shape has a line of symmetry?

A  **B**  **C**

12. How many TVs were sold in June?

May
June
July
Each ▢ means 9 TVs.

13. If you connect the points, what figure will be made?

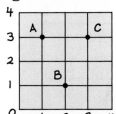

ANOTHER LOOK

Space Figures

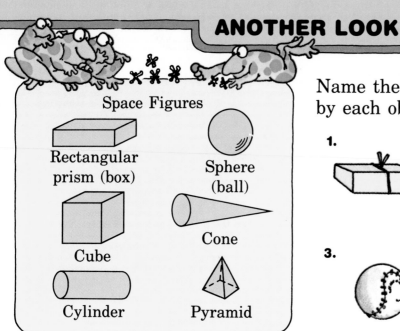

Rectangular prism (box)

Sphere (ball)

Cube

Cone

Cylinder

Pyramid

Plane Figures

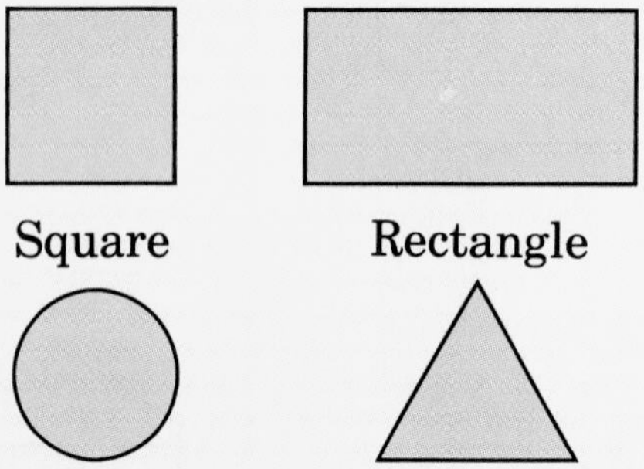

Square

Rectangle

Circle

Triangle

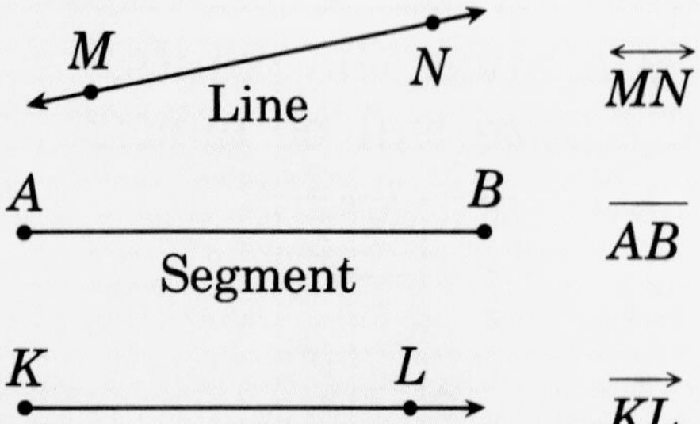

M ——— N
Line
$\overleftrightarrow{MN}$

A ——— B
Segment
$\overline{AB}$

K ——— L
Ray
$\overrightarrow{KL}$

Name the space figure suggested by each object.

1.
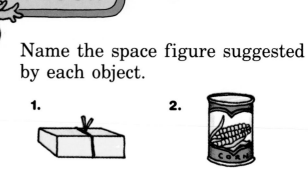

2.

3.

4.

Name the plane figure suggested by each object.

5.

6.

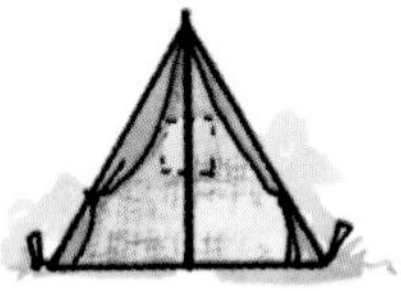

7.

8.

Tell whether each object suggests a line, segment, or ray.

9.
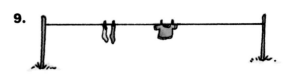

10.

Space Perception

This triangle, with all sides equal, has been carefully cut from a piece of green tagboard. It has an F (front) on one side and B (back) on the other. It can be put back into its hole six different ways.

flip

hole

   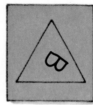 

Look at the figures below. First guess how many ways each figure can be put back into its hole. Draw each figure on graph paper. Cut it out and check your guess.

1.

Square

2.

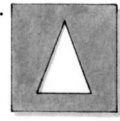

Isosceles triangle

3.

Rectangle

CUMULATIVE REVIEW

Give the letter for the correct answer.

1.
$$\begin{array}{r} 14 \\ \times\ 3 \\ \hline \end{array}$$
A 32
B 42
C 17
D not given

2.
$$\begin{array}{r} 65 \\ \times\ 5 \\ \hline \end{array}$$
A 325
B 305
C 70
D not given

3.
$$\begin{array}{r} 236 \\ \times\ 4 \\ \hline \end{array}$$
A 824
B 944
C 844
D not given

4.
$$\begin{array}{r} 115 \\ \times\ 4 \\ \hline \end{array}$$
A 449
B 440
C 460
D not given

5.
$$\begin{array}{r} 735 \\ \times\ 6 \\ \hline \end{array}$$
A 4,410
B 441
C 4,280
D not given

6.
$$\begin{array}{r} \$0.23 \\ \times\ 6 \\ \hline \end{array}$$
A $10.38
B $1.28
C $1.38
D not given

7.
$$\begin{array}{r} \$10.05 \\ \times\ 4 \\ \hline \end{array}$$
A $40.20
B $4.20
C $14.20
D not given

What fraction is shaded?

8. **A** $\frac{1}{3}$ **B** $\frac{2}{3}$ **C** $\frac{3}{4}$ **D** not given

9. **A** $\frac{2}{3}$ **B** $\frac{3}{6}$ **C** $\frac{2}{6}$ **D** not given

Which statement is correct?

10. **A** $\frac{1}{2} = \frac{2}{8}$ **B** $\frac{1}{2} = \frac{2}{6}$ **C** $\frac{1}{2} = \frac{2}{4}$ **D** not given

11. **A** $\frac{1}{3} < \frac{1}{2}$ **B** $\frac{1}{3} > \frac{1}{2}$ **C** $\frac{1}{2} < \frac{1}{3}$ **D** not given

12. Reduce $\frac{12}{20}$ to the lowest terms.

A $\frac{3}{5}$ **B** $1\frac{2}{5}$ **C** $\frac{6}{10}$ **D** not given

13. Hans gave 2 apples to each of his 12 friends. How many apples did Hans give away?

A 10 **B** 24 **C** 6 **D** not given

14. One tomato costs $0.35. How much do 3 tomatoes cost?

A $10.05 **B** $0.95 **C** $1.05 **D** not given

MULTIPLICATION: 2-Digit Factors

Patrick sometimes meets his mother at the college. She is a student studying computer programming. First she learned to write directions. The directions are called a program. She writes the program in a certain language. Writing it is fun. It is like answering a puzzle. Next she tests her program. She tries it on the computer. She catches mistakes. This is "debugging." It means taking the "bugs" out. Her last lesson took 12 hours to write. Debugging it took 3 times as long. Patrick is interested in his mother's courses. She tells him about what she is learning. Patrick wants to do that kind of work someday, too.

Special Products: Mental Math

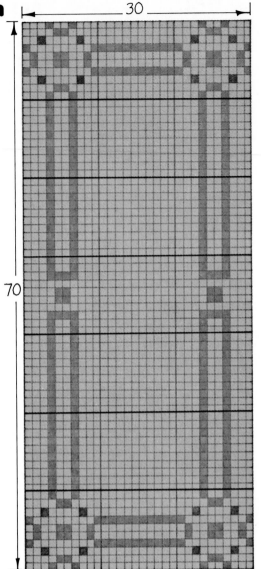

30

70

Janice and Roy covered the top of a table with tile. There are 70 rows with 30 pieces of tile in each row. How many pieces of tile did they use?

Since we want the total for equal rows, we multiply.

THINK
7 tens × 3 tens = 21 hundreds

70 × 30 = 2,100

21 hundreds = 2 thousand, 1 hundred

Janice and Roy used 2,100 pieces of tile.

Other Examples

10 × 60 = 600   **20 × 40 = 800**   **50 × 40 = 2,000**

Warm Up   Find the products mentally.

1. 10 × 10	**2.** 10 × 40	**3.** 10 × 80	**4.** 10 × 30
5. 60 × 10	**6.** 40 × 10	**7.** 70 × 10	**8.** 90 × 10
9. 70 × 20	**10.** 50 × 50	**11.** 90 × 80	**12.** 80 × 50
13. 20 × 10	**14.** 80 × 10	**15.** 40 × 20	**16.** 40 × 30
17. 50 × 30	**18.** 30 × 60	**19.** 20 × 90	**20.** 80 × 70

Practice Find the products. Write answers only.

1. 10×10
2. 10×30

3. 40×10
4. 10×60

5. 40×20
6. 20×20

7. 90×50
8. 50×60
9. 60×40
10. 80×30

11. 20×60
12. 90×20
13. 70×30
14. 80×40

15. 90×10
16. 20×70
17. 40×80
18. 60×80

★ 19. $3 \times 10 \times 40$
★ 20. $10 \times 2 \times 20$
★ 21. $8 \times 10 \times 10$

★ 22. $5 \times 10 \times 50$
★ 23. $10 \times 4 \times 20$
★ 24. $4 \times 10 \times 80$

Mixed Applications

25. There are 40 rows with 60 pieces of tile in each row. How many pieces of tile are there?

26. A garden is shaped like a triangle with sides 30 meters, 50 meters, and 40 meters. What is the perimeter?

THINK

🖩 **Using a Calculator**

Guess the number of zeros in each product. Then multiply on the calculator to check your guess.

200×500	$800 \times 4,000$
$40 \times 5,000$	$4,000 \times 50$
$7,000 \times 40$	$90,000 \times 20$
500×800	$500 \times 6,000$

MATH

Multiplying by Multiples of Ten

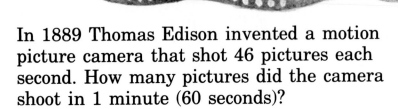

In 1889 Thomas Edison invented a motion picture camera that shot 46 pictures each second. How many pictures did the camera shoot in 1 minute (60 seconds)?

Since there are the same number of pictures each second, we multiply.

Multiply by the digit in the ones' place. → Multiply by the digit in the tens' place.

$$\begin{array}{r} 46 \\ \times\ 60 \\ \hline 0 \end{array}$$

$0 \times 46 = 0$

$$\begin{array}{r} 3 \\ 46 \\ \times\ 60 \\ \hline 2{,}760 \end{array}$$

6 tens × 46 = 276 tens

Edison's motion picture camera shot 2,760 pictures in 1 minute.

Other Examples

$$\begin{array}{r} 64 \\ \times\ 10 \\ \hline 640 \end{array}$$
1 ten × 4 = 4 tens

$$\begin{array}{r} 3 \\ 46 \\ \times\ 50 \\ \hline 2{,}300 \end{array}$$
5 tens × 6 = 30 tens

$$\begin{array}{r} 4 \\ 75 \\ \times\ 80 \\ \hline 6{,}000 \end{array}$$

$$\begin{array}{r} 40 \\ \times\ 30 \\ \hline 1{,}200 \end{array}$$

Warm Up Multiply.

1. $\begin{array}{r}12\\ \times 30\\ \hline\end{array}$	2. $\begin{array}{r}31\\ \times 40\\ \hline\end{array}$	3. $\begin{array}{r}98\\ \times 10\\ \hline\end{array}$	4. $\begin{array}{r}45\\ \times 20\\ \hline\end{array}$	5. $\begin{array}{r}63\\ \times 50\\ \hline\end{array}$	6. $\begin{array}{r}24\\ \times 90\\ \hline\end{array}$
7. $\begin{array}{r}13\\ \times 70\\ \hline\end{array}$	8. $\begin{array}{r}32\\ \times 80\\ \hline\end{array}$	9. $\begin{array}{r}28\\ \times 50\\ \hline\end{array}$	10. $\begin{array}{r}76\\ \times 30\\ \hline\end{array}$	11. $\begin{array}{r}25\\ \times 40\\ \hline\end{array}$	12. $\begin{array}{r}82\\ \times 60\\ \hline\end{array}$

Practice Find the products.

1. 37×10
2. 23×30
3. 81×20
4. 63×40
5. 70×60
6. 36×40

7. 12×90
8. 42×70
9. 89×30
10. 25×80
11. 44×40
12. 13×50

13. 54×50
14. 70×20
15. 29×70
16. 86×10
17. 38×90
18. 41×60

19. 60×35

20. 20×32

21. 70×74

22. Multiply 79 by 50.

23. Multiply 51 by 90.

Mixed Applications

24. Movie companies use cameras that shoot 24 pictures each second. How many pictures could be shot in 1 minute? (60 seconds = 1 minute)

25. A slow-motion camera takes 54 pictures each second. A movie-company camera takes 24 pictures each second. How many more pictures each second are taken by the slow-motion camera?

26. **DATA HUNT** Find the number of pictures a home movie camera shoots in 1 second. How many pictures would it shoot in 1 minute?

THINK

Estimation

Estimate to find which of these answers is about 500.

A $1,783 - 1,291 = \square$
B $82 \times 4 = \square$
C $156 \div 3 = \square$
D $235 + 275 = \square$
E $10 \times 48 = \square$
F $6,268 - 5,117 = \square$

MATH

Multiplication and Addition

Gretchen works at a greenhouse. She planted 2 rows of pink flowers and 10 rows of blue flowers. There are 24 flowers in each row. Here is how Gretchen figures out how many flowers she planted.

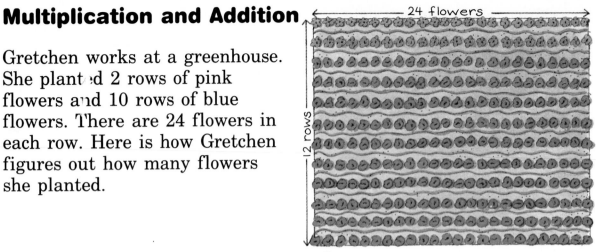

24 flowers

12 rows

Multiply to find the number of pink flowers.	Multiply to find the number of blue flowers.	Add to find the total number of flowers.

$$\begin{array}{r} 24 \\ \times\ 2 \\ \hline 48 \end{array}$$ pink flowers

$$\begin{array}{r} 24 \\ \times 10 \\ \hline 240 \end{array}$$ blue flowers

$$\begin{array}{r} 48 \\ + 240 \\ \hline 288 \end{array}$$
48 pink flowers
240 blue flowers
288 flowers

Gretchen planted 288 flowers.

How many flowers did each person plant?

1. Jon's flowers
   25 flowers in each row
   5 rows of red
   10 rows of blue

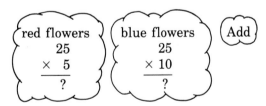

red flowers
$$\begin{array}{r} 25 \\ \times\ 5 \\ \hline ? \end{array}$$

blue flowers
$$\begin{array}{r} 25 \\ \times 10 \\ \hline ? \end{array}$$

Add

2. Bonnie's flowers
   18 flowers in each row
   4 rows of yellow
   10 rows of orange

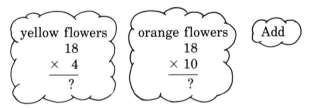

yellow flowers
$$\begin{array}{r} 18 \\ \times\ 4 \\ \hline ? \end{array}$$

orange flowers
$$\begin{array}{r} 18 \\ \times 10 \\ \hline ? \end{array}$$

Add

3. Hal's flowers
   36 flowers in each row
   3 rows of red
   10 rows of blue

★ 5. Sylvi's flowers
   18 flowers in each row
   12 rows

4. Dana's flowers
   32 flowers in each row
   8 rows of yellow
   20 rows of orange

★ 6. Corey's flowers
   24 flowers in each row
   16 rows

PROBLEM SOLVING
Choosing a Calculation Method

QUESTION · DATA · PLAN · ANSWER · CHECK

Your choice!

Pencil-Paper · Mental Math · Estimation · Calculator

You may use any of these methods to solve the problems, but use each method at least once.

1. Manuel planted 30 rows of flowers. There are 10 flowers in each row. How many flowers did Manuel plant?

2. Jodie planted 134 pansies and 67 daisies. How many flowers did she plant?

3. Norman planted 345 flowers. 180 of them were red. The rest were yellow. How many yellow flowers did he plant?

4. Beth put 345 plants in pots to sell. She sold them all for $1.29 each. How much did she get for her plants?

5. Rex bought 98 plants. He paid $1.95 each for them. Did Rex's plants cost more or less than $200?

6. Takeo planted 5 rows of daisies. He also planted 10 rows of pansies. There are 12 flowers in each row. How many flowers did he plant?

7. *Strategy Practice* Aaron planted 2 bulbs the first day, 4 bulbs the second day, 6 bulbs the third day, and so on. One day he planted 22 bulbs. How many did he plant the next day?

Multiplying with 2-Digit Factors

A small tugboat is 23 m long. An aircraft carrier is 13 times as long as the tugboat. How long is an aircraft carrier?

Since we want the total for equal lengths, we multiply.

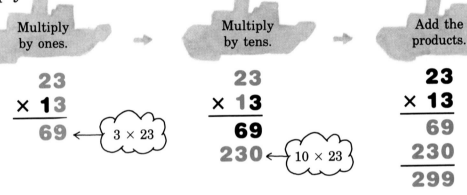

Multiply by ones.	Multiply by tens.	Add the products.
23 × 13 69 ← 3 × 23	23 × 13 69 230 ← 10 × 23	23 × 13 69 230 299

The aircraft carrier is 299 m long.

Other Examples

```
   14
 × 12
   28  ← 2 × 14
  140  ← 10 × 14
  168
```

```
   32
 × 23
   96  ← 3 × 32
  640  ← 20 × 32
  736
```

```
   20
 × 42
   40  ← 2 × 20
  800  ← 40 × 20
  840
```

Warm Up   Multiply.

1. 22 × 13
2. 12 × 24
3. 22 × 31
4. 11 × 43
5. 70 × 11
6. 14 × 31

7. 33 × 12
8. 34 × 22
9. 22 × 14
10. 20 × 33
11. 24 × 12
12. 30 × 22

Practice Find the products.

1. $\begin{array}{r} 32 \\ \times\ 12 \\ \hline \end{array}$
2. $\begin{array}{r} 21 \\ \times\ 23 \\ \hline \end{array}$
3. $\begin{array}{r} 12 \\ \times\ 14 \\ \hline \end{array}$
4. $\begin{array}{r} 40 \\ \times\ 22 \\ \hline \end{array}$
5. $\begin{array}{r} 24 \\ \times\ 20 \\ \hline \end{array}$
6. $\begin{array}{r} 30 \\ \times\ 18 \\ \hline \end{array}$

7. $\begin{array}{r} 12 \\ \times\ 34 \\ \hline \end{array}$
8. $\begin{array}{r} 78 \\ \times\ 11 \\ \hline \end{array}$
9. $\begin{array}{r} 43 \\ \times\ 21 \\ \hline \end{array}$
10. $\begin{array}{r} 33 \\ \times\ 13 \\ \hline \end{array}$
11. $\begin{array}{r} 11 \\ \times\ 59 \\ \hline \end{array}$
12. $\begin{array}{r} 12 \\ \times\ 21 \\ \hline \end{array}$

13. $\begin{array}{r} 10 \\ \times\ 43 \\ \hline \end{array}$
14. $\begin{array}{r} 32 \\ \times\ 30 \\ \hline \end{array}$
15. $\begin{array}{r} 22 \\ \times\ 42 \\ \hline \end{array}$
16. $\begin{array}{r} 30 \\ \times\ 22 \\ \hline \end{array}$
17. $\begin{array}{r} 31 \\ \times\ 13 \\ \hline \end{array}$
18. $\begin{array}{r} 14 \\ \times\ 41 \\ \hline \end{array}$

19. 24×21
20. 33×15
21. 44×19

22. 67×11
23. 40×21
24. 12×43

25. Multiply 14 times 21.
26. Multiply 34 times 22.

27. Multiply 41 times 12.
28. Multiply 32 times 23.

Mixed Applications

29. A small tugboat is 23 m long. A passenger liner is 12 times longer. What is the length of the passenger liner?

30. A small boat is 28 m long. A large boat is 54 m long. How much longer is the large boat?

SKILLKEEPER

Add or subtract.

1. $\begin{array}{r} 8 \\ +\ 6 \\ \hline \end{array}$
2. $\begin{array}{r} 5 \\ +\ 7 \\ \hline \end{array}$
3. $\begin{array}{r} 13 \\ -\ 8 \\ \hline \end{array}$
4. $\begin{array}{r} 17 \\ -\ 9 \\ \hline \end{array}$
5. $\begin{array}{r} 0 \\ +\ 6 \\ \hline \end{array}$

6. $\begin{array}{r} 11 \\ -\ 2 \\ \hline \end{array}$
7. $\begin{array}{r} 6 \\ -\ 1 \\ \hline \end{array}$
8. $\begin{array}{r} 3 \\ 6 \\ +\ 2 \\ \hline \end{array}$
9. $\begin{array}{r} 5 \\ 5 \\ +\ 6 \\ \hline \end{array}$
10. $\begin{array}{r} 7 \\ 0 \\ +\ 1 \\ \hline \end{array}$

More Multiplying with 2-Digit Factors

A basketball court is 26 m long and 14 m wide. What is the area of a basketball court in square meters?

Since we want the area of a rectangle, we multiply the length by the width.

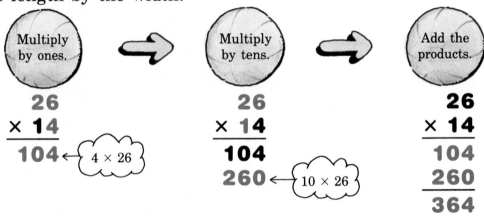

The area of the basketball court is 364 square meters.

Other Examples

34	42	54	25
× 24	× 32	× 65	× 48
136 ← 4 × 34	84 ← 2 × 42	270 ← 5 × 54	200 ← 8 × 25
680 ← 20 × 34	1260 ← 30 × 42	3240 ← 60 × 54	1000 ← 40 × 25
816	1,344	3,510	1,200

Warm Up   Multiply.

1. 53
   × 15

2. 52
   × 26

3. 33
   × 34

4. 53
   × 41

5. 42
   × 62

6. 25
   × 84

Practice Find the products.

1. $\begin{array}{r} 16 \\ \times\ 53 \\ \hline \end{array}$
2. $\begin{array}{r} 64 \\ \times\ 36 \\ \hline \end{array}$
3. $\begin{array}{r} 34 \\ \times\ 14 \\ \hline \end{array}$
4. $\begin{array}{r} 10 \\ \times\ 39 \\ \hline \end{array}$
5. $\begin{array}{r} 25 \\ \times\ 52 \\ \hline \end{array}$
6. $\begin{array}{r} 37 \\ \times\ 43 \\ \hline \end{array}$

7. $\begin{array}{r} 76 \\ \times\ 19 \\ \hline \end{array}$
8. $\begin{array}{r} 52 \\ \times\ 70 \\ \hline \end{array}$
9. $\begin{array}{r} 94 \\ \times\ 45 \\ \hline \end{array}$
10. $\begin{array}{r} 86 \\ \times\ 86 \\ \hline \end{array}$
11. $\begin{array}{r} 30 \\ \times\ 40 \\ \hline \end{array}$
12. $\begin{array}{r} 46 \\ \times\ 51 \\ \hline \end{array}$

13. $\begin{array}{r} 60 \\ \times\ 68 \\ \hline \end{array}$
14. $\begin{array}{r} 44 \\ \times\ 77 \\ \hline \end{array}$
15. $\begin{array}{r} 92 \\ \times\ 93 \\ \hline \end{array}$
16. $\begin{array}{r} 87 \\ \times\ 50 \\ \hline \end{array}$
17. $\begin{array}{r} 73 \\ \times\ 27 \\ \hline \end{array}$
18. $\begin{array}{r} 63 \\ \times\ 15 \\ \hline \end{array}$

19. 23×66
20. 64×35
21. 95×28

22. 72×23
23. 88×77
24. 46×46

25. Find the product of 18 and 42.
26. Find the product of 37 and 55.

27. Find the product of 42 and 75.
28. Find the product of 63 and 53.

Mixed Applications

29. The ice rink is a rectangle 64 m long and 33 m wide. What is the area of the ice rink?

30. How much greater is the length of the basketball court (on page 302) than the width?

31. Write a story problem that can be solved using the following: $25 \times 12 = 300$

> **THINK**
>
> **Using a Calculator**
>
> What number times itself gives 1,024?
>
> $$\text{▮▮} \times \text{▮▮} = 1{,}024$$
>
> same number
>
> Use guess and check to find the number.
>
> **MATH**

More Practice, page 427, Set B

303

Estimating Products Using Rounding

A hummingbird's heart beats 29 times faster than a camel's. About how many times does a hummingbird's heart beat in 1 minute?

Since you want an answer that is only **close** to the exact answer, you **estimate** by rounding and multiplying in your head.

HEARTBEATS IN 1 MINUTE

CAMEL	31	HORSE	44
CHEETAH	75	PIG	72
GIRAFFE	66		

Think of the problem. → 29 × 31

Round and multiply. → **30 × 30 = 900**

A hummingbird's heart beats **about** 900 times in 1 minute.

Other Examples

13 × 37

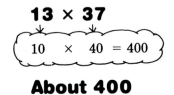

10 × 40 = 400

About 400

33 × $6.75

30 × $7 = $210

About $210

Practice Estimate the products. Round 2-digit numbers to the nearest ten and money to the nearest dollar.

1. 12 × 29
2. 38 × 21
3. 61 × 49
4. 52 × 19
5. 18 × 19
6. 11 × 47
7. 32 × 61
8. 48 × 78
9. 12 × $1.15
10. 24 × $1.65
11. 68 × $4.10
12. 19 × $4.95
13. 11 × 72
14. 19 × 39
15. 28 × 21
16. 48 × 12

17. **DATA BANK** See page 402. A canary's heart beats about 22 times faster than an elephant's. About how many times does a canary's heart beat in 1 minute?

PROBLEM SOLVING
Using Estimation

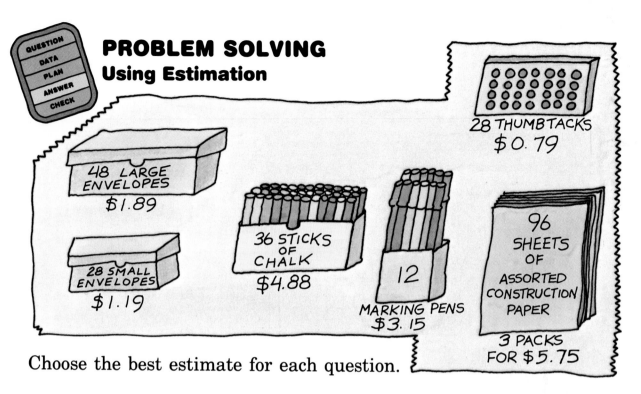

Choose the best estimate for each question.

1. About how many large envelopes are in 3 boxes?

   A 90   **B** 150   **C** 60

2. About how many dollars would it cost to buy 18 boxes of small envelopes?

   A $20   **B** $40   **C** $30

3. About how many more dollars does a box of chalk cost than a pack of marking pens?

   A $1   **B** $8   **C** $2

4. About how many dollars does 1 pack of paper cost?

   A $6   **B** $2   **C** $18

5. About how many sheets of paper are in 50 packs?

   A 50   **B** 500   **C** 5,000

6. About how many dollars does it cost to buy 1 pack of thumbtacks and 1 pack of marking pens?

   A $4   **B** $5   **C** $40

7. About how many dollars does it cost to buy 5 boxes of chalk and 3 packs of paper?

   A $25   **B** $31   **C** $43

8. *Strategy Practice* Each time 5 boxes of clips are sold, 3 cards of tacks are sold. How many cards of tacks are sold when 40 boxes of clips are sold? Complete the table.

Clips	5	10	15	20	25
Tacks	3	6	9	12	15

Multiplying with 2- and 3-Digit Factors

Work with a group.
You will need index cards.

Part 1

1. Make these cards.

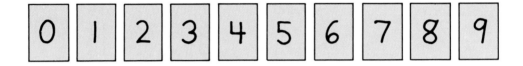

2. Turn the cards face down and mix them up.

3. Pick any four cards. Arrange them to make a multiplication problem with two 2-digit factors.

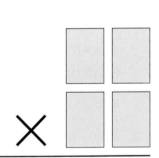

- Take turns making different problems, using the same four cards.
- Record each problem and its answer.
- How might you arrange the cards to get the largest possible product? The smallest possible product?
- Explain how you did it.

4. Pick four new cards and repeat the activity. Try to get the largest product. The smallest product. How can estimation help you?

Part 2

5. Play "Target Multiplication" with your group.
- Shuffle the number cards and pick four of them.

- Choose a number from the target.
- Work together to make a multiplication problem whose product will be as close as possible to your target number. Record your problem and its product.

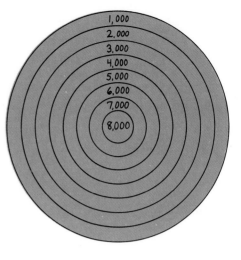

6. Talk about these questions:
   - How far from your target number is the product?
   - How can you use estimation to get closer to your target number?

7. Play the game again. Choose one of these ways:
   A Pick four new cards but use the same target number.
   B Pick a new target number but use the same four cards.
   C Pick a new target number and four new cards.

8. Play the game several times. Record your problems and products.

9. Play the game again. This time pick five cards and multiply a 3-digit factor by a 2-digit factor.

10. Talk about your results. What strategies did you discover for coming close to your target numbers?

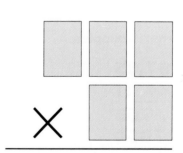

Multiplying Money

FOURTH GRADE CAR WASH
FRIDAY AND SATURDAY
$3.75
each car

A fourth grade class held a car wash to make money for a class field trip. They washed 21 cars on Friday. How much money did they collect on Friday?

Since we want the total for equal amounts, we multiply.

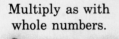

Multiply as with whole numbers. ➤ Show the product using dollars and cents.

$$\begin{array}{r} \$3.75 \\ \times\ \ 21 \\ \hline 375 \\ 7500 \\ \hline 7875 \end{array}$$

$$\begin{array}{r} \$3.75 \\ \times\ \ 21 \\ \hline 375 \\ 7500 \\ \hline \$78.75 \end{array}$$

Use estimation to check
$20 \times \$4 = \$80$
$78.75 is close to $80. It checks.

The class collected $78.75 on Friday.

Other Examples

$$\begin{array}{r} \$7.65 \\ \times\ \ 11 \\ \hline 765 \\ 7650 \\ \hline \$84.15 \end{array}$$
$10 \times \$8$ is about $80

$$\begin{array}{r} \$4.25 \\ \times\ \ 28 \\ \hline 3400 \\ 8500 \\ \hline \$119.00 \end{array}$$
$30 \times \$4$ is about $120

$$\begin{array}{r} \$0.95 \\ \times\ \ 41 \\ \hline 95 \\ 3800 \\ \hline \$38.95 \end{array}$$
$40 \times \$1$ is about $40

Warm Up Find the amounts. Write the answers with dollars and cents. Use estimation to check.

1. $\begin{array}{r} \$4.85 \\ \times\ \ 21 \end{array}$
2. $\begin{array}{r} \$2.05 \\ \times\ \ 29 \end{array}$
3. $\begin{array}{r} \$0.86 \\ \times\ \ 12 \end{array}$
4. $\begin{array}{r} \$7.80 \\ \times\ \ 52 \end{array}$
5. $\begin{array}{r} \$6.32 \\ \times\ \ 14 \end{array}$

Practice Find the amounts.
Write the answers with dollars and cents.

1. $3.24
    × 18

2. $9.38
    × 38

3. $3.75
    × 22

4. $0.75
    × 44

5. $1.24
    × 32

6. $2.78
    × 12

7. $6.05
    × 49

8. $1.99
    × 20

9. $7.10
    × 29

10. $6.09
    × 11

11. $0.85
    × 23

12. $4.95
    × 51

13. $0.98
    × 79

14. $8.07
    × 58

15. $7.81
    × 33

16. 11 × $3.80

17. 17 × $2.35

18. 20 × $0.85

19. 56 × $9.22

20. 72 × $3.36

21. 19 × $0.37

22. 13 × $7.07

23. 41 × $0.83

24. 36 × $8.54

Mixed Applications

25. The class washed 52 cars on Saturday. How much money did they collect on Saturday?

26. An additional $5.75 was charged to wax a car after it was washed. What was the total charge to wash and wax a car?

27. On two days last year, the fourth grade class washed a total of 45 cars at $3.50 each. How much money did they collect for that car wash?

28. Write a story to match this multiplication problem.
    $39 × \$2.25 = \$87.75$

SKILLKEEPER

Multiply.

1. 22
    × 4

2. 19
    × 5

3. 20
    × 4

4. 33
    × 3

5. 62
    × 3

6. 75
    × 7

7. 17
    × 5

8. 706
    × 3

9. 465
    × 2

10. 234
    × 6

PROBLEM SOLVING
Using Data from a Floor Plan

Mr. Jackson is a building contractor. He builds schools. This is the floor plan for a new building at Hagginwood School.

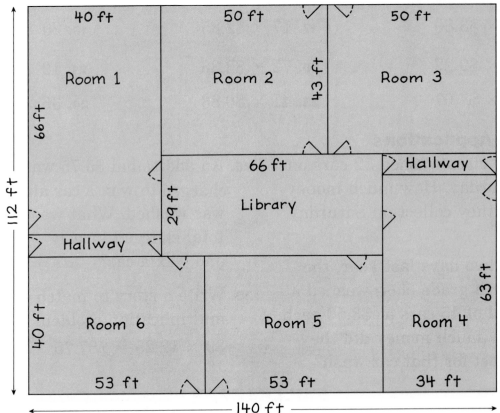

Floor plan for new building at Hagginwood School

△ door

Mr. Jackson used data from the floor plan to find the area of Room 4. Room 4 is 63 ft long and 34 ft wide. Since he wanted the area of a rectangle, Mr. Jackson used the formula of length times width. The area of Room 4 is 2,142 square feet.

310

Use data from the floor plan to answer these questions.

1. How many classrooms will the new building have?

2. What is the total number of rooms in the floor plan?

3. How long is the wall between Room 2 and Room 3?

4. How long is the wall between Room 6 and Room 5?

5. What is the area of Room 1 in square feet?

6. What is the area of the library in square feet?

7. There is 2,160 square feet of carpet for Room 3. Is there enough carpet to cover the floor?

8. There is 2,106 square feet of red carpet. Is there enough carpet to cover the floor in Room 6?

9. How many square feet of carpet will it take to cover the floor in Room 5?

10. What is the difference between the library's length and width?

11. What is the perimeter of the building?

12. **Strategy Practice** Mr. Jackson placed 32 chairs in the library and divided the rest equally among the 6 classrooms. Each classroom got 25 chairs. How many chairs did Mr. Jackson start with?

APPLIED PROBLEM SOLVING

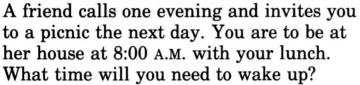

A friend calls one evening and invites you to a picnic the next day. You are to be at her house at 8:00 A.M. with your lunch. What time will you need to wake up?

Some Things to Consider

- Your mother and father will not be able to help you get ready.
- You need to pack your lunch.
- You need to fix your breakfast.
- You need to get yourself ready—wash, brush your teeth, dress, and so on.

- You need 15 minutes to walk to your friend's house.
- You want to allow plenty of time so you are not late.

Some Questions to Answer

1. How long will it take to fix your lunch?
2. How long does it take you to fix and eat your breakfast?
3. How much time do you take to get yourself ready?
4. How much extra time do you plan to allow?
5. How long does it take you to make your bed?

What Is Your Decision?

What time do you want to wake up?

Multiply.

1. 20×40 **2.** 60×10 **3.** 90×80 **4.** 50×70

5. $\begin{array}{r} 27 \\ \times\ 30 \\ \hline \end{array}$ **6.** $\begin{array}{r} 57 \\ \times\ 40 \\ \hline \end{array}$ **7.** $\begin{array}{r} 39 \\ \times\ 70 \\ \hline \end{array}$ **8.** $\begin{array}{r} 82 \\ \times\ 10 \\ \hline \end{array}$ **9.** $\begin{array}{r} 74 \\ \times\ 50 \\ \hline \end{array}$

10. $\begin{array}{r} 21 \\ \times\ 32 \\ \hline \end{array}$ **11.** $\begin{array}{r} 47 \\ \times\ 11 \\ \hline \end{array}$ **12.** $\begin{array}{r} 30 \\ \times\ 23 \\ \hline \end{array}$ **13.** $\begin{array}{r} 78 \\ \times\ 34 \\ \hline \end{array}$ **14.** $\begin{array}{r} 63 \\ \times\ 28 \\ \hline \end{array}$

Estimate the products. Round to the nearest ten, hundred, or dollar.

15. 78×51 **16.** 22×780 **17.** $13 \times \$4.75$

Multiply.

18. $\begin{array}{r} 387 \\ \times\ 26 \\ \hline \end{array}$ **19.** $\begin{array}{r} 152 \\ \times\ 65 \\ \hline \end{array}$ **20.** $\begin{array}{r} \$9.63 \\ \times\ 39 \\ \hline \end{array}$ **21.** $\begin{array}{r} \$2.38 \\ \times\ 44 \\ \hline \end{array}$ **22.** $\begin{array}{r} \$6.38 \\ \times\ 25 \\ \hline \end{array}$

Solve.

23. How much do 24 boxes of pencils cost?

24. What is the total area of this house in square feet?

$1.19

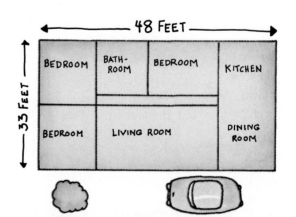

ANOTHER LOOK

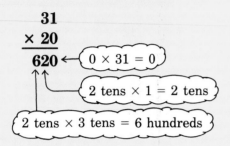

Multiplying by Tens

$$\begin{array}{r} 31 \\ \times\ 20 \\ \hline 620 \end{array}$$

- $0 \times 31 = 0$
- 2 tens $\times$ 1 = 2 tens
- 2 tens $\times$ 3 tens = 6 hundreds

1. $\begin{array}{r} 52 \\ \times\ 10 \\ \hline \end{array}$	**2.** $\begin{array}{r} 28 \\ \times\ 30 \\ \hline \end{array}$	**3.** $\begin{array}{r} 16 \\ \times\ 20 \\ \hline \end{array}$
4. $\begin{array}{r} 65 \\ \times\ 50 \\ \hline \end{array}$	**5.** $\begin{array}{r} 81 \\ \times\ 40 \\ \hline \end{array}$	**6.** $\begin{array}{r} 33 \\ \times\ 90 \\ \hline \end{array}$
7. $\begin{array}{r} 34 \\ \times\ 70 \\ \hline \end{array}$	**8.** $\begin{array}{r} 27 \\ \times\ 60 \\ \hline \end{array}$	**9.** $\begin{array}{r} 14 \\ \times\ 80 \\ \hline \end{array}$

Multiply by Ones and Then Tens

$$\begin{array}{r} 31 \\ \times\ 23 \\ \hline 93 \\ 620 \\ \hline 713 \end{array}$$

- 3×31
- 20×31
- Add

10. $\begin{array}{r} 14 \\ \times\ 21 \\ \hline \end{array}$	**11.** $\begin{array}{r} 56 \\ \times\ 11 \\ \hline \end{array}$	**12.** $\begin{array}{r} 32 \\ \times\ 13 \\ \hline \end{array}$
13. $\begin{array}{r} 24 \\ \times\ 22 \\ \hline \end{array}$	**14.** $\begin{array}{r} 13 \\ \times\ 31 \\ \hline \end{array}$	**15.** $\begin{array}{r} 20 \\ \times\ 32 \\ \hline \end{array}$
16. $\begin{array}{r} 22 \\ \times\ 23 \\ \hline \end{array}$	**17.** $\begin{array}{r} 21 \\ \times\ 43 \\ \hline \end{array}$	**18.** $\begin{array}{r} 12 \\ \times\ 33 \\ \hline \end{array}$

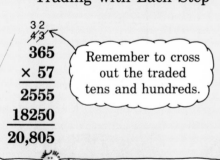

Trading with Each Step

$$\begin{array}{r} 3\ 2 \\ 4\ 3 \\ 365 \\ \times\ 57 \\ \hline 2555 \\ 18250 \\ \hline 20{,}805 \end{array}$$

Remember to cross out the traded tens and hundreds.

19. $\begin{array}{r} 424 \\ \times\ 46 \\ \hline \end{array}$	**20.** $\begin{array}{r} 657 \\ \times\ 35 \\ \hline \end{array}$
21. $\begin{array}{r} 338 \\ \times\ 26 \\ \hline \end{array}$	**22.** $\begin{array}{r} 245 \\ \times\ 19 \\ \hline \end{array}$
23. $\begin{array}{r} 617 \\ \times\ 43 \\ \hline \end{array}$	**24.** $\begin{array}{r} 363 \\ \times\ 58 \\ \hline \end{array}$

ENRICHMENT

Estimating by Clustering

Len took a 4-day bike trip. He rode these distances.

Monday:	27 miles
Tuesday:	34 miles
Wednesday:	32 miles
Thursday:	29 miles

About how far did he ride?
Since all of the distances are close to 30, we can multiply to estimate the sum.

4×30

27 + 34 + 32 + 29

$\boxed{120}$

estimate

Len rode about 120 miles.

Estimate each sum. Use multiplication when you can.

> All of the numbers are close to 50.
> THINK: 4×50

1. $52 + 49 + 47 + 51$

> All of the numbers are close to 20.
> THINK: 5×20

2. $19 + 24 + 22 + 18 + 21$

> All of the numbers are close to 60.
> THINK: 3×60

> All of the numbers are close to 30.
> THINK: 5×30

3. $64 + 58 + 59$

4. $25 + 34 + 28 + 26 + 33$

5. $59 + 64 + 63 + 58$

6. $41 + 36 + 37 + 42 + 39$

7. $82 + 76 + 81$

8. $17 + 24 + 18 + 23 + 19$

9. $27 + 32 + 28 + 34$

10. $92 + 86 + 94$

11. $68 + 74 + 72 + 71$

12. $46 + 52 + 53 + 51 + 49$

Give the letter for the correct answer.

1. $7)\overline{88}$

  A 12 R7 **B** 12 R4
  C 12 R8 **D** not given

2. $3)\overline{58}$

  A 19 R2 **B** 12 R2
  C 19 R1 **D** not given

3. $5)\overline{66}$

  A 11 R1 **B** 13 R1
  C 11 R3 **D** not given

4. $3)\overline{\$0.75}$

  A $0.25 **B** $2.50
  C $0.52 **D** not given

5. $4)\overline{509}$

  A 126 R5 **B** 102 R1
  C 127 R1 **D** not given

6. $3)\overline{280}$

  A 93 R1 **B** 73 R1
  C 9 R3 **D** not given

7. $2)\overline{\$7.50}$

  A $3.75 **B** $3.25
  C $3.15 **D** not given

Name each figure.

8.

  A cylinder
  B sphere
  C circle
  D not given

9.

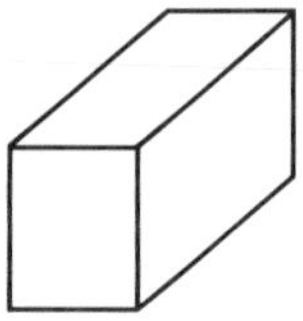

  A square
  B cube
  C rectangular prism
  D not given

10.

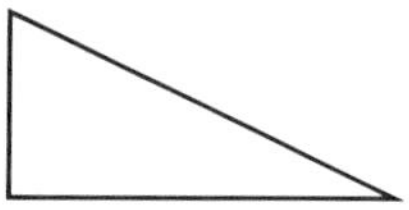

  A rectangle
  B triangle
  C quadrilateral
  D not given

11.

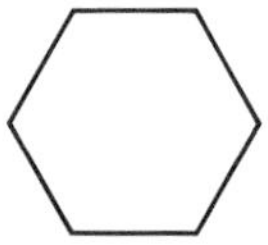

  A hexagon
  B octagon
  C pentagon
  D not given

12. 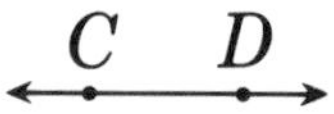 $C \quad D$

  A CD
  B $\overline{CD}$
  C $\overleftrightarrow{CD}$
  D not given

13. Holly can put 4 pictures on each page of her photo album. How many pages will she need for 53 pictures?

  A 13 **B** 12
  C 14 **D** not given

14. Jake bought 2 pairs of socks for $5.20. How much did each pair of socks cost?

  A $10.40 **B** $2.60
  C $2.10 **D** not given

Natalie stood next to her Uncle Charles. They were with a group of news reporters. The speech by Governor Smith was just over. They headed back to the news room. Charles entered his story into the computer. Natalie watched the screen. Charles told Natalie about newspaper deadlines. They are very important. He had 125 minutes to finish this story. This was 5 times as long as for yesterday's story. Charles finished his story. He let Natalie push the "send" button. This sent the story to the city editor. Last minute changes were made there. Then the story was ready to be printed.

Using Division Facts: Mental Math

Carmen has 150 pennies. Each penny wrapper holds 50 pennies. How many wrappers can she fill?

Since we separate the coins equally into wrappers, we divide.

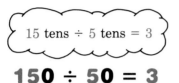

$$15 \text{ tens} \div 5 \text{ tens} = 3$$

$$150 \div 50 = 3$$

OR

$$5 \text{ tens} \overline{)15 \text{ tens}} = 3$$

$$50 \overline{)150} = 3$$

Carmen can fill 3 penny wrappers.

Other Examples

$$2 \text{ tens} \overline{)8 \text{ tens}} = 4 \qquad 6 \text{ tens} \overline{)48 \text{ tens}} = 8 \qquad 8 \text{ tens} \overline{)40 \text{ tens}} = 5$$

$$
\begin{array}{r} 4 \\ 20\overline{)80} \\ \underline{80} \\ 0 \end{array}
\qquad
\begin{array}{r} 8 \\ 60\overline{)480} \\ \underline{480} \\ 0 \end{array}
\qquad
\begin{array}{r} 5 \\ 80\overline{)400} \\ \underline{400} \\ 0 \end{array}
$$

Warm Up Divide. Give the quotients aloud.

1. $60 \div 20$ 2. $80 \div 40$ 3. $60 \div 30$ 4. $70 \div 70$ 5. $60 \div 10$

6. $50 \div 50$ 7. $80 \div 20$ 8. $90 \div 30$ 9. $40 \div 20$ 10. $90 \div 90$

11. $140 \div 20$ 12. $210 \div 70$ 13. $200 \div 50$ 14. $80 \div 10$ 15. $120 \div 60$

16. $180 \div 30$ 17. $320 \div 40$ 18. $300 \div 60$ 19. $240 \div 80$ 20. $270 \div 30$

21. $60 \div 10$ 22. $360 \div 40$ 23. $150 \div 30$ 24. $350 \div 50$ 25. $360 \div 90$

Practice Divide.

1. $10\overline{)70}$ 2. $90\overline{)90}$ 3. $30\overline{)90}$ 4. $20\overline{)40}$ 5. $40\overline{)80}$

6. $30\overline{)60}$ 7. $10\overline{)40}$ 8. $60\overline{)60}$ 9. $20\overline{)60}$ 10. $10\overline{)10}$

11. $30\overline{)120}$ 12. $20\overline{)120}$ 13. $20\overline{)160}$ 14. $40\overline{)240}$ 15. $60\overline{)360}$

16. $80\overline{)160}$ 17. $20\overline{)100}$ 18. $50\overline{)400}$ 19. $70\overline{)210}$ 20. $90\overline{)540}$

21. $20\overline{)180}$ 22. $30\overline{)240}$ 23. $80\overline{)640}$ 24. $20\overline{)80}$ 25. $50\overline{)100}$

26. $40\overline{)280}$ 27. $10\overline{)30}$ 28. $50\overline{)450}$ 29. $60\overline{)240}$ 30. $80\overline{)80}$

31. $70\overline{)490}$ 32. $40\overline{)280}$ 33. $30\overline{)90}$ 34. $70\overline{)140}$ 35. $90\overline{)360}$

36. $270 \div 90$ 37. $60 \div 30$ 38. $540 \div 60$

39. $210 \div 30$ 40. $150 \div 50$ 41. $420 \div 70$

42. How many 30s are in 270?

43. How many 80s are in 240?

Mixed Applications

44. Joshua has 160 nickels. Each nickel wrapper holds 40 nickels. How many nickel wrappers can he fill?

45. Tanya placed 50 pennies in each wrapper. How many pennies can she put in 9 wrappers?

46. **DATA HUNT** Find the number of dimes that a dime wrapper holds. How many wrappers could you fill if you had 150 dimes?

THINK

Using a Calculator

Guess the number of zeros in each quotient. Then divide with the calculator to check your guess.

A $270 \div 30$ **E** $8,000 \div 20$
B $600 \div 20$ **F** $900 \div 300$
C $2,400 \div 40$ **G** $18,000 \div 900$
D $3,000 \div 50$ **H** $40,000 \div 80$

MATH

Dividing by Multiples of Ten

Eric Heiden won 5 gold medals in speed skating at the 1980 Winter Olympics. Give Eric's time for the 5,000-meter race in minutes and seconds. (There are 60 seconds in 1 minute.)

Since there are the same number of seconds in each minute, we divide.

Eric Heiden's Race Time in Seconds*

500-meter race	38 seconds
1,000-meter race	75 seconds
1,500-meter race	116 seconds
5,000-meter race	422 seconds
10,000-meter race	868 seconds

*Race times to the nearest second

Decide Where to Start.	→	Dividing Ones · Divide · Multiply · Subtract · Compare

$60\overline{)422}$

$60\overline{)4}$ not enough hundreds

$60\overline{)42}$ or tens

$60\overline{)422}$ ← 422 ones

$$\begin{array}{r} 7 \text{ R2} \\ 60\overline{)422} \\ -420 \\ \hline 2 \end{array}$$

CHECK
$$\begin{array}{r} 60 \\ \times\ 7 \\ \hline 420 \\ +\ \ 2 \leftarrow \text{remainder} \\ \hline 422 \end{array}$$

Eric Heiden skated the 5,000-meter race in 7 minutes and 2 seconds.

Other Examples

$$\begin{array}{r} 6 \text{ R18} \\ 40\overline{)258} \\ -240 \\ \hline 18 \end{array} \qquad \begin{array}{r} 2 \text{ R12} \\ 30\overline{)72} \\ -60 \\ \hline 12 \end{array} \qquad \begin{array}{r} 8 \text{ R40} \\ 70\overline{)600} \\ -560 \\ \hline 40 \end{array}$$

Warm Up Divide. Check your answers.

1. $10\overline{)65}$ 2. $20\overline{)89}$ 3. $40\overline{)96}$ 4. $70\overline{)290}$ 5. $50\overline{)275}$

6. $20\overline{)105}$ 7. $60\overline{)200}$ 8. $80\overline{)356}$ 9. $30\overline{)105}$ 10. $90\overline{)618}$

Practice Divide and check.

1. $40\overline{)83}$ 2. $20\overline{)54}$ 3. $10\overline{)93}$

4. $30\overline{)159}$ 5. $50\overline{)313}$ 6. $60\overline{)195}$

7. $80\overline{)500}$ 8. $20\overline{)67}$ 9. $30\overline{)285}$

10. $50\overline{)491}$ 11. $70\overline{)400}$ 12. $90\overline{)193}$

13. $151 \div 20$ 14. $92 \div 60$ 15. $638 \div 70$

16. $222 \div 30$ 17. $500 \div 90$ 18. $311 \div 40$

19. Divide 73 by 40.   20. Divide 258 by 60.

21. Divide 612 by 90.   22. Divide 305 by 40.

Mixed Applications

23. Give Eric's time for the 1,500-meter race in minutes and seconds.

24. Write and answer a question for this story.
    Michael Woods skated the 5,000-meter race in 431 seconds.

25. **DATA BANK** See page 402. How many seconds greater was the winner's time in the 3,000 m race than in the 1,500 m race?

THINK

Guess and Check

Look at the cups below. You want each cup to have the same amount of water. Finish the directions so that this will happen.

cup 1   cup 2   cup 3

Pour ____ mL from cup 1 to cup 2 and ____ mL from cup 3 to cup 2.

MATH

1-Digit Quotients

Brad's soccer team has $66 to buy soccer balls. How many balls can they buy? How much money will they have left?

Since each of the balls costs the same amount, we divide.

Decide Where to Start.	→	Round the Divisor and Estimate.	→	Dividing Ones
				· Divide
				· Multiply
				· Subtract
				· Compare

about 30

$$28\overline{)66}$$

$$28\overline{)66}$$

about 30

2 R10
$$28\overline{)66}$$
$$-\ 56$$
$$\overline{\quad 10}$$

$28\overline{)6}$ not enough tens

$28\overline{)66}$ ← 66 ones

2
$3\overline{)6}$

Try 2.

Check
28
× 2
56
+ 10 ← remainder
66

Brad's team can buy 2 soccer balls. They will have $10 left.

Other Examples

(40)   **1 R35**
$$43\overline{)78}$$
$$-\ 43$$
$$\overline{\quad 35}$$

(20)   **2 R11**
$$15\overline{)41}$$
$$-\ 30$$
$$\overline{\quad 11}$$

0 R59
$$67\overline{)59}$$
$$-\ \ 0$$
$$\overline{\quad 59}$$

2
$$33\overline{)66}$$
$$-\ 66$$
$$\overline{\quad\ 0}$$

Warm Up   Divide and check.

1. $12\overline{)49}$ 2. $23\overline{)75}$ 3. $76\overline{)92}$ 4. $48\overline{)35}$ 5. $34\overline{)68}$

6. $41\overline{)85}$ 7. $58\overline{)73}$ 8. $44\overline{)38}$ 9. $23\overline{)69}$ 10. $19\overline{)67}$

Practice Divide and check.

1. $32\overline{)53}$ 2. $18\overline{)42}$ 3. $29\overline{)92}$ 4. $43\overline{)92}$ 5. $54\overline{)83}$

6. $68\overline{)65}$ 7. $24\overline{)59}$ 8. $37\overline{)58}$ 9. $13\overline{)26}$ 10. $21\overline{)35}$

11. $29\overline{)75}$ 12. $35\overline{)80}$ 13. $19\overline{)83}$ 14. $53\overline{)55}$ 15. $68\overline{)75}$

16. $87\overline{)78}$ 17. $42\overline{)45}$ 18. $53\overline{)92}$ 19. $14\overline{)30}$ 20. $27\overline{)62}$

21. $82 \div 17$ 22. $72 \div 39$ 23. $32 \div 31$

24. $75 \div 55$ 25. $62 \div 53$ 26. $44 \div 28$

27. What is 89 divided by 11?   28. What is 92 divided by 23?

29. What is 83 divided by 34?   30. What is 65 divided by 38?

Mixed Applications

31. Soccer bags are $17. The team has $80. How many bags can they buy? How much money will be left?

32. Soccer shoes cost $17 a pair. What would it cost to buy 15 pairs of soccer shoes?

SKILLKEEPER

Multiply.

1. $\begin{array}{r} 22 \\ \times 13 \end{array}$ 2. $\begin{array}{r} 11 \\ \times 43 \end{array}$ 3. $\begin{array}{r} 24 \\ \times 12 \end{array}$ 4. $\begin{array}{r} 12 \\ \times 30 \end{array}$ 5. $\begin{array}{r} 70 \\ \times 11 \end{array}$

6. $\begin{array}{r} 31 \\ \times 13 \end{array}$ 7. $\begin{array}{r} 42 \\ \times 32 \end{array}$ 8. $\begin{array}{r} 17 \\ \times 42 \end{array}$ 9. $\begin{array}{r} 286 \\ \times 23 \end{array}$ 10. $\begin{array}{r} 305 \\ \times 82 \end{array}$

More Practice, page 429, Set A

Changing Estimates

Sometimes you have to change your estimated quotient.

Erin made 50 dinner rolls. She puts 16 rolls into each bag. How many bags can she fill?

$$
\begin{array}{r}
\overset{\fbox{20}}{}\ \ \mathbf{2} \\
16\overline{)50} \\
-\,32 \\
\hline
\mathbf{18} \leftarrow \text{greater} \\
\text{than } 16
\end{array}
\qquad
\begin{array}{r}
\mathbf{3\ R2} \\
16\overline{)50} \\
-\,48 \\
\hline
\mathbf{2}
\end{array}
$$

Erin had to change her estimate from 2 to 3.

Erin can fill 3 bags. There will be 2 remaining rolls.

How many dozen rolls did Erin make?

$$
\begin{array}{r}
\overset{\fbox{10}}{}\ \ \mathbf{5} \\
12\overline{)50} \\
-\,60 \leftarrow \text{too} \\
\text{large}
\end{array}
\qquad
\begin{array}{r}
\mathbf{4\ R2} \\
12\overline{)50} \\
-\,48 \\
\hline
\mathbf{2}
\end{array}
$$

Erin made 4 dozen and 2 rolls.

Erin had to change her estimate from 5 to 4.

Warm Up

Decide which estimates must be changed and then change them. Finish the division.

1. $\overset{\fbox{20}}{}\ ^{4}\ 17\overline{)88}$
2. $\overset{\fbox{30}}{}\ ^{2}\ 28\overline{)86}$
3. $\overset{\fbox{40}}{}\ ^{1}\ 39\overline{)54}$
4. $\overset{\fbox{20}}{}\ ^{4}\ 16\overline{)97}$

5. $\overset{\fbox{30}}{}\ ^{2}\ 34\overline{)65}$
6. $\overset{\fbox{40}}{}\ ^{2}\ 42\overline{)85}$
7. $\overset{\fbox{10}}{}\ ^{4}\ 13\overline{)42}$
8. $\overset{\fbox{10}}{}\ ^{5}\ 14\overline{)52}$

Divide. Change your estimate if necessary.

9. $27\overline{)55}$
10. $35\overline{)82}$
11. $13\overline{)40}$
12. $15\overline{)79}$

Practice Divide. Change your estimates if necessary.

1. $13\overline{)35}$ 2. $12\overline{)49}$ 3. $19\overline{)42}$ 4. $18\overline{)72}$ 5. $23\overline{)45}$

6. $31\overline{)91}$ 7. $27\overline{)58}$ 8. $14\overline{)83}$ 9. $35\overline{)80}$ 10. $42\overline{)81}$

11. $21\overline{)95}$ 12. $24\overline{)95}$ 13. $16\overline{)98}$ 14. $15\overline{)60}$ 15. $28\overline{)65}$

16. $36\overline{)75}$ 17. $32\overline{)70}$ 18. $17\overline{)71}$ 19. $25\overline{)75}$ 20. $34\overline{)62}$

21. $56 \div 18$ 22. $80 \div 26$ 23. $66 \div 15$

24. $78 \div 39$ 25. $59 \div 42$ 26. $93 \div 45$

27. How many 12s are in 46?   28. How many 16s are in 94?

29. How many 29s are in 75?   30. How many 23s are in 60?

Mixed Applications

31. Evan made 60 bran muffins. How many dozen muffins did he make?

32. Evan had 7 bags of muffins and 8 extra muffins. Each bag held 15 muffins. How many muffins did he have?

33. A bakery makes 1,750 rolls each day. How many days will it take them to make 7,000 rolls?

THINK

Logical Reasoning

Pretend you cut in half a string 76 cm long. Then you cut each piece in half. What would be the length of each piece of string?

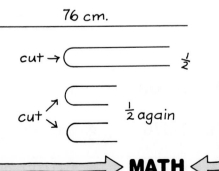

MATH

325

More 1-Digit Quotients

Mr. Burton used 279 units of electricity in his house in October (31 days). At this rate, how many units of electricity would he use each day in October?

Since we want the number of units each day, we divide.

Decide Where to Start.	$\longrightarrow$	Dividing Ones · Divide · Multiply · Subtract · Compare

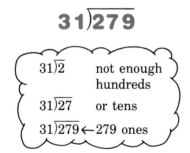

$$31\overline{)279}$$

31)2   not enough hundreds

31)27   or tens

31)279 ← 279 ones

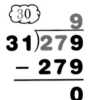

$$\begin{array}{r} (30) \quad\ \ 9 \\ 31\overline{)279} \\ -279 \\ \hline 0 \end{array}$$

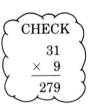

CHECK
$$\begin{array}{r} 31 \\ \times\ \ 9 \\ \hline 279 \end{array}$$

Mr. Burton would use 9 units of electricity each day.

Other Examples

$$\begin{array}{r} 6\ \textbf{R37} \\ 48\overline{)325} \\ -288 \\ \hline 37 \end{array} \qquad \begin{array}{r} 8\ \textbf{R1} \\ 23\overline{)185} \\ -184 \\ \hline 1 \end{array} \qquad \begin{array}{r} \$0.06 \\ 36\overline{)\$2.16} \\ -2\ 16 \\ \hline 0 \end{array}$$

Warm Up   Divide and check.

1. $51\overline{)376}$ 2. $78\overline{)342}$ 3. $43\overline{)285}$ 4. $61\overline{)370}$ 5. $26\overline{)\$2.08}$

6. $18\overline{)141}$ 7. $13\overline{)100}$ 8. $93\overline{)500}$ 9. $48\overline{)399}$ 10. $35\overline{)\$2.45}$

Practice Divide and check.

1. $28\overline{)250}$
2. $63\overline{)260}$
3. $51\overline{)185}$
4. $92\overline{)652}$
5. $35\overline{)\$2.45}$

6. $44\overline{)245}$
7. $37\overline{)58}$
8. $72\overline{)377}$
9. $19\overline{)153}$
10. $25\overline{)\$2.00}$

11. $78\overline{)311}$
12. $57\overline{)425}$
13. $41\overline{)372}$
14. $21\overline{)85}$
15. $67\overline{)\$6.03}$

16. $75\overline{)600}$
17. $22\overline{)195}$
18. $16\overline{)38}$
19. $89\overline{)346}$
20. $43\overline{)\$3.01}$

21. $395 \div 53$
22. $388 \div 72$
23. $478 \div 48$

24. $100 \div 26$
25. $300 \div 39$
26. $222 \div 34$

27. Divide 496 by 66.
28. Divide 309 by 72.

29. Divide 120 by 15.
30. Divide 834 by 88.

Mixed Applications

31. A toy store used 120 units of electricity in 1 day (24 hours). At this rate, how many units were used each hour?

32. A service station paid $45 a day for electricity one week and $37 a day the next week. How much greater was the electric bill for the first week?

33. Write and then solve a division story problem for the data below.

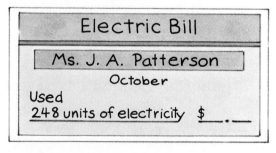

Electric Bill

Ms. J. A. Patterson
October

Used
248 units of electricity $ ___ . ___

THINK

Estimation

Estimate this product.
$$9 \times 8 \times 7 \times 6 \times 5 \times 4 \times 3 \times 2 \times 1$$
Do you think the product is
A less than 100,000?
B between 100,000 and 500,000?
C more than 500,000?
Find the product.
Was your estimate close?

MATH

PROBLEM SOLVING
Using Data from a Line Graph

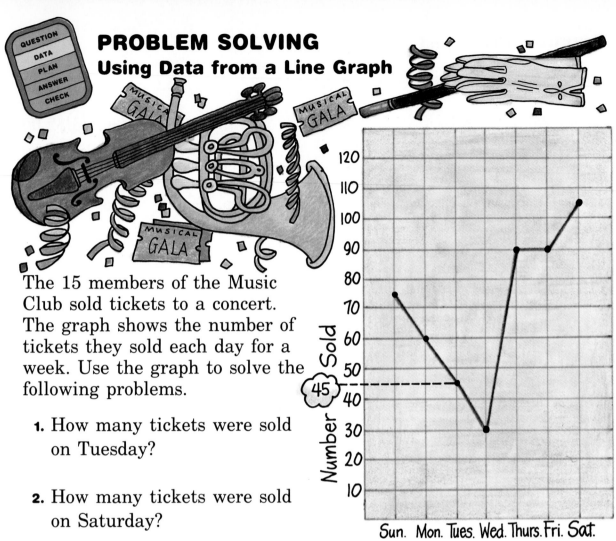

Ticket Sales

The 15 members of the Music Club sold tickets to a concert. The graph shows the number of tickets they sold each day for a week. Use the graph to solve the following problems.

1. How many tickets were sold on Tuesday?

2. How many tickets were sold on Saturday?

3. On which day were the fewest tickets sold?

4. How many more tickets were sold on Saturday than on Sunday?

5. How many tickets were sold on the first three days?

6. The tickets cost $3.75 each. How much money was collected on Wednesday?

7. If each member sold the same number of tickets on Saturday, how many tickets did each member sell?

8. **Strategy Practice** Lindy sold tickets for 8 days in a row. She sold the most tickets on the second day. The last day that she sold tickets was Wednesday. On which day of the week did Lindy sell the most tickets?

328

PROBLEM SOLVING
Multi-step Problems

Solve.

1. There are 72 instruments in the orchestra. 26 are violins and 9 are clarinets. How many other instruments are in the orchestra?

2. James practices the violin the same number of hours every day. He practiced 183 hours in March (31 days) and April (30 days). How many hours does he practice a day?

3. In the week before the concert the Music Club sold 495 tickets. On the day of the concert they sold another 108 tickets. Each ticket cost $3. How much money did the Music Club collect?

4. The shortest clarinet is 35 cm. The longest one is 29 cm more than 7 times the shortest. How long is the longest clarinet?

5. The orchestra practiced 225 minutes one week and 180 minutes the next. Each practice session was 45 minutes long. How many sessions did they have?

6. The orchestra had $400 to spend. They spent all but $96 on 38 music stands. What was the cost of each stand?

7. Ms. Adams bought 12 tickets. How much change did she get from $50 if the tickets cost $3.75 each?

8. There were 430 people at the Saturday night concert. 295 of them sat in chairs. The rest sat on benches. Each bench holds 15 people. How many benches were needed?

9. **Strategy Practice** There were 25 people in the front row. There were 3 more children than adults. How many children sat in the front row?

More Dividing by Tens

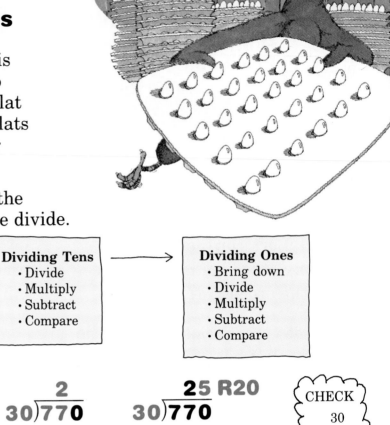

The Aristocrat Restaurant is planning to use 770 eggs to serve breakfast. Each egg flat holds 30 eggs. How many flats of eggs should the manager order?

Since we want to separate the eggs into equal amounts, we divide.

Decide Where to Start.	→	Dividing Tens • Divide • Multiply • Subtract • Compare	→	Dividing Ones • Bring down • Divide • Multiply • Subtract • Compare

$$30\overline{)770}$$

$30\overline{)7}$ not enough hundreds

$30\overline{)77}$ ← 77 tens

$$\begin{array}{r} 2 \\ 30\overline{)770} \\ -\ 60 \\ \hline 17 \end{array}$$

$$\begin{array}{r} 25\ \text{R20} \\ 30\overline{)770} \\ -\ 60\downarrow \\ \hline 170 \\ -\ 150 \\ \hline 20 \end{array}$$

CHECK
$$\begin{array}{r} 30 \\ \times\ 25 \\ \hline 150 \\ 60 \\ \hline 750 \\ \text{remainder} \rightarrow +\ 20 \\ \hline 770 \end{array}$$

Ms. Aris needs 25 full flats and 20 extra eggs, so she should order 26 flats of eggs.

Other Examples

$$\begin{array}{r} 23\ \text{R12} \\ 40\overline{)932} \\ -\ 80 \\ \hline 132 \\ -\ 120 \\ \hline 12 \end{array}$$

$$\begin{array}{r} 16\ \text{R35} \\ 50\overline{)835} \\ -\ 50 \\ \hline 335 \\ -\ 300 \\ \hline 35 \end{array}$$

$$\begin{array}{r} \$0.30 \\ 20\overline{)\$6.00} \\ -\ 6\ 0 \\ \hline 00 \\ -\ 0 \\ \hline 0 \end{array}$$

Warm Up   Divide and check.

1. $40\overline{)445}$ 2. $10\overline{)356}$ 3. $40\overline{)800}$ 4. $30\overline{)683}$ 5. $20\overline{)\$7.40}$

Practice Divide and check.

1. $20\overline{)235}$ 2. $30\overline{)386}$ 3. $30\overline{)615}$ 4. $40\overline{)495}$ 5. $60\overline{)\$6.00}$

6. $10\overline{)234}$ 7. $20\overline{)400}$ 8. $30\overline{)742}$ 9. $20\overline{)285}$ 10. $30\overline{)\$9.60}$

11. $20\overline{)935}$ 12. $10\overline{)678}$ 13. $60\overline{)255}$ 14. $50\overline{)750}$ 15. $80\overline{)\$9.60}$

16. $794 \div 10$ 17. $999 \div 30$ 18. $350 \div 20$

19. $587 \div 40$ 20. $419 \div 30$ 21. $835 \div 20$

22. What is 800 divided by 40?   23. What is 105 divided by 10?

24. What is 333 divided by 20?   25. What is 938 divided by 90?

Mixed Applications

26. The Aristocrat Restaurant used 28 flats of eggs one Sunday morning. How many eggs were used?

27. Make up a story problem that would be solved using this division example:

$$30\overline{)470}^{\;15\ R20}$$

2-Digit Quotients

The aquarium park bought 700 kg of mackerel to feed the dolphins. Each case of food has 25 kg of mackerel. How many cases did the park buy?

Since we want the total number of equal cases, we divide.

Decide Where to Start.	→	Dividing Tens	→	Dividing Ones
		• Divide		• Bring down
		• Multiply		• Divide
		• Subtract		• Multiply
		• Compare		• Subtract
				• Compare

• not enough hundreds, 25 > 7
• divide the tens, 25 < 70

$$25\overline{)700}$$

$$\begin{array}{r} \text{(30)} \quad 2 \\ 25\overline{)700} \\ -\ 50 \\ \hline 20 \end{array}$$

$$\begin{array}{r} \text{(30)} \quad 28 \\ 25\overline{)700} \\ -\ 50\downarrow \\ \hline 200 \leftarrow 30\overline{)200} \\ -\ 200 \\ \hline 0 \end{array}$$

The aquarium park bought 28 cases of mackerel.

Other Examples

$$\begin{array}{r} 19\ \text{R23} \\ 38\overline{)745} \\ -\ 38 \\ \hline 365 \\ -\ 342 \\ \hline 23 \end{array}$$

$$\begin{array}{r} 20\ \text{R15} \\ 43\overline{)875} \\ -\ 86 \\ \hline 15 \\ -\ \ 0 \\ \hline 15 \end{array}$$

$$\begin{array}{r} \$0.58 \\ 16\overline{)\$9.28} \\ -\ 80 \\ \hline 1\ 28 \\ -\ 1\ 28 \\ \hline 0 \end{array}$$

Warm Up Divide and check.

1. $21\overline{)345}$
2. $47\overline{)564}$
3. $39\overline{)790}$
4. $57\overline{)900}$
5. $35\overline{)\$7.35}$

Practice Divide and check.

1. $18\overline{)205}$ **2.** $32\overline{)684}$ **3.** $43\overline{)868}$ **4.** $27\overline{)604}$ **5.** $56\overline{)\$6.72}$

6. $21\overline{)900}$ **7.** $12\overline{)257}$ **8.** $66\overline{)635}$ **9.** $83\overline{)867}$ **10.** $44\overline{)\$8.36}$

11. $29\overline{)590}$ **12.** $31\overline{)600}$ **13.** $15\overline{)750}$ **14.** $43\overline{)294}$ **15.** $17\overline{)\$3.57}$

16. $26\overline{)793}$ **17.** $13\overline{)125}$ **18.** $25\overline{)800}$ **19.** $88\overline{)935}$ **20.** $13\overline{)\$8.32}$

21. $483 \div 24$ **22.** $732 \div 12$ **23.** $567 \div 19$

24. $805 \div 44$ **25.** $356 \div 28$ **26.** $660 \div 33$

27. Divide 314 by 19.   **28.** Divide 783 by 34.

29. Divide 500 by 28.   **30.** Divide 610 by 32.

Mixed Applications

31. The park bought 900 kg of seal food. Each box has 12 kg of food. How many boxes did the park buy?

32. The dolphins ate 525 kg of food in 3 weeks. At this rate, how many kilograms of food did they eat each day?

33. The park spent $2,852 on food for the whales during January (31 days). At this rate, how much did the park spend for food each day?

┌ THINK ┐

Divisibility

Any number is divisible by another number if the remainder is 0.

Example
$$24\overline{)480} \quad \overset{20}{}$$
480 is divisible by 24

Which of these numbers is 480 divisible by?

12, 18, 36, 41, 60, 96

MATH

PROBLEM SOLVING
Using Data from an Advertisement

Use the information on the packages to solve the following problems.

1. How many plates are in a package of paper plates?

2. What is the price of 1 paper plate?

3. How many ounces does the package of hamburger buns weigh?

4. How much does the box of trash bags cost in dollars and cents?

5. How many ounces does each hamburger bun weigh?

6. What is the price of each napkin?

7. How many ounces of juice will the 51 foam cups hold?

8. How many packages of paper plates can be bought with $10.00?

Smith's Foam Cups
51 cups
6 oz.
$2.55

Cheese-O CHEESE SLICES
72 slices   11 oz
$6.48

Wonder NAPKINS
10 in. x 10 in.
120¢   60

HANDY Trash Bags
2 ply
15 BAGS FOR 30 gal. Trash Cans
390¢

9. If you bought 5 boxes of plastic tableware, how many pieces would you have?

10. What would be the price of one trash bag?

11. How much does it cost to buy 3 packages of hamburger buns?

12. What is the price of 1 slice of cheese?

13. If you need 125 sandwich bags, how many boxes should you buy?

14. If you buy 4 packages of hamburger buns and use 39 of them, how many buns will be left?

15. If you use $5.00 to buy 1 package of napkins and 1 package of cups, how much change will you get?

16. *Strategy Practice* Meg, Tad, Evie, Dan, and Kari are in line at the market. Kari is between Meg and Tad. Dan is between Tad and Kari. Tad is ahead of Evie. Meg is first in line. Who is last?

APPLIED PROBLEM SOLVING

QUESTION
DATA
PLAN
ANSWER
CHECK

You are helping to plan a class party at a park. It is your job to bring the drinks. There are 30 people in your class. The drinks come in 1-liter bottles. How many bottles should you buy?

Some Things to Consider

- The party is outdoors in June. It may be hot.
- Games are planned that will require running.
- The party will last 4 hours.
- There is no water at the park.
- Each person will drink from 2 to 5 glasses.
- A liter will fill about 5 glasses.

Some Questions to Answer

1. How many glasses of drink will you need if each person drinks 2 glasses?
2. How many glasses of drink will you need if each person drinks 5 glasses?
3. How many liters would you buy if you wanted to fill 100 glasses?

What Is Your Decision?

How many bottles of drink will you buy for the party?

Divide.

1. $40\overline{)80}$ **2.** $10\overline{)10}$ **3.** $20\overline{)60}$ **4.** $50\overline{)450}$ **5.** $30\overline{)240}$

6. $20\overline{)27}$ **7.** $30\overline{)68}$ **8.** $50\overline{)67}$ **9.** $20\overline{)76}$ **10.** $40\overline{)91}$

11. $43\overline{)58}$ **12.** $22\overline{)75}$ **13.** $37\overline{)85}$ **14.** $32\overline{)98}$ **15.** $12\overline{)40}$

16. $12\overline{)49}$ **17.** $25\overline{)75}$ **18.** $41\overline{)85}$ **19.** $15\overline{)65}$ **20.** $35\overline{)80}$

21. $32\overline{)245}$ **22.** $47\overline{)490}$ **23.** $63\overline{)250}$ **24.** $21\overline{)\$1.68}$ **25.** $18\overline{)\$1.08}$

26. $20\overline{)678}$ **27.** $30\overline{)390}$ **28.** $40\overline{)495}$ **29.** $20\overline{)\$5.00}$ **30.** $70\overline{)\$9.60}$

31. $42\overline{)504}$ **32.** $37\overline{)462}$ **33.** $26\overline{)500}$ **34.** $32\overline{)\$6.08}$ **35.** $19\overline{)\$3.61}$

Solve.

36. There were 520 people at the Sunday night concert. 325 of them sat in chairs. The rest sat on benches. How many people sat on benches?

37. What is the price of each envelope?

ANOTHER LOOK

Use division facts.

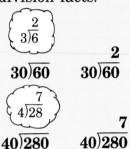

$$3\overline{)6} = 2$$

$$30\overline{)60}$$ $$30\overline{)60} = 2$$

$$4\overline{)28} = 7$$

$$40\overline{)280}$$ $$40\overline{)280} = 7$$

Put an X to show where to start.

$$\overset{X}{40\overline{)85}}$$ $$\overset{X}{40\overline{)235}}$$

not enough tens,
40 > 8

start with ones,
40 < 85

not enough hundreds,
40 > 2

not enough tens,
40 > 23

start with ones,
40 < 235

Change estimates.

$$2\overline{)6} = 3$$

$$\overset{3}{24\overline{)67}}$$
$$-\ 72 \leftarrow \text{too large}$$

Try a smaller number.

$$24\overline{)67} = 2\ R19$$
$$\underline{-\ 48}$$
$$19$$

$$3\overline{)8} = 2$$

$$\overset{2}{26\overline{)89}}$$
$$\underline{-\ 52}$$
$$37 \leftarrow \text{greater than 26}$$

Try a larger number.

$$26\overline{)89} = 3\ R11$$
$$\underline{-\ 78}$$
$$11$$

Find the quotients.

1. $2\overline{)8}$ 2. $3\overline{)9}$ 3. $4\overline{)36}$

$20\overline{)80}$ $30\overline{)90}$ $40\overline{)360}$

4. $2\overline{)14}$ 5. $5\overline{)35}$ 6. $8\overline{)32}$

$20\overline{)140}$ $50\overline{)350}$ $80\overline{)320}$

Put an X to show where to start.

7. $30\overline{)75}$ 8. $10\overline{)43}$ 9. $20\overline{)96}$

10. $40\overline{)324}$ 11. $60\overline{)552}$ 12. $30\overline{)267}$

13. $38\overline{)268}$ 14. $31\overline{)182}$ 15. $17\overline{)123}$

Divide.

16. $40\overline{)83}$ 17. $30\overline{)75}$ 18. $20\overline{)55}$

19. $50\overline{)308}$ 20. $80\overline{)751}$ 21. $60\overline{)378}$

22. $43\overline{)81}$ 23. $22\overline{)80}$ 24. $13\overline{)67}$

25. $27\overline{)85}$ 26. $16\overline{)72}$ 27. $35\overline{)78}$

Logical Reasoning

Colored arrows can be used to show relationships. The 10 letters below represent 10 people. The colored arrows show some of the ways these people are related to each other.

➡ points to a person's father.
➡ points to a person's mother.

The 10 people include a grandfather and grandmother, their 3 children, and 5 grandchildren.

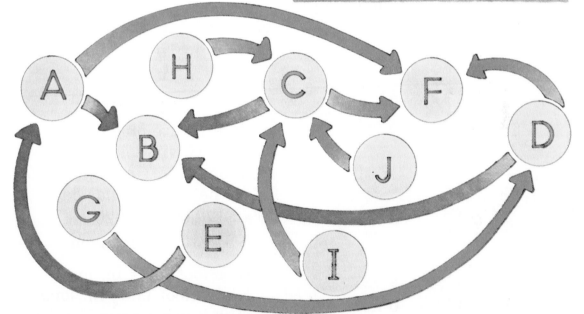

1. What letter represents the grandmother?
2. What letter represents the grandfather?
3. How are C and D related?

CUMULATIVE REVIEW

Give the letter for the correct answer.

1. $\dfrac{3}{6}$ **A** $\dfrac{5}{6}$ **B** $\dfrac{5}{12}$

$+\dfrac{2}{6}$ **C** 5 **D** not given

2. $\dfrac{1}{10}$ **A** 4 **B** $\dfrac{4}{10}$

$+\dfrac{3}{10}$ **C** $\dfrac{4}{20}$ **D** not given

3. $\dfrac{6}{10}$ **A** $\dfrac{3}{10}$ **B** $\dfrac{9}{10}$

$-\dfrac{3}{10}$ **C** $\dfrac{3}{0}$ **D** not given

4. $\dfrac{5}{8}$ **A** $\dfrac{9}{8}$ **B** $\dfrac{1}{0}$

$-\dfrac{4}{8}$ **C** $\dfrac{1}{8}$ **D** not given

5. $3\dfrac{2}{4}$ **A** $1\dfrac{1}{4}$ **B** $5\dfrac{3}{4}$

$+2\dfrac{1}{4}$ **C** $5\dfrac{3}{8}$ **D** not given

6. $7\dfrac{7}{10}$ **A** $4\dfrac{4}{10}$ **B** $3\dfrac{4}{20}$

$-4\dfrac{3}{10}$ **C** $3\dfrac{4}{10}$ **D** not given

7. 26 **A** 520 **B** 52

$\times 20$ **C** 420 **D** not given

8. 23 **A** 26 **B** 276

$\times 12$ **C** 69 **D** not given

9. 65 **A** 585

$\times 27$ **B** $1{,}655$

        C $1{,}755$

        D not given

10. $\$0.54$ **A** $\$1.00$

$\times\ \ 20$ **B** $\$1.08$

        C $\$10.08$

        D not given

11. $\$0.78$ **A** $\$32.76$

$\times\ \ 42$ **B** $\$32.66$

        C $\$2.96$

        D not given

12. $\$6.85$ **A** $\$234.05$

$\times\ \ 33$ **B** $\$226.05$

        C $\$42.00$

        D not given

13. Records are on sale for $6.88 each. Gavin sold 25 records in one day. How much money did he take in that day?

A $172.00   **B** $17.20

C $48.10   **D** not given

14. Eli's foot is $7\dfrac{2}{4}$ in. long. Kara's foot is $6\dfrac{1}{4}$ in. long. How much longer is Eli's foot than Kara's foot?

A $13\dfrac{3}{4}$ in.   **B** $1\dfrac{3}{4}$ in.

C $1\dfrac{1}{4}$ in.   **D** not given

DECIMALS

Jenny Chen is on a gymnastics team. She trains about 15 hours a week. Jenny does best on the balance beam. It is only about 10.2 cm wide. She begins new tricks on a line on the floor. Then she works out on a low beam. Finally she is ready for the high beam. It is about 1.19 m high. Jenny works very hard. Sometimes she becomes very tired. Then she wonders if it is worth all the work. Other times it is very rewarding. Once Jenny's team was judged first place champions. Jenny felt like she was on top of the world.

Tenths

The glass holds two tenths of a
liter. For two tenths, you can
write a fraction or a **decimal.**

Fraction	Decimal
$\dfrac{2}{10}$	**0.2**
	↑
	Decimal point

We read, "**two tenths.**"

two tenths

1 LITER

The bucket holds one and three
tenths liters. For one and three
tenths you can write a mixed
number or a decimal.

Mixed number	Decimal
$1\dfrac{3}{10}$	**1.3**
	↑
	Decimal point

We read, "**one and three tenths.**"

Warm Up Write a decimal for each amount.

1.

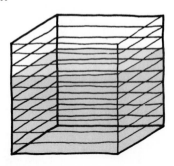

2.

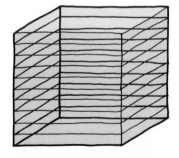
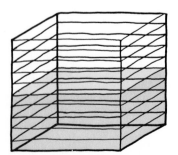

Practice Write a decimal for each amount.
You can see only the front of each box.

Example

1.

answer 2.4

2.

3.

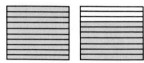

4.

5.

6.

7.

THINK

Patterns

Give the next 3 decimals.

1. 2.2, 2.3, 2.4, __?__, __?__, __?__

2. 2.6, 2.7, 2.8, __?__, __?__, __?__

3. 9.7, 9.8, 9.9, __?__, __?__, __?__

4. 24.6, 24.7, 24.8, __?__, __?__, __?__

MATH

Tenths and Hundredths

Work with a group.

Each person will need eight pieces of 10-by-10 grid paper, index cards, and scissors. Your group will also need a number cube.

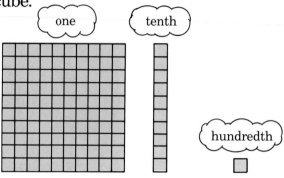

Part 1

1. Use the grid paper to make ones, tenths, and hundredths.

   - Leave six 10-by-10 grids whole (ones).
   - Cut one grid into 10 strips (tenths).
   - Cut another grid into 100 squares (hundredths).

2. Take some tenth strips.
   - Write a fraction for that part of the whole.
   - Write a decimal to show that number of tenths.
   - Compare strips in your group.

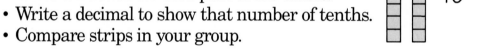

$\frac{2}{10}$ or 0.2

3. Next, take some hundredth squares.

   - Write a fraction for that part of the whole.
   - Write a decimal to show that number of hundredths.

   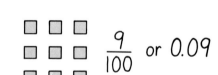

   $\frac{9}{100}$ or 0.09

   - Compare squares in your group.

4. Show some tenth strips. Write the decimal.

   - Now ask a partner to show the same decimal, using hundredth squares.
   - Talk about why you can do it.

5. Show several different ways you could use your grid pieces to model 1.00.

Part 2

6. Work with your group on this "Roll and Write" activity.

   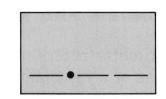

   - Make a card like this for each person.
   - Take turns. Roll a number cube. Each person writes that number on any line of his or her card.
   - Roll the cube two more times. Each person writes the numbers on his or her card.
   - Model your number with the pieces from Part 1.
   - Compare the numbers your group wrote. Put the number cards in order from smallest to largest.

   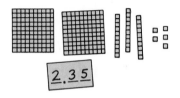

7. Repeat the activity several times.

   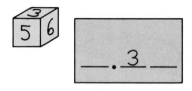

Part 3

8. Try the "Roll and Write" activity again. This time roll the cube only once.

   - Each person writes that number on a different line.
   - Write a 0 on each of the other lines.
   - Compare the numbers your group wrote. Put the cards in order from smallest to largest.
   - Model the numbers to check your work.

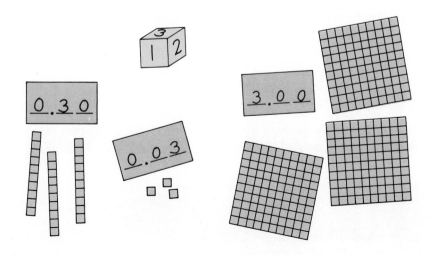

Decimals and Measurement

Centimeter rulers usually show tenths of a centimeter.

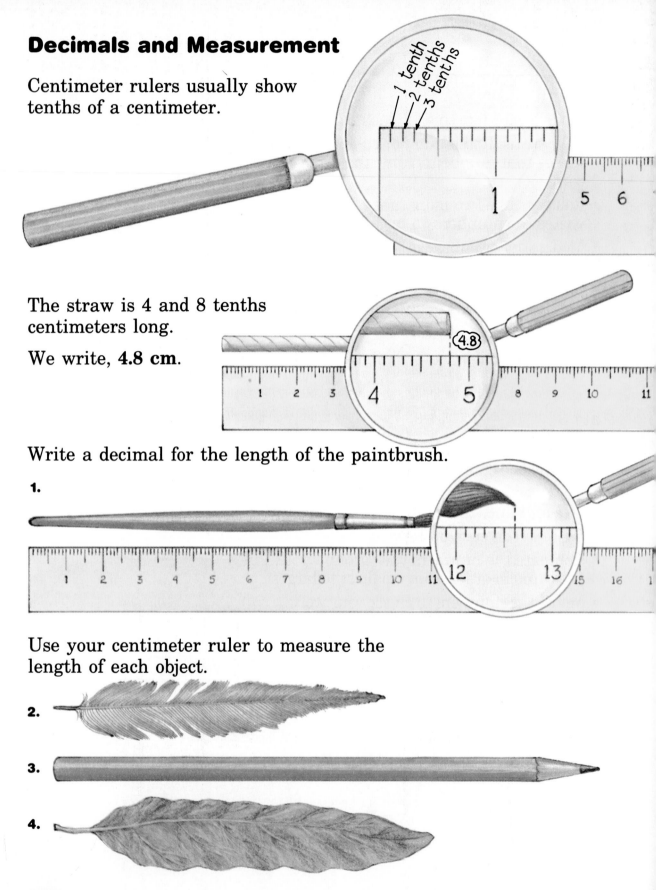

1 tenth
2 tenths
3 tenths

1   5 6

The straw is 4 and 8 tenths centimeters long.

We write, **4.8 cm**.

4.8

1 2 3 4   5   8 9 10 11

Write a decimal for the length of the paintbrush.

1.

1 2 3 4 5 6 7 8 9 10 11 12   13 15 16 1

Use your centimeter ruler to measure the length of each object.

2.

3.

4.

Decimals and Money

100 pennies will buy as much as 1 dollar.

1 penny is one hundredth of a dollar.

 $\frac{1}{100}$ dollar   We write, **$0.01.**

3 pennies are three hundredths of a dollar.

 $\frac{3}{100}$ dollar   We write, **$0.03.**

For 3 dollars and 27 pennies,

We think, "**three and twenty-seven hundredths dollars.**"
We write, **$3.27.**
We read, "**three dollars and twenty-seven cents.**"

Write each amount using the dollar sign and a decimal point.

1. 2 dollars and 25 pennies

2. 7 dollars and 78 pennies

3. 5 dollars and 7 pennies

4. 6 dollars and 10 pennies

5. 9 dollars and 1 dime

6. 4 dollars and 2 dimes

7. 1 dollar, 3 dimes, and 4 pennies

8. 3 dollars, 6 dimes, and 7 pennies

9. 8 dollars, 7 dimes, and 9 pennies

10. 5 dollars, 4 dimes, and 0 pennies

11. 7 dollars, 0 dimes, and 6 pennies

12. 9 dollars, 3 dimes, and 6 pennies

Comparing Decimals

A horse ran at a speed of 69.3 km/h (kilometers per hour). A dog ran at a speed of 69.1 km/h. Which animal was faster?

Compare the speeds to see which is faster.

Line up the decimal points. → Start at the left. Find the first place where the digits are different. → Compare these digits. → The numbers compare the same way the digits compare.

69.3　　　　**69.3**　　　　*is greater than*　　**69.3 > 69.1**
69.1　　　　**69.1**　　　　　**3 > 1**

The horse was faster than the dog.

Other Examples

is less than
0.26 < 0.29　　　　**0.40 > 0.04**　　　　**2.47 < 2.59**
24.0 = 24　　　　**32.4 > 32**　　　　**0.6　= 0.60**

Warm Up　Give >, <, or = for each ▓.

1. 0.35 ▓ 0.37　　　　2. 0.80 ▓ 0.8　　　　3. 2.38 ▓ 2.46

4. 3.40 ▓ 3.4　　　　5. 24　▓ 24.3　　　　6. 0.08 ▓ 0.70

7. 3.82 ▓ 3.78　　　　8. 2.30 ▓ 2.06　　　　9. 2.4　▓ 2.40

10. 0.56 ▓ 0.59　　　　11. 5.06 ▓ 5.60　　　　12. 65.4 ▓ 65

348

Practice Give $>$, $<$, or $=$ for each  .

1. 0.56 ⬤ 0.52
2. 2.56 ⬤ 2.51
3. 0.20 ⬤ 0.02
4. 24 ⬤ 24.1
5. 3.6 ⬤ 3.60
6. 0.65 ⬤ 0.68
7. 3.81 ⬤ 3.76
8. 0.20 ⬤ 0.02
9. 0.7 ⬤ 0.70
10. 0.60 ⬤ 0.6
11. 0.37 ⬤ 0.73
12. 0.07 ⬤ 0.70
13. 4.8 ⬤ 4.80
14. 4.38 ⬤ 4.4
15. 8.20 ⬤ 8.2
16. 6.28 ⬤ 6.30
17. 32.6 ⬤ 32
18. 0.29 ⬤ 0.32
19. 0.1 ⬤ 0.10
20. 0.41 ⬤ 0.35
21. 0.61 ⬤ 6.1

22. Which number is greater, 2.87 or 2.91?
23. Which number is less, 0.30 or 0.03?
24. Which number is greater, 0.29 or 0.3?
25. Which number is less, 32.4 or 32.6?

Give each set of decimals in order, from smallest to largest.

26. 3.6, 2.8, 4.1
27. 5.6, 5.2, 5.4
28. 0.37, 0.41, 0.34

Solve.

29. A rabbit ran 48.2 km/h. A fox ran 48.1 km/h. Which one ran faster?

30. A bird flew 72.2 km/h. Was this faster or slower than the dog's speed given on page 348?

THINK

Ordering Decimals

Put the numbers in order from smallest to largest.
Write the letter for each number above that number.
You will have the name of one of the fastest animals.

t	e	c	h	e	a	h
1.20	0.98	0.87	1.3	1.02	1.27	0.91

→ MATH ←

Adding Decimals

The chef mixed the two cans of juice together. How many liters of juice did he have?

Since we want the total amount, we add.

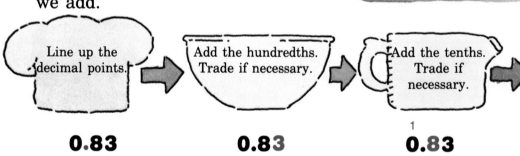

Line up the decimal points.	Add the hundredths. Trade if necessary.	Add the tenths. Trade if necessary.	Add the whole numbers. Place the decimal point.
0.83 + 0.95	0.8**3** + 0.9**5** **8**	¹ 0.83 + 0.95 78	¹ 0.83 + 0.95 1.78

17 tenths is 1 whole and 7 tenths.

The chef had 1.78 liters of juice.

Other Examples

¹ 27.6 + 38.9 66.5	¹ 13.27 + 62.56 75.83	¹ ¹ $6.56 + 9.85 16.41	¹ 0.36 + 0.29 0.65

13 hundredths is 1 tenth and 3 hundredths.

Warm Up Add.

1. 48.3 + 17.8	2. 6.47 + 0.38	3. 23.78 + 37.69	4. $3.76 + 9.38	5. 0.78 + 0.92

Practice Add.

1.	78.3 + 16.8	**2.**	27.6 + 32.9	**3.**	7.60 + 1.83
4.	8.32 + 9.16	**5.**	3.78 + 1.99	**6.**	0.95 + 0.81
7.	0.67 + 0.85	**8.**	42.8 + 76.9	**9.**	3.85 + 4.76

10. 30.68 + 42.39   **11.** 74.83 + 60.67

12. $3.95 + 2.69   **13.** $4.38 + 2.76   **14.** 7.95 + 8.69   **15.** $3.85 + 1.88   **16.** $54.67 + 31.28

17. 3.62 + 4.81   **18.** 76.3 + 81.9   **19.** 46.28 + 18.75

20. 9.6 + 8.9   **21.** 0.36 + 0.89   **22.** $2.95 + $3.79

23. Add 3.75 to 2.80.   **24.** Add 6.78 to 0.95.

Mixed Applications

25. One can had 0.83 L. Another had 1.74 L. How many liters were in both cans?

26. **DATA HUNT** Find the number of liters in each of two different sizes of canned fruit juices. Find how many more liters are in the larger size.

27. **DATA BANK** See page 399. The cook mixed a No. 2 can of juice with a No. 1 tall can of juice. How many liters of juice was this in all? 1.06 L

┌─ **THINK** ──────────────┐

 **Using a Calculator**

1. Show 8.0 on your calculator. Now show 8.7 by adding one number to 8.0.

2. Show 3.00 on your calculator. Now show 3.67 by adding one number to 3.00.

➡ **MATH** ⬅

└──────────────────────────┘

Subtracting Decimals

A serving of roast beef contains 23.40 grams of protein. The same size serving of turkey contains 28.13 grams of protein. How much more protein does the turkey have?

Since we want to find out how much more, we subtract.

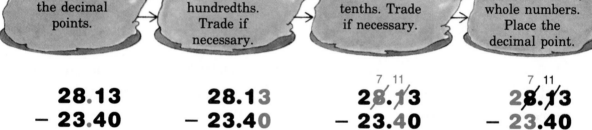

Line up the decimal points.	Subtract the hundredths. Trade if necessary.	Subtract the tenths. Trade if necessary.	Subtract the whole numbers. Place the decimal point.
28.13 − 23.40	28.13 − 23.40 3	2⁷.1̸¹¹3 − 23.40 73	2̸⁷8.1̸¹¹3 − 23.40 4.73

A turkey has 4.73 grams more protein.

Other Examples

$$
\begin{array}{r} {\scriptstyle 7\ 12} \\ 7.8\!\!\!/2 \\ -\ 3.56 \\ \hline 4.26 \end{array}
\qquad
\begin{array}{r} {\scriptstyle 8\ \ 11\ 14} \\ 9.2\!\!\!/4\!\!\!/ \\ -\ 1.67 \\ \hline 7.57 \end{array}
\qquad
\begin{array}{r} {\scriptstyle 6\ \ 12} \\ 6\!\!\!/7.2\!\!\!/ \\ -\ 26.7 \\ \hline 40.5 \end{array}
\qquad
\begin{array}{r} {\scriptstyle 2\ 11\ 16} \\ \$3\!\!\!/2.6\!\!\!/3 \\ -\ 28.93 \\ \hline \$\ 3.70 \end{array}
$$

Warm Up   Subtract.

1. 6.71
 − 3.28

2. 5.39
 − 1.62

3. 3.54
 − 2.69

4. 48.23
 − 39.50

5. $43.27
 − $17.36

Practice Subtract.

1. 9.24
− 3.70

2. 6.85
− 2.39

3. 4.48
− 1.24

4. 3.37
− 1.69

5. 2.43
− 1.58

6. 67.2
− 34.3

7. 6.25
− 5.75

8. 38.6
− 9.8

9. 27.4
− 14.9

10. 2.86
− 1.95

11. 32.46
− 17.83

12. 26.41
− 14.82

13. 13.40
− 6.17

14. 28.65
− 19.82

15. 67.62
− 53.46

16. $3.95
− 1.98

17. $2.76
− 0.98

18. $4.65
− 1.95

19. $32.45
− 17.60

20. $49.25
− 17.69

21. 32.4 − 17.9

22. 3.28 − 1.75

23. 2.76 − 1.90

24. $83.42 − $76.04

25. $29.75 − $19.95

26. $38.27 − $6.95

27. Subtract 3.75 from 6.82.

28. Subtract 37.50 from 62.35.

Mixed Applications

29. There are 17.9 grams of protein in a serving of lamb. The same size serving of white fish has 25.2 grams of protein. How much more protein does the fish have?

30. Find the total number of grams of protein for the two meats and the two vegetables given below.
    veal—23.0   chicken—28.1
    broccoli—3.3   spinach—2.3

THINK

Magic Squares

Complete this magic square. Remember, the sums in all directions (→ ↑ ↗ ↖) must be the same. In this square, the sum is 4.2.

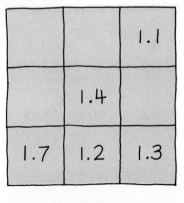

MATH

More Adding and Subtracting Decimals

Marlo's time in the race was 52.15 seconds. Dawn's time was 54.8 seconds. How many seconds' difference was there?

Since we want the difference in the two times, we subtract.

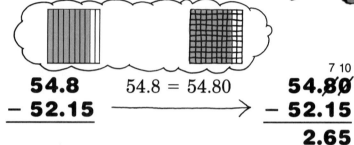

$$
\begin{array}{r} 54.8 \\ -\ 52.15 \\ \hline \end{array}
\qquad 54.8 = 54.80 \qquad
\begin{array}{r} {}^{7\ 10} \\ 54.8\!\!\!/0 \\ -\ 52.15 \\ \hline 2.65 \end{array}
$$

The difference in times was 2.65 seconds.

Other Examples

$$
\begin{array}{r} 4.76 \\ +\ 2.8 \\ \hline \end{array}
\rightarrow
\begin{array}{r} 4.76 \\ +\ 2.80 \\ \hline 7.56 \end{array}
\qquad
\begin{array}{r} 79 \\ -\ 26.38 \\ \hline \end{array}
\rightarrow
\begin{array}{r} {}^{8\ \ 9\ 10} \\ 79.0\!\!\!/0 \\ -\ 26.38 \\ \hline 52.62 \end{array}
$$

Find the sums and differences.

1. $\begin{array}{r}42.7\\+\ \ 8.69\\\hline\end{array}$	**2.** $\begin{array}{r}64.8\\-\ 21.34\\\hline\end{array}$	**3.** $\begin{array}{r}2.69\\+\ 8\\\hline\end{array}$	**4.** $\begin{array}{r}64\\-\ 18.3\\\hline\end{array}$	**5.** $\begin{array}{r}93\\-\ 75.46\\\hline\end{array}$
6. $\begin{array}{r}6.82\\+\ 57\\\hline\end{array}$	**7.** $\begin{array}{r}48.6\\-\ 15.37\\\hline\end{array}$	**8.** $\begin{array}{r}28.4\\+\ 17.67\\\hline\end{array}$	**9.** $\begin{array}{r}56.2\\+\ 75\\\hline\end{array}$	**10.** $\begin{array}{r}13.0\\-\ \ 7.23\\\hline\end{array}$

11. $14.3 + 32$

12. $16.4 - 3.25$

13. $75 + 16.4$

14. $58 - 13.43$

15. $18.35 + 9.6$

16. $76.1 - 2.85$

More Practice, page 432, Set B

PROBLEM SOLVING
Using Data from a Map

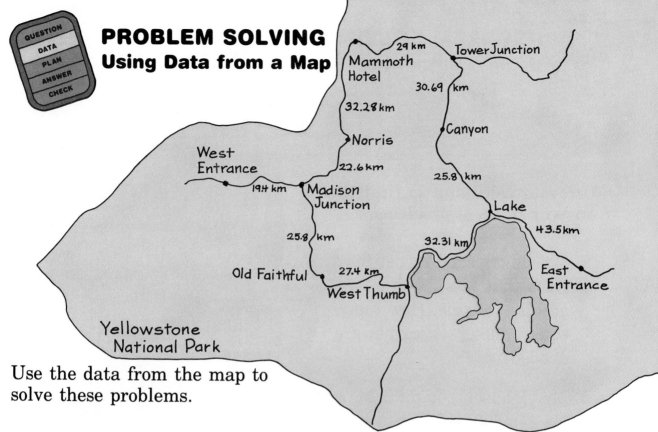

Use the data from the map to solve these problems.

1. How far is it from Madison Junction to Mammoth Hotel?

2. How much farther is it from Lake to West Thumb than from Lake to Canyon?

3. How far is it from West Thumb to Madison Junction?

4. How much closer is it from Canyon to Lake than from Canyon to Tower Junction?

5. How far would you drive if you made 4 one-way trips between Mammoth Hotel and Tower Junction?

6. Which is farther, Madison Junction to Mammoth Hotel or Madison Junction to West Thumb?

★ 7. A group on bicycles took 3 hours to go from the West Entrance to Norris. About how far did they travel each hour?

8. *Strategy Practice* Some visitors started at Madison Junction and drove to one place and back. They traveled 45.2 km. Where did they go?

PROBLEM SOLVING
Using a Calculator

QUESTION
DATA
PLAN
ANSWER
CHECK

Use your calculator to **find the answer** to these problems.

1. Mr. Fry needed carpet for a room that was 7.4 m long and 5.8 m wide. How many square meters of carpet are needed?

2. Mr. Johnson bought a house for $75,600. He had to have $\frac{1}{4}$ of that amount in cash. How much cash did he have to have?

3. Joel paid $985.00 for a couch. He bought a matching chair for $495.50. How much more was the couch?

4. Mr. Lee has 5 water heaters for his apartments. Their total weight is 158.76 kg. How much does each one weigh?

5. Ms. Lopez has 3 houses for sale at $69,500, $72,950, and $68,750. What is the average price of the houses?

6. Ms. Lee sold two houses for $59,790 and $68,900. She makes $0.02 on each dollar. How much did she make for selling these two houses? Hint: Multiply the total sales by 0.02.

7. **Strategy Practice** Mr. Jensen sells houses. He is supposed to sell the amounts listed below.

March	April	May
$39,500	$40,250	$41,000
June	July	August
$41,750	$42,500	

How much should he sell in August?

Decimal Practice

Find the sums.

1. $\begin{array}{r} 8.6 \\ + 7.5 \\ \hline \end{array}$	**2.** $\begin{array}{r} 27.3 \\ + 58.9 \\ \hline \end{array}$	**3.** $\begin{array}{r} 128.2 \\ + 276.4 \\ \hline \end{array}$	**4.** $\begin{array}{r} 58.7 \\ + 65.9 \\ \hline \end{array}$	**5.** $\begin{array}{r} 378.4 \\ + 126.7 \\ \hline \end{array}$
6. $\begin{array}{r} 3.42 \\ + 1.86 \\ \hline \end{array}$	**7.** $\begin{array}{r} 0.27 \\ + 0.58 \\ \hline \end{array}$	**8.** $\begin{array}{r} 28.75 \\ + 19.82 \\ \hline \end{array}$	**9.** $\begin{array}{r} 4.67 \\ + 2.88 \\ \hline \end{array}$	**10.** $\begin{array}{r} 0.76 \\ + 0.95 \\ \hline \end{array}$

Find the differences.

11. $\begin{array}{r} 3.8 \\ - 2.6 \\ \hline \end{array}$	**12.** $\begin{array}{r} 7.2 \\ - 1.8 \\ \hline \end{array}$	**13.** $\begin{array}{r} 24.3 \\ - 10.6 \\ \hline \end{array}$	**14.** $\begin{array}{r} 82.3 \\ - 17.6 \\ \hline \end{array}$	**15.** $\begin{array}{r} 42.7 \\ - 17.8 \\ \hline \end{array}$
16. $\begin{array}{r} 3.67 \\ - 1.28 \\ \hline \end{array}$	**17.** $\begin{array}{r} 0.36 \\ - 0.18 \\ \hline \end{array}$	**18.** $\begin{array}{r} 26.35 \\ - 9.82 \\ \hline \end{array}$	**19.** $\begin{array}{r} 4.60 \\ - 1.88 \\ \hline \end{array}$	**20.** $\begin{array}{r} 24.82 \\ - 8.95 \\ \hline \end{array}$

Find the sums and differences.

21. $\begin{array}{r} 26.1 \\ - 17.35 \\ \hline \end{array}$	**22.** $\begin{array}{r} 54 \\ + 8.76 \\ \hline \end{array}$	**23.** $\begin{array}{r} 35 \\ - 4.8 \\ \hline \end{array}$	**24.** $\begin{array}{r} 0.8 \\ - 0.36 \\ \hline \end{array}$	**25.** $\begin{array}{r} 13.8 \\ + 6.75 \\ \hline \end{array}$
26. $\begin{array}{r} 42.83 \\ + 75 \\ \hline \end{array}$	**27.** $\begin{array}{r} 26.1 \\ - 9.75 \\ \hline \end{array}$	**28.** $\begin{array}{r} 58.3 \\ + 75 \\ \hline \end{array}$	**29.** $\begin{array}{r} 86.7 \\ + 19.38 \\ \hline \end{array}$	**30.** $\begin{array}{r} 58 \\ - 29.4 \\ \hline \end{array}$

31. $27.6 + 35.8$ **32.** $83.2 - 16.7$ **33.** $7.86 + 9.27$

34. $4.86 - 2.39$ **35.** $84.83 + 26.75$ **36.** $76.34 - 28.09$

37. $38 + 19.2$ **38.** $69.24 + 27.9$ **39.** $7.8 - 2.36$

40. $54 - 7.6$ **41.** $38 - 27.67$ **42.** $75 + 28.63$

43. $96.1 - 27.87$ **44.** $67.2 + 96$ **45.** $56.1 - 29.36$

PROBLEM SOLVING
Mixed Practice

QUESTION
DATA
PLAN
ANSWER
CHECK

Solve these problems about the weather.

1. Hawaii has an average of 177.6 cm of rain per year. Nevada has an average of 18.8 cm. How much more rain does Hawaii average than Nevada?

2. Chicago had 85.12 cm of rain one year. The following year 96.62 cm of rain fell. How much rain did Chicago have in the two years?

3. The highest temperature ever for Alaska and Hawaii is the same, 37.78°C. The highest temperature for anywhere in the United States is 18.87°C higher. What is this highest temperature?

4. Dry snow is 10 times as deep as water. How deep would the snow be for 12 cm of water?

5. Wind moving 9 km/h is called a light breeze. A wind of 85 km/h is called a strong gale. How much faster is the gale?

6. In Tahoe, California, about 272 cm of snow fell in 4 days. If the same amount fell each day, how much snow fell each day?

7. In Juneau, Alaska, the average July temperature is 13°C. The average for July in Phoenix, Arizona, is about 32°C. How many degrees cooler is Juneau?

8. Dallas had 46.74 cm of snow one year. The next year only 6.35 cm of snow fell. What was the difference in snowfall in the two years?

9. A wind of 14 km/h is called a gentle breeze. A wind 5 times that fast is called a fresh gale. How fast is that?

10. One January, Seattle had 15 cm of rain. If that same amount had fallen as moist snow, it would have been 6 times that deep. How deep is that?

11. The average temperature in Boston in July is 24°C. The average temperature in March in Boston is only $\frac{1}{6}$ of that. What is the average for March?

12. The average wind speed for Salt Lake City is 14 km/h. The highest wind in Salt Lake City was 16 km/h faster than 7 times the average. How fast was that?

13. The wind was a gentle breeze of 14 km/h. A storm came up and the wind grew to 5 times what it was. Then it decreased by 25 km/h. How fast was it then?

14. **DATA HUNT** Find out what the difference in temperature is inside your classroom and outside your school.

15. **DATA BANK** See page 401. What is the difference in average rainfall between Seattle and Cincinnati?

16. *Strategy Practice* One year a city had 8 cm of snow for each 5 cm of rain. How much snow did they have if they had 40 cm of rain that year? Complete the table.

Rain	5	10	15
Snow	8	16	24

359

Mixed Skills Practice

Computation

Find the answers.

1. $\begin{array}{r} 376 \\ +\ 189 \end{array}$
2. $\begin{array}{r} 812 \\ -\ 175 \end{array}$
3. $\begin{array}{r} 567 \\ +\ 984 \end{array}$
4. $\begin{array}{r} \$23.75 \\ +\ 19.98 \end{array}$
5. $\begin{array}{r} 703 \\ -\ 469 \end{array}$
6. $\begin{array}{r} \$10.00 \\ -\ 3.95 \end{array}$

7. $\begin{array}{r} 642 \\ \times\ 7 \end{array}$
8. $\begin{array}{r} 589 \\ \times\ 4 \end{array}$
9. $\begin{array}{r} 36 \\ \times\ 40 \end{array}$
10. $\begin{array}{r} 72 \\ \times\ 38 \end{array}$
11. $\begin{array}{r} 68 \\ \times\ 25 \end{array}$
12. $\begin{array}{r} \$3.26 \\ \times\ 54 \end{array}$

13. $8\overline{)368}$
14. $6\overline{)432}$
15. $67\overline{)335}$
16. $24\overline{)840}$
17. $19\overline{)1,899}$
18. $42\overline{)2,876}$

19. $\begin{array}{r} \frac{3}{8} \\ +\ \frac{1}{8} \end{array}$
20. $\begin{array}{r} 5\frac{1}{4} \\ +\ 6\frac{1}{2} \end{array}$
21. $\begin{array}{r} \frac{1}{4} \\ +\ \frac{3}{8} \end{array}$
22. $\begin{array}{r} \frac{7}{8} \\ -\ \frac{3}{8} \end{array}$
23. $\begin{array}{r} \frac{3}{4} \\ -\ \frac{1}{2} \end{array}$
24. $\begin{array}{r} 5\frac{3}{4} \\ -\ 1\frac{1}{8} \end{array}$

Mental Math

Write only the answers.

25. $70 + 80$
26. $600 + 900$
27. $120 - 80$
28. $1,400 - 500$

29. 3×80
30. 6×70
31. 40×90
32. 50×70

33. $210 \div 7$
34. $320 \div 80$
35. $4,800 \div 60$
36. $2,800 \div 40$

Estimation

Estimate.

37. $49 + 23$
38. $395 + 408$
39. $82 - 29$
40. $689 - 207$

41. 3×29
42. 6×58
43. $4 \times \$3.95$
44. $6 \times \$7.98$

45. $79 \div 4$
46. $121 \div 3$
47. $\$11.95 \div 3$
48. $\$23.98 \div 6$

APPLIED PROBLEM SOLVING

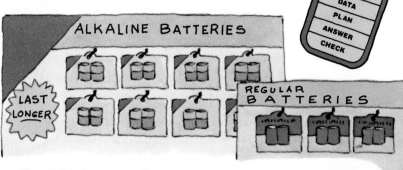

Your flashlight needs new batteries. You find two kinds of batteries at the store. One kind is alkaline, which costs $2.75 a pair. The other is regular, which costs $0.95 a pair. Both kinds fit your flashlight. Which pair of batteries will you buy?

Some Things to Consider

- You have $5.00 but there are some other things you would like to buy.

- The store clerk tells you that alkaline batteries will last 3 to 4 times as long as regular batteries.

- The flashlight will give the same amount of light using either pair of batteries.

Some Questions to Answer

1. Do you want to spend as much as $2.75 for batteries at this time?

2. About how many pairs of regular batteries can you buy for $2.75?

3. What is $3 \times \$0.95$?

4. What is $4 \times \$0.95$?

What Is Your Decision?

Will you buy the regular batteries or the alkaline batteries?

PROBLEM SOLVING
Using the Strategies

Use one or more of the strategies listed to solve each problem below.

PROBLEM-SOLVING STRATEGIES

CHOOSE THE OPERATIONS

DRAW A PICTURE

GUESS AND CHECK

MAKE A LIST

MAKE A TABLE

FIND A PATTERN

WORK BACKWARD

USE LOGICAL REASONING

1. At the grocery, Carol bought the same number of apples as oranges. She had the same number of yellow apples as red apples. How many pieces of fruit did Carol have if she had 5 red apples?

2. Carol wanted to buy one kind of meat and one vegetable for her meal. Her choices of meat were beef, veal, and lamb. Her choices of vegetables were beets, peas, and carrots. How many different meals could Carol choose?

3. Carol bought 2 dozen (24) cans of orange juice. She had 12 more small cans than large cans. How many large cans did she buy?

4. In the check-out line, Carol was behind Sue. Larry was in front of Sue and behind Ann. Carol was between Sue and Bob. Who was last in line?

Write a decimal for each picture.

1. **2.** **3.**

Use your centimeter ruler. Write a decimal for the length of each rod.

4. **5.**

Write each amount using a dollar sign and a decimal point.

6. 3 dollars and 37 pennies

7. 2 dollars and 3 dimes

8. 1 dollar, 5 dimes, and 7 pennies

9. 6 dollars, 0 dimes, and 4 pennies

Give the sign >, <, or = for each 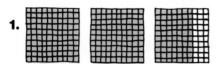 .

10. 4.8 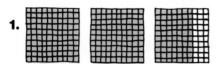 3.9

11. 6.27 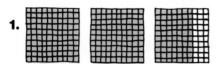 6.29

12. 45.20 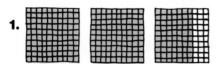 45.2

Find the sums and differences.

13. 0.86 + 0.37

14. 24.5 + 56.8

15. 27.65 + 13.84

16. $9.87 + 4.95

17. 28.24 − 13.61

18. 6.74 − 1.36

19. 47.2 − 19.8

20. 7.38 + 47

21. 74.6 − 16.28

22. 67.2 + 13.86

Solve.

23. How far is it from Nome to Bend?

24. How much farther is it from Bend to Hope than from Hope to Nome?

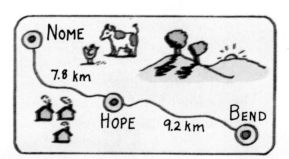

Write a decimal.

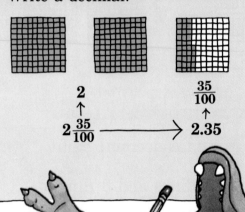

$$2\frac{35}{100} \longrightarrow 2.35$$

with 2 pointing to the whole squares and $\frac{35}{100}$ pointing to the partial square.

Write a decimal for each picture.

1.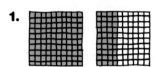

2.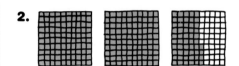

Compare.

35.62 ● 35.64

The whole numbers are equal. The tenths are equal. The second number has more hundredths.

35.62 < 35.64

Write >, <, or = for each ●.

3. 2.6 ● 2.5   **4.** 8.2 ● 7.9

5. 0.35 ● 0.41   **6.** 0.67 ● 0.71

7. 0.7 ● 0.70   **8.** 3.60 ● 3.6

9. 5.82 ● 5.9   **10.** 4.6 ● 4.59

11. 7.86 ● 7.68   **12.** 5.9 ● 6

13. 37 ● 36.9   **14.** 28.1 ● 27.9

Add or subtract.

$$
\begin{array}{r}
{\scriptstyle 1\ 1\ 1} \\
36.28 \\
+\ 47.96 \\
\hline
84.24
\end{array}
\qquad
\begin{array}{r}
{\scriptstyle 6\ 1114} \\
7.24 \\
-\ 1.76 \\
\hline
5.48
\end{array}
$$

Add the whole numbers. Write the decimal point between the ones and tenths.

Add or subtract.

15.
$$
\begin{array}{r}
3.8 \\
+\ 2.7 \\
\hline
\end{array}
$$
16.
$$
\begin{array}{r}
5.86 \\
+\ 3.95 \\
\hline
\end{array}
$$
17.
$$
\begin{array}{r}
16.82 \\
+\ 23.67 \\
\hline
\end{array}
$$

18.
$$
\begin{array}{r}
48.1 \\
-\ 17.6 \\
\hline
\end{array}
$$
19.
$$
\begin{array}{r}
3.85 \\
-\ 1.69 \\
\hline
\end{array}
$$
20.
$$
\begin{array}{r}
27.83 \\
-\ 12.95 \\
\hline
\end{array}
$$

21.
$$
\begin{array}{r}
26.75 \\
+\ 13.93 \\
\hline
\end{array}
$$
22.
$$
\begin{array}{r}
48.96 \\
-\ 16.34 \\
\hline
\end{array}
$$
23.
$$
\begin{array}{r}
75.96 \\
-\ 6.83 \\
\hline
\end{array}
$$

Negative and Positive Numbers

The number line below shows how **negative** and **positive** numbers can be used to describe the seconds **before** and **after** a rocket blast-off.

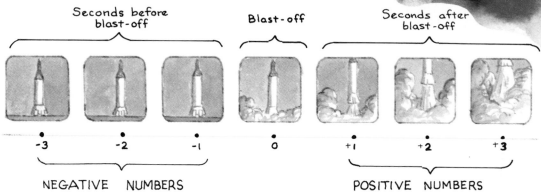

Seconds before blast-off   Blast-off   Seconds after blast-off

-3   -2   -1   0   +1   +2   +3

NEGATIVE NUMBERS   POSITIVE NUMBERS

We read ⁻3 as "**negative three**." We read ⁻2 as "**negative two**."

The graph below shows the changes in speed of a jet airplane during lift-off. Negative numbers show seconds before lift-off and positive numbers show seconds after lift-off.

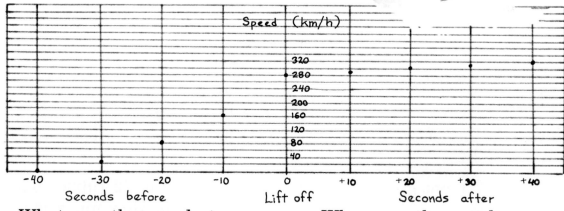

Speed (km/h)

320
280
240
200
160
120
80
40

-40   -30   -20   -10   0   +10   +20   +30   +40
Seconds before   Lift off   Seconds after

1. What was the speed at ⁻20 seconds?

2. What was the speed at lift-off?

3. When was the speed 80 km/h?

4. How many seconds was it from 0 to 300 km/h?

CUMULATIVE REVIEW

Give the letter for the correct answer.
Which are right angles?

1. a.
     b.
  A figure a
  B figure b
  c figures a and b
  D not given

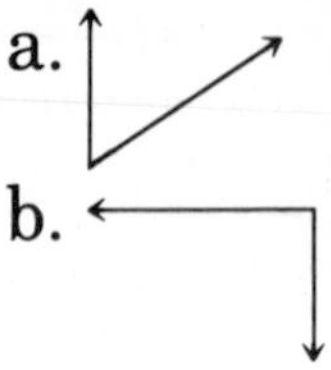

2. 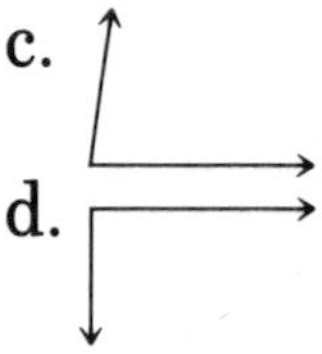 c.
     d.
  A figure c
  B figure d
  c figures c and d
  D not given

Which figure is congruent to the first?

3. 
  A 
  B 
  C 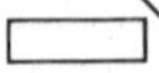
  D not given

4.
  A 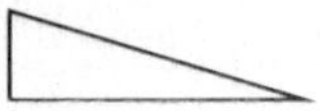
  B 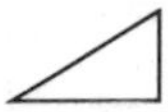
  C 
  D not given

Which is a line of symmetry?

5. A 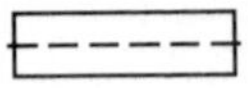   **B**
  C    **D** not given

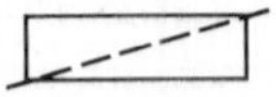

6. A    **B** 
  C 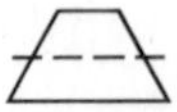   **D** not given

7. $20\overline{)35}$ **A** 1 R15   **B** 1 R5
  c 1 R51   **D** not given

8. $40\overline{)77}$ **A** 1 R7   **B** 1 R37
  c 1 R40   **D** not given

9. $23\overline{)88}$ **A** 3 R18   **B** 3 R9
  c 3 R19   **D** not given

10. $43\overline{)250}$ **A** 5 R35   **B** 6 R2
  c 5 R45   **D** not given

11. $36\overline{)290}$ **A** 8 R20   **B** 8 R2
  c 8 R52   **D** not given

12. $23\overline{)\$2.07}$ **A** $0.90   **B** $0.09
  c $9.00   **D** not given

13. Tammy's soccer team practices for 45 minutes each time they meet. The team practiced 405 minutes in April. How many times did they meet?
  A 9   **B** 7
  c 6   **D** not given

14. A package of 32 rubber bands costs $2.24. How much is it for each rubber band?
  A $2.56   **B** $71.68
  c $0.07   **D** not given

MEASUREMENT: Customary Units

The clouds were low and dark. The wind was growing stronger. The temperature had dropped. So had the air pressure. Sean and Brian had made weather instruments. They used them to take exact readings. Then they made a decision. They guessed it would snow in the next hour. They were right. It soon began to snow. The next day the snowfall stopped. They used a measuring stick to find how deep the snow was. It came up to about their knees. The two boys ran home. They met again at the hill. This time they had their sleds.

Customary Units for Length

The pictures help you think about **customary** units for measuring length.

This is an **inch** (in.) unit.

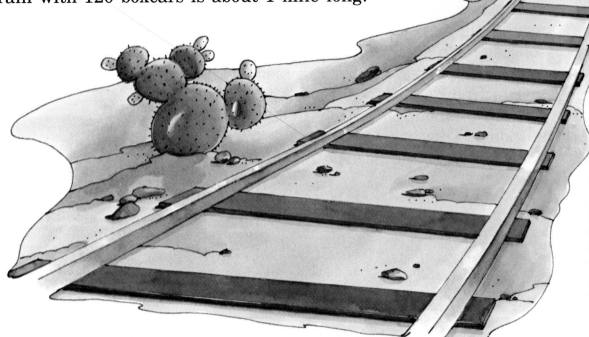

1 **foot** (ft) = 12 inches.

1 **yard** (yd) = 36 inches or 3 feet.

1 **mile** (mi) = 1,760 yards or 5,280 feet.

A train with 120 boxcars is about 1 mile long.

Warm Up   Choose the unit that makes the statement reasonable.

1. The pencil is 7 __?__ long.

2. It is 128 __?__ to Detroit.

3. The football field is 100 __?__ long.

4. Tommy is 4 __?__ tall.

5. The ceiling is 3 __?__ high.

6. The teacher's desk is 27 __?__ high.

7. It is 3 __?__ across the lake.

8. The door is 7 __?__ high.

Practice Choose the unit that makes the statement reasonable.

1. The basketball player is 6 __?__ tall.

2. Mr. Calvo's car is about 2 __?__ long.

3. The classroom is 5 __?__ wide.

4. The jet is flying 6 __?__ high

5. Teri's foot is 8 __?__ long.

6. Ryan can reach 8 __?__ high.

7. Ms. Soto drove 48 __?__.

8. It is 275 __?__ to Dallas.

Choose the better estimate.

9. How wide is the desk?
   A 1 foot   B 1 yard

10. How long is the street?
    A 4 yards   B 4 miles

11. How tall is the school?
    A 16 inches   B 16 feet

12. How wide is the river?
    A 120 yards   B 120 miles

Copy and complete the tables.

13.

Feet	1	2	3	4	5
Inches	12	24	▓	▓	▓

14.

Yards	1	2	3	4	5
Feet	3	6	▓	▓	▓

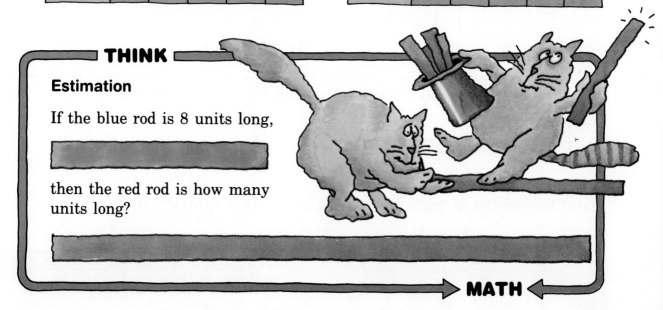

THINK

Estimation

If the blue rod is 8 units long,

then the red rod is how many units long?

MATH

Using Fractions in Measurement

Robin and Sharon are building a tree house. They need nails that have different lengths. They are also using boards of many different sizes.

Examples

The length of this nail is $2\frac{1}{4}$ inches.

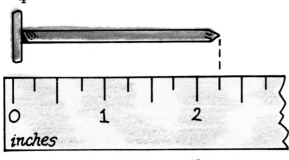

This board is $1\frac{3}{4}$ inches wide.

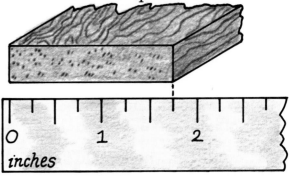

The length of this nail is $2\frac{1}{2}$ inches to the nearest quarter inch.

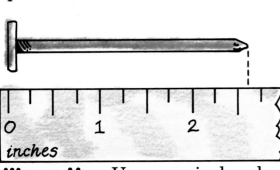

This board is 2 inches wide to the nearest quarter inch.

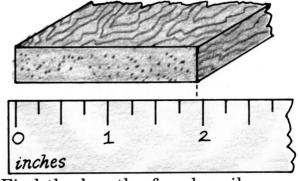

Warm Up Use your inch ruler. Find the length of each nail.

1.

2.

Find the width of each board to the nearest quarter inch.

3.

4.

Practice Find the length or width.

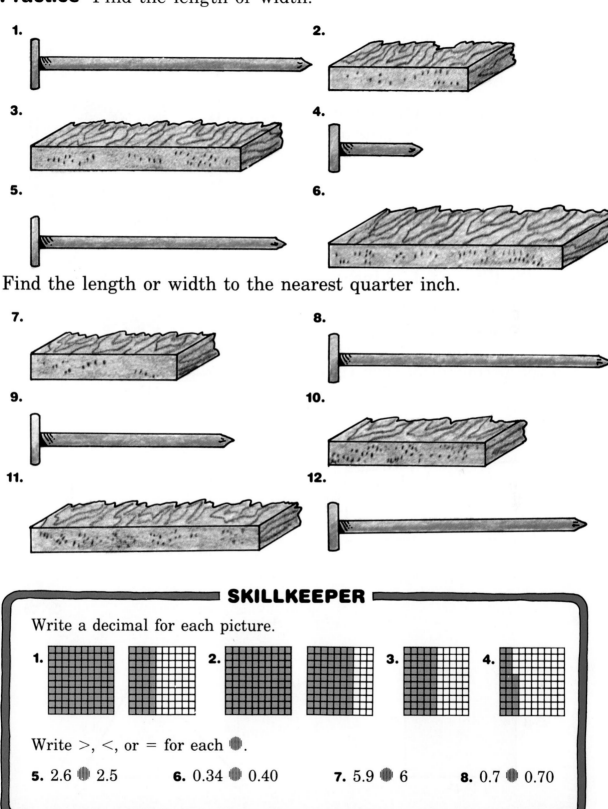

1.

2.

3.

4.

5.

6.

Find the length or width to the nearest quarter inch.

7.

8.

9.

10.

11.

12.

371

Perimeter

Elisa framed her butterfly collection with yarn. How much yarn did she use?

Since we want the total distance around, we add the lengths of the sides.

$$\begin{aligned} 27 \\ 12 \\ 27 \\ +\ 12 \\ \hline 78 \end{aligned}$$ Elisa used 78 inches of yarn.

The **distance around** a figure is the **perimeter** of the figure.

Find the perimeter of each figure.

1.

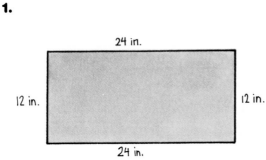

24 in.

12 in.   12 in.

24 in.

2.

56 ft

41 ft   41 ft

56 ft

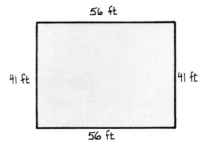

3.

73 yd

83 yd   83 yd

73 yd

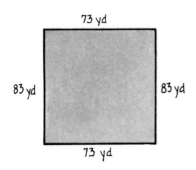

4.

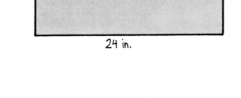

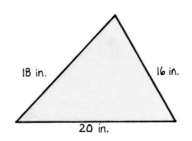

18 in.   16 in.

20 in.

372

PROBLEM SOLVING
Length and Perimeter

Solve.

1. Joe ran around the edge of the field. How far did he run?

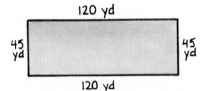

120 yd

45 yd   45 yd

120 yd

2. Jan ran 880 yd. How much farther must she run to run a mile? (1 mile = 1,760 yd)

3. The distance around the track is 440 yd. Leon ran around the track 3 times. How far did he run?

4. How far do baseball players run when they run all the way around the diamond?

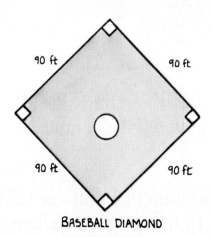

90 ft   90 ft

90 ft   90 ft

BASEBALL DIAMOND

5. Joy hiked 54 mi in 3 days. If she walked the same number of miles each day, how far did she hike each day?

6. How far is it from Hillview to Center to Upton to Hillview?

UPTON

62 mi   38 mi

HILLVIEW   40 mi   CENTER

7. A square field is 87 yd on each side. How far is it around the field?

8. Marta walked $5\frac{1}{4}$ mi in the morning and $6\frac{1}{2}$ mi in the afternoon. How far did she walk that day?

9. *Strategy Practice* A rectangle has a perimeter of 28 in. The length is 4 in. more than the width. How long is the rectangle?

373

Cups, Pints, Quarts, and Gallons

The milk comes in half-pint containers at Jim's school. Each half pint is 1 **cup**. Jim drinks 5 containers each week. Is that more or less than a quart?

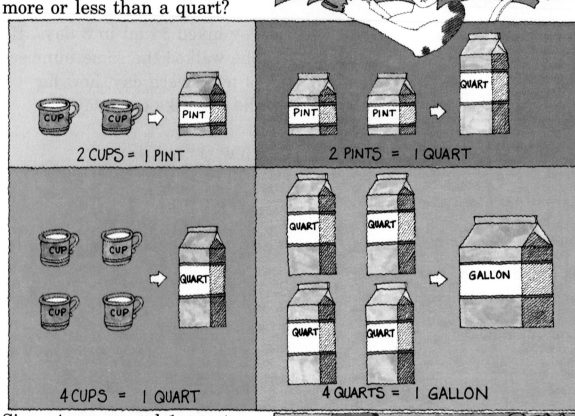

2 CUPS = 1 PINT

2 PINTS = 1 QUART

4 CUPS = 1 QUART

4 QUARTS = 1 GALLON

Since 4 cups equal 1 quart, 5 cups is more than a quart.

Give the missing numbers.

1. 1 pint = __?__ cups.

2. 2 pints = __?__ cups.

3. 1 quart = __?__ cups.

4. 2 quarts = __?__ cups.

5. 1 gallon = __?__ quarts.

6. 5 gallons = __?__ quarts.

Choose the better estimate.

7. Water in a tub
   A 8 pints   **B** 8 gallons

8. Gasoline in a full car tank
   A 15 quarts   **B** 15 gallons

PROBLEM SOLVING
Capacity

Solve.

1. The cook made 8 quarts of fruit punch for a party. How many cups is this?

2. The cook made 5 gallons of vegetable soup. How many quarts is this?

3. Half-pint containers of milk come in boxes of 24. How many quarts of milk are in a box? (1 half pint = 1 cup)

4. One day 225 containers of milk were used. The next day only 196 containers were used. How many more containers were used the first day?

5. How many quarts of milk were used on the day 196 containers were used? (4 containers = 1 quart)

6. The cook used 2 gallons of milk to make soup. How many pints of milk is this?

7. There are 16 cups in a gallon. How many cups of soup can a cook get from 25 gallons?

8. A recipe for fruit punch calls for 7 cups of pineapple juice and 9 cups of orange juice. How many cups of juice would it take to make 5 recipes?

9. The school ordered 15 boxes of milk. In each box there were 24 containers. On the first day 295 containers were used. How many were left?

10. **Strategy Practice** The cook uses 5 cups of whole-wheat flour for each 2 cups of white flour. How many cups of white flour are needed to go with 35 cups of whole-wheat flour? Complete the table.

Whole-wheat flour	5	10	15
White flour	2	4	6

375

Estimating Weight: Ounces, Pounds, and Tons

The **ounce** (oz), **pound** (lb), and **ton** (T) are customary units of weight.

5 nickels

about 1 ounce

pint of milk

about 1 pound

compact car

about 1 ton

16 ounces = 1 pound   2,000 pounds = 1 ton

Choose the unit that makes the statement reasonable.

1. Hand calculator

10 _?_

2. Roasting chicken

$3\frac{1}{2}$ _?_

3. Elephant

3 _?_

4. Typewriter

8 _?_

5. Truck

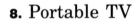

4 _?_

6. Small box of paper clips

2 _?_

7. Bulldozer

12 _?_

8. Portable TV

20 _?_

9. Orange

8 _?_

Estimating Temperature

The customary unit for measuring temperature is the **degree Fahrenheit** (°F). The thermometer shows some common temperatures.

Choose the best estimate.

1. Hot faucet water
- **A** 60°F
- **B** 90°F
- **C** 150°F

2. Cool fall day
- **A** 90°F
- **B** 40°F
- **C** 10°F

3. Temperature of your body
- **A** 148°F
- **B** 98°F
- **C** 38°F

4. Inside a freezer
- **A** 10°F
- **B** 40°F
- **C** 60°F

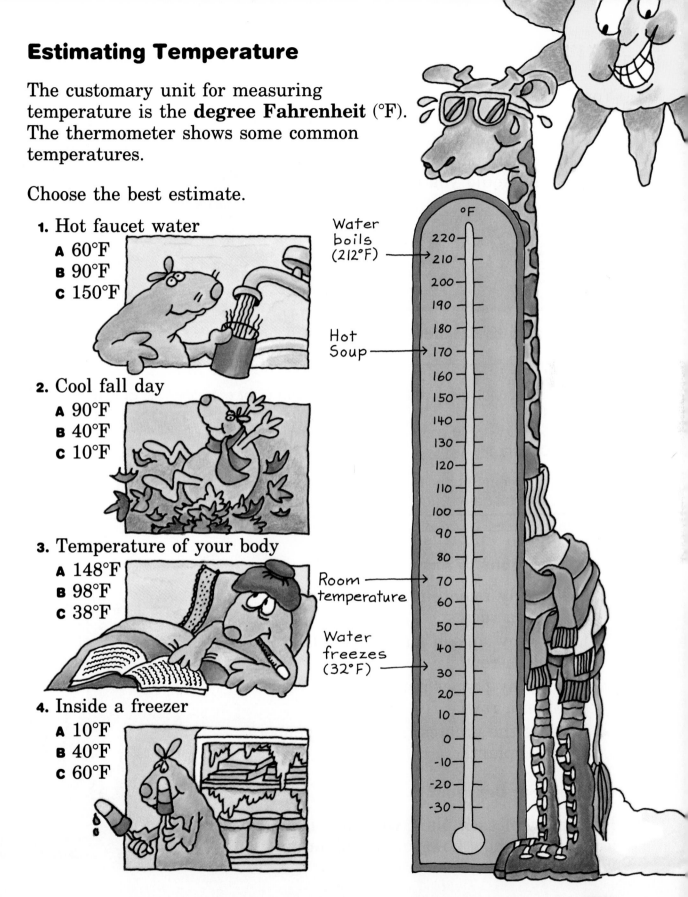

Water boils (212°F)

Hot Soup

Room temperature

Water freezes (32°F)

°F
- 220
- 210
- 200
- 190
- 180
- 170
- 160
- 150
- 140
- 130
- 120
- 110
- 100
- 90
- 80
- 70
- 60
- 50
- 40
- 30
- 20
- 10
- 0
- -10
- -20
- -30

APPLIED PROBLEM SOLVING

QUESTION
DATA
PLAN
ANSWER
CHECK

You want to plant a small vegetable garden. Your garden area is 9 feet by 12 feet. You have decided to plant tomatoes, summer squash, and green peppers. How many of each plant should you buy?

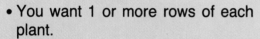

ROWS

12 FEET

9 FEET

Some Things to Consider

- You want 1 or more rows of each plant.
- You don't want to plant closer than 1 foot from the edge.
- You want only one row of squash.
- You don't want more than 2 rows of peppers.
- Amount of space needed between plants: tomatoes—2 to 3 ft, squash—2 to 3 ft, peppers—1 ft

Some Questions to Answer

1. How many tomato plants should you plant in a row?

2. How many squash plants should you plant in a row?

3. How many pepper plants should you plant in a row?

4. What is the greatest number of peppers you will plant?

What Is Your Decision?

How many of each plant will you buy? Draw a picture to show how you are planning your garden.

Which unit would you use? Write inches, feet, yards, or miles.

1. The baby was 18 __?__ long.

2. Mr. White drove 125 __?__ before stopping.

3. The basketball player was 2 __?__ tall.

4. Jo jumped across a creek that was 10 __?__ wide.

Find the length of each nail to the nearest quarter inch.

5.

6.

Find the perimeter of each figure.

7.

	126 ft	
42 ft		42 ft
	126 ft	

8.

	14 yd	
14 yd		14 yd
	14 yd	

Give the missing number.

9. 1 quart = __?__ cups

10. 1 gallon = __?__ quarts

11. 1 pint = __?__ cups

12. 1 quart = __?__ pints

Write ounces, pounds, or tons for each weight.

13. pickup truck
 2 __?__

14. wrist watch
 $1\frac{1}{2}$ __?__

15. 3 books
 6 __?__

Choose the best estimate.

16. Hot summer day
 A 90°F   **B** 10°F   **C** 30°F

17. Ice water
 A 60°F   **B** 33°F   **C** 0°F

Solve.

18. A square field is 175 ft on each side. How far is it around the field?

19. The tank holds 72 gallons of water. How many quarts is this? 1 gallon = 4 quarts.

ANOTHER LOOK

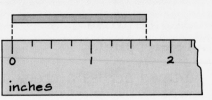

$1\frac{1}{2}$ inches to the nearest half inch.
$1\frac{3}{4}$ inch to the nearest quarter inch.

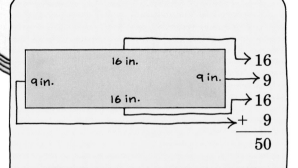

The perimeter of the rectangle is 50 inches.

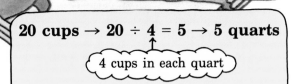

20 cups → 20 ÷ 4 = 5 → 5 quarts

4 cups in each quart

4 quarts → 4 × 2 = 8 → 8 pints

2 pints in each quart

Find the length
to the nearest half inch.

1.

2.

to the nearest quarter inch.

3.

4.

Find the perimeter.

5.
14 yd
8 yd 8 yd
14 yd

6.
25 ft
15 ft
20 ft

7.
25 in.
25 in. 25 in.
25 in.

8.
15 yd
15 yd 17 yd
9 yd

Find the missing numbers.

9. 12 cups = __?__ quarts

10. 2 quarts = __?__ pints

11. 6 gallons = __?__ quarts

12. 16 quarts = __?__ gallons

Estimating Area

The example below shows how you can count squares and parts of squares to **estimate** area.

Estimate the area of this circle.

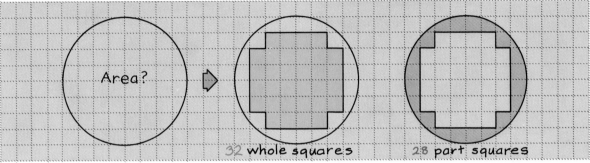

32 whole squares   28 part squares

Estimate that the part squares **average** $\frac{1}{2}$ unit per square.

$\frac{1}{2}$ of $28 = 14$

Area of the red region ⟶ 32 square units
Estimated area of the blue region ⟶ 14 square units
Estimated area of the circle ⟶ 46 square units

Estimate the area of each region.

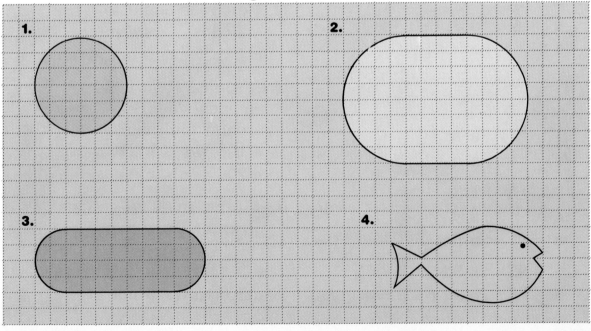

1.

2.

3.

4.

CUMULATIVE REVIEW

Give the letter for the correct answer.

Give the decimal shown.

1.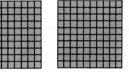

   A 27.0   **B** 2.3
   C 2.7   **D** not given

2.

   A 4.4
   B 0.44
   C 4.04
   D not given

Which amount is correct?

3. 2 dollars and 26 pennies
   A $2.26   **B** $2.62
   C $200.26 **D** not given

4. 1 dollar, 0 dimes, and 4 pennies
   A $1.40   **B** $14.00
   C $1.04   **D** not given

Which answer is correct?

5. 5.24 ▦ 5.26
   A >   **B** <
   C =   **D** not given

6. 32.7 ▦ 32.70
   A >   **B** <
   C =   **D** not given

7. 3.85   **A** 8.61   **C** 7.61
   + 4.76   **B** 8.51   **D** not given

What is the best unit?

8. The pencil is 7 __?__ long.
   A inches **B** yards
   C feet   **D** not given

9. The boy is 4 __?__ tall.
   A inches **B** yards
   C miles   **D** not given

10. It is 275 __?__ to Dallas
    A inches **B** yards
    C miles   **D** not given

11. Give the perimeter.

    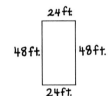
    24ft
    48ft.   48ft.
    24ft.

    A 72 ft
    B 96 ft
    C 144 ft
    D not given

12. 1 quart is equal to
    A 4 cups   **B** 4 pints
    C 4 gallons **D** not given

13. A square field is 54 yards on each side. How far is it around the field?
    A 108 yards **B** 216 yards
    C 206 yards **D** not given

14. A tank holds 20 gallons of water. How many quarts is this? (1 gallon = 4 quarts)
    A 5 quarts **B** 24 quarts
    C 80 quarts **D** not given

TECHNOLOGY RESOURCE BANK

Computer Instruction

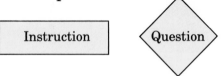

Flowcharts

Flowcharts show a step-by-step way of doing things. They are used to plan instructions for computers. Special shapes are used for the different steps.

(START)   or   (STOP)   [Instruction]   < Question >

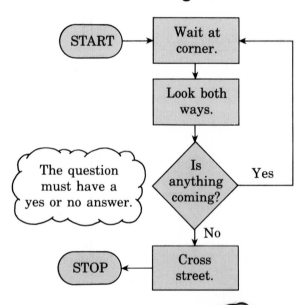

Sharpening a Pencil

(START)
↓
Put pencil in sharpener.
↓
Turn handle.
↓
Take pencil out of sharpener.
↓
(STOP)

Crossing the Street

(START) → Wait at corner.
↓
Look both ways.
↓
Is anything coming? — Yes
↓ No
Cross street. → (STOP)

The question must have a yes or no answer.

1. What is the second step in sharpening a pencil?

2. What do you do after you turn the handle?

3. What is the step after you wait at the corner?

4. If a car is coming, what do you do?

5. If there is nothing coming, what do you do?

384

Give the missing instructions.

1. Going to a Movie

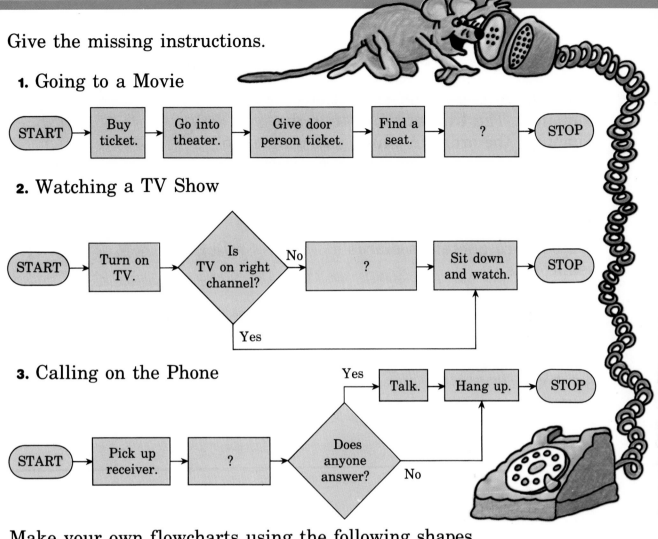

START → Buy ticket. → Go into theater. → Give door person ticket. → Find a seat. → ? → STOP

2. Watching a TV Show

START → Turn on TV. → Is TV on right channel? — No → ? → Sit down and watch. → STOP
Yes ↑

3. Calling on the Phone

START → Pick up receiver. → ? → Does anyone answer? — Yes → Talk. → Hang up. → STOP
No

Make your own flowcharts using the following shapes.

4. Washing your Hands

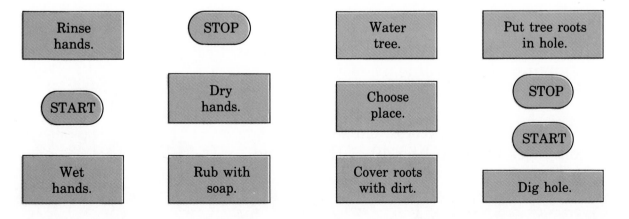

Rinse hands.
STOP
START
Dry hands.
Wet hands.
Rub with soap.

5. Planting a Tree

Water tree.
Put tree roots in hole.
Choose place.
STOP
START
Cover roots with dirt.
Dig hole.

Computer Instruction

Using Computer Programs

A **program** is a set of instructions for the computer. The **line number** tells the computer the order in which you want it to follow instructions. The programs below use special words such as PRINT, END, and RUN. They also use special symbols for multiplication (∗) and division (/). Other symbols are quotation marks (" ") and semicolons (;).

PROGRAM

```
10 PRINT "12 * 3"
20 PRINT 12 * 3
30 END
RUN
```

Press RETURN or ENTER.

RUN

```
12 * 3
36
```

```
10 PRINT 96/3
20 PRINT "96/3"
30 PRINT "96/3 = ";
40 PRINT 96/3
50 END
RUN
```

```
32
96/3
96/3 = 32
```

1. What did the quotation marks cause the computer to do to line 10 of the first program?

2. What did the semicolon cause the computer to do to line 40 of the second program?

386

When we want the computer to erase the
last program, we use the command NEW.
Write the RUN for each of these programs.

1. NEW
   10 PRINT 27 * 4
   20 END

2. NEW
   10 PRINT "27 * 4"
   20 END

3. NEW
   10 PRINT "27 * 4 = "
   20 PRINT 27 * 4
   30 END

4. NEW
   10 PRINT "27 * 4 = ";
   20 PRINT 27 * 4
   30 END

5. NEW
   10 PRINT "91/7"
   20 PRINT 91/7
   30 PRINT "91/7 = "
   40 PRINT 91/7
   50 END

6. NEW
   10 PRINT "83 + 79"
   20 PRINT 83 + 79
   30 PRINT "83 + 79 = ";
   40 PRINT 83 + 79
   50 END

7. NEW
   10 PRINT "152 - 86 = "
   20 PRINT 152 - 86
   30 END

8. NEW
   10 PRINT "38 * 6 = ";
   20 PRINT 38 * 6
   30 END

★Write a program for each RUN.

9. 8 + 4

10. 12

11. 8 + 4
    12

12. 8 + 4 = 12

13. 7 * 9
    63

14. 7 * 9 = 63

Computer Drawings

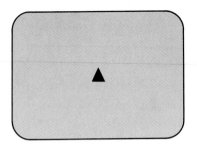

Logo is a special computer language. You can use it to draw pictures on a computer screen. A small triangle △, called a *turtle*, can move around to draw pictures. But you must tell the turtle what to do. The pictures show you how to make the turtle move and draw.

The turtle

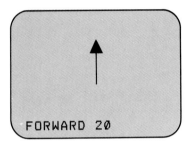

Move forward
20 units.

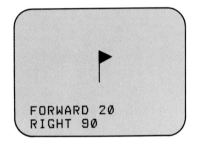

Turn right
90 degrees.

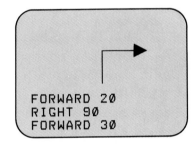

Move forward
30 units.

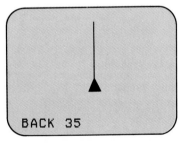

Move back 35 units.

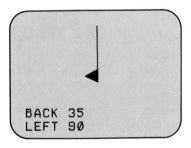

Turn left 90 degrees.

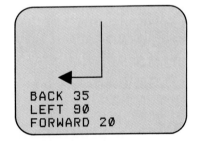

Move forward 20 units.

The turtle was told to draw a triangle that is 30 units long on each side.

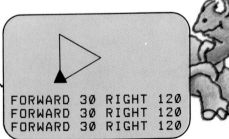

Give the missing word for each picture.

1.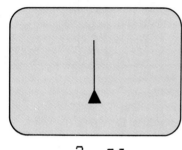

_?__ 40

2.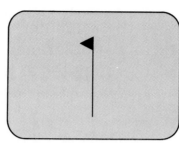

FORWARD 50
_?__ 90

3.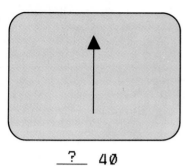

_?__ 30

4.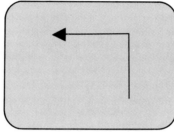

FORWARD 40
_?__ 90
FORWARD 40

5.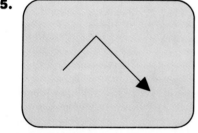

RIGHT 45 FORWARD 30
RIGHT 90 _?__ 40

6.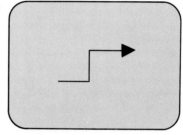

RIGHT 90 FORWARD 20
_?__ 90 FORWARD 20
RIGHT 90 FORWARD 20

7. Write commands to make the turtle draw this rectangle.

 20 units

40 units

★ **8.** Write commands to make the turtle draw this shape.

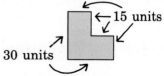

15 units

30 units

Using GOTO

Another important word the computer understands is GOTO. In the program below, GOTO 40 tells the computer to jump to line 40.

Program

```
10  PRINT  "GOOD"
20  GOTO 40
30  PRINT  "NIGHT,"
40  PRINT  "MORNING,"
50  END
```

Screen

```
RUN
GOOD
MORNING,
```

Notice that the computer jumped over line 30.

Program A

```
10  PRINT  "WHAT'S"
20  GOTO 40
30  PRINT  "OLD?"
40  PRINT  "NEW?"
50  END
```

Program B

```
10  PRINT  "HAVE"
20  GOTO 50
30  PRINT  "DAY,"
40  GOTO 70
50  PRINT  "A NICE"
60  GOTO 30
70  END
```

RUN A

```
RUN
WHAT'S
NEW?
```

RUN B

```
RUN
HAVE
A NICE
DAY,
```

1. What line did the computer jump over in Program A?

2. What did the computer do after printing HAVE in Program B?

3. What did the computer do after printing DAY in Program B?

390

Write the RUN for each program.

1.
```
10 PRINT "HOW OLD "
20 GOTO 40
30 PRINT "IS SHE?"
40 PRINT "ARE YOU?"
50 END
```

2.
```
10 PRINT "24 TIMES 6
   EQUALS"
20 GOTO 40
30 PRINT 24/6
40 PRINT 24 * 6
50 END
```

3.
```
10 PRINT "HOW"
20 GOTO 50
30 PRINT "YOU?"
40 GOTO 70
50 PRINT "ARE"
60 GOTO 30
70 END
```

4.
```
10 PRINT "54 DIVIDED
   BY 9"
20 GOTO 50
30 PRINT 54/9
40 GOTO 70
50 PRINT "EQUALS"
60 GOTO 30
70 END
```

5.
```
10 PRINT "TWINKLE
   TWINKLE"
20 GOTO 70
30 PRINT "HOW I"
40 PRINT "WONDER"
50 PRINT "WHERE
   YOU ARE."
60 GOTO 90
70 PRINT "LITTLE
   STAR"
80 GOTO 30
90 END
```

6.
```
10 PRINT "IF YOU
   KNOW"
20 GOTO 70
30 PRINT "ALSO
   KNOW"
40 GOTO 90
50 PRINT "THEN
   YOU"
60 GOTO 30
70 PRINT "9 * 7 = ";
   9 * 7
80 GOTO 50
90 PRINT "7 * 9 = ";
   7 * 9
100 END
```

★ **7.** Write a program of your own using GOTO. Give the RUN.

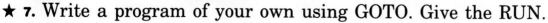

Computer-Assisted Problem Solving

Problem 1 (For use after page 17)
How many dogs, cats, and birds are owned by members of your class? How many pets in all are owned by your class?

Program 1
```
10   REM HOW MANY PETS?
20   INPUT "HOW MANY DOGS ARE
     OWNED? ";D
30   INPUT"HOW MANY CATS ARE
     OWNED? ";C
40   INPUT"HOW MANY BIRDS
     ARE OWNED? ";B
50   PRINT:PRINT "DOGS-----";
60   FOR X = 1 TO D:PRINT "*";
     :NEXT X
70   PRINT:PRINT "CATS-----";
80   FOR X = 1 TO C:PRINT "*";
     :NEXT X
90   PRINT:PRINT "BIRDS----";
100  FOR X = 1 TO B:PRINT "*";
     :NEXT X
110  PRINT:PRINT "THE TOTAL NUMBER
     OF PETS IN THE CLASS IS
     "B+C+D"."
120  END
```

Problem 2 (For use after page 77)
Suppose you have $100 to spend. You can buy any five items below as long as the total does not go over $100. What items would you buy? Estimate the total and see if you have enough money. Using Program 2, below, enter the prices from this list.

Albums:	$29.95	Toys:	$19.95
Watch:	$ 9.95	Lunch:	$ 6.49
Books:	$ 7.79	Clothes:	$43.39
	Video Game:	$23.29	

Program 2
```
10   REM ESTIMATING A TOTAL
20   T = 0
30   FOR Z = 1 TO 5
40   PRINT : INPUT "ENTER THE
     COST OF ONE ITEM WITHOUT
     THE $";P
50   T = T + P
60   NEXT Z
70   PRINT : PRINT "YOUR ITEMS
     COST $";T;"."
80   PRINT : IF T > 100 THEN
     PRINT "YOUR TOTAL IS OVER
     $100. CHOOSE AGAIN.":
     GOTO 20
90   END
```

Problem 3 (For use after page 125)
It's your birthday and your mother has bought 18 favors for your party. Your mother says you can invite any number of guests to your party as long as everyone gets the same number of favors. What different numbers of guests can you invite? How many favors will each get? Don't forget to include yourself as a member of the party.

Program 3
```
10   REM BIRTHDAY
20   INPUT "HOW MANY FAVORS DO
     YOU HAVE? ";F
30   FOR P = 2 TO F
40   IF F/P = INT(F/P) THEN PRINT
     "YOU AND "P-1" GUESTS GET
     "F/P" "FAVORS."
50   NEXT P
60   END
```

Problem 4 (For use after page 241)

Using five blue cards numbered 1–5 and five red cards numbered 1–5, answer the following questions.

1. What fraction of the cards is red?
2. What fraction of the cards is even numbered?
3. What fractions of the cards are blue and odd numbered?

Use the program below to help you solve these problems.

Program 4

```
10  REM CARDS
20  PRINT "ENTER YOUR FRACTION
    WITH A COMMA BETWEEN
    NUMERATOR AND DENOMINATOR."
30  PRINT:PRINT "EXAMPLE: ENTER
    6/10 AS 6,10."
40  PRINT:INPUT "WHAT FRACTION
    IS RED? ";A,B
50  IF A/B < > .5 THEN PRINT "TRY
    AGAIN.": GOTO 40
60  PRINT:PRINT "CORRECT!"
70  PRINT:INPUT "WHAT FRACTION
    IS EVEN NUMBERED?";C,D
80  IF C/D < > .4 THEN PRINT "TRY
    AGAIN.": GOTO 70
90  PRINT:PRINT "CORRECT!"
100 PRINT:INPUT "WHAT FRACTIONS
    ARE BLUE AND ODD? ";E,F
110 IF E/F < > .3 THEN PRINT
    "TRY AGAIN.":GOTO 100
120 PRINT: PRINT "CORRECT!"
130 END
```

Problem 5 (For use after page 379)

Milk comes in containers of various sizes. If a pint of milk costs $0.40, a quart costs $0.72, and a gallon costs $2.40, how much does each cost per cup? Which is the best buy?

Program 5

```
10  REM BUYING MILK
20  INPUT "HOW MUCH FOR EACH
    PINT? ";P
30  PRINT:INPUT "HOW MUCH FOR
    EACH QUART? ";Q
40  PRINT:INPUT "HOW MUCH FOR
    EACH GALLON? ";G
50  PC = INT(1000*P/2 + .005)/
    1000
60  QC = INT(1000*Q/4 + .005)/
    1000
70  GC = INT(1000*G/16 + .005)/
    1000
80  PRINT:PRINT "PRICE PER CUP
    FOR PINT QUANTITY IS $"PC
90  PRINT:PRINT "PRICE PER CUP
    FOR QUART QUANTITY IS $"QC
100 PRINT:PRINT "PRICE PER CUP
    FOR GALLON QUANTITY IS $"GC
110 PRINT:IF PC<QC AND PC<GC
    THEN PRINT "PINT IS THE
    BEST BUY.":GOTO 140
120 PRINT:IF QC<PC AND QC<GC
    THEN PRINT "QUART IS THE
    BEST BUY.":GOTO 140
130 PRINT:PRINT "GALLON IS THE
    BEST BUY."
140 END
```

Problem 6 (For use after page 289)

Can you use a unit segment and estimate the length of a given segment to the nearest unit? Program 6 will help you improve your measurement and estimation skills.

Computer-Assisted Problem Solving

Program 6

```
10   REM  ESTIMATING LENGTH
20   U = INT (4*RND (1) + 3)
30   S = INT (6*RND (1) + 4)*
     U: IF S < U THEN 20
40   L = INT (S / U + .5): IF L =
     1 THEN 20
50   FOR N = 1 TO U: PRINT "_";:
     NEXT N: PRINT "1 UNIT"
60   PRINT : PRINT
70   FOR N = 1 TO S: PRINT "_";:
     NEXT N
80   PRINT : PRINT : INPUT
     "ESTIMATE THE LENGTH ";E
90   PRINT "LENGTH","EST.",
     "DIFF."
100  PRINT L,E, ABS (L - E)
110  INPUT "TRY AGAIN?(Y/N)";Y$
120  IF LEFT$ (Y$,1) = "Y" THEN 20
130  END
```

Problem 7 (For use after page 45)

You want to save some money from your allowance for presents. How much can you save by December 1st if you start now? **Data:** Plan to save $\frac{1}{2}$ your weekly allowance.

Data Needed: How many weeks from now until December 1st? Estimate your total amounts and use Program 7 to check.

Program 7

```
10   REM SAVINGS
20   INPUT "WHAT IS YOUR WEEKLY
     ALLOWANCE IN DOLLARS? $";A
30   PRINT : INPUT "HOW MANY WEEKS
     WILL YOU SAVE MONEY?";W
40   PRINT "WEEK", "SAVINGS"
50   FOR N = 1 TO W:S = A / 2:T =
     T + S
60   PRINT N,T: NEXT N
70   END
```

Problem 8 (For use after page 103)

You want to plant 32 tomato plants in your garden. You want to plant them in equal rows with no plants left over. What are your choices for planting? How many choices are there? Use the computer program below to check your answers.

Program 8

```
10   REM   TOMATO PLANTS
20   T = 0
30   INPUT "HOW MANY TOMATO
     PLANTS ? ";P
40   PRINT "ROWS","PLANTS"
50   FOR R = 1 TO P
60   FOR S = 1 TO P
70   IF R*S < > P THEN 110
80   T = T + 1
90   PRINT R,S
100  PRINT
110  NEXT S
120  NEXT R
130  PRINT : PRINT "THE NUMBER
     OF WAYS TO PLANT IS "T"."
140  END
```

Problem 9 (For use after page 337)

Choose a partner and play the Largest Remainder Game. The computer will give you a divisor. You then choose a 3-digit dividend. Your partner will then do the same. The computer divides the two numbers and calculates the remainders for each player. The player with the larger remainder wins.

Program 9

```
 10   REM LARGEST REMAINDER
 20   D(1) = INT (79*RND(1)+15):
      D(2) = D(1) + INT
      (10*RND(1)-6)
 30   IF D(2) = D(1) THEN 20
 40   FOR N = 1 TO 2:GOSUB 160:
      NEXT N
 50   PRINT:PRINT "HERE ARE THE
      REMAINDERS"
 60   PRINT:PRINT "PLAYER 1",
      "PLAYER 2"
 70   FOR N = 1 TO 2:PRINT R(N),
 80   NEXT N
 90   PRINT:PRINT
100   IF R(1) > R(2) THEN PRINT
      "PLAYER 1 WINS!":GOTO 130
110   IF R(1) = R(2) THEN PRINT
      "YOU TIE!":GOTO 130
120   PRINT "PLAYER 2 WINS!"
130   INPUT "DO YOU WANT TO PLAY
      AGAIN?(Y/N)";Y$
140   IF LEFT$(Y$,1) = "Y"
      THEN 20
150   END
160   PRINT "PLAYER ";N;": YOUR
      DIVISOR IS ";D(N)
170   INPUT "TYPE A 3-DIGIT
      NUMBER ";K(N)
180   IF K(N) < 100 OR K(N) > 999
      THEN PRINT "3 DIGITS
      PLEASE!":GOTO 170
190   Q(N) = K(N)/D(N):S(N) =
      INT(Q(N)):R(N)=K(N)
      - S(N)*D(N)
200   RETURN
```

Problem 10 (For use after page 155)

Suppose you can run at a pace of 3 km for every 17 minutes. How long would it take you to run 5 km? 10 km?

Program 10

```
10   REM RUNNING
20   INPUT "HOW MANY MINUTES FOR
     3 KM? ";P
30   INPUT "HOW FAR DID YOU
     RUN? ";D
40   PRINT:PRINT "IT TOOK YOU
     ABOUT "INT(D*P/3)" MINUTES."
50   PRINT:INPUT "DO YOU WANT TO
     TRY AGAIN? (Y/N) ";Y$
60   IF LEFT$(Y$,1) = "Y" THEN
     GOTO 20
70   END
```

Problem 11 (For use after page 185)

How many days do you spend watching TV in a year? Estimate how many days of TV watching equals 24 hours. Then estimate about how many times this could happen in a year. Use the program below to check your estimate.

Data Needed: The number of minutes you watch TV each day.

Program 11

```
 10   REM  TV WATCHING
 20   INPUT "HOW MANY MINUTES DO
      YOU WATCH TV EACH DAY? ";M
 30   T = M*365
 40   H = INT (T/60)
 50   D = INT (H/24)
 60   PRINT "IN A YEAR YOU WATCH TV
      ABOUT"
 70   PRINT T" MINUTES"
 80   PRINT H" HOURS"
 90   PRINT D" DAYS"
100   END
```

Computer-Assisted Problem Solving

Problem 12 (For use after page 215)

The following are the statistics for Ryne Iceberg, the star second baseman of the Chicago Pugs:

Total times at bat:	154
Hits:	45
Walks:	8
Hit by Pitch:	2
Sacrifices:	9

Walks, hit by pitch, and sacrifices must be subtracted from total at bats to find official at bats. Use the program below to divide the number of hits by the official times at bat to calculate his batting average to the nearest thousandth.

Program 12

```
10   REM   BATTING AVERAGE
20   INPUT "WHAT IS THE PLAYER'S
     NAME? ";N$
30   PRINT : INPUT "HOW MANY AT
     BATS? ";B
40   PRINT : INPUT "HOW MANY
     HITS?";H
50   PRINT : INPUT "HOW MANY
     WALKS? ";W
60   PRINT : INPUT "HOW MANY TIMES
     HIT BY A PITCH? ";P
70   PRINT : INPUT "HOW MANY
     SACRIFICES? ";S
80   OF = B - (W + P + S)
90   A = H/OF:A = INT (1000 * A +
     .0005)/1000
100  PRINT "BATTING AVERAGE FOR
     "N$" IS "A
110  END
```

Problem 13 (For use after page 261)

In Tim's class 4 out of every 5 students have brown eyes. How many of the 30 students in the class have brown eyes? Use the computer program below to find equivalent fractions that will help you solve this problem.

Program 13

```
10   REM   EQUIVALENT FRACTIONS
20   PRINT : INPUT "NUMERATOR OF
     THE FRACTION? ";N
30   PRINT : INPUT "DENOMINATOR OF
     THE FRACTION? ";D
40   PRINT : INPUT "HOW MANY
     EQUIVALENT FRACTIONS DO YOU
     WANT? ";E
50   PRINT : PRINT "HERE ARE YOUR
     EQUIVALENT FRACTIONS: "
60   FOR Z = 2 TO E + 1
70   PRINT Z*N"/"Z* D,
80   NEXT Z
90   PRINT : INPUT "ANOTHER
     TRY?(Y/N)" ;Y$
100  IF LEFT$ (Y$,1) = "Y" THEN
     GOTO 20
110  END
```

Problem 14 (For use after page 361)

If Sonia bought one item from each group and spent $2.62, what could she have ordered? There are 2 choices in each group. Use estimation to make your choices. Use the computer to check your estimate.

A		B		C	
Hamburger	1.39	Fries	.65	Milk	.45
Pizza	1.19	Salad	.98	Juice	.58

Program 14

```
10  REM    MENU
20  PRINT : INPUT "WHAT IS THE
    TOTAL COST? ";T
30  PRINT : PRINT "ENTER THE COST
    OF EACH ITEM.":T1 = 0
40  FOR N = 1 TO 3: INPUT C(N)
50  T1 = T1 + C(N): NEXT N
60  IF T1 < > T THEN PRINT "THIS
    TOTAL IS "T1: GOTO 90
70  PRINT "YOU HAVE FOUND THE
    CHOICES!"
80  PRINT C(1)" + "C(2)" + "C(3)"
    = "T1: GOTO 110
90  INPUT "DO YOU WANT TO TRY
    AGAIN?(Y/N) ";Y$
100 IF LEFT$ (Y$,1) = "Y" THEN
    30
110 END
```

Problem 15 (For use after page 313)

How much allowance will you receive on Sunday if you get $0.10 on Monday, $0.20 on Tuesday, $0.40 on Wednesday, and so on, doubling the amount each day? What is your total allowance for the week? Estimate, then use the computer to find out.

Program 15

```
10  REM ALLOWANCE
20  T = 0:P = .05
30  INPUT "HOW MANY DAYS TO
    CALCULATE?";L
40  PRINT : PRINT "DAY", "PAY",
    "TOTAL"
50  FOR D = 1 TO L
60  P = P * 2:T = T + P
70  PRINT D, "$"P,"$"T
80  NEXT D
90  END
```

Calculator-Assisted Problem Solving

Problem 16 (For use with page 75)

Jack bought 2 items. Their total cost was less than $20 but more than $19. Use estimation to help you decide what Jack might have bought. Use your calculator to check your answers. There are several possible answers.

ITEM	PRICE
Clock	$ 7.48
Brush	$ 4.69
Sunglasses	$ 5.19
Umbrella	$12.49
Hand mirror	$ 3.98
Calculator	$ 4.99
Radio	$14.75
Basket	$ 6.98

Problem 17 (For use with page 181)

DATA BANK See page 403. A 727 airplane was full on 5 flights between Denver and Chicago. Another airline used a 757 airplane for the same 5 flights. On these flights, 4 were full and the fifth flight had 9 empty seats. How many more people did the 757 carry?

Problem 18 (For use with page 205)

Greenleaf and Evergreen are two nurseries. Their plants are of equal quality. Which nursery has the better buy for each plant?

	Item	Greenleaf	Evergreen
1.	Rose Bushes	6 for $10.50	2 for $ 3.38
2.	Plum Trees	3 for $ 5.94	5 for $ 9.45
3.	Cedar Trees	4 for $25.96	3 for $20.37
4.	Pine Trees	5 for $44.90	6 for $52.74

Calculator-Assisted Problem Solving

Problem 19 (For use with page 71)
Below is a record of a savings account. It shows **deposits** (money put in) and **withdrawals** (money taken out). **Interest** is money the bank puts into the account. The **balance** is the amount of money in the account. Give the missing balances for each date.

	Date	Deposit	Withdrawal	Interest	Balance
1.	Nov. 3	$54.64			$ 54.64
2.	Nov. 11		$29.88		
3.	Nov. 14	$49.75			
4.	Nov. 25		$37.79		
5.	Dec. 1			$0.57	
6.	Dec. 7	$48.95			

Problem 20 (For use with page 359)
The table shows three different rates for telephone calls between two cities.

1. How much can you save on a 10-minute call if you phone on a weekend rather than during a weekday?

2. What is the savings between the day rate and evening rate for a 10-minute call?

	Full Day Rate		Evening Rate		Holiday, Weekend, and Night Rate	
From Danville to Lakeport	First minute	Each additional minute	First minute	Each additional minute	First minute	Each additional minute
	$0.47	$0.36	$0.32	$0.26	$0.18	$0.15

Problem 21 (For use with page 207)
DATA BANK See page 401. Find the average depth of the 4 oceans (Pacific, Atlantic, Indian, and Arctic). What is the average depth of the four seas listed? How much deeper is the average of the oceans than that of the seas?

Problem 22 (For use with page 311)
DATA BANK See page 400. Find the area of the base of each pyramid. Assume that each base is a square. Since you are given the perimeter of the base, you will need to find the length of one side before you can find the area.

Canning and Freezing Cookbook

STANDARD CAN SIZES

CAN	SIZE	CAN	SIZE
No. 1	0.30 L	No. 2½	0.83 L
No. 300	0.41 L	No. 3	0.95 L
No. 1 tall	0.47 L	No. 5	1.74 L
No. 2	0.59 L	No. 10	3.08 L
No. 3 squat	0.65 L		

Recipe for Finger Paint

Materials:

125 mL cornstarch
250 mL cold water
1 envelope unflavored gelatin
500 mL boiling water
Food coloring

Directions:

1. Mix cornstarch with 185 mL cold water in a saucepan.
2. Soak gelatin in 65 mL cold water in a bowl.
3. Stir the boiling water into the cornstarch mixture. Cook over medium heat. Bring to boil. Mixture should be clear.
4. Remove from heat. Stir in the gelatin mixture.
5. Cool. Put small amounts of mixture into various containers. Each container will be a different color. Stir in enough drops of food coloring into each jar until desired color is reached.

PYRAMIDS
Perimeters of Square Bases and Heights

Giza

Great Pyramid
Perimeter: 920 m
Height: 137 m

2nd Pyramid
Perimeter: 864 m
Height: 144 m

3rd Pyramid
Perimeter: 436 m
Height: 66 m

North Stone Pyramid
Perimeter: 880 m
Height: 99 m

Dashur

South Stone Pyramid
Perimeter: 760 m
Height: 101 m

Nile

Pyramid of Senwosret I
Perimeter: 420 m
Height: 61 m

Pyramid of Maidum
Perimeter: 576 m
Height: 92 m

Maidum

TYPES OF RAINFALL

TYPE	AMOUNT
Trace	Unmeasurable
Light rain	About $\frac{1}{10}$ inch per hour
Moderate rain	About $\frac{3}{10}$ inch per hour
Heavy rain	Greater than $\frac{3}{10}$ inch per hour

PARK FOLDER

Volcanoes

Name	State	Height
Mt. Baker	WA	3,285 m
Glacier Peak	WA	3,213 m
Mt. Rainier	WA	4,392 m
Mt. Adams	WA	3,751 m
Mt. St. Helens	WA	2,547 m
Mt. Hood	OR	3,424 m
Mt. Jefferson	OR	3,199 m
Crater Lake	OR	2,486 m
Mt. Shasta	CA	4,317 m
Lassen Peak	CA	3,187 m
Mauna Loa	HI	4,169 m
Mt. Katmai	AK	2,047 m

Great Trees of the American Forest

Name	Maximum Height	Maximum Diameter
Douglas fir	76 m	244 cm
Loblolly pine	30 m	91 cm
Slash pine	30 m	91 cm
Shortleaf pine	30 m	91 cm
Longleaf pine	37 m	76 cm
Yellow poplar	37 m	182 cm
Sugar maple	30 m	121 cm
White oak	30 m	121 cm

Travelers' Guide to Average Annual Rainfall

City	Rainfall
Atlanta, GA	123 cm
Boston, MA	108 cm
Chicago, IL	87 cm
Cincinatti, OH	102 cm
Cleveland, OH	89 cm
Denver, CO	39 cm
Detroit, MI	79 cm
Honolulu, HI	58 cm
Houston, TX	122 cm
Juneau, AK	139 cm
Miami, FL	152 cm
New York, NY	106 cm
St. Louis, MO	91 cm
San Francisco, CA	50 cm
Seattle, WA	99 cm
Washington, DC	99 cm

—*Registry of Ships*—

FERRYBOATS

Name	Location	Number of Cars	Length of Boat
Elwha	Seattle, WA	162	116 m
Illahee	Seattle, WA	75	78 m
Tillikum	Seattle, WA	100	94 m
Kittitas	Seattle, WA	100	100 m
Columbia	Vancouver, B.C.	180	127 m
Malastina	Vancouver, B.C.	132	124 m
Taku	Vancouver, B.C.	105	107 m

OCEANS OF THE WORLD

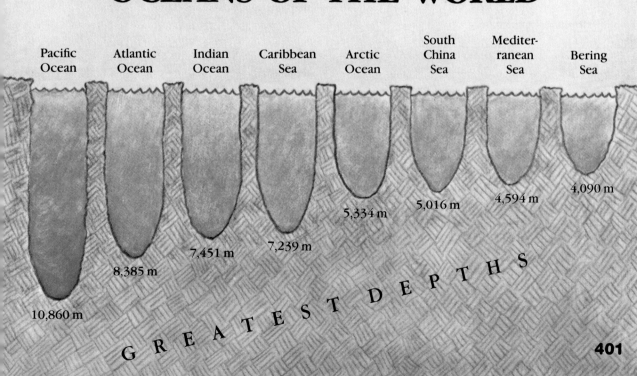

Pacific Ocean	Atlantic Ocean	Indian Ocean	Caribbean Sea	Arctic Ocean	South China Sea	Mediterranean Sea	Bering Sea
10,860 m	8,385 m	7,451 m	7,239 m	5,334 m	5,016 m	4,594 m	4,090 m

GREATEST DEPTHS

•ARTHUR'S ANIMAL ALMANAC•

Record Ages of Animals

Name	Age
Elephant	61 years
Horse	54 years
Hippopotamus	41 years
Rhinoceros	40 years
Bear	34 years
Monkey	25 years
Cat	23 years
Dog	22 years

Animal Heartbeats in 1 Minute

Animal	Heartbeat
Bat	750
Cat	120
Dog	90
Elephant	33
Goat	90
Hamster	450
Lion	44
Monkey	192
Mouse	534
Rat	328
Sheep	75
Skunk	166
Squirrel	249

SPORTS PAGE

1980 WINTER OLYMPICS SPEED SKATING WOMEN'S EVENTS

500-METER RACE

		Seconds*
1. Karin Enke, East Germany		
2. Leah Mueller, U.S.A.		42
3. Natalia Petruseva, U.S.S.R.		42
		43

1,000-METER RACE

1. Natalia Petruseva, U.S.S.R.		
2. Leah Mueller, U.S.A.		84
3. Silvia Albrecht, East Germany		86
		87

1,500-METER RACE

1. Annie Borckink, Netherlands		
2. Ria Visser, Netherlands		131
3. Sabine Becker, East Germany		133
		133

3,000-METER RACE

1. Bjoerg Eva Jensen, Norway		
2. Sabine Becker, East Germany		272
3. Beth Heiden, U.S.A.		273
		274

*Race time to nearest second

AIRPLANE SEATING CAPACITY

AIRPLANE	NUMBER OF PERSONS
DC-10	380
L-1011	400
727	189
747	550
757	237
767	289

MAJOR WORLD AIRPORTS

NAME	NUMBER OF PASSENGERS (IN A RECENT YEAR)
Chicago O'Hare	44,238,000
Atlanta International	29,977,000
Los Angeles International	28,361,000
London Heathrow	23,775,000
Tokyo Haneda	23,190,000
JFK, New York	22,545,000
San Francisco International	20,249,000
Dallas-Ft. Worth	17,318,000
Denver Stapleton	15,281,000
La Guardia, New York	15,087,000

403

Appendix

More Practice

Set A   For use after page 3

Add.

1.	5 + 6	2.	7 + 4	3.	4 + 4	4.	0 + 8	5.	9 + 1	6.	3 + 5	7.	5 + 0
8.	6 + 6	9.	8 + 9	10.	4 + 6	11.	3 + 9	12.	1 + 6	13.	7 + 8	14.	6 + 7
15.	7 + 7	16.	3 + 0	17.	7 + 9	18.	3 + 2	19.	4 + 3	20.	8 + 8	21.	2 + 4
22.	2 + 9	23.	2 + 0	24.	8 + 6	25.	4 + 9	26.	9 + 6	27.	3 + 8	28.	3 + 3
29.	7 + 8	30.	0 + 9	31.	7 + 7	32.	9 + 4	33.	7 + 9	34.	1 + 8	35.	4 + 5

Set B   For use after page 5

Subtract.

1.	15 − 7	2.	11 − 8	3.	5 − 5	4.	8 − 6	5.	18 − 9	6.	7 − 3	7.	9 − 3
8.	17 − 8	9.	15 − 9	10.	9 − 5	11.	12 − 7	12.	7 − 0	13.	10 − 7	14.	13 − 4
15.	16 − 8	16.	13 − 5	17.	11 − 7	18.	14 − 9	19.	8 − 5	20.	12 − 8	21.	14 − 6
22.	11 − 10	23.	7 − 2	24.	10 − 6	25.	8 − 8	26.	13 − 8	27.	14 − 7	28.	6 − 5

Add.

1. 5	**2.** 7	**3.** 4	**4.** 3	**5.** 7	**6.** 1	**7.** 4
2	1	5	3	3	9	4
+ 6	+ 4	+ 5	+ 7	+ 2	+ 1	+ 4

8. 5	**9.** 4	**10.** 2	**11.** 1	**12.** 2	**13.** 6	**14.** 4
4	6	6	5	3	4	2
+ 0	+ 3	+ 2	+ 3	+ 6	+ 6	+ 1

Write the standard number.

1. five hundred eighty nine

2. one hundred seventy

3. three hundred four

4. six hundred thirty-six

5. seven hundred forty

6. four hundred seventy-one

7. two hundred sixty

8. nine hundred sixty-four

Write the standard number. Use a comma to separate thousands.

1. five thousand, four hundred

2. eight thousand, three hundred eighty-four

3. two thousand, five hundred thirty

4. seven thousand, one hundred seventy-six

5. one thousand, two hundred twenty-five

Set A   For use after page 29

Write > or < for each ▦ .

1.   73 ▦ 64   **2.**   46 ▦ 48   **3.**   676 ▦ 667

4.   538 ▦ 358   **5.**   312 ▦ 318   **6.** 2,000 ▦ 1,999

7. 5,267 ▦ 5,270   **8.** 8,363 ▦ 8,636   **9.** 3,450 ▦ 3,440

Set B   For use after page 31

Round to the nearest ten.

1. 28 → ▥   **2.** 83 → ▥   **3.** 65 → ▥   **4.** 34 → ▥

5. 71 → ▥   **6.** 46 → ▥   **7.** 17 → ▥   **8.** 52 → ▥

Round to the nearest hundred.

1. 285   **2.** 3,796   **3.** 733   **4.** 5,806

5. 461   **6.** 6,055   **7.** 866   **8.** 150

Set C   For use after page 33

Round to the nearest thousand.

1. 4,499   **2.** 8,207   **3.** 2,600   **4.** 5,653

5. 6,233   **6.** 7,492   **7.** 9,010   **8.** 6,874

Round to the nearest dollar.

1. $1.79   **2.** $68.16   **3.** $13.49   **4.** $72.28

5. $2.55   **6.** $64.95   **7.** $3.18   **8.** $87.32

Set A   For use after page 35

Write the standard number. Use a comma to separate thousands.

1. thirty-six thousand

2. five hundred seventy-nine thousand

3. two hundred eight thousand, four hundred thirteen

4. nine hundred three thousand, two hundred twenty

5. three hundred one thousand, four hundred

Set B   For use after page 36

Write > or < for each ⬤ .

1. 37,530 ⬤ 36,351   2. 21,568 ⬤ 21,658   3. 89,709 ⬤ 100,000

4. 413,268 ⬤ 413,260   5. 75,200 ⬤ 85,200   6. 586,490 ⬤ 86,490

7. 15,600 ⬤ 16,500   8. 610,000 ⬤ 609,000   9. 55,783 ⬤ 55,800

Set C   For use after page 39

Write the standard number.

1. eight million, seven hundred twelve thousand

2. forty-nine million

3. five hundred sixty-eight million, three hundred sixty-five thousand

4. seven hundred million, five hundred thousand

5. sixty-three million

Set A   **For use after page 51**

Find the sums.

1.	2.	3.	4.	5.	6.
38 + 9	35 + 44	342 + 80	36 + 53	475 + 92	747 + 14

7.	8.	9.	10.	11.	12.
810 + 528	661 + 70	52 + 63	8 + 46	920 + 654	95 + 51

13.	14.	15.	16.	17.	18.
805 + 621	628 + 54	418 + 750	39 + 39	632 + 241	266 + 451

19.	20.	21.	22.	23.	24.
22 + 48	265 + 205	605 + 821	26 + 57	123 + 94	200 + 847

Set B   **For use after page 53**

Find the sums.

1.	2.	3.	4.	5.	6.
715 + 916	685 + 77	263 + 98	702 + 859	457 + 382	375 + 829

7.	8.	9.	10.	11.	12.
316 + 607	67 + 285	447 + 285	918 + 836	607 + 798	288 + 554

13.	14.	15.	16.	17.	18.
307 + 21	18 + 16	279 + 111	81 + 47	714 + 600	369 + 41

19.	20.	21.	22.	23.	24.
$3.26 + 2.97	$9.05 + 0.36	$2.17 + 6.84	$6.75 + 9.50	$3.88 + 2.55	$2.82 + 8.54

25.	26.	27.	28.	29.	30.
$1.96 + 2.37	$5.25 + 3.83	$4.59 + 2.45	$8.20 + 0.98	$7.39 + 3.26	$5.56 + 8.67

Set A   For use after page 55

Find the sums.

1.	2,964 + 5,682	**2.**	6,587 + 2,744	**3.**	4,532 + 1,607	**4.**	16,518 + 8,385	**5.**	3,358 + 3,692
6.	55,295 + 64,968	**7.**	64,615 + 34,607	**8.**	36,395 + 44,120	**9.**	3,643 + 5,818	**10.**	36,385 + 24,120
11.	$15.85 + 8.65	**12.**	$21.80 + 23.93	**13.**	$47.36 + 16.87	**14.**	$58.65 + 27.40	**15.**	$29.52 + 63.75
16.	$58.40 + 3.66	**17.**	$46.15 + 46.07	**18.**	$78.11 + 18.29	**19.**	$18.54 + 6.83	**20.**	$48.12 + 39.68

Set B   For use after page 57

Estimate by rounding to the nearest ten.

1.	75 + 34	**2.**	33 + 59	**3.**	46 + 21	**4.**	56 + 37	**5.**	98 + 43

Estimate by rounding to the nearest hundred or dollar.

6.	242 + 757	**7.**	$5.95 + 1.39	**8.**	618 + 333	**9.**	$8.11 + 2.95

Estimate by rounding to the nearest thousand.

10.	1,684 + 7,450	**11.**	5,258 + 7,500	**12.**	3,277 + 1,584	**13.**	4,623 + 2,418	**14.**	7,681 + 2,154

Set A   **For use after page 61**

Add.

1. 16 4 + 59	**2.** 236 425 + 237	**3.** 37 26 + 17	**4.** 6,520 831 + 1,272	**5.** 335 26 + 796	**6.** 5,625 2,910 + 3,335
7. 64 47 28 + 35	**8.** $3.83 5.35 7.68 + 0.54	**9.** 746 75 434 + 8	**10.** 563 87 412 + 29	**11.** $1.95 6.28 1.39 + .97	**12.** 52 43 18 + 77
13. $8.84 3.29 5.92 + 1.99	**14.** 7,965 4,208 1,860 + 3,222	**15.** 2,746 318 7,852 + 67	**16.** $5.24 7.12 6.18 + 4.70	**17.** 1,039 5,762 2,834 + 4,220	**18.** $6.75 2.94 .66 + 2.82

Set B   **For use after page 63**

Subtract.

1. 43 − 8	**2.** 30 − 18	**3.** 81 − 36	**4.** 56 − 17	**5.** 80 − 26	**6.** 77 − 25
7. 62 − 48	**8.** 50 − 36	**9.** $6.24 − 1.30	**10.** 138 − 85	**11.** 640 − 326	**12.** $3.79 − 1.45
13. 146 − 72	**14.** 629 − 149	**15.** 512 − 190	**16.** $6.70 − 2.34	**17.** 314 − 181	**18.** 327 − 85
19. 476 − 228	**20.** 559 − 167	**21.** $3.50 − 1.24	**22.** 859 − 384	**23.** 750 − 370	**24.** $4.11 − 2.70
25. 62 − 24	**26.** 158 − 92	**27.** $3.89 − 1.79	**28.** 473 − 57	**29.** 146 − 72	**30.** 341 − 281

Find the differences.

1.	227 − 139	**2.**	244 − 87	**3.**	365 − 79	**4.**	$6.41 − 3.97	**5.**	885 − 693	**6.**	720 − 388
7.	213 − 144	**8.**	351 − 267	**9.**	$8.13 − 2.28	**10.**	644 − 356	**11.**	904 − 578	**12.**	$5.68 − 1.79
13.	851 − 285	**14.**	513 − 175	**15.**	439 − 281	**16.**	518 − 269	**17.**	$3.26 − 1.48	**18.**	540 − 288
19.	842 − 264	**20.**	$5.36 − 0.78	**21.**	355 − 196	**22.**	$7.61 − 3.95	**23.**	533 − 184	**24.**	866 − 278

Find the differences.

1.	904 − 361	**2.**	701 − 646	**3.**	203 − 186	**4.**	$4.00 − 1.61	**5.**	805 − 377	**6.**	300 − 85
7.	601 − 388	**8.**	400 − 168	**9.**	$3.07 − 1.48	**10.**	801 − 44	**11.**	606 − 57	**12.**	107 − 78
13.	703 − 58	**14.**	904 − 718	**15.**	500 − 239	**16.**	200 − 97	**17.**	508 − 329	**18.**	$3.05 − 2.86
19.	100 − 77	**20.**	$7.08 − 3.99	**21.**	606 − 138	**22.**	903 − 357	**23.**	404 − 98	**24.**	208 − 155
25.	207 − 44	**26.**	907 − 249	**27.**	$5.08 − 4.09	**28.**	400 − 231	**29.**	706 − 29	**30.**	809 − 679

Subtract.

1. 4,430 − 726	**2.** 6,429 − 5,161	**3.** 5,000 − 2,435	**4.** $72.28 − 14.16	**5.** 84,520 − 15,635

6. $32.77
− 14.84
	7. 2,628
	  − 879
		8. 4,036
		− 2,154
			9. $36.64
			  − 8.36
				10. 63,560
				− 18,684

11. 77,252 − 44,683	**12.** 52,941 − 34,356	**13.** $24.36 − 10.85	**14.** 35,721 − 9,845	**15.** 8,826 − 5,471
16. 94,714 − 6,836	**17.** 49,267 − 25,074	**18.** 19,234 − 11,655	**19.** 89,165 − 22,618	**20.** $92.58 − 50.64

Estimate by rounding to the nearest ten.

1. 42 − 33	**2.** 63 − 38	**3.** 84 − 16	**4.** 59 − 24	**5.** 72 − 46

Estimate by rounding to the nearest hundred or dollar.

6. 318 − 186	**7.** 683 − 321	**8.** $8.71 − 2.56	**9.** 442 − 276

Estimate by rounding to the nearest thousand.

10. 6,980 − 2,140	**11.** 5,825 − 2,066	**12.** 3,912 − 1,510	**13.** 7,258 − 4,517	**14.** 8,245 − 2,058

Set A For use after page 83

Multiply.

1. $\begin{array}{r} 2 \\ \times\, 8 \\ \hline \end{array}$
2. $\begin{array}{r} 3 \\ \times\, 2 \\ \hline \end{array}$
3. $\begin{array}{r} 2 \\ \times\, 5 \\ \hline \end{array}$
4. $\begin{array}{r} 3 \\ \times\, 7 \\ \hline \end{array}$
5. $\begin{array}{r} 3 \\ \times\, 9 \\ \hline \end{array}$
6. $\begin{array}{r} 2 \\ \times\, 6 \\ \hline \end{array}$
7. $\begin{array}{r} 2 \\ \times\, 7 \\ \hline \end{array}$

8. $\begin{array}{r} 3 \\ \times\, 5 \\ \hline \end{array}$
9. $\begin{array}{r} 3 \\ \times\, 7 \\ \hline \end{array}$
10. $\begin{array}{r} 2 \\ \times\, 2 \\ \hline \end{array}$
11. $\begin{array}{r} 3 \\ \times\, 8 \\ \hline \end{array}$
12. $\begin{array}{r} 2 \\ \times\, 1 \\ \hline \end{array}$
13. $\begin{array}{r} 3 \\ \times\, 3 \\ \hline \end{array}$
14. $\begin{array}{r} 3 \\ \times\, 4 \\ \hline \end{array}$

Set B For use after page 85

Multiply.

1. $\begin{array}{r} 4 \\ \times\, 8 \\ \hline \end{array}$
2. $\begin{array}{r} 4 \\ \times\, 5 \\ \hline \end{array}$
3. $\begin{array}{r} 5 \\ \times\, 1 \\ \hline \end{array}$
4. $\begin{array}{r} 4 \\ \times\, 6 \\ \hline \end{array}$
5. $\begin{array}{r} 3 \\ \times\, 6 \\ \hline \end{array}$
6. $\begin{array}{r} 4 \\ \times\, 5 \\ \hline \end{array}$
7. $\begin{array}{r} 3 \\ \times\, 2 \\ \hline \end{array}$

8. $\begin{array}{r} 4 \\ \times\, 7 \\ \hline \end{array}$
9. $\begin{array}{r} 5 \\ \times\, 2 \\ \hline \end{array}$
10. $\begin{array}{r} 4 \\ \times\, 9 \\ \hline \end{array}$
11. $\begin{array}{r} 5 \\ \times\, 3 \\ \hline \end{array}$
12. $\begin{array}{r} 4 \\ \times\, 2 \\ \hline \end{array}$
13. $\begin{array}{r} 4 \\ \times\, 4 \\ \hline \end{array}$
14. $\begin{array}{r} 2 \\ \times\, 9 \\ \hline \end{array}$

15. $\begin{array}{r} 4 \\ \times\, 1 \\ \hline \end{array}$
16. $\begin{array}{r} 4 \\ \times\, 0 \\ \hline \end{array}$
17. $\begin{array}{r} 5 \\ \times\, 4 \\ \hline \end{array}$
18. $\begin{array}{r} 7 \\ \times\, 3 \\ \hline \end{array}$
19. $\begin{array}{r} 1 \\ \times\, 5 \\ \hline \end{array}$
20. $\begin{array}{r} 4 \\ \times\, 3 \\ \hline \end{array}$
21. $\begin{array}{r} 5 \\ \times\, 0 \\ \hline \end{array}$

Set C For use after page 91

Multiply.

1. $\begin{array}{r} 6 \\ \times\, 9 \\ \hline \end{array}$
2. $\begin{array}{r} 7 \\ \times\, 9 \\ \hline \end{array}$
3. $\begin{array}{r} 9 \\ \times\, 0 \\ \hline \end{array}$
4. $\begin{array}{r} 3 \\ \times\, 4 \\ \hline \end{array}$
5. $\begin{array}{r} 9 \\ \times\, 4 \\ \hline \end{array}$
6. $\begin{array}{r} 2 \\ \times\, 7 \\ \hline \end{array}$
7. $\begin{array}{r} 5 \\ \times\, 5 \\ \hline \end{array}$

8. $\begin{array}{r} 1 \\ \times\, 9 \\ \hline \end{array}$
9. $\begin{array}{r} 5 \\ \times\, 6 \\ \hline \end{array}$
10. $\begin{array}{r} 6 \\ \times\, 3 \\ \hline \end{array}$
11. $\begin{array}{r} 9 \\ \times\, 8 \\ \hline \end{array}$
12. $\begin{array}{r} 7 \\ \times\, 0 \\ \hline \end{array}$
13. $\begin{array}{r} 3 \\ \times\, 9 \\ \hline \end{array}$
14. $\begin{array}{r} 8 \\ \times\, 4 \\ \hline \end{array}$

15. $\begin{array}{r} 9 \\ \times\, 9 \\ \hline \end{array}$
16. $\begin{array}{r} 2 \\ \times\, 9 \\ \hline \end{array}$
17. $\begin{array}{r} 0 \\ \times\, 4 \\ \hline \end{array}$
18. $\begin{array}{r} 1 \\ \times\, 9 \\ \hline \end{array}$
19. $\begin{array}{r} 9 \\ \times\, 5 \\ \hline \end{array}$
20. $\begin{array}{r} 1 \\ \times\, 6 \\ \hline \end{array}$
21. $\begin{array}{r} 5 \\ \times\, 9 \\ \hline \end{array}$

Find the products.

1. $\begin{array}{r} 7 \\ \times\ 6 \\ \hline \end{array}$ 2. $\begin{array}{r} 8 \\ \times\ 5 \\ \hline \end{array}$ 3. $\begin{array}{r} 6 \\ \times\ 8 \\ \hline \end{array}$ 4. $\begin{array}{r} 7 \\ \times\ 7 \\ \hline \end{array}$ 5. $\begin{array}{r} 7 \\ \times\ 8 \\ \hline \end{array}$ 6. $\begin{array}{r} 9 \\ \times\ 9 \\ \hline \end{array}$ 7. $\begin{array}{r} 5 \\ \times\ 6 \\ \hline \end{array}$

8. $\begin{array}{r} 0 \\ \times\ 4 \\ \hline \end{array}$ 9. $\begin{array}{r} 8 \\ \times\ 8 \\ \hline \end{array}$ 10. $\begin{array}{r} 1 \\ \times\ 7 \\ \hline \end{array}$ 11. $\begin{array}{r} 6 \\ \times\ 6 \\ \hline \end{array}$ 12. $\begin{array}{r} 8 \\ \times\ 6 \\ \hline \end{array}$ 13. $\begin{array}{r} 3 \\ \times\ 9 \\ \hline \end{array}$ 14. $\begin{array}{r} 6 \\ \times\ 7 \\ \hline \end{array}$

Find these factors.

1. $4 \times \text{▓} = 28$ 2. $\text{▓} \times 9 = 81$ 3. $\text{▓} \times 7 = 21$ 4. $5 \times \text{▓} = 0$

5. $8 \times \text{▓} = 72$ 6. $\text{▓} \times 5 = 40$ 7. $4 \times \text{▓} = 32$ 8. $7 \times \text{▓} = 56$

9. $\text{▓} \times 9 = 54$ 10. $9 \times \text{▓} = 45$ 11. $8 \times \text{▓} = 16$ 12. $4 \times \text{▓} = 16$

13. $7 \times \text{▓} = 42$ 14. $\text{▓} \times 9 = 27$ 15. $\text{▓} \times 9 = 36$ 16. $6 \times \text{▓} = 48$

Find the quotients.

1. $8 \div 2 =$ 2. $24 \div 3 =$ 3. $14 \div 2 =$ 4. $15 \div 3 =$

5. $18 \div 3 =$ 6. $10 \div 2 =$ 7. $4 \div 2 =$ 8. $9 \div 3 =$

9. $2\overline{)16}$ 10. $3\overline{)21}$ 11. $2\overline{)12}$ 12. $2\overline{)16}$ 13. $3\overline{)27}$

14. $3\overline{)12}$ 15. $2\overline{)14}$ 16. $3\overline{)15}$ 17. $3\overline{)6}$ 18. $2\overline{)18}$

19. $2\overline{)12}$ 20. $3\overline{)15}$ 21. $2\overline{)10}$ 22. $3\overline{)3}$ 23. $3\overline{)9}$

24. $2\overline{)8}$ 25. $3\overline{)18}$ 26. $2\overline{)4}$ 27. $2\overline{)2}$ 28. $3\overline{)24}$

Divide. Think about fact families or missing factors.

1. $20 \div 5 =$ **2.** $16 \div 4 =$ **3.** $10 \div 5 =$ **4.** $8 \div 4 =$

5. $40 \div 5 =$ **6.** $12 \div 4 =$ **7.** $25 \div 5 =$ **8.** $36 \div 4 =$

9. $4\overline{)20}$ **10.** $5\overline{)30}$ **11.** $4\overline{)24}$ **12.** $5\overline{)40}$ **13.** $5\overline{)15}$

14. $5\overline{)45}$ **15.** $4\overline{)28}$ **16.** $4\overline{)36}$ **17.** $5\overline{)35}$ **18.** $4\overline{)8}$

19. $6\overline{)30}$ **20.** $4\overline{)24}$ **21.** $8\overline{)64}$ **22.** $7\overline{)49}$ **23.** $6\overline{)42}$

24. $5\overline{)25}$ **25.** $4\overline{)28}$ **26.** $3\overline{)27}$ **27.** $7\overline{)63}$ **28.** $4\overline{)12}$

Find the quotients.

1. $35 \div 7 =$ **2.** $54 \div 6 =$ **3.** $12 \div 6 =$ **4.** $21 \div 7 =$

5. $30 \div 6 =$ **6.** $42 \div 7 =$ **7.** $28 \div 7 =$ **8.** $18 \div 6 =$

9. $7\overline{)14}$ **10.** $6\overline{)24}$ **11.** $7\overline{)49}$ **12.** $7\overline{)63}$ **13.** $6\overline{)36}$

14. $6\overline{)42}$ **15.** $7\overline{)28}$ **16.** $6\overline{)6}$ **17.** $6\overline{)48}$ **18.** $7\overline{)56}$

Divide.

1. $8 \div 8 =$ **2.** $27 \div 9 =$ **3.** $56 \div 8 =$ **4.** $81 \div 9 =$

5. $32 \div 8 =$ **6.** $63 \div 9 =$ **7.** $40 \div 8 =$ **8.** $16 \div 8 =$

9. $8\overline{)72}$ **10.** $9\overline{)36}$ **11.** $8\overline{)48}$ **12.** $9\overline{)18}$ **13.** $9\overline{)54}$

14. $8\overline{)24}$ **15.** $8\overline{)64}$ **16.** $9\overline{)45}$ **17.** $9\overline{)72}$ **18.** $9\overline{)9}$

Set A   For use after page 162

Find these products. Use the grouping shown.

1. $(2 \times 3) \times 3$ 2. $(4 \times 1) \times 10$ 3. $5 \times (4 \times 2)$

4. $4 \times (2 \times 100)$ 5. $5 \times (2 \times 3)$ 6. $(3 \times 3) \times 10$

7. $7 \times (1 \times 10)$ 8. $3 \times (3 \times 2)$ 9. $(1 \times 8) \times 800$

Find these products. Use any grouping you want.

1. $4 \times 2 \times 2$ 2. $5 \times 1 \times 9$ 3. $7 \times 1 \times 5$

4. $2 \times 3 \times 100$ 5. $6 \times 1 \times 10$ 6. $5 \times 2 \times 50$

7. $3 \times 3 \times 100$ 8. $2 \times 2 \times 10$ 9. $2 \times 3 \times 1,000$

Set B   For use after page 167

Multiply.

1.	$\begin{array}{r} 21 \\ \times\ 3 \\ \hline \end{array}$	2.	$\begin{array}{r} 27 \\ \times\ 3 \\ \hline \end{array}$	3.	$\begin{array}{r} 15 \\ \times\ 5 \\ \hline \end{array}$	4.	$\begin{array}{r} 32 \\ \times\ 3 \\ \hline \end{array}$	5.	$\begin{array}{r} 46 \\ \times\ 2 \\ \hline \end{array}$
6.	$\begin{array}{r} 12 \\ \times\ 7 \\ \hline \end{array}$	7.	$\begin{array}{r} 19 \\ \times\ 4 \\ \hline \end{array}$	8.	$\begin{array}{r} 25 \\ \times\ 3 \\ \hline \end{array}$	9.	$\begin{array}{r} 24 \\ \times\ 4 \\ \hline \end{array}$	10.	$\begin{array}{r} 15 \\ \times\ 4 \\ \hline \end{array}$
11.	$\begin{array}{r} 18 \\ \times\ 3 \\ \hline \end{array}$	12.	$\begin{array}{r} 27 \\ \times\ 3 \\ \hline \end{array}$	13.	$\begin{array}{r} 16 \\ \times\ 6 \\ \hline \end{array}$	14.	$\begin{array}{r} 38 \\ \times\ 2 \\ \hline \end{array}$	15.	$\begin{array}{r} 12 \\ \times\ 5 \\ \hline \end{array}$
16.	$\begin{array}{r} 13 \\ \times\ 7 \\ \hline \end{array}$	17.	$\begin{array}{r} 33 \\ \times\ 2 \\ \hline \end{array}$	18.	$\begin{array}{r} 17 \\ \times\ 4 \\ \hline \end{array}$	19.	$\begin{array}{r} 46 \\ \times\ 2 \\ \hline \end{array}$	20.	$\begin{array}{r} 13 \\ \times\ 4 \\ \hline \end{array}$
21.	$\begin{array}{r} 23 \\ \times\ 3 \\ \hline \end{array}$	22.	$\begin{array}{r} 30 \\ \times\ 2 \\ \hline \end{array}$	23.	$\begin{array}{r} 42 \\ \times\ 2 \\ \hline \end{array}$	24.	$\begin{array}{r} 12 \\ \times\ 2 \\ \hline \end{array}$	25.	$\begin{array}{r} 17 \\ \times\ 5 \\ \hline \end{array}$

Set A   For use after page 169

Find the products.

1. 53
   × 4

2. 72
   × 5

3. 24
   × 4

4. 45
   × 6

5. 86
   × 5

6. 12
   × 8

7. 62
   × 3

8. 22
   × 7

9. 88
   × 2

10. 76
    × 8

11. 36
    × 3

12. 57
    × 6

13. 16
    × 9

14. 70
    × 5

15. 49
    × 2

16. 34
    × 5

17. 63
    × 4

18. 15
    × 6

19. 74
    × 6

20. 18
    × 3

21. 77
    × 4

22. 82
    × 8

23. 92
    × 7

24. 56
    × 2

25. 63
    × 4

26. 37
    × 3

27. 14
    × 7

28. 49
    × 6

29. 15
    × 9

30. 63
    × 8

Set B   For use after page 171

Find the products.

1. 130
   × 4

2. 161
   × 7

3. 128
   × 3

4. 116
   × 5

5. 411
   × 8

6. 314
   × 4

7. 601
   × 5

8. 232
   × 4

9. 81
   × 7

10. 183
    × 3

11. 206
    × 2

12. 512
    × 5

13. 721
    × 6

14. 681
    × 2

15. 92
    × 6

16. 59
    × 2

17. 74
    × 8

18. 115
    × 6

19. 532
    × 3

20. 63
    × 8

Set A   For use after page 173

Find the products.

1.	636 × 4	2.	254 × 6	3.	842 × 5	4.	312 × 8	5.	69 × 9
6.	605 × 3	7.	250 × 7	8.	708 × 2	9.	435 × 8	10.	582 × 5
11.	751 × 9	12.	320 × 5	13.	491 × 4	14.	88 × 3	15.	286 × 7
16.	164 × 6	17.	487 × 2	18.	185 × 3	19.	625 × 9	20.	125 × 4

Set B   For use after page 179

Find the products.

1.	4,512 × 7	2.	1,475 × 6	3.	7,004 × 5	4.	2,351 × 3	5.	5,267 × 8
6.	3,418 × 4	7.	2,358 × 2	8.	1,059 × 9	9.	4,289 × 6	10.	1,286 × 7
11.	8,537 × 3	12.	4,230 × 5	13.	2,006 × 8	14.	944 × 4	15.	3,172 × 8
16.	867 × 5	17.	5,616 × 2	18.	5,009 × 6	19.	6,031 × 9	20.	3,548 × 2
21.	6,009 × 3	22.	242 × 7	23.	2,071 × 4	24.	319 × 3	25.	1,428 × 6

Multiply. Write the answers with dollars and cents.

1. $0.45 $\times$ 7	**2.** $5.26 $\times$ 8	**3.** $3.02 $\times$ 4	**4.** $8.59 $\times$ 9	**5.** $0.78 $\times$ 5
6. $10.62 $\times$ 6	**7.** $0.32 $\times$ 8	**8.** $15.16 $\times$ 3	**9.** $9.33 $\times$ 5	**10.** $41.50 $\times$ 7
11. $55.35 $\times$ 8	**12.** $60.07 $\times$ 6	**13.** $7.89 $\times$ 2	**14.** $75.36 $\times$ 3	**15.** $20.06 $\times$ 5
16. $19.83 $\times$ 9	**17.** $67.38 $\times$ 2	**18.** $35.18 $\times$ 4	**19.** $25.16 $\times$ 7	**20.** $85.42 $\times$ 6

Find the quotients and remainders.

1. $2\overline{)3}$	**2.** $3\overline{)6}$	**3.** $3\overline{)8}$	**4.** $8\overline{)4}$	**5.** $6\overline{)21}$
6. $5\overline{)6}$	**7.** $4\overline{)9}$	**8.** $7\overline{)46}$	**9.** $9\overline{)41}$	**10.** $8\overline{)36}$
11. $2\overline{)17}$	**12.** $5\overline{)36}$	**13.** $4\overline{)0}$	**14.** $9\overline{)78}$	**15.** $7\overline{)6}$
16. $6\overline{)30}$	**17.** $8\overline{)61}$	**18.** $9\overline{)47}$	**19.** $3\overline{)16}$	**20.** $5\overline{)14}$
21. $2\overline{)13}$	**22.** $4\overline{)22}$	**23.** $7\overline{)16}$	**24.** $6\overline{)15}$	**25.** $8\overline{)65}$
26. $9\overline{)39}$	**27.** $5\overline{)47}$	**28.** $2\overline{)9}$	**29.** $3\overline{)22}$	**30.** $7\overline{)38}$
31. $4\overline{)35}$	**32.** $6\overline{)49}$	**33.** $5\overline{)28}$	**34.** $8\overline{)15}$	**35.** $3\overline{)10}$
36. $4\overline{)29}$	**37.** $3\overline{)33}$	**38.** $6\overline{)50}$	**39.** $7\overline{)60}$	**40.** $9\overline{)85}$
41. $7\overline{)37}$	**42.** $6\overline{)22}$	**43.** $8\overline{)42}$	**44.** $3\overline{)20}$	**45.** $9\overline{)50}$

Find the quotients and remainders.

1. $2\overline{)21}$ 2. $4\overline{)88}$ 3. $5\overline{)91}$ 4. $5\overline{)86}$ 5. $6\overline{)80}$

6. $3\overline{)35}$ 7. $9\overline{)99}$ 8. $7\overline{)36}$ 9. $2\overline{)34}$ 10. $8\overline{)75}$

11. $5\overline{)68}$ 12. $8\overline{)94}$ 13. $2\overline{)91}$ 14. $6\overline{)53}$ 15. $4\overline{)79}$

16. $3\overline{)55}$ 17. $7\overline{)81}$ 18. $9\overline{)86}$ 19. $3\overline{)92}$ 20. $8\overline{)82}$

21. $4\overline{)65}$ 22. $6\overline{)70}$ 23. $2\overline{)69}$ 24. $7\overline{)88}$ 25. $5\overline{)59}$

26. $9\overline{)96}$ 27. $3\overline{)64}$ 28. $8\overline{)84}$ 29. $4\overline{)45}$ 30. $2\overline{)53}$

31. $7\overline{)74}$ 32. $6\overline{)92}$ 33. $4\overline{)55}$ 34. $5\overline{)62}$ 35. $3\overline{)88}$

Find the quotients and remainders.

1. $3\overline{)416}$ 2. $5\overline{)681}$ 3. $8\overline{)994}$ 4. $2\overline{)625}$ 5. $6\overline{)818}$

6. $4\overline{)727}$ 7. $7\overline{)925}$ 8. $3\overline{)640}$ 9. $6\overline{)934}$ 10. $4\overline{)551}$

11. $2\overline{)750}$ 12. $8\overline{)941}$ 13. $5\overline{)704}$ 14. $7\overline{)808}$ 15. $5\overline{)593}$

16. $3\overline{)700}$ 17. $4\overline{)791}$ 18. $6\overline{)788}$ 19. $2\overline{)547}$ 20. $8\overline{)892}$

21. $7\overline{)796}$ 22. $5\overline{)839}$ 23. $3\overline{)334}$ 24. $4\overline{)633}$ 25. $7\overline{)799}$

26. $6\overline{)677}$ 27. $8\overline{)937}$ 28. $2\overline{)248}$ 29. $5\overline{)909}$ 30. $3\overline{)587}$

31. $7\overline{)884}$ 32. $6\overline{)893}$ 33. $4\overline{)450}$ 34. $2\overline{)335}$ 35. $8\overline{)884}$

36. $6\overline{)696}$ 37. $4\overline{)510}$ 38. $2\overline{)392}$ 39. $5\overline{)718}$ 40. $2\overline{)221}$

41. $3\overline{)987}$ 42. $9\overline{)998}$ 43. $8\overline{)916}$ 44. $3\overline{)753}$ 45. $4\overline{)893}$

Set A   For use after page 201

Divide and check.

1. $3\overline{)124}$ 2. $7\overline{)810}$ 3. $6\overline{)200}$ 4. $2\overline{)137}$ 5. $4\overline{)543}$

6. $9\overline{)425}$ 7. $5\overline{)663}$ 8. $8\overline{)383}$ 9. $3\overline{)707}$ 10. $7\overline{)400}$

11. $4\overline{)564}$ 12. $2\overline{)845}$ 13. $5\overline{)109}$ 14. $6\overline{)507}$ 15. $9\overline{)377}$

16. $8\overline{)178}$ 17. $3\overline{)573}$ 18. $7\overline{)306}$ 19. $4\overline{)326}$ 20. $6\overline{)728}$

21. $9\overline{)267}$ 22. $5\overline{)586}$ 23. $8\overline{)977}$ 24. $2\overline{)479}$ 25. $7\overline{)918}$

26. $3\overline{)278}$ 27. $6\overline{)805}$ 28. $5\overline{)285}$ 29. $4\overline{)629}$ 30. $9\overline{)840}$

31. $8\overline{)893}$ 32. $2\overline{)197}$ 33. $7\overline{)243}$ 34. $3\overline{)359}$ 35. $5\overline{)427}$

Set B   For use after page 203

Divide.

1. $7\overline{)636}$ 2. $6\overline{)604}$ 3. $9\overline{)98}$ 4. $2\overline{)801}$ 5. $5\overline{)750}$

6. $3\overline{)91}$ 7. $4\overline{)431}$ 8. $7\overline{)846}$ 9. $8\overline{)819}$ 10. $3\overline{)901}$

11. $5\overline{)502}$ 12. $9\overline{)365}$ 13. $6\overline{)744}$ 14. $2\overline{)81}$ 15. $4\overline{)823}$

16. $8\overline{)480}$ 17. $3\overline{)32}$ 18. $7\overline{)721}$ 19. $5\overline{)450}$ 20. $9\overline{)995}$

21. $4\overline{)83}$ 22. $2\overline{)612}$ 23. $8\overline{)721}$ 24. $6\overline{)62}$ 25. $3\overline{)311}$

26. $9\overline{)546}$ 27. $7\overline{)75}$ 28. $5\overline{)52}$ 29. $2\overline{)416}$ 30. $4\overline{)203}$

31. $8\overline{)325}$ 32. $6\overline{)363}$ 33. $3\overline{)272}$ 34. $5\overline{)203}$ 35. $7\overline{)354}$

36. $3\overline{)61}$ 37. $4\overline{)363}$ 38. $8\overline{)882}$ 39. $3\overline{)306}$ 40. $5\overline{)505}$

41. $7\overline{)216}$ 42. $9\overline{)814}$ 43. $2\overline{)507}$ 44. $6\overline{)612}$ 45. $5\overline{)900}$

Divide.

1. $5)\overline{\$0.30}$ 2. $8)\overline{\$1.44}$ 3. $2)\overline{\$0.18}$ 4. $4)\overline{\$7.56}$ 5. $7)\overline{\$0.56}$

6. $3)\overline{\$4.56}$ 7. $6)\overline{\$7.86}$ 8. $9)\overline{\$0.72}$ 9. $5)\overline{\$6.40}$ 10. $2)\overline{\$1.60}$

11. $4)\overline{\$0.92}$ 12. $7)\overline{\$4.41}$ 13. $8)\overline{\$8.00}$ 14. $3)\overline{\$0.78}$ 15. $6)\overline{\$2.70}$

16. $9)\overline{\$5.67}$ 17. $2)\overline{\$8.06}$ 18. $5)\overline{\$4.60}$ 19. $4)\overline{\$3.88}$ 20. $7)\overline{\$8.61}$

21. $6)\overline{\$8.04}$ 22. $3)\overline{\$1.50}$ 23. $8)\overline{\$9.76}$ 24. $2)\overline{\$0.90}$ 25. $9)\overline{\$8.46}$

26. $3)\overline{\$6.00}$ 27. $4)\overline{\$0.36}$ 28. $6)\overline{\$0.48}$ 29. $5)\overline{\$8.90}$ 30. $7)\overline{\$2.59}$

31. $2)\overline{\$2.02}$ 32. $6)\overline{\$0.36}$ 33. $7)\overline{\$9.17}$ 34. $8)\overline{\$3.28}$ 35. $4)\overline{\$2.80}$

36. $3)\overline{\$9.30}$ 37. $5)\overline{\$0.50}$ 38. $5)\overline{\$9.25}$ 39. $4)\overline{\$8.04}$ 40. $2)\overline{\$9.18}$

Find the averages of these numbers.

1. 88, 36, 14   2. 16, 11, 14, 15   3. 10, 13, 15, 22

4. 55, 74, 39   5. 115, 149, 108, 132   6. 121, 84, 66, 109

7. 19, 10, 7, 8   8. 37, 15, 29   9. 137, 111, 124

10. 13, 9, 17, 6, 15   11. 37, 17, 9, 21   12. 64, 35, 12

13. 43, 12, 8   14. 15, 7, 12, 5, 21   15. 72, 46, 26

16. 32, 65, 24, 47   17. 40, 16, 7   18. 17, 23, 36, 12

19. 33, 22, 17   20. 16, 34, 8, 2   21. 112, 39, 5

22. 56, 12, 8, 24   23. 17, 6, 73   24. 61, 25, 21, 5

Set A   **For use after page 227**

Multiply the numerator and denominator by
2, 3, and 4 to find a set of equivalent fractions.

1. $\frac{1}{4} = \frac{}{} = \frac{}{} = \frac{}{}$ **2.** $\frac{1}{3} = \frac{}{} = \frac{}{} = \frac{}{}$ **3.** $\frac{2}{5} = \frac{}{} = \frac{}{} = \frac{}{}$

4. $\frac{3}{8} = \frac{}{} = \frac{}{} = \frac{}{}$ **5.** $\frac{3}{4} = \frac{}{} = \frac{}{} = \frac{}{}$ **6.** $\frac{5}{9} = \frac{}{} = \frac{}{} = \frac{}{}$

7. $\frac{1}{6} = \frac{}{} = \frac{}{} = \frac{}{}$ **8.** $\frac{1}{2} = \frac{}{} = \frac{}{} = \frac{}{}$ **9.** $\frac{4}{5} = \frac{}{} = \frac{}{} = \frac{}{}$

Set B   **For use after page 229**

Reduce each fraction to lowest terms.

1. $\frac{6}{8}$ **2.** $\frac{3}{9}$ **3.** $\frac{4}{16}$ **4.** $\frac{18}{24}$ **5.** $\frac{8}{12}$ **6.** $\frac{3}{9}$

7. $\frac{2}{10}$ **8.** $\frac{4}{6}$ **9.** $\frac{6}{15}$ **10.** $\frac{25}{45}$ **11.** $\frac{6}{12}$ **12.** $\frac{6}{24}$

13. $\frac{4}{8}$ **14.** $\frac{6}{9}$ **15.** $\frac{18}{60}$ **16.** $\frac{15}{24}$ **17.** $\frac{2}{8}$ **18.** $\frac{10}{15}$

19. $\frac{2}{20}$ **20.** $\frac{3}{15}$ **21.** $\frac{6}{30}$ **22.** $\frac{15}{18}$ **23.** $\frac{3}{24}$ **24.** $\frac{12}{16}$

Set C   **For use after page 231**

Write $>$, $<$, or $=$, for each ⬤.

1. $\frac{1}{5}$ ⬤ $\frac{1}{3}$ **2.** $\frac{1}{2}$ ⬤ $\frac{1}{3}$ **3.** $\frac{1}{10}$ ⬤ $\frac{1}{5}$ **4.** $\frac{1}{4}$ ⬤ $\frac{1}{5}$ **5.** $\frac{2}{4}$ ⬤ $\frac{5}{10}$

6. $\frac{1}{3}$ ⬤ $\frac{1}{10}$ **7.** $\frac{2}{5}$ ⬤ $\frac{1}{2}$ **8.** $\frac{3}{4}$ ⬤ $\frac{5}{8}$ **9.** $\frac{1}{5}$ ⬤ $\frac{3}{10}$ **10.** $\frac{1}{5}$ ⬤ $\frac{2}{10}$

11. $\frac{3}{4}$ ⬤ $\frac{2}{3}$ **12.** $\frac{3}{5}$ ⬤ $\frac{6}{10}$ **13.** $\frac{7}{10}$ ⬤ $\frac{4}{5}$ **14.** $\frac{5}{10}$ ⬤ $\frac{4}{5}$ **15.** $\frac{8}{10}$ ⬤ $\frac{4}{5}$

16. $\frac{1}{2}$ ⬤ $\frac{2}{3}$ **17.** $\frac{2}{3}$ ⬤ $\frac{2}{5}$ **18.** $\frac{4}{10}$ ⬤ $\frac{3}{5}$ **19.** $\frac{2}{5}$ ⬤ $\frac{1}{4}$ **20.** $\frac{9}{10}$ ⬤ $\frac{4}{5}$

Set A   For use after page 233

Find the missing numbers.

1. $\frac{1}{2}$ of 8   2. $\frac{1}{3}$ of 21   3. $\frac{1}{5}$ of 10   4. $\frac{1}{4}$ of 8

5. $\frac{1}{8}$ of 16   6. $\frac{1}{4}$ of 12   7. $\frac{1}{2}$ of 10   8. $\frac{1}{3}$ of 3

9. $\frac{1}{5}$ of 25   10. $\frac{1}{8}$ of 32   11. $\frac{1}{4}$ of 16   12. $\frac{1}{2}$ of 20

13. $\frac{1}{8}$ of 8   14. $\frac{1}{4}$ of 24   15. $\frac{1}{3}$ of 9   16. $\frac{1}{2}$ of 14

Set B   For use after page 235

Find the missing numbers.

1. $\frac{2}{3}$ of 9   2. $\frac{2}{5}$ of 10   3. $\frac{3}{8}$ of 8

4. $\frac{2}{4}$ of 8   5. $\frac{5}{3}$ of 16   6. $\frac{2}{3}$ of 12

7. $\frac{2}{5}$ of 5   8. $\frac{3}{4}$ of 24   9. $\frac{4}{5}$ of 15

10. $\frac{2}{4}$ of 16   11. $\frac{3}{8}$ of 24   12. $\frac{3}{4}$ of 16

Set C   For use after page 239

Write as a whole number or mixed number.
Reduce all fraction parts to lowest terms.

1. $\frac{8}{4}$ 2. $\frac{5}{2}$ 3. $\frac{6}{3}$ 4. $\frac{26}{4}$ 5. $\frac{10}{2}$

6. $\frac{41}{8}$ 7. $\frac{17}{3}$ 8. $\frac{16}{4}$ 9. $\frac{47}{5}$ 10. $\frac{18}{6}$

11. $\frac{40}{6}$ 12. $\frac{12}{2}$ 13. $\frac{11}{4}$ 14. $\frac{15}{2}$ 15. $\frac{9}{3}$

16. $\frac{18}{3}$ 17. $\frac{8}{3}$ 18. $\frac{24}{8}$ 19. $\frac{20}{8}$ 20. $\frac{22}{5}$

424

Find the sums.

1. $\frac{2}{5} + \frac{2}{5}$ 2. $\frac{1}{4} + \frac{2}{4}$ 3. $\frac{4}{6} + \frac{1}{6}$ 4. $\frac{4}{8} + \frac{2}{8}$

5. $\frac{3}{10} + \frac{3}{10}$ 6. $\frac{3}{5} + \frac{1}{5}$ 7. $\frac{1}{3} + \frac{1}{3}$ 8. $\frac{4}{10} + \frac{5}{10}$

9. $\begin{array}{r} \frac{1}{8} \\ + \frac{2}{8} \\ \hline \end{array}$ 10. $\begin{array}{r} \frac{1}{5} \\ + \frac{2}{5} \\ \hline \end{array}$ 11. $\begin{array}{r} \frac{1}{10} \\ + \frac{3}{10} \\ \hline \end{array}$ 12. $\begin{array}{r} \frac{2}{6} \\ + \frac{2}{6} \\ \hline \end{array}$ 13. $\begin{array}{r} \frac{1}{10} \\ + \frac{8}{10} \\ \hline \end{array}$ 14. $\begin{array}{r} \frac{3}{8} \\ + \frac{1}{8} \\ \hline \end{array}$

Find the differences.

1. $\frac{9}{10} - \frac{6}{10}$ 2. $\frac{7}{8} - \frac{2}{8}$ 3. $\frac{6}{8} - \frac{2}{8}$ 4. $\frac{4}{5} - \frac{2}{5}$

5. $\frac{12}{8} - \frac{6}{8}$ 6. $\frac{11}{10} - \frac{6}{10}$ 7. $\frac{4}{4} - \frac{1}{4}$ 8. $\frac{5}{6} - \frac{1}{6}$

9. $\begin{array}{r} \frac{4}{6} \\ - \frac{2}{6} \\ \hline \end{array}$ 10. $\begin{array}{r} \frac{3}{5} \\ - \frac{2}{5} \\ \hline \end{array}$ 11. $\begin{array}{r} \frac{5}{4} \\ - \frac{3}{4} \\ \hline \end{array}$ 12. $\begin{array}{r} \frac{8}{10} \\ - \frac{6}{10} \\ \hline \end{array}$ 13. $\begin{array}{r} \frac{4}{8} \\ - \frac{1}{8} \\ \hline \end{array}$ 14. $\begin{array}{r} \frac{5}{5} \\ - \frac{1}{5} \\ \hline \end{array}$

Find the sums and differences.

1. $\frac{3}{8} + \frac{6}{8}$ 2. $\frac{8}{10} + \frac{8}{10}$ 3. $\frac{3}{4} + \frac{2}{4}$ 4. $\frac{4}{6} + \frac{4}{6}$

5. $\begin{array}{r} 2\frac{2}{3} \\ + 1\frac{1}{3} \\ \hline \end{array}$ 6. $\begin{array}{r} 6\frac{2}{4} \\ - 1\frac{1}{4} \\ \hline \end{array}$ 7. $\begin{array}{r} 4\frac{1}{6} \\ + 3\frac{2}{6} \\ \hline \end{array}$ 8. $\begin{array}{r} 12\frac{6}{8} \\ - 6\frac{2}{8} \\ \hline \end{array}$ 9. $\begin{array}{r} 5\frac{3}{10} \\ + 1\frac{4}{10} \\ \hline \end{array}$ 10. $\begin{array}{r} 8\frac{1}{2} \\ - 4\frac{1}{2} \\ \hline \end{array}$

11. $\begin{array}{r} 3\frac{1}{2} \\ + 2\frac{1}{2} \\ \hline \end{array}$ 12. $\begin{array}{r} 4\frac{5}{8} \\ + 4\frac{2}{8} \\ \hline \end{array}$ 13. $\begin{array}{r} 8\frac{6}{10} \\ - 7\frac{3}{10} \\ \hline \end{array}$ 14. $\begin{array}{r} 2\frac{2}{3} \\ - 1\frac{1}{3} \\ \hline \end{array}$ 15. $\begin{array}{r} 2\frac{1}{4} \\ + 3\frac{1}{4} \\ \hline \end{array}$ 16. $\begin{array}{r} 9\frac{4}{6} \\ - 3\frac{3}{6} \\ \hline \end{array}$

Set A   For use after page 255

Add.

1. $\frac{5}{8}$
   $+\frac{2}{4}$

2. $\frac{2}{10}$
   $+\frac{2}{5}$

3. $\frac{2}{9}$
   $+\frac{1}{3}$

4. $\frac{1}{2}$
   $+\frac{4}{6}$

5. $\frac{3}{4}$
   $+\frac{1}{2}$

6. $\frac{1}{6}$
   $+\frac{2}{3}$

7. $\frac{6}{10}$
   $+\frac{3}{5}$

8. $\frac{2}{8}$
   $+\frac{2}{4}$

9. $\frac{1}{3}$
   $+\frac{5}{6}$

10. $\frac{3}{10}$
    $+\frac{3}{5}$

Set B   For use after page 257

Subtract.

1. $\frac{6}{8}$
   $-\frac{1}{4}$

2. $\frac{2}{3}$
   $-\frac{2}{9}$

3. $\frac{4}{5}$
   $-\frac{3}{10}$

4. $\frac{3}{4}$
   $-\frac{3}{8}$

5. $\frac{1}{3}$
   $-\frac{1}{6}$

6. $\frac{5}{8}$
   $-\frac{1}{2}$

7. $\frac{1}{2}$
   $-\frac{1}{8}$

8. $\frac{2}{3}$
   $-\frac{2}{6}$

9. $\frac{6}{8}$
   $-\frac{1}{2}$

10. $\frac{7}{8}$
    $-\frac{3}{4}$

Set C   For use after page 297

Multiply.

1. 63
   $\times 80$

2. 48
   $\times 30$

3. 75
   $\times 40$

4. 43
   $\times 10$

5. 27
   $\times 60$

6. 38
   $\times 20$

7. 12
   $\times 40$

8. 16
   $\times 70$

9. 97
   $\times 50$

10. 64
    $\times 30$

11. 77
    $\times 90$

12. 58
    $\times 80$

Find the products.

1. 12   2. 31   3. 43   4. 30   5. 14   6. 44
  × 23   × 42   × 11   × 24   × 12   × 34

7. 10   8. 40   9. 24   10. 22   11. 41   12. 32
  × 42   × 14   × 31   × 43   × 21   × 13

13. 22   14. 33   15. 24   16. 34   17. 21   18. 11
  × 43   × 24   × 22   × 41   × 32   × 20

Multiply.

1. 16   2. 33   3. 52   4. 25   5. 64   6. 72
  × 83   × 46   × 70   × 41   × 15   × 39

7. 55   8. 63   9. 75   10. 86   11. 37   12. 44
  × 27   × 52   × 42   × 62   × 43   × 56

13. 18   14. 38   15. 42   16. 24   17. 43   18. 46
  × 26   × 21   × 35   × 84   × 19   × 66

Multiply.

1. 300   2. 642   3. 684   4. 259   5. 135
  × 21   × 53   × 15   × 36   × 47

6. 407   7. 500   8. 76   9. 384   10. 708
  × 63   × 28   × 52   × 18   × 24

Set A   For use after page 309

Find the amounts.

1. $2.79 × 32	**2.** $1.15 × 46	**3.** $8.08 × 29	**4.** $0.68 × 15	**5.** $5.27 × 24
6. $4.73 × 36	**7.** $9.06 × 53	**8.** $5.61 × 42	**9.** $8.34 × 16	**10.** $3.10 × 45
11. $4.50 × 57	**12.** $0.72 × 13	**13.** $8.65 × 31	**14.** $6.72 × 26	**15.** $5.98 × 78

Set B   For use after page 319

Divide.

1. $20\overline{)80}$ **2.** $60\overline{)180}$ **3.** $10\overline{)90}$ **4.** $40\overline{)240}$ **5.** $90\overline{)360}$

6. $70\overline{)420}$ **7.** $30\overline{)90}$ **8.** $70\overline{)280}$ **9.** $30\overline{)120}$ **10.** $50\overline{)450}$

11. $20\overline{)100}$ **12.** $40\overline{)200}$ **13.** $40\overline{)80}$ **14.** $80\overline{)640}$ **15.** $10\overline{)10}$

16. $50\overline{)350}$ **17.** $60\overline{)540}$ **18.** $20\overline{)80}$ **19.** $50\overline{)400}$ **20.** $30\overline{)60}$

Set C   For use after page 321

Divide.

1. $30\overline{)78}$ **2.** $70\overline{)92}$ **3.** $40\overline{)333}$ **4.** $80\overline{)266}$

5. $60\overline{)153}$ **6.** $40\overline{)178}$ **7.** $30\overline{)56}$ **8.** $50\overline{)122}$

9. $50\overline{)285}$ **10.** $30\overline{)95}$ **11.** $90\overline{)508}$ **12.** $60\overline{)185}$

13. $20\overline{)99}$ **14.** $70\overline{)383}$ **15.** $80\overline{)490}$ **16.** $20\overline{)53}$

Set A   **For use after page 323**

Divide and check.

1. $15\overline{)48}$ 2. $47\overline{)96}$ 3. $33\overline{)47}$ 4. $25\overline{)56}$

5. $39\overline{)34}$ 6. $14\overline{)30}$ 7. $22\overline{)92}$ 8. $52\overline{)67}$

9. $23\overline{)32}$ 10. $16\overline{)71}$ 11. $37\overline{)75}$ 12. $26\overline{)85}$

13. $46\overline{)73}$ 14. $64\overline{)60}$ 15. $36\overline{)87}$ 16. $63\overline{)79}$

17. $56\overline{)90}$ 18. $74\overline{)65}$ 19. $45\overline{)90}$ 20. $18\overline{)95}$

21. $27\overline{)39}$ 22. $34\overline{)61}$ 23. $41\overline{)89}$ 24. $24\overline{)89}$

25. $18\overline{)38}$ 26. $25\overline{)77}$ 27. $12\overline{)80}$ 28. $27\overline{)89}$

29. $35\overline{)79}$ 30. $17\overline{)91}$ 31. $11\overline{)96}$ 32. $36\overline{)56}$

Set B   **For use after page 327**

Divide and check.

1. $23\overline{)100}$ 2. $14\overline{)\$1.26}$ 3. $42\overline{)376}$ 4. $36\overline{)61}$

5. $64\overline{)504}$ 6. $31\overline{)300}$ 7. $73\overline{)467}$ 8. $24\overline{)123}$

9. $12\overline{)\$1.08}$ 10. $74\overline{)457}$ 11. $86\overline{)735}$ 12. $52\overline{)232}$

13. $45\overline{)258}$ 14. $27\overline{)\$2.43}$ 15. $62\overline{)388}$ 16. $16\overline{)\$1.28}$

17. $29\overline{)180}$ 18. $32\overline{)74}$ 19. $56\overline{)400}$ 20. $76\overline{)342}$

21. $46\overline{)235}$ 22. $41\overline{)\$2.87}$ 23. $22\overline{)185}$ 24. $18\overline{)151}$

25. $32\overline{)100}$ 26. $13\overline{)\$5.20}$ 27. $62\overline{)190}$ 28. $56\overline{)240}$

29. $17\overline{)145}$ 30. $22\overline{)204}$ 31. $42\overline{)\$1.68}$ 32. $66\overline{)462}$

Divide and check.

1. 30)536   2. 10)324   3. 40)687   4. 50)650

5. 40)748   6. 60)700   7. 20)435   8. 10)462

9. 20)$7.00   10. 70)955   11. 30)812   12. 40)579

13. 50)805   14. 10)$4.60   15. 30)$8.70   16. 40)475

17. 10)143   18. 30)421   19. 90)963   20. 20)787

21. 20)666   22. 40)563   23. 80)988   24. 50)$9.00

25. 30)427   26. 40)$4.80   27. 70)960   28. 10)196

29. 20)$3.80   30. 60)863   31. 50)550   32. 80)872

Divide and check.

1. 14)279   2. 22)354   3. 41)892   4. 35)961

5. 46)703   6. 57)665   7. 11)$7.92   8. 64)828

9. 42)622   10. 36)504   11. 23)490   12. 39)400

13. 73)$8.76   14. 81)857   15. 45)786   16. 86)946

17. 12)277   18. 37)395   19. 18)388   20. 26)$4.68

21. 34)414   22. 44)$8.36   23. 27)344   24. 38)667

25. 22)436   26. 31)961   27. 47)549   28. 55)$9.90

29. 67)843   30. 37)999   31. 43)$6.45   32. 91)932

Set A   For use after page 349

Give >, <, or = for each ⬤ .

1. 0.27 ⬤ 0.30   2. 7.60 ⬤ 7.6   3. 0.03 ⬤ 0.30

4. 4.8 ⬤ 3.9   5. 6.27 ⬤ 6.29   6. 2.5 ⬤ 2.6

7. 0.41 ⬤ 0.35   8. 0.72 ⬤ 0.68   9. 0.8 ⬤ 0.80

10. 45.20 ⬤ 45.2   11. 4.50 ⬤ 4.5   12. 6.8 ⬤ 5.72

13. 5.6 ⬤ 5.59   14. 7.67 ⬤ 7.76   15. 4.9 ⬤ 5

16. 34.9 ⬤ 35   17. 24.1 ⬤ 23.9   18. 5.5 ⬤ 5.48

19. 0.39 ⬤ 0.4   20. 38 ⬤ 38.1   21. 0.1 ⬤ 0.10

22. 0.30 ⬤ 0.03   23. 0.51 ⬤ 5.1   24. 36.4 ⬤ 36.6

25. 0.27 ⬤ 0.72   26. 6.80 ⬤ 6.8   27. 0.20 ⬤ 0.2

Set B   For use after page 351

Add.

1. 3.68
   + 4.19

2. 42.7
   + 69.1

3. 4.83
   + 1.47

4. 58.26
   + 17.35

5. 8.3
   + 7.2

6. 6.85
   + 5.93

7. $78.23
   + 12.85

8. 28.61
   + 76.32

9. 84.1
   + 67.3

10. 5.38
    + 1.96

11. 75.62
    + 33.91

12. 98.46
    + 13.53

13. 69.75
    + 3.86

14. $0.68
    + 0.73

15. 54.2
    + 86.5

16. 56.72
    + 31.84

17. $8.73
    + 47.00

18. 47.6
    + 16

19. 27.6
    + 12.73

20. $7.89
    + 5.94

Subtract.

1. 14.0
  − 9.6

2. 56.8
  − 24.5

3. 27.65
  − 13.84

4. 9.87
  − 4.95

5. 38.42
  − 16.31

6. 7.64
  − 3.16

7. $47.20
  − 19.80

8. 47.52
  − 8.73

9. 47.60
  − 17.82

10. 32.75
  − 12.08

11. 42.7
  − 15.8

12. 2.83
  − 1.57

13. 4.76
  − 3.85

14. $42.39
  − 30.68

15. 32.9
  − 27.6

16. $6.45
  − 2.81

17. 8.32
  − 4.60

18. 76.54
  − 43.38

19. 76.28
  − 35.64

20. $42.35
  − 16.10

Find the sums and differences.

1. 0.6
  − 0.27

2. 43
  + 6.78

3. 12.7
  + 5.67

4. 67.43
  − 29.08

5. 68
  − 34.9

6. 8.62
  + 75

7. 15.38
  − 6.9

8. 14.0
  + 3.27

9. 48.2
  + 16.77

10. 49.62
  − 39.7

11. 78
  − 14.33

12. 6.92
  + 9

13. 73.74
  − 27.65

14. 67.1
  + 8.52

15. 17.53
  − 6.9

16. 75
  + 68.23

17. 3.75
  + 4.93

18. 15.8
  − 6.6

19. 48
  − 17.76

20. 6.3
  + 1.6

21. 21.3
  + 13.6

22. 17.8
  − 8

23. 63.1
  + 4.3

24. 54
  − 12.8

25. 11
  + 14.9

Table of Measures

Metric System		Customary System	

Length

Metric System		Customary System	
1 centimeter (cm)	10 millimeters (mm)	1 foot (ft)	12 inches (in.)
1 decimeter (dm)	100 millimeters (mm) 10 centimeters (cm)	1 yard (yd)	36 inches (in.) 3 feet (ft)
1 meter (m)	1,000 millimeters (mm) 100 centimeters (cm) 10 decimeters (dm)	1 mile (m)	5,280 feet (ft) 1,760 yards (yd)
1 kilometer (km)	1,000 meters (m)		

Area

Metric System		Customary System	
1 square meter (m^2)	100 square decimeters (dm^2) 10,000 square centimeters (cm^2)	1 square foot (ft^2)	144 square inches $(in.^2)$

Volume

Metric System		Customary System	
1 cubic decimeter (dm^3)	1,000 cubic centimeters (cm^3) 1 liter (L)	1 cubic foot (ft^3)	1,728 cubic inches $(in.^3)$

Capacity

Metric System		Customary System	
		1 cup (c)	8 fluid ounces (fl oz)
		1 pint (pt)	16 fluid ounces (fl oz) 2 cups (c)
1 teaspoon	5 milliliters (mL)		
1 tablespoon	12.5 milliliters (mL)	1 quart (qt)	32 fluid ounces (fl oz) 4 cups (c) 2 pints (pt)
1 liter (L)	1,000 milliliters (mL) 1,000 cubic centimeters (cm^3) 1 cubic decimeter (dm^3) 4 metric cups	1 gallon (gal)	128 fluid ounces (fl oz) 16 cups (c) 8 pints (pt) 4 quarts (qt)

Weight

Metric System		Customary System	
1 gram (g)	1,000 milligrams (mg)	1 pound (lb)	16 ounces (oz)
1 kilogram (kg)	1,000 grams (g)		

Time

Metric System		Customary System	
1 minute (min)	60 seconds (s)	1 year (yr)	365 days 52 weeks 12 months
1 hour (h)	60 minutes (min)		
1 day (d)	24 hours (h)		
1 week (w)	7 days (d)	1 decade	10 years
1 month (mo)	about 4 weeks	1 century	100 years

Glossary

a.m. A way to indicate the times from 12:00 midnight to 12:00 noon.

addend One of the numbers to be added.

Example:

angle Two rays from a single point.

area The measure of a region, expressed in square units.

average The quotient obtained when the sum of the numbers in a set is divided by the number of addends.

capacity The volume of a space figure given in terms of liquid measurement.

centimeter (cm) A unit of length in the metric system. 100 centimeters equal 1 meter.

circle A plane figure in which all the points are the same distance from a point called the center.

congruent figures Figures that have the same size and shape.

congruent triangles

cube A space figure that has squares for all of its faces.

cup (c) A unit for measuring liquids. 1 quart equals 4 cups.

cylinder A space figure that has a circle for a face.

cylinder

decimal A number that shows tenths by using a decimal point.

3.2 ←— decimal
↑
decimal point

degree Celsius (°C) A unit for measuring temperature in the metric system.

degree Fahrenheit (°F) A unit for measuring temperature in the customary system of measurement.

denominator The number below the line in a fraction.

$\frac{3}{4}$ ←— denominator

difference The number obtained by subtracting one number from another.

digits The symbols used to write numerals: 0, 1, 2, 3, 4, 5, 6, 7, 8, and 9.

dividend A number to be divided.

$\frac{4}{7\overline{)28}}$ ←— dividend

divisor The number by which a dividend is divided.

divisor ——→ $7\overline{)28}$

edge One of the segments making up any of the faces of a space figure.

END An instruction in a computer program that tells the computer to stop.

equation A number sentence involving the use of the equality symbol.

Examples: 9 + 2 = 11
8 − 4 = 4

equivalent fractions Fractions that name the same amount.

Example: $\frac{1}{2}$ and $\frac{2}{4}$

estimate To find an answer that is close to the exact answer.

even number A whole number that has 0, 2, 4, 6, or 8 in the ones' place.

face One of the plane figures (regions) making up a space figure.

factors Numbers that are multiplied together to form a product.

factors ——→ 6 × 7 = 42

flowchart A chart that shows a step-by-step way of doing something.

foot (ft) A unit for measuring length. 1 foot equals 12 inches.

fraction   A number that expresses parts of a whole or a set.

Example: $\frac{3}{4}$

gallon (gal)   A unit of liquid measure. 1 gallon equals 4 quarts.

GOTO   An instruction in a computer program that tells the computer to jump to a specified line.

gram (g)   The basic unit for measuring weight in the metric system. A paper clip weighs about 1 gram.

graph   A picture that shows information in an organized way.

grouping property   When the grouping of addends or factors is changed, the sum or product is the same.

greater than   The relationship of one number being larger than another number.

Example: $6 > 5$, read "6 is greater than 5."

hexagon   A polygon with six sides.

inch (in.)   A unit for measuring length. 12 inches equal 1 foot.

intersecting lines   Lines that have one common point.

kilogram (kg)   A unit of weight in the metric system. 1 kilogram is 1,000 grams.

kilometer (km)   A unit of length in the metric system. 1 kilometer is 1,000 meters.

length   The measure of distance from one end to the other end of an object.

less than   The relationship of being smaller than another number.

Example: $5 < 6$, read "5 is less than 6."

line   A straight path that is endless in both directions.

line of symmetry   A line on which a figure can be folded so that the two parts fit exactly.

 line of symmetry

liter (L)   A metric unit used to measure liquids. 1 liter equals 1,000 cubic centimeters.

Logo   A special computer language that is used for computer graphics.

lowest terms   A fraction is in lowest terms if the numerator and denominator have no common factor greater than 1.

meter (m)   A unit of length in the metric system. 1 meter is 100 centimeters.

mile (mi)   A unit for measuring length. 1 mile equals 5,280 feet.

milliliter (mL)   A metric unit for measuring capacity. 1,000 milliliters equal 1 liter.

mixed number   A number that has a whole number part and a fractional part, such as $2\frac{3}{4}$.

multiple   A number that is the product of a given number and a whole number.

negative number   A number that is less than zero.

number pair   Two numbers that are used to give the location of a point on a graph.

Example: (3,2)

numeral   A symbol for a number.

numerator   The number above the line in a fraction. $\frac{3}{4}$ ←——— numerator

octagon   A polygon with eight sides.

odd number   A whole number that has 1, 3, 5, 7, or 9 in the ones' place.

one property   In multiplication, when either factor is 1, the product is the other factor. In division, when 1 is the divisor, the quotient is the same as the dividend.

order property   When the order of addends or factors is changed, the sum or product is the same.

ordinal number   A number that is used to tell order.

Example: first, fifth

ounce (oz)   A unit for measuring weight. 16 ounces equal 1 pound.

p.m.   A way to indicate the times from 12:00 noon to 12:00 midnight.

parallel lines   Lines in the same plane that do not intersect.

pentagon   A polygon with five sides.

perimeter   The distance around a figure.

pint (pt)   A unit for measuring liquid. 2 pints equal 1 quart.

place value   The value given to the place a digit occupies in a number.

Example:

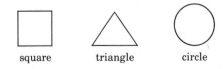

plane figures   Figures that lie on a flat surface.

Examples:

square   triangle   circle

point   A single, exact location, often represented by a dot.

polygon A closed figure formed by line segments.

pound (lb) A customary unit for measuring weight. 1 pound equals 16 ounces.

prime number A whole number greater than 1, whose only factors are itself and 1.

PRINT An instruction in a computer program that tells the computer to print something.

product The result of the multiplication operation.

$$6 \times 7 = 42 \longleftarrow \text{product}$$

program The set of instructions that tells a computer what to do.

quadrilateral A polygon with four sides.

quart (qt) A unit for measuring liquids. 1 quart equals 4 cups.

quotient The number (other than the remainder) that is the result of the division operation.

$$45 \div 9 = 5 \qquad\qquad 6 \longleftarrow \text{quotient}$$
$$\uparrow \qquad\qquad 7\overline{)45}$$
$$\text{quotient} \qquad -\ 42$$
$$\overline{3}$$

ray A part of a line having only one endpoint.

ray

rectangle A plane figure with four sides and four right angles.

rectangular prism A space figure with six faces. It has the shape of a box.

remainder The number less than the divisor that remains after the division process is completed.

Example: 6
$7\overline{)47}$
$-\ 42$
$\overline{5} \longleftarrow \text{remainder}$

right angle An angle that has the same shape as the corner of a square.

rounding Replacing a number with a number that tells about how many.

Example: 23 rounded to the nearest 10 is 20.

RUN What appears on the video screen when a computer program is used.

segment A straight path from one point to another.

similar figures Two or more figures having the same shape but not necessarily the same size.

space figure A figure that is not flat but that has volume.

cube   cylinder

sphere A space figure that has the shape of a round ball.

square A plane figure that has four equal sides and four equal corners.

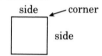
side   corner
side

sum The number obtained by adding numbers.

Example: 3
$+\ 2$
$\overline{5} \longleftarrow \text{sum}$

symmetric figure A plane figure that can be folded in half so that the two halves match.

ton A unit for measuring weight. 1 ton equals 2,000 pounds.

trading To make a group of ten from one of the next highest place value, or one from ten of the next lowest place value.

Examples: 1 hundred can be traded for 10 tens; 10 ones can be traded for 1 ten.

triangle A plane figure with three segments as sides.

unit An amount or quantity used as a standard of measurement.

vertex (vertices) The common point of any two sides of a polygon.

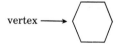
vertex $\longrightarrow$

volume The number of units of space that a space figure holds.

yard (yd) A unit for measuring length. 1 yard equals 3 feet.

zero property In addition, when one addend is 0, the sum is the other addend. In multiplication, when either factor is 0, the product is 0.

Index

facts through 18, 4–5, 10–11
of fractions, 248–249
of fractions, 256–257
of mixed numbers, 250–251
with money, 62–65, 68–75,
  352–354
practice the facts, 10
problem-solving applications
  (*see* Problem-solving
  applications)
with time, 134–135
zero property of, 6–7
zeros in, 68–69
Sum, 2
Symmetric figures, 278–279

T

Tables, 122, 124, 133, 207, 231,
  267, 369, 375
Tally charts, 15
Technology. *See* Calculator
  activities; Calculator-assisted
  problem solving; Computer-
  assisted problem solving;
  Computer instruction/
  literacy; Flowcharts.
Technology Resource Bank,
  383–403
Temperature
  Celsius, 151, 434
  Fahrenheit, 377, 434
Tens, place value, 24–25
Tenths, 342–343, 344–345
Thermometer
  Celsius, 151
  Fahrenheit, 377
Thousands, place value,
  26–27, 34–35
Time,
  a.m. and p.m., 132
  addition and subtraction with,
    134–135, 137
  calendar, 136
  digital, 130–131
  estimating, 131, 152
  hours and minutes, 130–131
  measures of, 433
  telling, 130–131
  zones, 137
Times/distance, data hunt, 140
Ton, 376
Trading
  in addition, 50–53

in multiplication, 166–173
in subtraction, 62–65, 70–71
Triangle, 268–269, 436
Two-step problems, 16, 67,
  109, 115, 119, 122–123, 133,
  152–153, 191, 197, 206–207,
  211, 233, 235–237, 305, 311,
  329, 335, 355, 359, 375

U

Understanding
  multiplication, 82
Understanding division, 108–109

V

Vertex, 268–269, 436
Volume, 146–147, 433, 436

W

Weight
  data hunt, 153
  estimating, 150, 376
  metric units of measurement,
    150, 433

Y

Yard, 368–369, 435

Z

Zero
  in division, 112
  as a factor, 86–87
  in the quotient, 202–205
  in subtraction, 68–69
Zero property
  of addition and subtraction,
    6–7
  of division, 112

ASP.NET 2.0

Your visual blueprint™ for developing Web applications

by Chris Love

Wiley Publishing, Inc.

ASP.NET 2.0: Your visual blueprint™ for developing Web applications

Published by
Wiley Publishing, Inc.
10475 Crosspoint Boulevard
Indianapolis, IN 46256

Published simultaneously in Canada

Library of Congress Control Number: 2006939444

ISBN: 978-0-470-01001-3

Manufactured in the United States of America

10 9 8 7 6 5 4 3 2 1

Contact Us

For general information on our other products and services please contact our Customer Care Department within the U.S. at 800-762-2974, outside the U.S. at 317-572-3993 or fax 317-572-4002.

For technical support please visit www.wiley.com/techsupport.

Trademark Acknowledgments

The Temple of Angkor Wat

Of the hundreds of temples built between 802 and 1220AD in the Cambodian jungle, the Temple of Angkor Wat is the largest and most breathtaking. Dedicated to the Hindu God Vishnu by King Suryavarman II in the 12th century, it displays magnificent examples of Khmer and Hindu art. Its outer gallery walls bear the world's longest continuous bas-relief—800 meters depicting stories from Hindu mythology. A new chapter in its history was unveiled in 2007, when scientific and archaeological studies revealed that the temple stood at the heart of a pre-industrial city larger than the storied Mayan communities.

For more about the archaeological wonders of Southeast Asia, see *Frommer's Southeast Asia*, available wherever books are sold or at

WILEY

Sales

Contact Wiley at (800) 762-2974 or (317) 572-4002.

PRAISE FOR VISUAL BOOKS...

"This is absolutely the best computer-related book I have ever bought. Thank you so much for this fantastic text. Simply the best computer book series I have ever seen. I will look for, recommend, and purchase more of the same."

—David E. Prince (NeoNome.com)

"I have several of your Visual books and they are the best I have ever used."

—Stanley Clark (Crawfordville, FL)

"I just want to let you know that I really enjoy all your books. I'm a strong visual learner. You really know how to get people addicted to learning! I'm a very satisfied Visual customer. Keep up the excellent work!"

—Helen Lee (Calgary, Alberta, Canada)

"I have several books from the Visual series and have always found them to be valuable resources."

—Stephen P. Miller (Ballston Spa, NY)

"This book is PERFECT for me — it's highly visual and gets right to the point. What I like most about it is that each page presents a new task that you can try verbatim or, alternatively, take the ideas and build your own examples. Also, this book isn't bogged down with trying to 'tell all' — it gets right to the point. This is an EXCELLENT, EXCELLENT, EXCELLENT book and I look forward to purchasing other books in the series."

—Tom Dierickx (Malta, IL)

"I have quite a few of your Visual books and have been very pleased with all of them. I love the way the lessons are presented!"

—Mary Jane Newman (Yorba Linda, CA)

"I am an avid fan of your Visual books. If I need to learn anything, I just buy one of your books and learn the topic in no time. Wonders! I have even trained my friends to give me Visual books as gifts."

—Illona Bergstrom (Aventura, FL)

"I just had to let you and your company know how great I think your books are. I just purchased my third Visual book (my first two are dog-eared now!) and, once again, your product has surpassed my expectations. The expertise, thought, and effort that go into each book are obvious, and I sincerely appreciate your efforts."

—Tracey Moore (Memphis, TN)

"Compliments to the chef!! Your books are extraordinary! Or, simply put, extra-ordinary, meaning way above the rest! THANK YOU THANK YOU THANK YOU! I buy them for friends, family, and colleagues."

—Christine J. Manfrin (Castle Rock, CO)

"I write to extend my thanks and appreciation for your books. They are clear, easy to follow, and straight to the point. Keep up the good work! I bought several of your books and they are just right! No regrets! I will always buy your books because they are the best."

—Seward Kollie (Dakar, Senegal)

"I am an avid purchaser and reader of the Visual series, and they are the greatest computer books I've seen. Thank you very much for the hard work, effort, and dedication that you put into this series."

—Alex Diaz (Las Vegas, NV)

Credits

Project Editor
Jade L. Williams

Acquisitions Editor
Jody Lefevere

Copy Editor
Kim Heusel

Technical Editor
Jim Duffy

Editorial Manager
Robyn Siesky

Business Manager
Amy Knies

Sr. Marketing Manager
Sandy Smith

Permissions Editor
Laura Moss

Manufacturing
Allan Conley
Linda Cook
Paul Gilchrist
Jennifer Guynn

Book Design
Kathryn Rickard

Production Coordinator
Patrick Redmond

Layout
Andrea Hornberger
Jennifer Mayberry
Christine Williams

Screen Artist
Jill A. Proll

Cover Illustration
Cheryl Grubbs

Proofreader
Broccoli Information Management

Quality Control
Laura Albert

Indexer
Infodex Indexing Services, Inc.

**Vice President and Executive
Group Publisher**
Richard Swadley

Vice President and Publisher
Barry Pruett

Composition Director
Debbie Stailey

Wiley Bicentennial Logo
Richard J. Pacifico

About the Author

Chris Love has over 14 years of experience in software design, development and architecture. He has been the principal developer for more than 250 small and medium ASP and ASP.NET Web sites over the past 7 years. These projects have exposed Chris to a wide range of Microsoft-related technologies to solve real business problems for his clients. He has learned to look objectively at his clients' business and offer pragmatic suggestions to make them more efficient and profitable.

Other responsibilities have included managing and maintaining production Windows servers for Web, database, and e-mail. He has learned to manage performance, security, and spam safeguards to keep his customers operating 24/7.

Chris' clients have also relied on his experience and expertise to help develop online marketing strategies, including search engine optimization and pay-per-click campaigns. Chris has begun to leverage this experience along with his ASP.NET expertise to build his own Web properties and practice his technical and marketing theories firsthand.

Chris has been active in a leadership role in the local user's group, TRINUG, for more than 5 years. He served as the Vice President for the first 3 years and is currently on the advisory board. He has also led monthly a Special Interest Group (SIG) where he covered practical ASP.NET programming techniques, including how to use httpHandlers, httpModules, extending the .NET framework and using third party tools. He frequently presents and organizes Code Camps around the country. He is a Full Mentor with Solid Quality Mentors in the Development Practice.

Author's Acknowledgments

I would like to thank all my close family and friends for supporting me not only on this book, but also all the effort to build a solid set of skills in a technical area that I love.

I would like to extend a special thanks to Jim Duffy for his efforts as the technical editor of the book.

TABLE OF CONTENTS

4 WORKING WITH NEW ASP.NET 2.0 WEB CONTROLS 80

5 VALIDATING USER INPUT 100

6 DISPLAYING RECORDS WITH DATA CONTROLS 112

TABLE OF CONTENTS

7 LEVERAGING THE MEMBERSHIP AND ROLE PROVIDERS 144

8 MANAGING ACCESS WITH THE ROLE PROVIDER . . .166

TABLE OF CONTENTS

HOW TO USE THIS BOOK

ASP.NET 2.0: Your visual blueprint™ for developing Web applications uses clear, descriptive examples to show you how to do something with ASP.NET. If you are already familiar with ASP.NET, you can use this book as a quick reference for many ASP.NET tasks.

Who Needs This Book

This book is for the experienced computer user who wants to find out more about ASP.NET. It is also for more experienced ASP.NET users who want to expand their knowledge of the different features that ASP.NET has to offer.

Book Organization

ASP.NET 2.0: Your visual blueprint™ for developing Web applications has 15 chapters and a companion Web site.

Chapter 1, "Getting Familiar with Visual Studio 2005," provides an introduction on how to use Visual Studio to manage ASP.NET Web sites. You will learn how to leverage many of the common and new features to quickly build and debug your Web applications.

Chapter 2, "Introducing ASP.NET," guides you through the fundamentals of how ASP.NET works, and how to program ASP.NET. You will learn how to program fundamental Web concepts in ASP.NET. Additionally you will understand ASP.NET specific concepts and the basic ASP.NET Web site configuration concepts.

Chapter 3, "Understanding Common Web Server Controls," will introduce and explain how to use each of the common ASP.NET Web controls. You will learn how to format controls, manage setting properties at design and run-time, and handle events.

Chapter 4, "Working with New ASP.NET 2.0 Web Controls," will explain how each of the newest Web controls work. These are controls added to the .NET Framework with the 2.0 release.

Chapter 5, "Validating User Input," teaches you how to apply the various Validation controls to a form.

Chapter 6, "Displaying Records with Data Controls," teaches you how to bind records to each of the data controls, such as the GridView and Repeater. You will also learn how to customize these controls, insert new, edit, and delete records through the data controls.

Chapter 7, "Leveraging the Membership and Role Providers," demonstrates how to use the Membership provider to manage user authentication. You will learn how to add, edit, and remove users from the site. You will also learn how to manage passwords and track the number of active users on the site.

Chapter 8, "Managing Access with the Role Provider," teaches you how to leverage the new Role provider to group users into logical groups. You will learn how to add, edit, and remove roles. You will also learn how the roles apply to user accounts.

Chapter 9, "Maintaining a Consistent User Interface with Membership Controls," teaches you how to leverage the new Membership controls. You will learn how to create new users, manage authentication, and protect content based on a user's authority.

Chapter 10, "Working with Navigation Controls and SiteMaps," teaches you how to use the new Navigation controls and SiteMap files.

Chapter 11, "Enhancing Web Sites with Master Pages, Themes, and Personalization," teaches you how to take advantage of Master Pages and Themes to create consistent and professional site layouts. The Personalization content shows you how to let users customize their experience.

Chapter 12, "Working with Data Objects," teaches you the fundamentals of connecting to and interacting with a database in .NET. You will learn how to bind records to data objects such as a DataSet.

Chapter 13, "Leveraging Basic Error Handling and Debugging Techniques," teaches you how to debug and track down errors in your application using the many features of ASP.NET and Visual Studio.

Chapter 14, "Going Beyond Basic ASP.NET," takes you beyond just understanding the basics of building ASP.NET Web pages by showing you some practical examples that most sites need to include. You will learn how to send e-mail messages and use httpModules and httpHandlers.

Finally, Chapter 15, "Applying Web Services and AJAX," teaches you how to create and consume Web services in your Web site. You will also learn how to use the new ASP.NET AJAX framework to enhance your user's experience.

What You Need to Use This Book

- Windows 2000, Windows XP, Windows 2003 Server, or Windows Vista
- PC with a Pentium processor running at 1 GHz or faster
- At least 512MB of total RAM installed on your computer; for best performance, I recommend at least 2 GB
- Visual Studio 2005 and SQL Server Express
- The .NET 2.0 framework

The Conventions in This Book

A number of styles have been used throughout *ASP.NET 2.0: Your visual blueprint™ for developing Web applications* to designate different types of information.

Courier Font

Indicates the use of code such as tags or attributes, scripting language code such as statements, operators, or functions, and code such as objects, methods, or properties.

Bold

Indicates information that you must type.

Italics

Indicates a new term.

Apply It

An Apply It section takes the code from the preceding task one-step further. Apply It sections allow you to take full advantage of ASP.NET code.

Extra

An Extra section provides additional information about the preceding task. Extra sections contain the inside information to make working with ASP.NET easier and more efficient.

What's on the Web Site

The Web site accompanying this book contains the sample files of the exercises found in *ASP.NET 2.0: Your visual blueprint for developing Web applications*. You may download the sample exercise files at `http://www.wiley.com/go/aspnet2` for your use.

Note from the Author

I would be happy to hear any comments you have about this book. My Blog is located at `http://ProfessionalASPNET.com`. I have set up two Web sites at `http://www.aspnetblueprint.com` and `http://www.aspnetroadmap.com` that contain a live version of the steps and links to Visual Studio Express and SQL Server Express. The sample exercise files for *ASP.NET 2.0: Your visual blueprint for developing Web applications* are also available at these sites after a simple registration.

Introduction to Visual Studio 2005

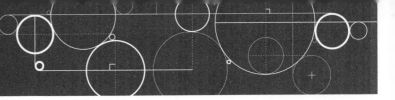

Visual Studio 2005 is the Integrated Development Environment (IDE) for the .NET platform. It was designed with the productivity of the developer and teams of developers in mind. There are different versions of Visual Studio available, ranging from Visual Studio Express to Visual Studio Team System. Each version has a different target market in mind.

The goal of the IDE is to make it as easy as possible for developers to create productive, bug-free applications. To accomplish this goal, Visual Studio offers a wide range of visual development tools and debugger interfaces. The IDE utilizes a series of movable and dockable windows that give developers quick access to information about the project or solution they are developing. Some of the standard windows include the Solution Explorer, Properties, Server Explorer, Class View, and ToolBox.

Visual Studio Project Types

Visual Studio gives developers the ability to create a variety of application projects, including Web sites, WinForm applications, class libraries, Console applications, as well as the new .NET 3.0 projects and custom templates exported by the developer. Projects can be developed in VB.NET, C#, J#, and C++. Support for mobile and compact development is also supported, but requires additional free SDK downloads from the Microsoft site.

Visual Studio File Types

Visual Studio offers the developer the ability to edit all kinds of files, including Web pages, WinForms, class files, style sheets, resource files, XML documents, databases, and JavaScript, as well as just about any file needed to build any of the supported applications. Files can be added as needed to a project at any time. If a file is added to a project and there is a special folder associated with that file type, Visual Studio prompts you to place the file in that folder. For example, if you add a new class file to a project it asks if you want to place the file in the App_Code folder.

Visual Studio Windows

Visual Studio 2005 offers most of the standard windows available in previous versions with some new additions. A new feature is the Error Notification Assistance window, which is available from most syntax errors. It offers an explanation of the error and some suggested corrections.

Another new feature is the Tag Navigator bar, which appears at the bottom of a design page. Clicking on a tag name in the bar sets the focus to that HTML element.

Visual Studio and Controls

The use of controls is vital to the development process on the Windows platform. Visual Studio provides full visual experience in both design and source view of Web pages and `WinForms`. Controls can either be dragged from the control ToolBox or created by hand in source view. If the control has a designer associated with it, you can also interact with the control at designtime and often invoke custom editors provided with the control.

Running and Testing Web Applications

Executing applications from the development environment is important, and Visual Studio provides several methods for you to execute the Web site you are developing. You can define a start page for the site that loads when you start the application either with or without debugging. You can also open any page or handler directly in a browser. Visual Studio 2005 ships with a built-in personal Web server that requires no configuration by the developer to conveniently serve the current Web site.

Code Snippets, Intellisense, and Code Reuse

Productivity is the primary reason development environments were created. Visual Studio 2005 introduces Code Snippets, the easy ability to export and import templates and files, and improved Intellisense capabilities. Code Snippets are an extendable library of code patterns that can be quickly embedded in an application from a context menu or set of keystrokes. Entire application projects or individual files from a project may be exported to be reused for other projects in the future. Intellisense has always been one of the best features of Visual Studio, and the 2005 edition has a much improved Intellisense feature.

Exporting Web Sites

Another new feature to Visual Studio 2005 is the ability to export projects, Web sites, and pages. In the past, creating a custom project type was a very complicated process. Now you can create a base project or Web site and choose to export the project or site as a template from the File menu. After starting the export process, a wizard walks you through the steps to export. After this is done, the project or site is added as a project type to the New Project or New Web Site choices. Similarly, a single file or page can be exported for consistent reuse in future projects.

Debugging in Visual Studio

Visual Studio offers a rich set of debugging tools, enabling you to step through application code, SQL Server Stored Procedures, and even through JavaScript. Breakpoints can easily be set by pressing F9 on the line to initiate debugging. Stepping through the application is done by pressing F10 to move to the next line of code or F11 to step into a method or property.

Debugging is initiated by pressing F5 or attaching to an existing process. The application does not necessarily have to be a .NET application. Remote debugging can even be done on a machine where your account has the appropriate credentials.

New features to Visual Studio are the DataTips and Design-Time Syntax notifications. DataTips are available when the mouse cursor is placed over the variable. This allows you to drill into complex data types in a modeless window. Syntax notifications indicate when code has been added to a page that violates proper syntax for the language, and works both in markup and code-behind pages.

Publishing Web Sites

Posting a finished Web site can be done right from Visual Studio. The Web Site Copy utility allows you to post and synchronize content from the development workstation to a remote server through FTP, XCopy, the local instance of IIS, or a remote site with FrontPage Extensions installed.

VISUAL STUDIO VERSION	DESCRIPTION
Visual Studio Express	This is a lightweight, free version of Visual Studio targeted at the novice, student, and hobbyist. While there are limitations to the capabilities, developers will find with this version that they can develop just about any application from Web sites to games.
Visual Studio Standard	This version of Visual Studio is targeted at the individual developer who builds n-tier applications and Web sites.
Visual Studio Professional	This is a step up from the Standard edition. It is targeted at developers in small teams and offers a slightly improved user experience, full XML editing, Crystal reports, remote debugging, SQL 2005 integration, and more.
Visual Studio Team System	This version is targeted to large development teams. It offers a full range of lifecycle, communication, and collaboration tools vital to the large team development and testing process.

Create a Web Site with Visual Studio 2005

To create a new Web site in Visual Studio 2005 you can either choose File and then New Web Site from the menu or click the New Web Site icon on the application toolbar. This displays the New Web Site dialog box. You will see a variety of Web site projects, depending on what is installed on your system.

Your options will include ASP.NET Web Site, ASP.NET Web Service, and Empty Web Site. In the New Web Site dialog box you will need to type the name of your Web site and the location on your computer that you want the site created.

One of the great new features of ASP.NET 2.0 is that you place the actual Web site anywhere you want and are not limited to a virtual Web site inside of IIS. Visual Studio 2005 ships with Personal Web Server, which is a virtual Web server built into the development environment. When you launch a Web site from within Visual Studio 2005 it opens the site in a new browser, but you see a path similar to http://localhost:5465/MyWebSite/default.aspx.

After you complete the creation of your new Web site, you will see a default.aspx, a web.config, global.asax, and style sheet files in your new site. You can now proceed in developing your new Web site, starting with the default.aspx page. You can add new pages, style sheets, themes, Master pages, and handlers by either right-clicking on the location in the solution explorer and selecting the file type or by typing the handler signature manually.

Visual Studio 2005 first shipped without a Web site project. Microsoft eventually released an update that included the concept of a Web site project. This allows developers to add additional projects to a Web site solution. You can do this by choosing File and then Add. Typically, a class library will be added to the solution.

Create a Web Site with Visual Studio 2005

① Click File → New → Web Site.

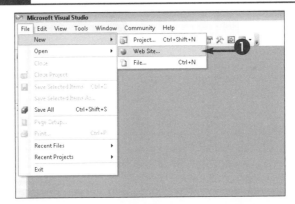

② Select ASP.NET Web Site from the New Web Site dialog box.

③ Set the path to the new Web site.

④ Click OK to create the new Web site.

Note: *You may have more or less project types to choose from depending on what has been installed on your workstation.*

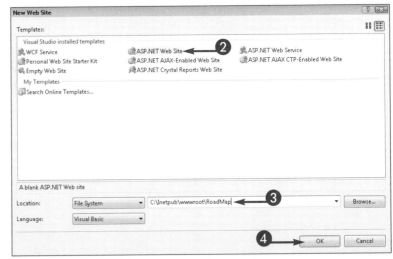

⑤ Open the Solution Explorer window.

Note: *Visual Studio leverages dockable and hideable windows. If a window is hidden, there will be a tab on the side of Visual Studio that will expand when you move the mouse over it.*

The new Web site will have a default.aspx page and a web.config file.

⑥ Double-click the default.aspx Web page to see the design code.

The Web page opens displaying its design code.

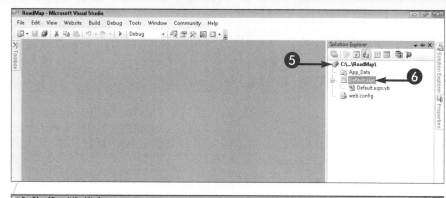

Extra

If you have installed any Starter Kits, Templates, ASP.NET AJAX, or possibly the ASP.NET 3.0 SDK, you will see more options. Starter Kits are specialized prebuilt projects that can be created as a base framework application to build your new Web site. Templates are very similar to Starter Kits, but are exported from Visual Studio, which is detailed later in this chapter. Recently, Microsoft released the ASP.NET 3.0 SDK, which is the latest version of the .NET framework, but is beyond the scope of this book.

You will notice a randomly assigned port, 5465 in this example, used by Personal Web Server to differentiate it from any standard install of IIS. The default installation of IIS will typically use port 80, the RFC-defined port for Web or HTTP activity. An RFC is a Request for Comment and is used to define standards for the Internet and many other network-related protocols. Protocols are executed over ports that range from 1 to 65555. Port 80 is the standard port for HTTP traffic. Another reason a nonstandard port is used is to make it harder for hackers to attack a development machine.

Add a Web Page to a Web Site

After you create a Web project, you need to add pages to the site. New pages or files may be added either through keystrokes or menu selections. Most developers opt for displaying the context menu from the root node of the Solution Explorer window. But the same can be accomplished for root pages of a site by pressing CTRL+N.

Adding new pages to a site through the context menu in the Solution Explorer gives you the ability to add the page to a subdirectory, whereas the keystroke only allows you to add a page to the Web site's root folder. To add a new page at any location in the site, right-click the folder to which you want to add the new page. In the context menu that appears, choose Add New Item.

The Add New Item dialog box that appears contains a long list of file types that may be added in this location.

For example, if you display this dialog box in the `App_Code` folder you only see file types for classes and other nonvisual items. There will generally be three file types you will add to a Web site: Web form (commonly referred to as a page), Master page, and Web user control.

If you are adding a new Web form, you are also given the option of selecting the associated Master page in the form of a check box in the lower portion of the dialog box. If you select this option you are prompted to select an existing Master page to associate with the new Web form. A *Master page* is a common template that can be applied to multiple pages in a Web site for a consistent layout. This is convenient because it creates the new Web form with all the code needed to leverage the Master page.

Add a Web Page to a Web Site

① Right-click the root of the Web site in the Solution window.

② Click Add New Item from the context menu.

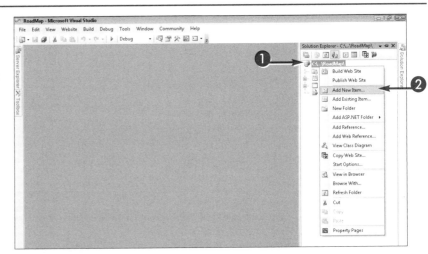

③ Select Web Form in the template list.

④ Type a name for your new file.

⑤ Click the Add button.

Note: Keep the Place code in a separate file option checked. You should also leave the Select Master Page option checked for this example.

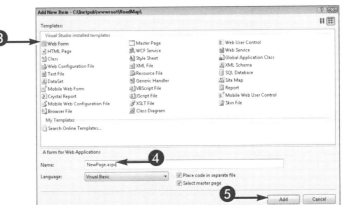

6 Type some text to indicate the page you added.

7 Click the Source tab at the bottom to view the page's markup.

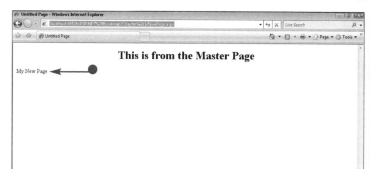

8 Open the page in a browser by right-clicking and selecting View in Browser.

● The new page appears showing the text you added in design mode.

Extra

There is a long list of potential files you can add to most folders in a Web site from the Add New Item dialog box. The dialog box is smart enough to filter this list to only allow file types that are supported in the folder. Some folders are marked with special attributes by Visual Studio, such as the App_Code and App_Data folders. There is a smaller subset of potential files for these folders; for example, App_Data only allows you to add SQL databases, XML files, Reports, Text files, and Class Diagrams.

The Add New Item dialog box offers two different views of the file types — Large Icons and Small Icons. The only differences are the icon size, large and small, and where the page type is displayed, below or to the right. This can be changed by selecting the corresponding icon in the top right corner of the dialog.

If you have installed any custom file templates in Visual Studio they are listed at the bottom of the Templates window in the My Templates section. You can learn more about these in the Export Template section.

E diting a Web page in Visual Studio 2005 involves two distinct paths — page design and program code, typically in the code-behind. By default, Visual Studio 2005 creates a Web page as two distinct files, the .aspx or design page and the .vb or .cs file (.vb is for a VB.NET file and .cs corresponds to C#). The .aspx file contains the HTML markup that defines how the page will be rendered to the browser. It contains standard HTML markup tags and attributes as well as the tags that define Web controls, such as a `TextBox`.

The Web page itself can be edited in either design or source views. The design view is a WYSIWYG visual format that allows the developer the ability to drag and drop elements and visually edit a page. You can change to source view to edit the page in the HTML markup. Each has distinct advantages. In the source view, for

example, most developers find it easier to manage finite details of a page. Design view allows the developer to see real time how a page may layout.

The code file is used to enter application logic to process data and inputs. It contains a class for the page and generally matches the name of the page with either a .vb or .cs extension. Each ASP.NET page has a life cycle marked by a series of events. These events can have handlers added to the code file that is executed when that event is raised. For more information about these events, see Chapter 2.

Methods, properties, and variables (known as class members) can be added to the page's class. These members can be called from event handlers to branch into the logical flow of the application to render the page or process user input as needed.

Edit a Web Page

① Open an existing Web page.

② Click the Design View tab to change to Design mode.

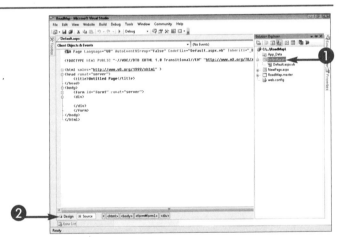

③ Click Layout → Insert Table to open the Insert Table dialog box.

④ Click the Template drop-down arrow and select Header, footer, and side.

⑤ Click OK.

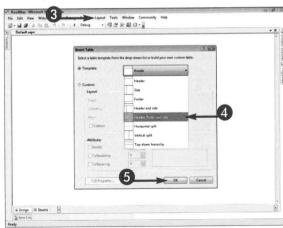

A preformatted table inserts into the document.

6 Select a cell (TD tag) in the table and then click the Ellipse button to open the Style Builder dialog box from the Properties window.

7 Set the Font Family to Arial.

8 Set the Font Color to White.

9 Set the Font Size to 24 px.

10 Click OK to store the settings.

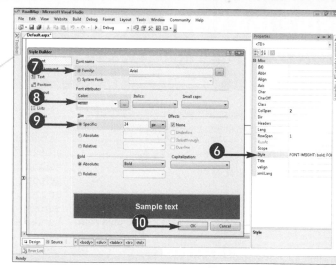

11 Type **ASP.NET Visual Blueprint** in the header cell.

You can now open the page in a browser to see the results.

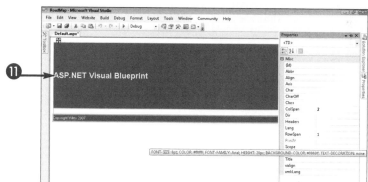

Extra

Most ASP.NET Web controls as well as Web user controls will have a SmartTag located in the top-right corner of the control in design view. The tag is a small square with a little arrow. Each control can have its own SmartTag functionality, but all are designed to give the programmer easier access to common programming or formatting functionality.

The SmartTag for a control will be a list of links or drop-down lists that have selections for common properties. Clicking one of the links typically displays a configuration dialog box for a particular property, such as setting the `datasource` for data control or a predefined style for many template controls. You can almost always access these same properties through the Properties window, in design view as attributes, or at runtime, but often the SmartTag interface optimizes the management of these properties.

Explore the Visual Studio 2005 Windows

Visual Studio 2005 was designed with productivity in mind. The IDE utilizes a series of content windows that can be moved and pinned to suit the developer's style while providing easy access to the tools and information needed to efficiently work on projects.

The main window used to edit files is called the document window. This window takes on slightly different views based on the file type being edited. A Web page has both a Design view and Source view. The Document window also includes a Tag navigator at the bottom of the window when editing a Web page, giving quick access to the underlying HTML tags. A code file has one view, but it has a pair of drop-down lists at the top to help the developer access and create event handlers for the page, controls, or base classes.

Other windows support the development process by providing quick access to information and project management to the developer. The Solution Explorer window contains a tree of projects, files, and folders that comprise an overall solution. Pages, files, and other project-related resources can be added and interacted with through simple mouse clicks. To open a file from the Solution Explorer, double-click the file.

The Properties window lists properties available to the developer from a control or HTML tag. Properties can be set inside the window and any custom property dialog box can be displayed. Some examples of a custom property dialog box are a color picker, style sheet builder, or items manager.

At the bottom of Visual Studio is a series of windows. These windows can vary, but often include Error List and Task List. These windows display a list of current solution errors and tasks defined by the developer. Other windows can be opened from the View menu and positioned at the left, right, or bottom of the IDE.

Explore the Visual Studio 2005 Windows

① With a Web site loaded, move your mouse over the Solution Explorer tab to make it visible.

Note: *The Solution Explorer window may be pinned open.*

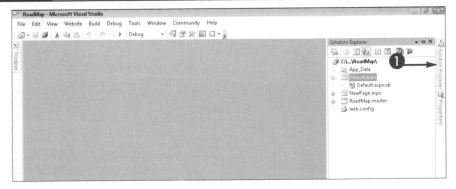

② Open an existing Web page.

③ Place the mouse cursor in a table cell.

Note: *This can vary based on the page you open. The properties for the selected HTML element or control will be displayed.*

④ Press F4 to see the Properties window for the page.

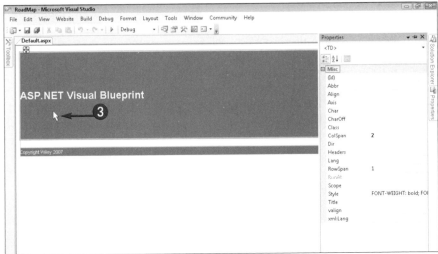

⑤ Position the mouse over the Error List tab.

● A list of errors currently acknowledged by Visual Studio appears.

⑥ Click View → Other Windows.

● A list of available windows in Visual Studio appears.

Note: *The list of available windows on your desktop will depend on the third-party add-ins you have installed.*

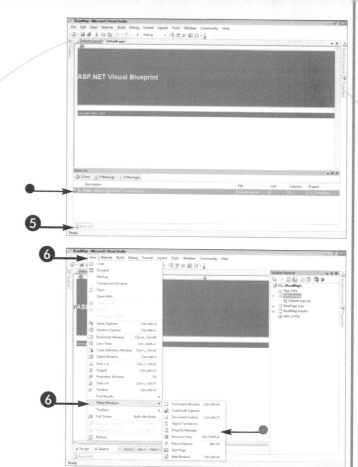

Extra

Visual Studio windows can be closed, moved, and pinned as needed. In the upper-right corner of each window, except the Document window, there is a down arrow, a push pin, and an X. The down arrow opens a menu with docking and hiding options for the window. The push pin allows you to either pin or keep the window open or allow it to collapse to the edge of the IDE. If a window is pinned, the Document window resizes to accommodate; otherwise the Document window stays beneath the unpinned window. Clicking the X closes the window. If you close the window you can still open it if you need it later, typically through the View menu or a keyboard shortcut.

While Visual Studio comes with a strong set of tools at the disposal of the developer, there are many third-party add-in tools that can be integrated into the development environment. Some of the common tools are source control, code generation, testing, and utility packages. Vendors for these utilities and tools often integrate an interface directly in Visual Studio to make it more convenient to work with their tool.

Add a Web Control to a Web Page

A Web control is an object that is typically used to collect information or display information to a user. It can also be used to manage extra attributes of controls and control groups. Web controls are analogous to Controls in a Smart Client application because they provide the programmer an object that can be programmed both on the Web form and in the application code.

Generally, a Web control inherits a series of base properties from the `WebControl` class that give you the ability to adjust various display settings, such as font color, bold, and background color. Some controls, such as the `PlaceHolder` control, have these properties suppressed. Other controls are composite controls, meaning they are composed of several controls but appear programmatically as one control.

Properties can be set either declaratively (in design mode) or at runtime (in the application code). Web controls all have an ID property that is by default created as the name of the control type and the current number of the controls without unique names on the page. For example `TextBox1` is the initial ID of the first `TextBox` placed on a page. You can change the name of any control to make it represent what it does; for example, `txtFirstName`. All controls should also have the `runat=server` set in the control definition.

```
<asp:TextBox ID="TextBox1" runat=
"server"></asp:TextBox>
```

You can quickly add controls to a page by selecting a control in the Visual Studio ToolBox and either dragging it to the location on the page you want the control displayed or double-clicking the item. If you double-click, it is added at the current location of the cursor in the page.

Add a Web Control to a Web Page

① Create a new Web page.

② Click the Design tab to switch to Design mode.

③ Open the ToolBox window in Visual Studio.

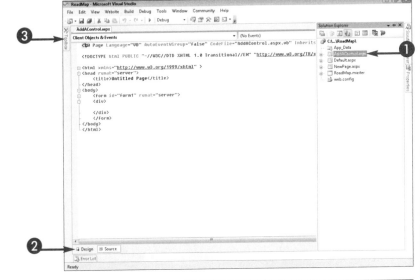

④ Double-click TextBox in the Standard tab list.

⑤ Press the Spacebar to add separation from the TextBox.

⑥ Position your mouse over the ToolBox and double-click the Button control to add it to your page.

⑦ Double-click the `Button` control to add a click event handler.

⑧ Type code to echo the value entered in the TextBox to the Label control.

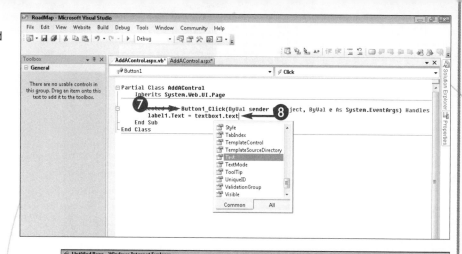

⑨ Open the page in a browser by right-clicking and selecting View in Browser.

⑩ Type some text in the `TextBox` control.

⑪ Click Submit.

● You should now see the value entered in the TextBox echoed in the `Label` control.

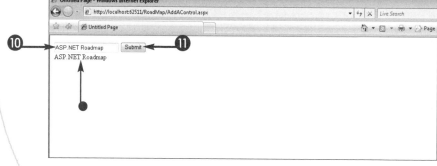

Extra

You can also create your own custom Web controls. The ASP.NET framework allows you to create your own controls from scratch or derive your controls from the `CompositeControl` class. If you create a control from scratch, you should inherit the class from WebControl to gain access to many core properties. Consider creating your own Web controls when you consistently reuse a set of markup and logic repeatedly in your Web sites.

You can also create a user control, which is much like a Web control, but is more like a small Web page. These are built in .ascx files that enable you to quickly build a set of reusable code in the same way you would build a Web page. User controls can be dragged onto the surface of a Web page just like a Web control. They will actually be a file in the Web solution and are not capable of being compiled into a reusable library.

Add a Reference to a Class Library

Many applications, including Web sites, rely on third-party class libraries as well as internal business libraries. These libraries are typically packaged as dynamic link libraries, or DLLs. Class libraries may contain a series of related classes, .NET controls, or resources.

You can add a reference to these libraries to your Web site by right-clicking the root node of the Web site in Solution Explorer to display the context menu. Choose Add Reference from the menu. In the Add Reference dialog box that appears, you will see a series of tabs — .NET, COM, Projects, Browse, and Recent.

The .NET tab contains a list of .NET DLLs that have been registered in the global assembly cache (GAC). The COM tab contains a list of COM objects registered on the machine. The Projects tab contains a list of the projects in

the current solution along with the Web site. The Browse tab resembles a File Open dialog box and lets you search the local computer and any network shares for the library you want to add. The Recent tab lists all the libraries that have been recently added to the project.

You can select any of the libraries from any of the tabs. In the case of tabs with a list, you can select multiple libraries to add to the Web site. For example, you can Ctrl+click items in the list box before clicking OK to add the references to your project.

A Visual Studio Solution can contain more than one project. For example, an enterprise application may contain a series of business logic libraries, a custom control library, and a Web site project. Each of these projects can reference each other as needed. Utilizing a library is a great way to package reusable code to reuse on multiple projects.

Add a Reference to a Class Library

① Right-click the root of the Web site in Solution Explorer.

② Click Add Reference.

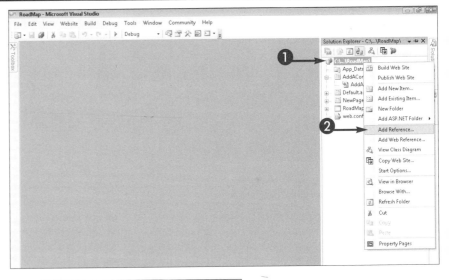

③ Scroll through the list of class libraries registered in the .NET tab to the System.Drawing component.

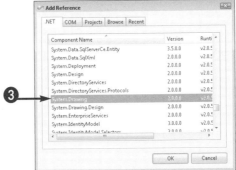

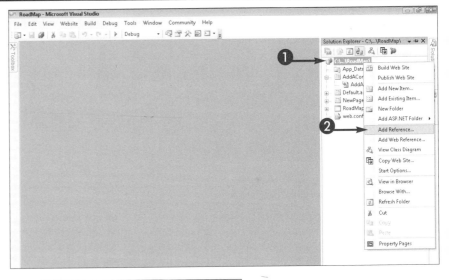

14

④ Click the Browse tab.

⑤ Browse your local computer to find an available component, a .dll, .exe, .ocx, or .tlb.

⑥ Select the component in the list.

⑦ Click OK to add the reference to the Web site.

Note: *If you are not aware of the location of a local component, you can add a reference to one of the components in the .NET tab.*

● The component you selected appears in the bin folder of the Web site. In this example, components were added on which the selected component is dependent upon.

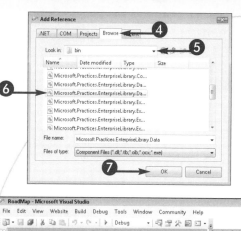

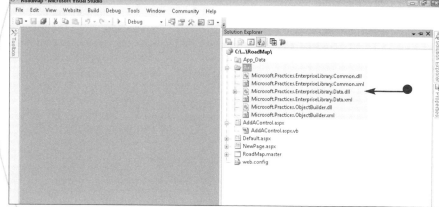

The web.config file contains a pages section that contains a namespaces section. Each namespace can be added to the namespaces section to make it available by default on each code page in the site. If you do not need a global reference to a namespace you can add it to your code page by adding an Imports (VB) or Using (C#) line to the header of the file.

Namespaces:

```
<pages>
 <namespaces>
 <clear/>
 <add namespace="System"/>
 <add namespace="System.Drawing"/>
 <add namespace="System.Data"/>
 </namespaces>
</pages>
```

Program a Page Using Code-Behind

Classic ASP programming uses an inline programming model, where any sort of programming logic is performed between a set of delimiters such as <% [Programming Here] %>. Several modern languages still utilize this style of programming: PHP, for example. ASP.NET offers a newer method of programming a Web application known as the code-behind model. This model separates design code from application logic, making it easier to debug and maintain application code. This allows the design portion of the site to be easier to maintain as well as define.

To help programmers transition from Classic ASP, ASP.NET supports the old inline method of coding. An intermediate model is also supported where you can define methods in the page header that are executed on the server. Again this model has limitations that make the code harder to maintain and scale as it grows.

The code-behind model is structured much like a traditional desktop application where you design your application's layout and then define the user interface logic in a supporting file. Code-behind files contain classes that are fully object-oriented. Depending on your language of choice, the code-behind file will either have the extension of .vb or .cs.

To access the code-behind file for a Web page, right-click on the page in the Solution window or right-click anywhere on the page in the Design editor window and select View Code. After you open the code file you can add event handlers and methods as you need to execute the page. Event handlers may be added by selecting the page events from the event drop-down list at the top left of the page and the event itself from the event drop-down list to its right. This automatically creates a handler method for the event. An ASP.NET page has several events that can be handled during its life cycle; the Load event is the most common event to handle.

Program a Page Using Code-Behind

① Open an existing Web page by double-clicking it in Solution Explorer.

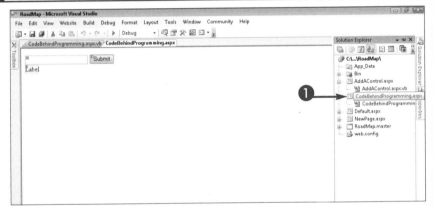

② Right-click anywhere on the page and choose View Code from the context menu.

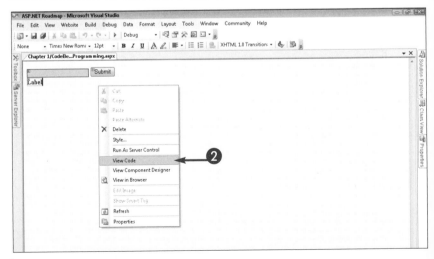

3 Add a Handler for the
Page Load event.

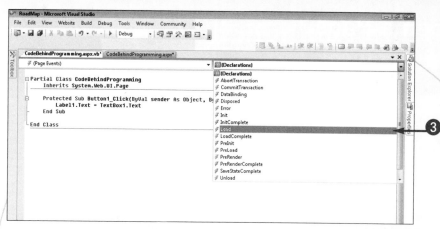

4 Add some code to set
the initial value in the
TextBox control.

*Note: In this example, a
page with the Add A
Control to a Web
Page section is
selected.*

You can now open the
page in a browser to
see the results.

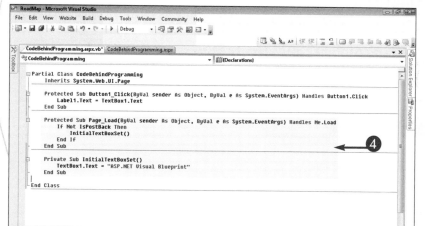

Extra

Most applications leverage the Page Load event
handler to begin processing local logic, but you are
not limited to this event as a place to begin
processing. You can create handlers for any of the
other events in the ASP.NET page life cycle. Other
important events are PreRender, Init, and
Error.

Always check if the page is being posted back to the
server through the IsPostback property. A post
back occurs when an input control such as a
Button is displayed, causing the form on the page
to post back to the server. Not every piece of code
should be executed each time a page is loaded. Data
binding, for example, should only be done the first
time a page is loaded or is explicitly invoked after a
change in the dataset.

You can create any code needed in the page's class
file, including functions that return values, sub
routines, properties, and enums. Instances of
controls on a page are created in the page's Init
event handler. If a control is created at runtime you
will need to create a new instance of this control
each time a page is processed.

Open a Page in a Browser

Developing a Web site involves checking the pages in a browser to verify they work and render correctly. You can quickly execute the site by pressing F5 (debug mode) or Ctrl+F5 (without debugging). This opens the default or start page for the site, which is typically the default.aspx page added to the site when it is first created. If you do not have a default page set for the Web site, you will be prompted to do so before executing the site.

Any page in the site can be set as the default page to open. There are two ways to define the start page for a Web site project. The easiest way to open an individual page is to right-click the page in the Solution window, then select Set as Start page from the context menu.

Alternatively, you can also open the properties for the Web site and open the Start Option section of the Properties dialog box. In the Start action section, you can choose to use the current page, a specific page, start an external program, a specific URL, or not to open a page at all. This gives you great flexibility in the start-up debug options for an ASP.NET 2.0 Web site.

If you are working the page file (.aspx), you can also right-click anywhere in the code or design surface to display a context menu. You can select View in Browser to open that page in a browser to begin validating how it is rendered and functions.

You are not limited to using the built-in Personal Web Server; you can also configure your application to run in a Virtual Web under a local instance of IIS or even on a remote machine running IIS.

Open a Page in a Browser

① Open the Solution Explorer window.

② Right-click any page in the solution.

③ Click View in Browser.

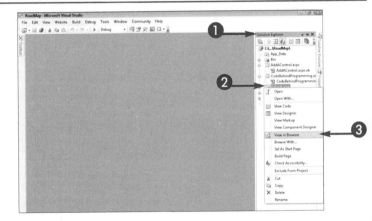

④ Open a page in Source view.

⑤ Right-click anywhere on the page.

⑥ Click View in Browser.

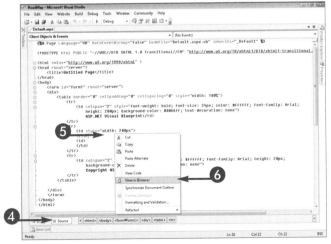

⑦ Click the Design tab to switch to Design mode.

⑧ Right-click anywhere on the page.

⑨ Click View in Browser.

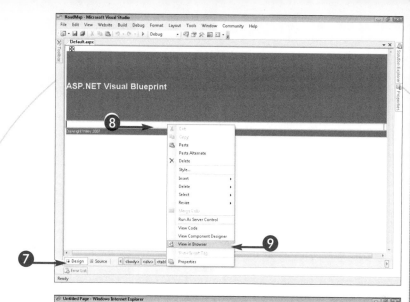

● The page opens in the browser.

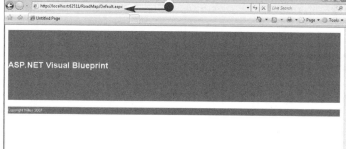

Extra

Traditionally, a Web developer's workstation will have a local version of the Web server installed. For classic ASP and ASP.NET developers, this is traditionally IIS. But as corporate security and support policies have evolved, developers are finding it harder to have a local copy of Web servers running on their development workstations because of the security exposure it offers. Visual Studio 2005 ships with the Personal Web Server, which is a small instance of an IIS Web server that is only invoked while the developer actively runs the Web site from Visual Studio. The nice thing about the Personal Web Server is it runs on any current edition of Windows XP, Windows Server, and Vista.

The Personal Web Server does not run over the traditional Web service HTTP port 80. Instead, it randomly selects a port number to run in the valid range of ports. Selecting a random port number makes it more difficult for a potential hacker to attack the local Web server instance. Personal Web Server, previously known as Casini, is available for free download at www.asp.net.

Use Code Snippets to Quickly Add Common Code

Rapidly developing applications is one of the most compelling attributes of the ASP.NET and Visual Studio experience. Visual Studio 2005 provides a new feature, Code Snippets, which make it very easy for a developer to add predefined code to an application. A Code Snippet is a little piece of code that performs a specific task or is a repeatable pattern, such as an `If Then` statement.

There are hundreds of Code Snippets that ship with Visual Studio and vary by language, project, and file type. The IDE is intelligent enough to offer only applicable snippets based on the code file's use. To add a Code Snippet, simply right-click in the code-behind file to display the context menu and click Insert Snippet.

A drop-down list appears right where your cursor is positioned with a top-level list of snippet categories such as networking, system, data, File IO, math, and common structures. Each time you select an item in the list, another drop-down list with subcategories is displayed or the code is placed in the file. After the code is in the file you can clean it up to fit your application. There may also be some sections that require you to type values or variables in order for the snippet to function. These are highlighted in green by default. For example, an `If Then` statement needs a conditional statement to evaluate.

Each snippet also has a shortcut to add it to a file. The shortcut for a snippet can be seen in the Tooltip window when the snippet is selected in the drop-down list. The shortcut is a value that can be typed in a file followed by pressing Tab to add the section. For example, `If Then` has a shortcut of If+Tab. Your can improve your programming efficiency by learning these shortcuts.

Use Code Snippets to Quickly Add Common Code

① Create a new Web page and then open the code file.

② Create a `Load` event handler for the page.

③ Right-click inside the `Load` event handler and click Insert Snippet.

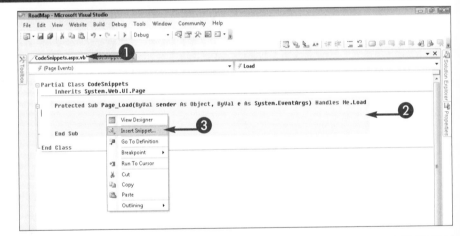

④ Select Common Code Patterns from the snippet drop-down list.

⑤ Select Conditionals and Loops from the next drop-down list.

⑥ Select If...ElseIf..Else..EndIf Statement from the final drop-down list.

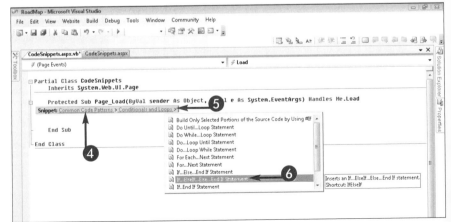

7 Add `Response .Write` calls to indicate the different cases of the `If` conditional statement.

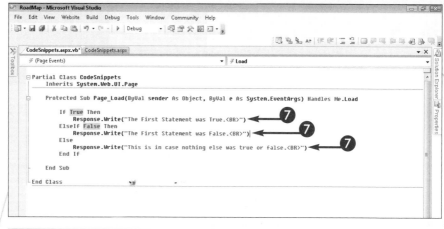

8 Open the file in a browser to see the text echoed from the `If` conditional statement.

● In this example, you should see the first string because you did not set any values in the conditional section and used the default of `True`.

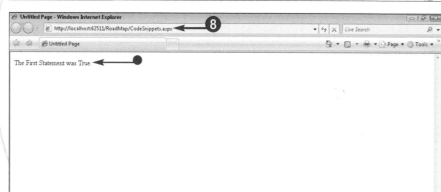

Extra

A Code Snippet is an XML text file with the .snippet extension that follows the Code Snippet XML schema. A snippet can display an input dialog box or message box, add import (VB) or using (C#) statements to a code file, and highlight areas that require a user to customize.

You can manage your code Snippet library with the Code Snippet Manager. The Code Snippet Manager can be opened from the Tools menu of Visual Studio or by pressing Ctrl+K, Ctrl+B. It allows you to add, remove, and import Code Snippets as well as navigate through all the installed snippets.

The syntax that defines a Code Snippet allows you to define a name, author, and description for the snippet. You can also add any namespace imports needed for the code. If the namespace is already included in the file, this is ignored. A snippet can also have variables or declarations that need to be customized by the developer.

Export Projects and Files

Visual Studio comes with several prebuilt projects, including Web, WinForm, Class Library, console applications, and so on. It has been possible for developers to create similar templates in previous versions of Visual Studio, but it was too difficult a task for the average developer or team to accomplish. Visual Studio 2005 includes a useful Export feature to assist a developer create a core or skeleton project with all the files, pages, and resources needed to provision a vertical-oriented site. The same Export feature can also create individual file templates that may be reused on future projects.

For example, a team that specializes in e-commerce solutions might create a core solution or set of customized solutions it can use to quickly get a project under way. The main advantage of a custom project template is that it includes all base pages, classes, and

resources consistently needed for all similar projects. You can think of it as a base class library to inherit your next set of projects from, saving hours of common programming.

Exporting a project is fairly straightforward. First, create a new Web site or class library project, or another base project you may want to customize. After you add all the core elements, such as pages, classes, and style sheets, you can export it intact. The Export Wizard can be launched from the File menu.

You are not limited to just exporting projects and Web sites; you can also export files. For example, most Web sites have a contact form. You can create a standard contact form and export it. Each time you create a new Web site, you can just add a new prebuilt contact form to the site.

Export Projects and Files

1 Open a Web site in Visual Studio.

2 Click File → Export Template.

Note: *You may need to add this to your menu by clicking Tools → Customize.*

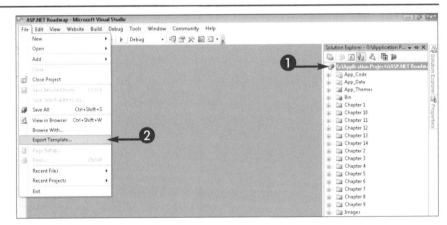

3 Click the Project template option.

4 Click here and select the Web project you want to export.

5 Click here and select the language for which the Web site is developed.

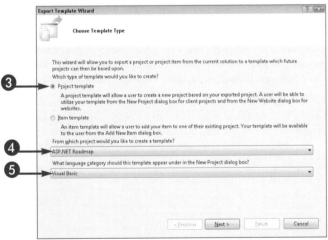

6 Change any of the Template option values you need to customize.

7 Select the Automatically import the template info Visual Studio option.

8 Select the Display an explorer window on the output files folder option.

9 Click Finish to export the Web site.

● Explorer opens to the Zip file that was exported. Depending on your system, the contents of the Zip file may display.

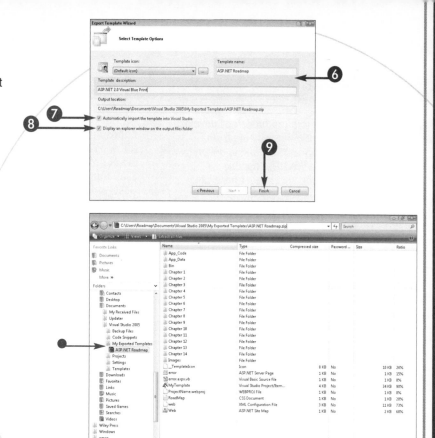

Visual Studio 2005 includes the ability to export and import settings for Visual Studio. This can be very helpful to a developer who works on a variety of projects. In this case, certain windows and layouts of the IDE can be more productive for each type of project.

Environment settings may be imported and exported from the Tools menu. Open the Tools menu and choose Import and Export Settings. The Import and Export Settings Wizard opens, and you have a choice to Export, Import, or Reset all Settings. The two screens allow you to select the settings to export and the name and location of the settings file. Similarly, the Import Settings will prompt you to indicate if you want to save the current settings and which set of settings you want to import. Resetting the settings returns Visual Studio to the initial state after install.

Publish a Web Site

Publishing a Web site to a production or development and quality assurance environments from a developer workstation can be done in several ways: XCopy deployment, the Copy Web Site option, Precompiling, or by building an Installer program.

XCopy deployment is simply copying all the files from one location to the other through a standard file copy operation. XCOPY is a command-line tool that can be used to copy entire directory or drive structures from one location to another. The term XCOPY deployment simply refers to the process of copying the Web application files from one location to another. This could also include a simple FTP operation to the server.

The Copy Web Site option refers to a built-in GUI inside of Visual Studio 2005 that helps manage the copying and synchronization of files from the development machine to another location. This GUI can be displayed by clicking

on the Copy Web Site icon on Solution Explorer or by choosing Website and then Copy Web Site. This GUI allows you to select the destination location. There are several destination options: File System, Local IIS, FTP Site, and Remote Site. After you connect to the destination you will see a file and directory structure for both the source and destination.

Synchronizing between the two locations can be done by selecting the files and directories you want to synchronize with the destination, then using the arrow buttons in the center of the window to perform the synchronization process. The first two buttons copy a file from the workstation to the destination, or the vice versa. The next option synchronizes between the two locations, selecting the most current version for copying to the other location. The remaining button allows you to terminate or cancel any operation while it is running.

Publish a Web Site

① Open a Web site in Visual Studio.

② Click the Copy Web Site icon at the top of the Solution Explorer window.

Note: *You must have a node in the Web site selected for this icon to be available.*

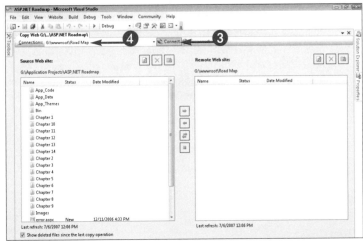

③ Click Connect at the top of the Copy Web Site window.

④ Select the destination Folder.

Note: *There are four possible destination types, each of which requires a set of connection values.*

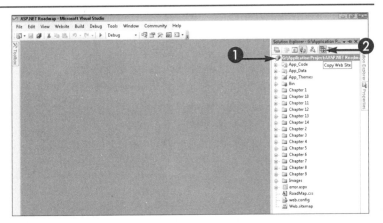

⑤ Select a group of files in the Web site to synchronize with the destination.

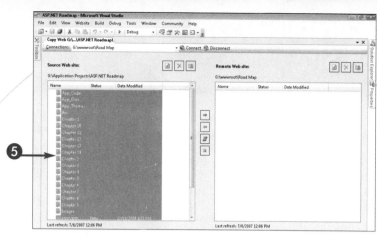

⑥ Click the Synchronize button to copy the selections to the destination location.

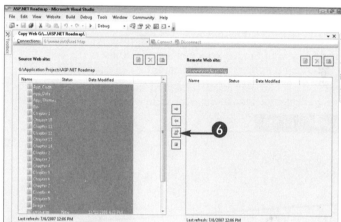

Extra

The Copy Web Site utility allows you to select from four destination types: File System, Local IIS, FTP Site, and Remote Site. Each destination type has a set of information required to make a connection.

File System is easiest because you just need to indicate the path to the destination folder on the local machine. This can also be a mapped drive. The Local IIS option provides a tree list of the local Web servers and their virtual webs. You can select any of these nodes to which you have write permission to synchronize your site.

The FTP Site option handles connecting over FTP protocol to a remote server. Note that you may need to type the destination folder because the Copy Web Site tool assumes the initial folder is the destination folder. The Remote Site option allows you to type a destination URL that is configured with FrontPage Server extensions.

Precompile a Web Site

By default, ASP.NET performs batch compiling on a Web application. This means that a site is compiled as it is used. The first time a page is requested it is compiled, which causes an initial performance hit. Every subsequent request for that page bypasses the compilation process and instead serves up the compiled page. If you make a change to the file it goes through the compilation process again.

ASP.NET 2.0 introduces precompilation, which gives you the ability to compile the Web site before it is deployed, thus bypassing the batch compilation penalty. There are two ways in which a Web site can be compiled: through the command line with the aspnet_compiler.exe utility or from the Build menu Publish Web Site option.

The aspnet_compiler accepts a few command-line switches to indicate the source Web site, either from the

IIS metabase or a physical path on the workstation and the destination folder. The Publish Web Site option displays a dialog box asking for the target location, and several compilation options. You can allow the compiled site to be updateable, use fixed naming and single page assemblies, or enable a strong name.

The output of the compilation will resemble the original site, but if you examine the compiled Web pages you will see they are merely a placeholder file to mark the original file. In the site's Bin folder are a series of randomly named DLL files that the application was compiled into. You can recognize the files because they will be named App_Web_ABCXYZ.dll, where ABCXYZ are random characters. Some files, such as XML, config, and HTML files, are not compiled.

Precompile a Web Site

① Click Build → Publish Web Site.

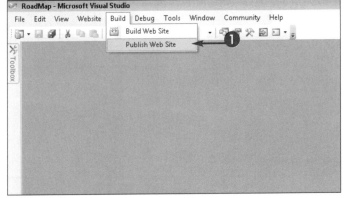

② Type the destination for the compiled Web site.

③ Deselect the Allow this precompiled site to be updateable option.

④ Deselect the Use fixed naming and single page assemblies option.

⑤ Deselect the Enable strong naming on precompiled assemblies option.

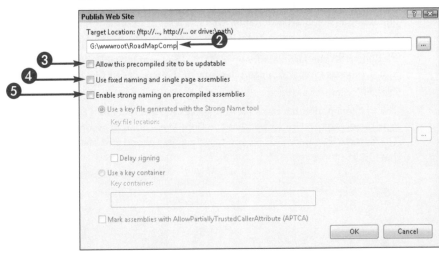

6 Click OK to compile the site.

Note: *You will not see anything happen, but if you examine the Output window you can see the result.*

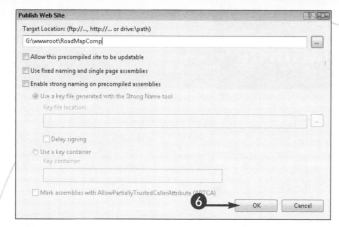

7 Open your Web browser.

8 Type in the destination's Bin folder.

● The compiled DLL files appear.

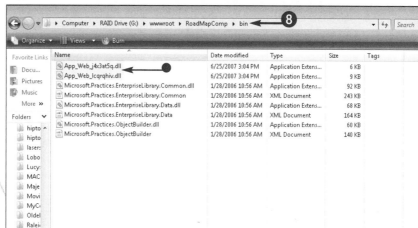

Extra

The Publish Web Site utility allows you to precompile the site to a destination location. It also gives you the ability to control certain aspects of how your site is compiled. The first choice, Allow this precompiled site to be updateable, retains the original .aspx files to enable them to be changed at a later time. This means you can make small changes to the design of a page and replace the file on the destination at any time.

Deselecting the first option means the site must be recompiled to apply any changes. Each page is still represented on the site, but with a place-holder file. Each of these files contains the following statement: "This is a marker file generated by the precompilation tool, and should not be deleted!"

The Use fixed naming and single page assemblies option causes the compiler to create a DLL file for each page in the Web site. The third option is to use a Strong name on the assembly, signed with the key of your choice.

Discover the ASP.NET Platform

ASP.NET provides a high-performance, scalable platform to build Web sites. The platform is built upon the .NET framework, IIS, and the Windows Server Platform. The .NET framework provides thousands of pre-built and tested classes that provide managed access to databases, the file system, network services, the request context, and much more.

Currently, there are millions of production Web sites on the Internet and company intranets built using the ASP.NET framework. Some higher-profile sites include MySpace.com, Continental Airlines, and many Fortune 500 companies.

An ASP.NET Web site is really a specialized application that runs on top of the IIS subsystem and the .NET framework. Unlike Classic ASP, its popular predecessor, and several competing platforms, such as PHP, ASP.NET does not utilize inline coding that is interpreted at runtime. ASP.NET is built in a very similar manner as a desktop application and is compiled when the site is first executed or can be precompiled before it is deployed.

While the classic inline coding model is supported by ASP.NET, the code-behind model is the preferred method to build ASP.NET applications because it offers a more optimal structure for architecture, maintenance, and performance.

An ASP.NET Web site is composed of Web or content pages, their supporting code-behind files, and several optional files. These optional files include a web.config, global.asax, style sheets, Themes, Skins, Master pages, user controls, and images. In addition, Web controls are special classes that encapsulate both user interface and application logic into reusable components that can be used across multiple sites or distributed as a third-party source of reliable code.

The global.asax file manages application and session event handlers. Master pages, Themes, Skins, Style sheets, and images are used to provide a professional-looking and consistent site. User controls can be thought of as mini pages that can be included on Web pages that provide the ability to program controls and logic in smaller segments.

The Web.Config File

A web.config file defines configuration settings for the Web application by overriding server-level settings defined in the machine.config file. The web.config file can contain custom configuration sections and settings for a particular site or class library. The ASP.NET 2.0 version of the web.config file includes several new upgrades over the previous versions, including a built-in section for `ConnectionStrings`, mail settings, and many more new options.

Code-Behind File

Application code is often contained in code files that sit behind the design code. Each code-behind file consists of a class that inherits from the `System.Web.UI.Page` class. It also may contain local event handlers for the events in the ASP.NET page life cycle, such as the `Load`, `Render`, and `Error` events. These events can be used to initiate custom business logic.

Web Pages

Web pages or forms are indicated with the .aspx extension in ASP.NET and are the most common file type in a Web site. ASP.NET Web pages are composed of HTML markup in the .aspx page, but may also include server-executed code and inline code. But most ASP.NET sites utilize the code-behind model to manage application code.

Master Pages

Maintaining a consistent look and feel to a Web site is important for a positive user experience, but it has not been that easy for many Web developers. Master pages have been added to the ASP.NET toolset to help developers maintain the consistent look and structure to a site needed for easy maintenance and better user experience.

Themes and Skins

Themes and Skins are new additions to the ASP.NET toolset to make it easier for developers to provide a high user experience with a lower maintenance threshold. Themes are used to define a consistent look to Web controls in the site and can utilize style sheets as well. A theme is stored in the /App_Theme folder.

User Controls

User controls are a smaller, reusable version of a Web page. While the development experience of user controls is similar to a Web page, they must reside in a Web page to operate. User controls are used to contain code and markup that are typically used multiple times in a site, making it easier for code reuse and maintenance.

Web Controls

Web controls take the concept of a user control to another level and typically contain compiled code controlling a specific control or related controls. Web controls are typically included in a class library to be used across multiple sites.

Maintaining State

Keeping track of user activity during a visit is a problem every Web site has because the Web is a stateless medium, meaning each request is entirely unique. ASP.NET solves this common problem through the use of `Session state`, a mechanism that utilizes a cookie on the user's machine to identify him or her on the server. The `Session` object can be used to store values specific to each session. A session can be set to expire at a predefined time frame, fixed, or on a sliding scale.

Page Directives

Each ASP.NET page has a set of optional Page Directives that tell the compiler about the page. There are 11 directives available for you that control attributes about the page itself, including OutputCache, References, Controls, Master pages, and more.

httpModules and httpHandlers

`HttpModules` are classes that can be plugged into the application request pipeline to invoke custom logic. All `httpModules` are derived from the `IHttpModule` interface and implement two methods, `Invoke` and `Dispose`. You can use `httpModules` to modify content before it is sent to the client or change the way a request is processed altogether.

`HttpHandlers` produce custom HTML or binary content based on the request and any parameters passed to the request. As a programmer, you can direct a request to an `httpHandler` and produce a specialized response based on the name of the resource requested, for example vcard.ashx, or parameters passed in the `Querystring`.

Application Life Cycle of ASP.NET

Events are raised in a specific order each time a page is requested through the ASP.NET engine. These events can all be intercepted by `httpModules` to perform custom logic and each serves a different purpose.

EVENT	DESCRIPTION
BeginRequest	This is the first event in the ASP.NET pipeline.
AuthenticateRequest	This event fires when a security module creates a user identity. This event only fires when the configured authentication mechanism authenticates the request. This means you can execute code only if the user has been authenticated on the site.
PostAuthenticateRequest	This event is raised after the `AuthenticateRequest` event.
AuthorizeRequest	This event is raised when ASP.NET has authorized the request.
PostAuthorizeRequest	This event is raised after the `AuthorizeRequest` event.
ResolveRequestCache	This event is raised after authorization to let caching modules know that any requests can now be served from cache.
PostResolveRequestCache	This event is raised after the `ResolveRequestCache` event.
PostMapRequestHandler	This event is raised when ASP.NET maps the request to the appropriate event handler.
AcquireRequestState	This event is raised when the request acquires state; for example, session state.
PostAcquireRequestState	This event is raised after the `AcquireRequestState` event.

Explore ASP.NET Page Life Cycle

Every time a user requests a page from an ASP.NET application, the .NET engine runs through a cycle of steps that processes the request and produces the appropriate content to the browser. These steps take care of initialization, instantiation of controls, state management, event handling, and finally, rendering output to the browser. When you understand the different stages of the ASP.NET page life cycle you will know where you write code for each particular task.

If you want to write custom Web controls you should become very intimate with the page life cycle because you need to be aware of when to handle specific code in the control, such as managing State, initializing any child controls, and running any logic code.

Each stage in the life cycle raises events that can have methods assigned to execute when each event is raised, called an event handler. An event is said to be raised

when it occurs and bubbles through the application. An event handler is simply a method that matches the required method signature for the event when the event is raised. Code can be placed in the event handler to process any logic you need at that point. For example, just about every page utilizes the OnLoad event handler to start the main body of processing.

If you author controls, they have a very similar event cycle and generally execute right after the page's event is raised. Controls that are created at runtime can have events out of sync from the page. This is a rare occurrence, and after the control is instantiated it begins to catch up to the current page event process.

Page event handlers all have the same parameter signature of a Sender and an EventArgs object. The Sender parameter is an Object type. The EventArgs parameter is a base type from which other event argument classes are derived.

Explore ASP.NET Page Life Cycle

① Create a new Web page.

② Open the properties for the document.

● You may need to select Document from the Element drop-down list at the top of the Properties window.

③ Set Trace to true.

④ Set Trace Mode to SortByTime.

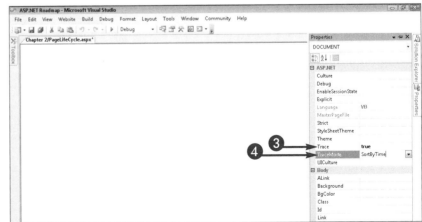

⑤ Add a page title to the document.

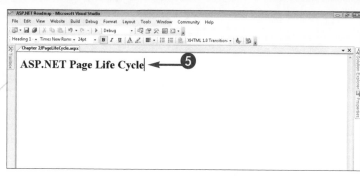

⑥ Open the page in a browser.

● The title you entered should be visible, followed by a series of trace information. The Trace Information section lists each step in the ASP.NET life cycle and how long it takes to execute.

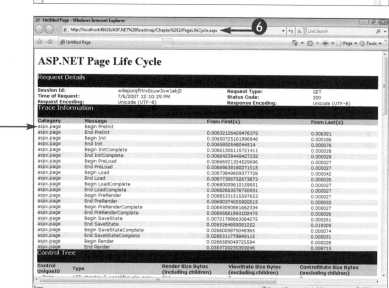

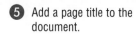

Extra

Each time a page is loaded you should check the `IsPostBack` property before processing any page initialization logic you may have. For example, you do not want to call the page's initial data binding methods when the page is submitted to the server. This causes any form data to be overwritten to the state in which it was sent to the browser when it first loaded.

The `IsPostBack` property is a Boolean so it will be either True or False. It can be called in any event handler to control the execution of code.

Using the IsPostBack Property in the Page_Load Method:

```
Protected Sub Page_Load(ByVal sender As Object, ByVal e As System.EventArgs) Handles Me.Load
If IsPostBack = False then
 'Process any page initialization methods, such as data binding.
End If
End Sub
```

Often you need to pass parameters or variables to a Web page, much like you would a console or desktop application. These parameters are used in your page to control how it behaves. Input parameters are sent over the Web as Post or Get variables. Post variables are passed in the request header, virtually invisible to the end user. Get variables are passed in the URL QueryString.

The QueryString is a series of variables appended to the end of a URL and delineated by a (?). The parameter names and values are separated by an (&). A typical URL with QueryString parameters looks something like this: www.mydomain.com?param1=value1&param2=value2.

QueryString variables are accessed through the Request object. The Request object provides access to information about the page, such as URL, headers, and parameters. QueryString parameters can be read by

calling Request.QueryString("[ParameterName]") or Request.("[ParameterName]")where [ParameterName] represents the variable name.

The Request.QueryString property is a NameValueCollection representing each of the QueryString variables sent by the client.

Calling the Request object and passing a parameter name, Request("[ParameterName]"), returns the first match the request finds. This method searches through a list of NameValue collections in the Request object in this order: QueryString, Form, Cookies, and Server variables. It is a good idea to explicitly call the collection you are looking for because it may not be the actual value you expect. It is a good practice to verify a parameter exists before accessing it. In VB.NET, you would check with the following code:

```
If IsNothing(request("[ParameterName]") =
False then ... End If
```

Read Input from the QueryString

① Create a new Web page and save it as QueryString.aspx.

② Add four hyperlink controls to the page.

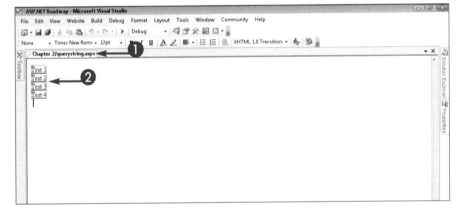

③ Set each hyperlink's NavigationUrl property to link to this page.

④ Set the QueryString parameters to a changing set of values for each hyperlink control.

⑤ Switch to the code-behind.

⑥ Add code to the `Page_Load` event to each of the values of the `QueryString` parameters.

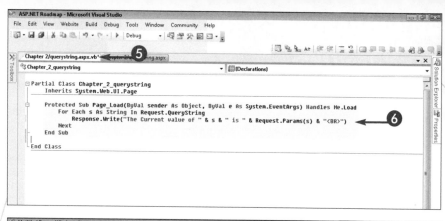

⑦ Open the page in a browser.

⑧ Click the various hyperlinks.

● The values change based on the link you click.

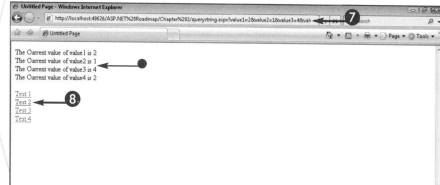

The Current value of value1 is 2
The Current value of value2 is 1
The Current value of value3 is 4
The Current value of value4 is 2

Test 1
Test 2
Test 3
Test 4

Apply It

It is a good practice to read `QueryString` values using the `Server.URLDecode` method to ensure data integrity. Web URLs cannot contain certain ASCII characters, but can contain a specially encoded ASCII version (available through `Server.URLEncode`). For example, a space character cannot be read by some browsers, but may be encoded as `%20`. This encoding mechanism also helps make the inputs safer from hacking attempts.

Read Each Variable Value from the QueryString Using URLDecode:
```
For Each item as string in Request.QueryString
  Respnse.Write(Server.URLDecode(Request.QueryString(item)))
Next
```

Read Input from Form Variables

ariables can be sent to a page in one of two methods — `Post` or `Get` variables. Variables are passed in the request header, typically as the result of a form being submitted. These are called `Form` variables. `Get` variables are passed in the URL in the form of the `QueryString`. You can read `Form` variables by calling the `Request.Form("[ParameterName]")` method or simply `Request("[ParameterName]")`.

`Form` or `Posted` variables are sent back to the server in the page header, invisible to the user. The page header is not rendered by the browser to the end user, but can be seen by network packet sniffers or tools like Fiddler (www.fidlertools.com). You can also set the `Trace=True` in the page directives to have all the `RequestObject` values echoed on the page.

HTML controls or Web controls are represented in the `Request.Form` collection. Hidden tags, such as the `ViewState`, are also included in this collection, so

practice caution when echoing these values on a page. This can be done by encoding any user input with the `httpUtility.HTMLEncode` method.

The `Request.Form` property is a `NameValueCollection` that holds Posted variables and their values. You can read Posted variables by calling Request.Form ("[VariableName]"). This method accepts one parameter, the variable name, and returns a string value. The `Request.Form` object is a `NameValueCollection`, just like the `Request.QueryString` object.

The `Request.Form` collection is a read-only property at runtime and cannot be programmatically set. This means that you cannot inject variables directly into the form collection that are posted back to the server. This is one of the reasons why the `ViewState` object is serialized to a `Hidden Input` control, so it will be passed back as a header value when the page is submitted.

Read Input from Form Variables

1. Create a new Web page.

2. Add an `Input` control from the HTML controls tab of the ToolBox.

3. Add a `TextBox` Web control.

4. Add a `Button` Web control.

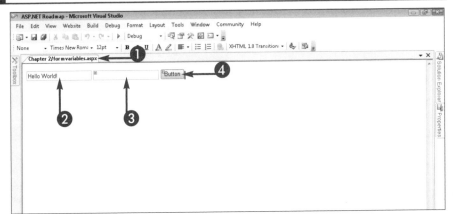

5. Double-click the `Button` control to create an event handler.

6. Add code to echo the values of the Form Collection.

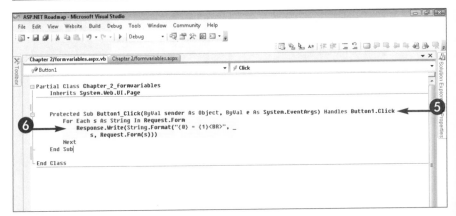

7 Open the page in a browser.

8 Type values in the Input and TextBox.

9 Click Submit (Button) to display the Form Values.

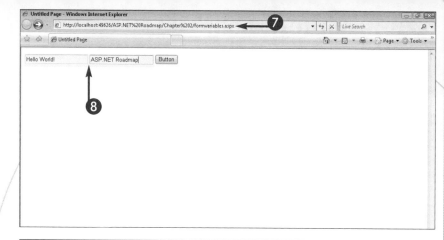

● The values of each of the controls as well as the `ViewState` and `Eventvalidation` hidden fields appear.

Use Application Cache to Persist Values

Many Web sites have common variables that are used on many pages throughout the site and for each session. Storing global variables is not a natural aspect of Web programming that is common to regular windows applications. Application State was created to preserve global variables in ASP.NET.

The Application State is stored in an instance of the `HttpApplication` class and is accessible by every class in the `System.Web` namespace as Application. The `HttpApplication` object is created upon the first page request for the Web site.

You can store your own objects in the `Application State`, including strings, integers, arrays, hash tables, and even custom types by calling the `Application` object and passing the name of the variable and a value like this Application("MyParameter") = MyValue. In a similar manner `Application State` values can be

accessed like this: `dim myvar as string = Application ("MyParameter")`. It is a good practice to type cast any custom objects, such as `dim myvar as MyClass = CType(Application ("MyParameter"), MyClass)`.

Because `Application State` is stored in memory, you need to determine if storing a value in the Application State is the optimal location. If you do not access the value across multiple user sessions or only on one page, consider another method of saving the state, like in the `ViewState` or `Session State`.

The `Application State` is not scalable by default in a Web Farm environment. If you are using a Web Farm, the `Application State` should be stored in a common medium, such as a database. Application State is reset each time the Web site is restarted or the Web.config file is changed. It is also a good idea to initialize Application State values in the `Application_Start` method.

Use Application Cache to Persist Values

① Create a new Web page.

② Add a `TextBox` control.

③ Add a `Button` control.

④ Double-click the `Button` control to create an event handler.

⑤ Add code to store values in the Application Cache.

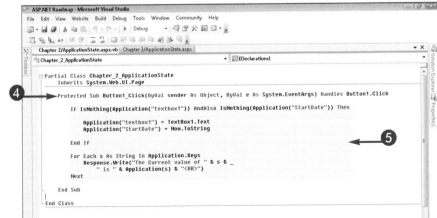

6 Open the page in a browser.

7 Type a value in the TextBox.

8 Click Submit (Go).

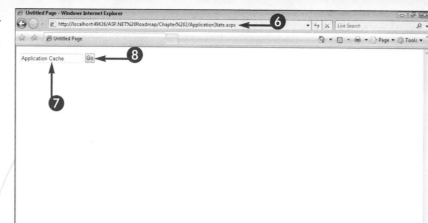

● The value of the TextBox and the time the form was submitted the first time appear.

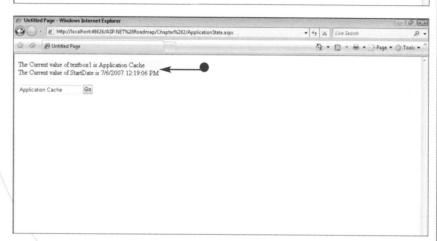

Extra

`Application State` is a free-threaded class, to which multiple users and pages can have access to get or set values. Therefore it is good practice to `Lock` and `Unlock` `Application State` variables to update their values.

Calling `Lock` blocks other clients from modifying any variable stored in the `Application` object. You can explicitly call `Unlock` to control when the object is available to other clients, or it is automatically called as soon as a page completes processing. When a page locks the `Application` object, any other page will wait to access the object until it is unlocked.

Using Application Locks to Set an Application Value:
```
Public Sub SetSomeApplicationVariable(sName as string, sValue as string)
Application.Lock()
Application(sName) = sValue
Application.UnLock()
End Sub
```

Use Session State to Persist Values

Persisting values across a user's session can be done in several manners, including cookies, hidden fields, and the Session object. The Session object is loaded after the AquireRequestState event fires in the life cycle of the Application. The Session object is released when the ReleaseRequestState event fires. Session is an HttpSessionState type, which is a collection of values and corresponding keys.

A Session is initiated upon the first request of a page in the Web site by a browser and is maintained as long as the user is active on the site. A Session is released when the user is inactive for a specified number of minutes — the default is 20. This value can be set in the site's web.config file by assigning the timeout attribute of the sessionState section, located in the system.web section of the web.config file.

To store and read Session values, reference the Session object and pass it the key for the value you want to work with. To store a value in the Session object, reference the Session property of the Page or control you are working with and the key or index and set it equal to the value, Session("FirstName") = "Chris". Reading a value is just as easy. You reverse the call to the Session object, txtFirstName.text = Session("FirstName"). It is good practice to check for a null value before processing a value in the Session object. If the value is not yet added you throw an exception if you try to reference the value.

A cookie is created on the client machine when a session is initiated that stores a randomly generated GUID used to reference the Session in memory. If the browser does not support cookies there are configuration options available to use cookieless sessions and to even auto-detect the use of cookies.

Use Session State to Persist Values

① Create a new Web page.

② Add a TextBox control.

③ Add a Button control.

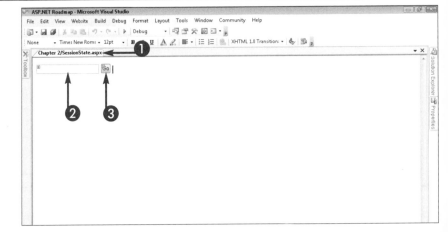

④ Double-click the Button control to create an event handler.

⑤ Add code to store values in the Session Cache.

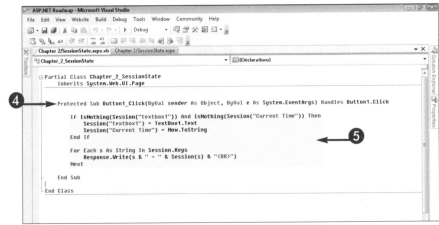

6 Open the page in a browser.

7 Type a value in the TextBox.

8 Click Submit (Go).

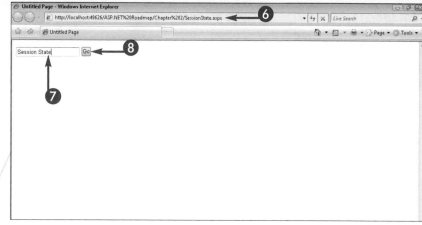

● The value of the TextBox and the time the form was submitted the first time appear. This will be different for each session. If you open the page in a second browser, different results appear.

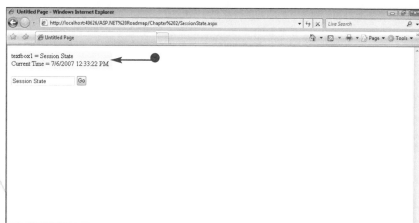

Extra

By default Session values are stored in memory, but can quickly be changed to use SQL Server, an ASP.NET session server, or a custom server. If you implement a Web farm you will need to use one of the alternate session storage mechanisms. This choice can be done in the web.config file by setting the SessionStateMode attribute to an appropriate choice such as Custom, InProc, Off, SQLServer, or StateServer.

Some applications do not need to use Session because they have no need to maintain values across the session; this can vary depending on the application design. Sometimes the architecture or enterprise rules dictate that session variables cannot be used. In these cases, you can increase the site's overall performance by choosing SessionStateMode=Off.

The SessionState is built on the provider model, which gives you another alternative to create your own mechanism to maintain state for your Web application. You need to define the custom provider in the sessionState section's providers subtag in the web.config file.

The custom provider is a class that derives from SessionStateStoreProviderBase and must override the CreateUninitializedItem, CreateNewStoreData, ResetItemTimeout, InitializeRequest, and EndRequest methods.

You are not limited in the medium you can store session objects in, so you could create your own SQL Server, Access, File, and so on.

Use ViewState to Page Persist Values

The Web is a stateless medium, meaning that each request is unique and the Web server knows nothing about the previous page content the user accessed. This can cause some problems when original values are needed to process a request. `ViewState` was created to preserve page and control data in ASP.NET.

The `ViewState` is a base 64-encoded hidden field value on every ASP.NET page and holds the values for each control on the page plus any variables set at runtime.

You can store your own objects in the `ViewState`, including strings, integers, arrays, and even custom types. You can store a variable in the `ViewState` by simply calling `ViewState` and passing the name of the variable and a value like this; `ViewState("MyParameter")` `= MyValue`. In a similar manner, `ViewState` values can be accessed like this: `dim myvar as string = ViewState ("MyParameter")`. It is good practice to type cast any

custom objects, `dim myvar as MyClass = CType(ViewState("MyParameter"), MyClass)`.

If you need to persist a value across multiple pages, consider another method of saving the state, like in the `Application` or `session state`.

By default, `ViewState` is enabled on each control. This is not always needed and can easily be set to false as a `Page Directive` or in the `EnableViewState` property of each control. The `GridView` and its predecessor, the `DataGrid`, are known as `ViewState` hogs; be careful in the number of controls displayed in either one of these controls.

`ViewState` data is serialized into XML and then encoded as `Base64`. This means the `ViewState` object can grow rather large on some pages. Large pages can cause performance issues, and you should test the performance of any page where large amounts of data are being stored in the `ViewState` object.

Use ViewState to Page Persist Values

① Create a new Web page.

② Add a `TextBox` control.

③ Add a `Button` control.

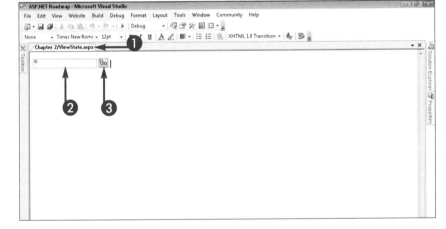

④ Double-click the `Button` control to create an event handler.

⑤ Add code to store values in the `ViewState`.

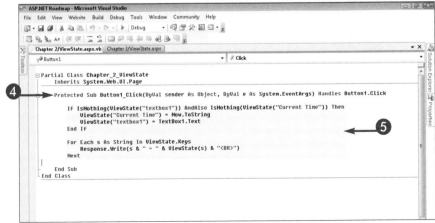

6 Open the page in a browser.

7 Type a value in the TextBox.

8 Click Submit (Go).

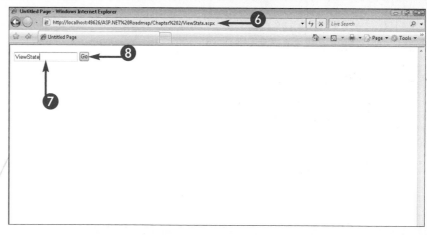

● The value of the `TextBox` and the time the form was submitted the first time appear.

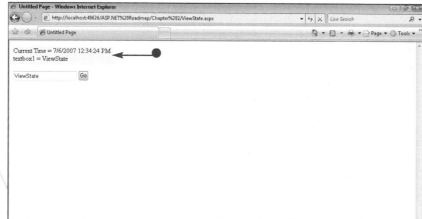

Cookies are another method of maintaining state and values across a session or across sessions and even computer restarts for a particular user. However, the nature of cookies makes them constantly suspect and should not be relied on to store sensitive information. Cookies can be stolen, sniffed, or faked by bad guys, or can become corrupted on the user's machine. Assume that a cookie is not a reliable method of persisting confidential data for a user. However, it is still a very useful mechanism to store temporary and nonsensitive data.

To store a `Cookie` on the user's computer you would create a new instance of an `HttpCookie` object and set its properties accordingly. The `Value` property holds the actual data you are storing on the client machine. It can be no larger than 4096 bytes in length. The Cookies collection can be stored through the `Response.Cookies` property.

Cookies can be targeted to live on the user's computer for a specific time period before they are deleted, which is often used to identify a user each time he or she returns to the site. The cookie object, `HttpCookie`, has an `Expires` property that manages a `DateTime` value. You can set the `Expire` time by adding a time period to the current time. If you want a cookie to persist forever, you would set the value to `DateTime.MaxValue`.

Cookies can be read through the `Request.Cookies` object. A site can have as many as 20 cookies assigned to it. You should ensure the cookie exists before you attempt to read it. If you read a nonexistent cookie you will throw a `NullReferenceException`. Cookies can be manually deleted by the user, a spyware program, or tampered with on the hard drive or in transit, so you want to be safe when reading cookie values.

Write and Read a User Cookie

1 Create a new Web page.

2 Add a new TextBox.

3 Add a Button.

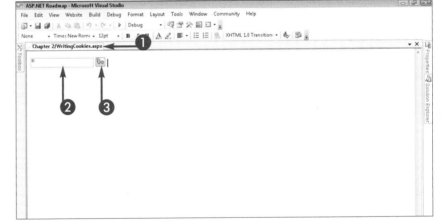

4 Double-click the Button control to create an event handler.

5 Add code to store values in a cookie.

6 Add code to read the cookie if it exists and echo the value to the browser.

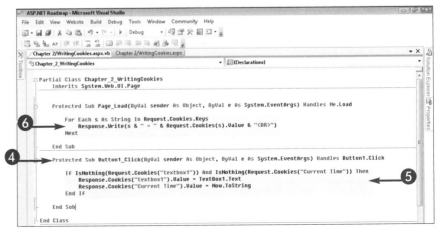

7 Open the page in a browser.

8 Type a value in the TextBox.

9 Click Submit (Go).

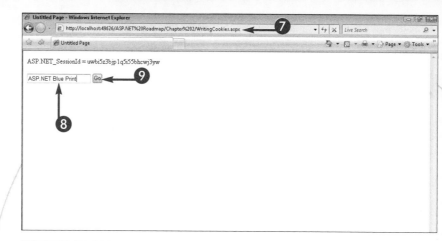

● The values you added to the cookie and the session ID appear in the Web page.

Extra

Cookies allow you to store multiple values by using subkeys or multivalue cookies. Subkeys are a name-value pair that store a name and a subkey value and look much like a multidimensional array. You cannot store more than 20 cookies for a site, although the size limitation is 4096 bytes. The overhead for each cookie is about 50 characters, which counts against the 4096 limit; so using a cookie with five subkeys saves us 200 characters of overhead.

There is no limit to the number of subkeys you can store. You can call the `HttpCookie.HasKeys` property to determine if the cookie is a multivalue cookie or normal.

Storing a Multivalue Cookie:
```
Response.Cookies("userInfo")("userId") = "3AF41A09-B0E1"
Response.Cookies("userInfo")("lastActivty") = DateTime.Now.ToString()
Response.Cookies("userInfo")("lastCategory") = "ASP.NET Cookies"
Response.Cookies("userInfo").Expires = DateTime.MaxValue
```

Delete a User Cookie

Technically, you cannot delete a cookie from a user's browser cache, but rather you control when a `cookie` expires. This is done by setting the expiration date to a time in the past, so the browser thinks it needs to delete the `cookie`. The `cookie` is not deleted until the next time the user makes a request for a resource on the site. You cannot use the `Response.Cookies.Remove` method because it simply tells the cookie not to overwrite the existing cookie.

ASP.NET Forms Authentication timeouts are tracked using this mechanism. By default, each time a user requests a page on the site the ASP.NET engine resets the timeout for the authenticated session to 20 minutes in the future. This forces the `cookie` to be deleted

if a user requests a page 20 minutes later and redirects him or her to the designated login page.

To set a `cookie` to a past expiration date you must first verify the `cookie` exists on the user's machine. If it does not exist you can then create a new `cookie`. You then need to set the `Expires` property to a date in the past. A simple way to do this is to call the `Now.AddDays(-1)` method.

Ironically, most cookie-related errors involve the expiration date. You should always set the `Expires` value of the cookie each time you set the cookie. If you fail to set the expiration date in the future, the cookie value will be deleted as soon as it is updated or the browser is closed. To set a cookie to be permanent, it is common practice to use `DateTime.MaxValue` as the `Expires` value.

Delete a User Cookie

① Create a new Web page.

② Add two buttons to the page.

③ Set the text of each button to Create and Delete, respectively.

④ Double-click each of the buttons to create event handlers.

⑤ Add code to the Create button handler to create a new cookie.

⑥ Add code to the Delete button handler to delete the cookie created by the other.

⑦ Add code to set the value of the cookie in the `Page Load` event.

You can now open the page in a browser, and create and delete cookies.

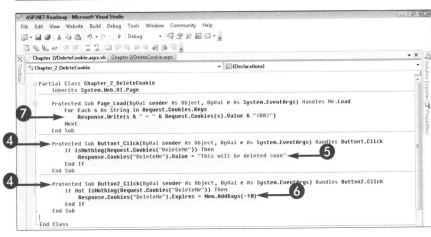

Use a Cookieless Session

Some users do not enable cookies either out of fear or because of corporate policies. This causes a problem tracking session state because ASP.NET tracks the SessionId as a cookie value on the client computer. ASP.NET has a Cookieless session option that allows the site to maintain a reference to the user's session without using a cookie. The drawbacks to this method are it is not search engine- or user-friendly and creates another public attack vector for hackers to compromise the site. The Cookieless session state is configured in the sessionState element of the web.config file by setting the cookieless attribute to true or one of the httpCookieMode values.

httpCookieMode is an enumeration of how a cookie is used on a Web site. The choices are AutoDetect, UseCookies, UseDeviceProfile, and UseUri.

Setting the cookieless attribute to UseUri causes the identifier to be stored in the URL. AutoDetect determines if the browser or end device supports cookies or not and uses the appropriate method.

The SessionId token is passed in the URL of each page as a directory name. It is a series of random characters to the visitor as part of the URL in the browser's address bar. This may potentially be a source of problems if users ever try to hack the session ID or to rewrite the URL themselves. In these instances the session is most likely lost, a problem for many applications such as an online shopping cart.

URL paths must be set relatively in order for cookieless sessions to work. You cannot use any hard-coded paths to your site. Any relative URL you set should be passed through the Response .ApplyAppPathModifier method to inject the session ID as needed.

Use a Cookieless Session

① Open the web.config file for a Web site in Visual Studio 2005.

② Add a <sessionState .. > section to the <system.web> section.

③ Set the cookieless attribute to UseUri.

④ Save the changes to the web.config file.

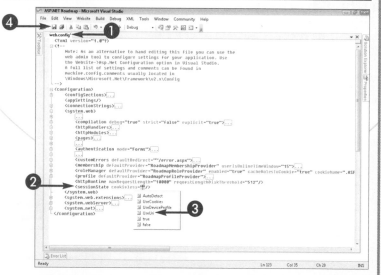

⑤ Open any Web page in the site.

● The SessionId is in the URL and is a random set of characters appended to the end of the domain, but ahead of the file name.

This uses Cookieless Sessions

Get Familiar with Page Directives

age directives are special instructions used to direct the page and user-control compilers as they process an ASP.NET Web page or user control. Page directives are included at the top of the Web page or user control source view in a directive block indicated by <%@ ...%>. There are 11 directives available with the Page directive being used on almost every ASP.NET page. A directive declaration consists of the directive and a series of attributes and their values.

Assembly Directive

The Assembly Directive links an assembly to a page so the classes and interfaces are available to the page. You do not have to include the Assembly Directive for an assembly that resides in the application's \Bin folder. An alternative is to use the <assemblies> section in the web.config file to link assemblies for the entire application.

Control Directive

The Control Directive is used to define a user control (.ascx) that is included in the page. There are 19 attributes that can be used to define the user control. The minimal attributes needed to define a user control directive are Src, TagName, and TagPrefix.

The Src attribute specifies the source of the file that defines the control. The TagName defines the default base ID and the second part of the TagName of the user control in the page's markup. For example, a user control named WebUserControl produces a default ID of WebUserControl1 for the first instance of the control. TagPrefix defines the first part of the TagName, uc1, for example. A typical user control tag looks like
<uc1:WebUserControl ID="
WebUserControl1" runat="server"/>.

Implements Directive

The Implements Directive indicates that the page implements a specific interface. The one attribute for the Implements Directive is Interface, which is the namespace and name of the interface.

Import Directive

The Import Directive explicitly imports a namespace into a page. This is useful when you are coding in the design page and not the code-behind page. If you are coding in the code-behind page you include the Import (using in C#) directive at the top of the file. You can alternatively define imported namespaces in the web.config file to make them available to all classes in the Web site.

Master Directive

The Master Directive specifies the Master page used by the page. You can only have one Master directive defined in a page, because there can only be one Master page assigned to a Web page in ASP.NET. There are many attributes available to define a Master Page in the Directive declaration. The MastérPageFile attribute designates the path to the Master page file (.master) that defines the Master page to be used. Other attributes are optional. The MasterPageFile attribute may also be used in the Page directive, and you will not have to use the Master directive in the page at all.

MasterType Directive

The `MasterType` directive defines a strongly typed reference to the Master page class being used by a Web page. There are two attributes available, `TypeName` and `VirtualPath`. The `TypeName` specifies the type name or class name for the Master page. The `VirtualPath` specifies the path to the actual class for the Master page. If the `VirtualPath` does not exist, the type must exist in one of the included assemblies of the Web site application.

PreviousPageType Directive

The `PreviousPageType` directive defines a strongly typed reference to the `Page` class used by the posting page in a cross-page `postback` or `Server.Transfer` operation. There are two attributes available, `TypeName` and `VirtualPath`. `TypeName` specifies the type name or class name for the Master page. `VirtualPath` specifies the path to the actual class for the previous page. If the `VirtualPath` does not exist, the type must exist in one of the included assemblies of the Web site application. You cannot have both attributes defined or the page will throw an exception.

OutputCache Directive

The `OutputCache` directive specifies the attributes associated with the Web page or user control. There are several attributes available for the `OutputCache` directive, but the `Duration` and `vary by attributes` are the most often used. The `Duration` attribute specifies the timeframe in seconds the cache should be maintained.

`VaryByParam` designates the cache to be unique based on a specific parameter or set of parameters passed in the `QueryString` or `Form` collection. You can specify more than one parameter as a list delimited by semicolons.

Reference Directive

The `Reference` directive specifies a page, user control, or file that should be dynamically compiled and linked to the Web page or user control. There are three attributes available — `Page`, `Control`, and `virtualPath`. Each designates the external resource to compile — only one of the three attributes may be defined.

Page Directive

Every page uses a `Page` directive; it defines attributes used by the Web page for the compiler. There are numerous attributes available to define how the page is compiled, but only a few that are commonly used.

The `Language` attribute specifies the programming language used in the Web page: VB or C#, for example. The `AutoEventWireup` attribute specifies if the page's events are automatically wired to methods that match the event name and signature. The `Inherits` attribute defines the code-behind class that defines the page. This class has to be derived from the `Page` class. Similarly, the `CodeFile` attribute specifies the source file for the `Page` class.

Other attributes can be used to define `theming`, `master pages`, `ViewState` settings, custom error page, asynchronous operations, `tracing`, and much more.

Register Directive

The `Register` directive specifies a relationship between a custom control and a Web page. There are five possible attributes that may be used — `assembly`, `namespace`, `Src`, `tagname`, and `tagprefix`. If the control is included in the \App_Code folder of the Web site you do not use the `assembly` attribute, but may use the `Src` attribute to specify the source file. The control is declaratively defined in the page's markup as a colon-separated pair: `<tagname:tagprefix .../>`.

Characterize the Web.Config File

The web.config file is the soul of any ASP.NET Web site. The web.config file is an XML document that organizes a wide range of configuration data the site needs to run. The machine.config file is a global configuration file that all sites on a server use for their base configuration and is located in the %SystemRoot%\Microsoft.NET\Framework\versionNumber\ CONFIG\ directory. Each Web site inherits settings from machine.config and uses web.config to override the global settings and may add more configuration settings. The web.config file is organized as a collection of XML elements that define specific settings for the site.

configSections Element

The configSections element allows developers to create their own custom configuration sections in the web.config file. Many third-party vendors use this feature to declare their own configuration sections. It has two attributes: name and type. The name attribute defines the name of the custom configuration section. The type attribute specifies the class that is responsible for deserializing the configuration XML into a class instance.

```
<section name="customConfigSection"
type="customClassName"/>
```

connectionStrings Element

The connectionStrings element specifies a collection of name/value pairs of connection strings used by the Web site. The connection strings are actually defined in a series of child <add> elements. Each add child element has two attributes: name and connectionString. The name element is the name used to reference the associated connection string. The connectionString attribute holds the actual connection string to the database. Additionally the connectionString element may contain a <clear> and <remove> child element. The clear element removes all references to any inherited connection strings, while remove deletes any reference to an inherited connection string by that name.

```
<add name="MyDB" connectionString=
"MyConnectionString"/>
```

system.web Element

The system.web element is the root element for many ASP.NET configuration sections. There are no attributes associated with this element; rather it can contain many child element sections.

appSettings Element

Since the inception of ASP.NET 1.0, the appSettings element has been used to store custom configuration data for a Web site. Many developers think of this section much like an .ini file was used in the early days of Windows. The appSettings section may contain any of three child elements; add, clear, and remove. The add element is a name/value pair used to define a custom setting.

```
<add key="SiteName" value="Widgets For
Your World"/>
```

The clear element removes all references to any inherited custom application settings, while remove deletes any reference to an inherited custom application setting by that name.

httpModules Element

The httpModules element configures the HTTP modules used in a Web site. It has no attributes, but may contain any of three optional child elements; add, clear, and remove.

The add element is a name/value pair used to add a module to the application. It has two required attributes: name and type. The type attribute is a comma-separated declaration of the class/assembly of the httpModules. The name attribute is a common name for the httpModule and may be used in the global.asax file to assign an event handler for the module.

```
<add name="MyModule"
type="myhttpModuleClassDef"/>
```

The clear element removes all references to any inherited httpModules, while remove deletes any reference to an inherited httpModule by that name.

httpHandlers Element

The `httphandlers` element maps requests to the appropriate handler. It has no attributes, but may contain any of three child elements; `add`, `clear`, and `remove`.

The `add` element is a name/value pair used to define the handler mapping. It has `verb`, `path`, `type`, and, optionally, `validate` attributes. The verb attribute specifies the action type and may be either `Get`, `Post`, `Put`, or `*` for all three. The `type` attribute is a comma-separated declaration of the class/assembly of the `httpHandler`. The `path` attribute specifies the URL that triggers the `httphanlder`; this may be a wildcard: `*.aspx`, for example. If the optional `validate` attribute is set to false the `httpHandler` class is not loaded until a matching request comes through the ASP.NET pipeline, which may increase site performance.

```
<add verb="*"  path="*.aspx"
type="httpHandlerAssembly,
httpHandlerClassName"/>
```

The `clear` element removes all references to any inherited `httpHandlers`, while `remove` deletes any reference to an inherited `httpHandler` by that name.

compilation Element

The `compilation` element configures all the compilation settings for the Web site and has a long series of optional attributes to control the compiler on the server. In addition, the element may have any of several child elements; `assemblies`, `buildproviders`, `codeSubDirectories`, `compilers`, or `expressionBuilders`.

The `assemblies` child element is the most often used element. It may contain any of three optional child elements; `add`, `clear`, and `remove`. The `add` element has one attribute, `assembly`, which defines an assembly to be used in the site. These `assemblies` reside either in the GAC or in the site's \bin folder.

The `clear` element removes all references to any inherited `assemblies`, while `remove` deletes any reference to inherited assemblies by that name.

Pages Element

The `Pages` element globally defines page settings, such as directives for pages and controls. It can have the following child elements: `controls`, `namespaces`, or `tagMapping`. The `controls` child element defines a collection of directives for controls with a matching tag prefix. The `namespaces` element defines a collection of directives to use during an assembly precompilation. The `tagMapping` element is used to define a collection of tag types that are remapped to other tag types at compile time.

customErrors Element

The `customErrors` element defines how custom error handling is handled for the Web site. Individual pages may override this setting in the page directives; otherwise, these settings are used. There are two attributes available: `mode` and, optionally, `defaultRedirect`.

The mode attribute is required and the options are `On`, `Off`, and `RemoteOnly`. `On` specifies that a custom error page be displayed when an unhandled exception occurs. The custom error page is specified in the `defaultRedirect` attribute, but if this is not set users see a generic error page. `Off` forces the detailed error message to be shown to the user. `RomoteOnly` specifies that custom errors are only shown to remote users and not on the local host, which is useful for debugging purposes. The `defaultRedirect` attribute specifies the path to the default URL of the custom error page.

authentication Element

The `authentication` element specifies how users are identified to the site. The element has one attribute, `mode`, which designates the method used to authenticate users. The options are `Windows`, `Forms`, `Passport`, and `None`.

`Windows` is the default setting and relies on IIS authentication: `Basic`, `Digest`, `Integrated Windows authentication`, or `certificates`. `Forms` authentication is the most common method for ASP.NET sites to authenticate their users. It also has additional child elements to define authentication further.

The `Passport` option forces the site to use Microsoft's Passport system for authentication. Choosing `None` tells the site you should only expect anonymous users or the application has another means for authentication not provided by the ASP.NET framework.

authorization Element

The `authorization` element controls access to URLs in the Web site. The element has two possible child elements: `allow` and `deny`. Each of the child elements can specify either a list of users or roles that can or cannot access the site or the designated URL. Additionally you can specify the action verbs: `Get`, `Post`, `Put`, or `*`.

Create a User Control

O ften programmers create controls to perform common tasks, but creating Web controls can be beyond many programmer's abilities and time constraints. Consistently copying and maintaining common code on multiple pages can lead to many maintenance issues. ASP.NET offers user controls as a happy medium to build reusable pieces of Web code. A user control gives you the ability to program much like you would a normal Web page, with design and code-behind pages. A user control inherits from the `System.Web.UI.UserControl` class, which is related to the `Page` class.

To add a user control to a Web project you add a new item to the site, just like a Web page, except you choose User Control in the Add New Item dialog box. A user control file ends in the .ascx extension and has a slightly

different icon from a Web page. If you switch to Design view you will notice the header of the file for a user control is similar to a regular Web page. It allows you to define similar page directives, but instead of containing a Page directive it contains a Control directive. There is no HTML markup included in the user control, either; you add this as you build the control. The control itself is rendered in the parent page and therefore does not need any HTML to work.

You can add markup and Web controls to a user control just as you would any Web page. When you want to include the user control on a Web page, simply click and drag the user control from the solution tree onto the surface of the Web page (in design view). You should see the user control rendered as if the markup and controls were actually part of the Web page itself.

Create a User Control

① Create a new Web page.

② Create a new user control.

③ Click and drag the new user control from Solution Explorer to the Web page.

④ Select Edit UserControl from the Smart Tag menu.

⑤ Click the Design tab to switch to Design view.

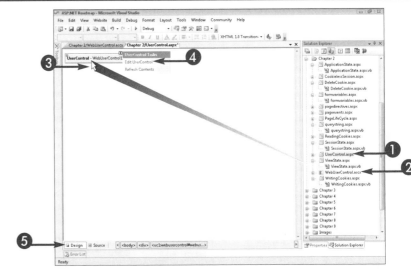

⑥ Add a text header to the user control and format as an H1.

7 Switch the Web page back and forth between Design and Source view until Design view displays the text in the user control.

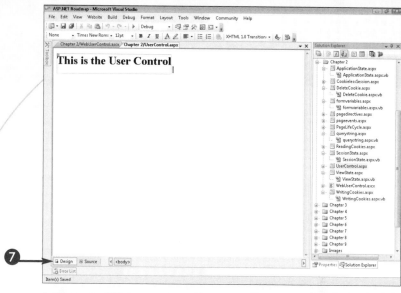

8 Open the page in a browser.

● The content from the user control in the web page appears.

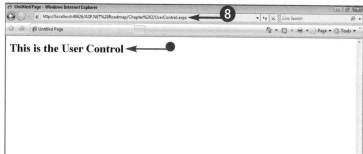

User controls are built from a class and can have public properties and methods. These methods may be accessed by the parent page by declaring an instance of the user control's class and setting it to the actual instance of the control in the `controls` collection. Any public property or method may then be accessed from the parent page. In the case of public properties, they may also be set declaratively in the page markup just like a Web control.

The `FindControl` method can be used on any `Page` or `Control` class to search through the collection of controls to find the instance of the desired control.

Example:
```
Dim uc1 As WebUserControl =
CType(FindControl("WebUserControl1"),
WebUserControl)
uc1.BackGroundColor = "#c3c3c3"
```

You can expose properties from a user control just like any other class in .NET. Any public property can be accessed by the parent page and may be set either declaratively or at runtime. You will even have full Intellisense available for the public properties.

Example:
```
<uc1:WebUserControl ID="WebUserControl1"
runat="server" HeaderText="Set from a Public
Property"/>
```

Display Text with the Literal and Label Controls

ASP.NET enables you to display dynamic, read-only text with the `Literal` and `Label` controls. The `Literal` control is used to display raw text and inherits its style from the page or HTML container. It is a useful control to display HTML strings or just plain text. The `Label` control extends the functionality of the `Literal` control by offering properties to format the appearance of the text. However, the `Label` control will not display HTML-formatted text or inherit style sheet classes.

The `Literal` control provides three properties to display text: `Text`, `Mode`, and `Visible`. The `Text` property gets or sets the text that will be displayed. The `Mode` property controls how the text is displayed. The options are `Transform`, `Passthrough`, and `Encode`. `Transform` is the default setting and strips any unsupported markup language elements.

`Passthrough` mode displays the raw, unformatted text.

`Encode` mode uses the `HttpUtility.Encode` method to convert the text to an HTML-encoded string. Using `Encode` displays any HTML markup as encoded characters, so you would see the actual HTML tags and attributes of the string. The `Encode` method provides a safe way to view HTML markup.

The `Label` control acts much like a `Literal` control, but it has properties to format how the text looks. These properties control the font, color, character size, bold, italics, border, and so on. You can also control the appearance of a `Label` control by setting the `StyleSheet` class (`CssClass` property) or specifying a theme.

Both controls can have their properties set at runtime. This is useful when displaying information from a database or echoing user input. The `EnableViewState` property turns on or off the `ViewState` for a control. Because the `Literal` and `Label` controls only display data, it is often good to set this property to false.

Display Text with the Literal and Label Controls

① Create a new Web page.

② Add a `Label` control to the page.

③ Add a `Literal` control to the page.

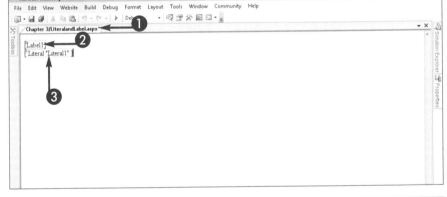

④ Set formatting properties for the `Label` control, such as Bold=True and ForeColor=Blue.

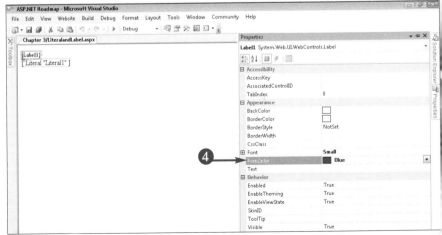

⑤ Add code to the class to set the `Label` control.

⑥ Add code to the class to set the `Literal` control.

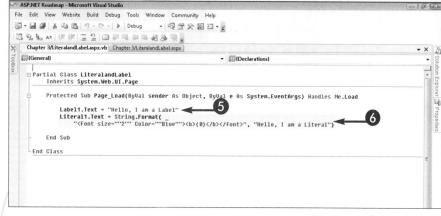

⑦ Open the page in a browser to view the `Label` and `Literal` controls.

● You can see the difference in the display style.

Extra

It is important to be careful what you echo in a `Label` or `Literal` control because users could enter a malicious client script into your site. By default, ASP.NET pages have the `ValidateRequest` page directive set to True. This is a feature that Microsoft added in the ASP.NET 1.1 release to protect against SQL injection attacks or cross-site scripting code. This setting is defined in the `machine.config` file and can be overridden for the entire site in the `Web.Config` file or on individual pages as a page directive. Take great caution in disabling this feature, but there are instances where this is the case.

Even if you keep the `ValidateRequest` option on, you should still take care to encode any values echoed from the user. You can do this with the `httpUtility.HTMLEncode` method. If you use the `Literal` control with the `Mode` set the `Encode`, the control automatically calls this method.

Encode a String to Safely Echo on the Page:
```
Label1.Text = httpUtility.HTMLEncode(UserEnteredText)
```

Add a TextBox and a Button to a Page and Echo the User Input

Web Controls are used in ASP.NET to collect user data and display information. The `TextBox` and `Button` controls are used on most forms to collect user data and submit it to the server for processing. The `TextBox` control is used to collect data from a user and the `Button` control is used to submit the form on the Web page.

The `TextBox` control has several properties you can set to adjust the way it is displayed. The `TextMode` property can be set to `Single`, `MultiLine`, or `Password`. The default setting is `Single`, which displays a one-line `TextBox`. A `MutliLine` `TextBox` displays an input field with the number of `Columns` and `Rows` specified in those properties. A password-formatted `TextBox` allows the user to type sensitive text that is represented with an asterisk (*) for each character entered. This is the proper way to gather password and other sensitive data, hiding

it from the user and anyone who may be viewing the page.

You can read and write the text in a `TextBox` at runtime by accessing the `Text` property of the `TextBox`.

```
TextBox1.Text = DefaultText
ReturnedText = TextBox1.Text
```

When the `Button` control is clicked, it fires an event that can be processed in an event handler defined in the page's class. You can create the event handler in the page's code class by simply double-clicking the button in Design view. The event handler may also be created in the Code view by selecting the `Button` in the Object drop-down list and then selecting Click Event in the Event drop-down list at the top of the page. You can process the data entered by the user from any control as you need to within the click event handler.

Add a TextBox and a Button to a Page and Echo the User Input

1 Create a new Web page.

2 Add a TextBox.

3 Add a Button control.

4 Rename the button Try Me.

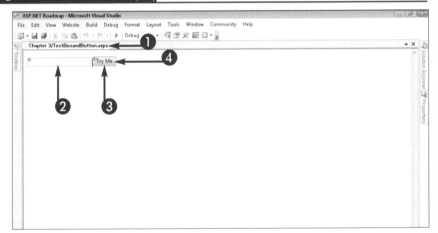

5 Create a `Click` event handler for the button by double-clicking the button.

6 Add code to echo the contents of the TextBox to the page.

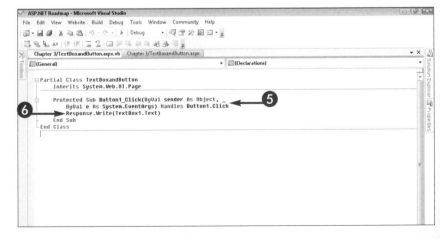

⑦ Open the page in a browser.

⑧ Type a string in the TextBox.

⑨ Click Try Me.

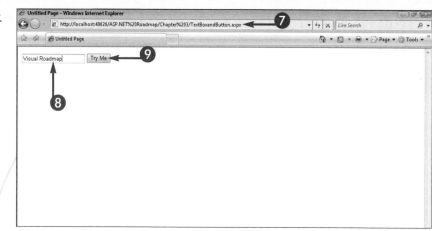

● The string in the TextBox is echoed to the page.

Apply It

Each page has a `Page_Load` event handler that is processed before any other control events are executed. This can cause problems if the `Page_Load` event handler gets or sets values of any controls on the page. The `Page` class has an `IsPostBack` property that indicates if the page is processing a form post (that is, the `Button` control being clicked) or is being loaded for the first time. Wrap any code that needs to be run the first time a page is loaded in an `if IsPostBack = false then` statement. This insulates this code from being executed when the page is posted back by the user.

Using the IsPostBack Property in the Page_Load Method:

```
Protected Sub Page_Load(ByVal sender As Object, ByVal e As System.EventArgs) Handles Me.Load
If IsPostBack = False then
    'Process any page initialization methods, such as data binding.
End If
End Sub
```

Using the LinkButton and ImageButton Control

The standard `Button` control is useful to submit forms back to the server, and it provides some properties to control the appearance of the button. Often you need to have more artistic control over the page and the standard `Button` will not do. The `LinkButton` and `ImageButton` controls perform the same post-back functionality as the `Button` control, but offer a greater range to control the visual aspects of a submit button.

The `LinkButton` control produces a standard anchor tag and contains many of the same appearance properties as the `Label` control. This allows you to define the `Font`, foreground color (`ForeColor`), text size (through a `FontInfo` object in the `Font` property), and `Border` attributes.

The `ImageButton` functions similarly to the `LinkButton`, but has properties to format the image that is displayed: `ImageURL`, `AlternateText`, and `ImageAlign`. The

`ImageURL` property is a string that gets or sets the URL to the image to be displayed. `AlternateText` gets or sets the `Alt` text attribute that is displayed when a user rolls the mouse over the image or reads by a Section 508 reader (for the blind). `ImageAlign` specifies how the image is aligned on the page or in the container. `Left`, `Right`, and `Middle` are some of the options available.

Both the `ImageButton` and `LinkButton` have additional properties including `CommandName`, `CommandArgument`, `CausesValidation`, `ValidationGroup`, and `PostBackURL`. These properties can be used when the page is posted back to the server to process the request. The `PostBackURL` is used for a `Cross-Page Postback`. The `CommandName` can be used to indicate a path for processing; the `CommandArgument` is a value you can associate with the `Button` control. You can bypass form validation by setting the `CausesValidation` property to false. `ValidationGroup` specifies what validation group will be applied to the button.

Using the LinkButton and ImageButton Control

① Create a new Web page.

② Add a `LinkButton` to the page.

③ Add an `ImageButton`.

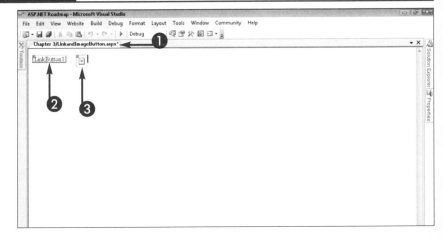

④ Change the `LinkButton`'s text to Click Me.

⑤ Set the `ImageButton`'s image property to an image of your choice.

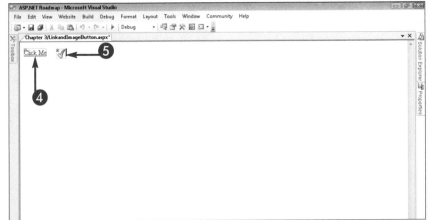

⑥ Add `Click` event handlers for each button.

⑦ Add code to echo to the page to which the button was clicked.

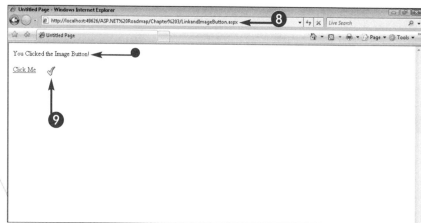

⑧ Open the page in a browser.

⑨ Click each button to verify the message for each button's display.

● A description of the button appears.

Apply It

All `web` controls can be used inside of `data` controls like the `GridView` and `DataList` to post actions back to the page. The `CommandName` and `CommandArgument` properties are very useful in this instance. When a `button` control is clicked on a `data` control, it fires an event, and a handler for the `data` control's `ItemCommand` event is executed. The `ItemCommand` event handler accepts two parameters, a source object and `CommandEventArgs`. The event arguments parameter provides a reference to the `button` control that was clicked. Generally, you can use a `Switch` statement to take your course of action.

Using a Switch Statement to Control Flow Based on the CommandName:
```
Protected Sub GridView1_RowCommand(ByVal sender As Object, _
 ByVal e As System.Web.UI.WebControls.GridViewCommandEventArgs) _
 Handles GridView1.RowCommand
 Select Case e.CommandName
  Case "Delete"
  'Call the Delete Item Method
   DeleteItem(e.CommandArgument)
  Case "Edit"
   'Call the Edit Item Method
   EditItem(e.CommandArgument)
 End Select
End Sub
```

Create a Link to a Page with the Hyperlink Control

The Web is built upon links between pages, and the HTML Anchor tag defines these links. The HyperLink Web control provides access to creating these links in ASP.NET. There are four properties in the HyperLink control that provide everything needed to link to another page: ImageURL, NavigationURL, Target, and Text.

The Text property is the actual text that is anchored in the link, such as Click Here. It is a good practice to make this text relevant to the content or purpose of the destination page.

The NavigationURL gets or sets the URL of the destination. The Target property tells the link where to open the destination page, in the current browser (or tab in Internet Explorer 7 or FireFox) or a new browser. To open the page in the same browser, '_Self', as the default value. If you give a name to a browser in an anchor tag then any link on your page or site will open destination pages targeted to the same name in the same browser. For example, if all your targets are set to NewWindow, then they will all open in the same browser or tab.

ImageURL is used to specify an image that is in the anchor tag and is also optional. This is useful because images are often objects that need to be linked to other pages and there is not any difference in the way text or an image is anchored in HTML. You should set border=0 for an image hyperlink or you will see a purple border around the image (unless you have this set differently in the page style sheet definition). If you specify an image, the Text property will be set to the Alt attribute of the rendered image.

Create a Link to a Page with the Hyperlink Control

① Create a new Web page.

② Add a HyperLink control.

③ Set the Text property to Professional ASP.NET.

④ Set the NavigateURL to www.professionalaspnet.com.

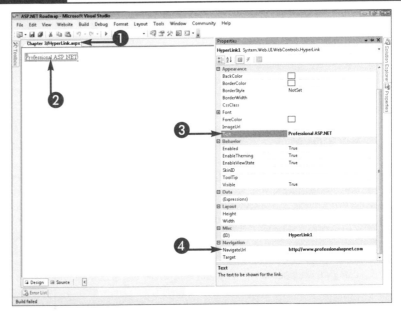

⑤ Set the ForeColor to #0000C0.

⑥ Set the BackColor to #FFFFC0.

⑦ Set the BorderColor to #000040.

⑧ Set the BorderStyle to Ridge.

⑨ Set the BorderWidth to 1.

Note: *This makes the link stand out on the page; you could also apply a* style sheet *class*

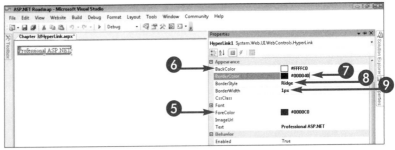

⑩ Open the page in a browser.

⑪ Click the URL to open
ProfessionalASPNET.com.

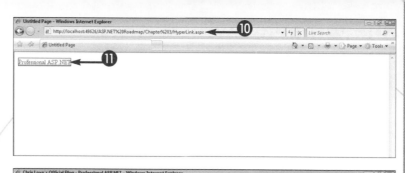

The ProfessionalASPNET.com
Web site opens.

Extra

Unless you need to process information from a user before navigating to a new page you should use either the `HyperLink` control or just a simple anchor tag `<a ...>`. This takes the user directly to the page or URL he or she wants to visit.

The `LinkButton` as well as any `Button`-derived control causes a post-back to the server for that page. This is useful when you need to process user input, such as on a user registration form. But if there is no server-side processing taking place and you are simply using the button as a means to redirect the user to another page or URL this causes extra work that can be avoided. It reduces the load on your server and increases the user experience.

You can use the `LinkButton` and other button controls to cause the form to post-back to another page by using the `PostBackUrl` property. It allows you to post the user input from the form directly to another page, so instead of processing the input on the registration page, it can be handled on the payment page.

Display Images with the Image Web Control

The Image control enables you to dynamically set an image and its properties at runtime or declaratively. The Image control has six public properties relevant to displaying an image: AlternateText, DescriptionURL, Enabled, GenerateEmptyAlternateText, ImageAlign, and ImageURL.

The ImageURL property is a string representing the URL or Src attribute to the actual image. Because this is a Web control running on the server, you can use the "~/" trick to map your image to the Web site root. This comes in handy with Master pages where the path to the page may not be the same as the Master page.

The ImageAlign property is an ImageAlign enum property that renders the corresponding Align attribute of the IMG tag. The Align attribute is useful to place images in a Paragraph or DIV to make the text wrap around the image. Alignment and spacing attributes may also be

controlled through a style sheet class or a theme. This might give you easier control over an image's appearance.

The DescriptionURL gets or sets the URL to the HTML page containing the image's detailed description. The detailed description is rendered in the longdesc attribute, a supplement to the Alt attribute of the image. This is a completely optional property, but can help with text-only browsers, and screen readers provide a set of rich information about the image.

The GenerateEmptyAlternateText property is a Boolean, set to false by default, that indicates if the Alt attribute should be rendered as an empty string if no AlternateText has been set. This is useful for section 508 compliance. The AlternateText property fills the Alt tag of the image with a short description of the image. The Enabled property, common to all Web controls, is a Boolean that allows you to enable or disable the image.

Display Images with the Image Web Control

① Create a new Web page.

② Add an Image control.

③ Select the picture you want to display.

④ Click OK.

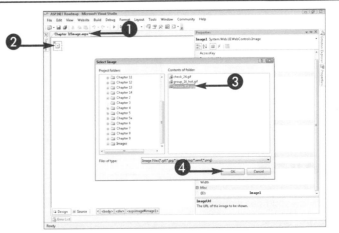

⑤ Set the AlternateText property.

⑥ Set the BorderColor property to #000040.

⑦ Set the BorderWidth to 3.

⑧ Set the BorderStyle to Dotted.

⑨ Set the ImageAlign property to Middle.

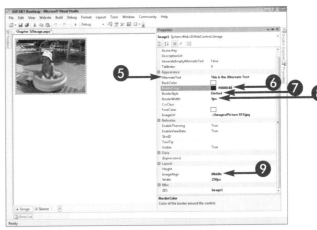

10 Open the page in a browser to see the image.

11 Position your cursor over the image to display the `AlternateText`.

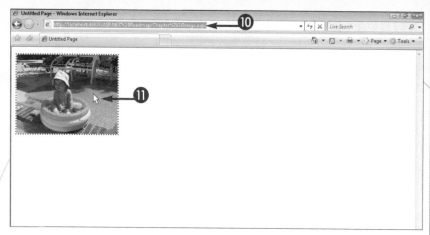

- A dotted border appears. You can control this and many other aspects through the properties and style sheets.

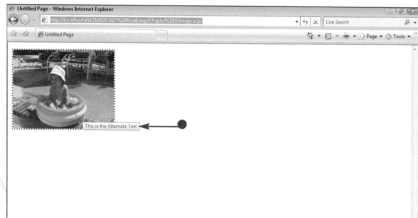

Apply It

Because this is a server-side Web control the `"~/"` trick may be used to map the URL to the root of the page's Web site. Any server-side control that references files in the same Web site can use `"~/"` to map the URL against the root of the Web site. For example, http://www.mysite.com/default.aspx could be shortened to '~/default.aspx'. A destination to a foreign Web site should contain the fully qualified URL with the http://, https://, or other prefixes needed to access the destination, http://www.foreignsite.com.

You can apply this technique to a normal HTML tag as well. Simply add a `runat=server id="AnAppropriateName"` in the tag definition. This causes an HTML control to be created in the page, providing full server-side control of the tag. You can now define root-based URLs for `IMG` and `A` tags.

Applying the Tilde Trick to an HTML Anchor Tag:
```
<a runat="server" id="AHomePage" href="~/default.aspx">Home</a>
```

Display a List in the DropDown and ListBox Controls

You can display a list in a number of ways in ASP.NET. The DropDown and ListBox controls are two ways to provide a user interaction with a list of values. Both controls inherit from the ListControl class, which provides base methods, properties, and events for list-type controls. A ListControl contains the Items property, which is a collection of ListItems. A ListItem is a data class that contains the Value and Text properties that are used by list controls. If no Value is specified, then the Value is assumed to be the Text property.

The difference between the DropDown list and the Listbox control is the ability to make multiple selections in the ListBox and how the data is presented. The DropDown List looks like a single TextBox with an arrow to DropDown the list of items to select. The ListBox looks like a multiline TextBox with each ListItem displayed on its own line.

Data for both controls can be set through the DataSource and Databind methods or in the page design or at runtime. The DataValueField and the DataTextField are properties you set to define the field names in the DataSource for the Value and the displayed Text of the control.

Indicating or discovering which items are selected in the ListBox can be done by looping or iterating through the Item collection and checking the Selected property of the item. The DropDown list does not allow multiple selections to be made, so it provides three methods to get the selection: SelectedIndex, SelectedValue, and SelectedItem.

The SelectedIndex gets the selected item's index, but not the actual values of the Item. The returned index can be used against the Items collection to get the actual ListItem selected. The SelectedValue returns the value for the selected Item. The SelectedItem property provides direct access to the selected item.

Display a List in the DropDown and ListBox Controls

1 Create a new Web page.

2 Add a ListBox from the ToolBox.

3 Add a DropDown list from the ToolBox.

4 Add a Button control.

5 Switch to code-behind and add a BindData method.

6 Populate the method with ListBox1.Items.Add and DropDownList1.Items.Add calls.

7 Add the BindData method to the Page_Load event handler.

8 Wrap it in a check for IsPostBack.

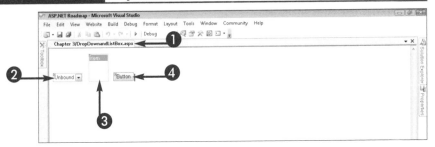

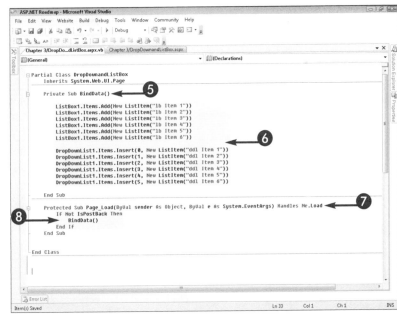

9 Add `SelectedIndex-Changed` event handlers for each list control.

10 Add code to each handler to echo the selected items back to the page.

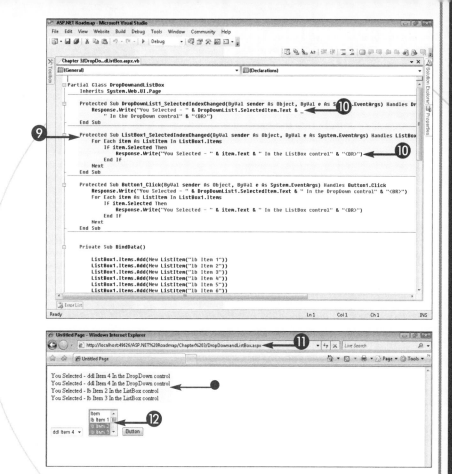

11 Load the page in a browser.

12 Select an item in either of the `ListControl`s.

● The `Text` property of the selection is echoed to the page.

Apply It

Items can be inserted into a list control's data at runtime by calling the `{ListControl}.Items.Add` or `{ListControl}.Items.Insert` methods. The `Items.Add` method takes a `ListItem` as a parameter. The `ListItem` constructor can be either a single string (the Text Field of the control) or two strings (the Value Field): new `ListItem`(100, "Green"). The `Items.Insert` method takes a number that represents the position in the collection as the first parameter and a `ListItem`: `Items.Insert`(0, new `ListItem`(-1, "Please Make Selection")). This will insert the new item at the desired position.

Adding ListItems to a List Control:
```
ListBox1.Items.Add(New ListItem("lb Item 1"))
DropDownList1.Items.Insert(0, New ListItem("lb Item 1"))
```

You can declaratively add items to the list in the page design view as well.

Example:
```
<asp:ListItem Text="Item " Value="1" Selected=true></asp:ListItem>
```

Collect User Input with CheckBoxes

The `CheckBox` control gives the user a flexible way to indicate a choice where selected choice may or may not be required. The `CheckBoxList` control groups a series of `CheckBox` controls together and is derived from the `ListControl`.

The `CheckBox` control has two primary properties: `Text` and `Checked`. The `Text` property is used to set the text that will be displayed on the page next to the check box itself. The `Checked` property can be set or retrieved to indicate the option has been selected. Both of these properties can be set at runtime or declaratively.

The `CheckBoxList` control contains a list of `CheckBox` controls. It has a `DataSource` property and a `Databind` method like a data control, but can also have its contents defined declaratively or added manually. The `DataTextField` and `DataValueField` are properties that define what fields in a data source correspond to the

text displayed and the value associated with each check box in the list. A `CheckBoxList` contains an `Items` property that is a collection of `ListItems`, a class used to represent name value pairs in several list controls like the `DropDownList` and `RadioButtonList`. Because it is a collection, items may be added at any time — design time or runtime. To add a new item to the list at runtime you call either the `Items.Add` or `Items.Insert` methods.

Determining which `CheckBoxes` have been selected upon post-back can be done by iterating through the list and determining which items are `Selected`. Similarly, you can set which items are selected at runtime by looping through the list and setting the `Selected` property to `True`.

The `CheckBoxList` control has a series of properties that allow you to control how the list is displayed on the page. The `RepeatColumns` property defines how many columns will be used to display the `CheckBoxes`. The `RepeatDirection` controls which direction items are rendered; the choices are `Horizontal` and `Vertical`.

Collect User Input with CheckBoxes

① Create a new Web page.

② Add a `CheckBox` control and a `CheckBoxList` control to the page.

③ Add a `Button` for each of the controls and set their text properties to Try Me.

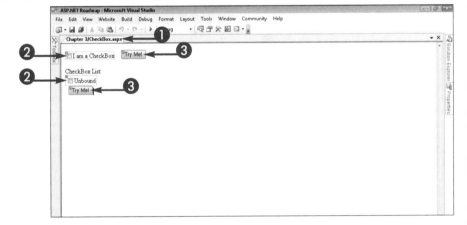

④ Switch to code-behind.

⑤ Create a new `ArrayList` and insert items in the `ArrayList`.

⑥ Set the `DataSource` of the `CheckBoxList` to the `ArrayList`.

⑦ Call the `CheckBoxList` `DataBind` method.

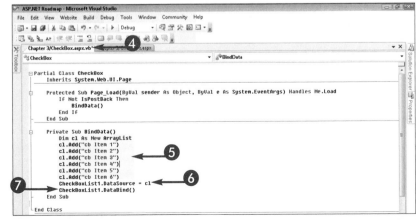

8 Add code to the button event handlers to echo the selections from the `CheckBox` and `ChecklBoxList` controls.

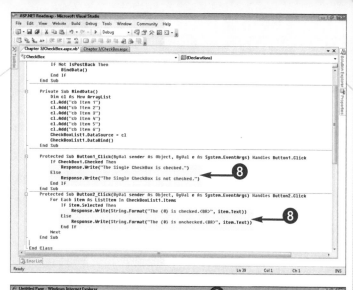

9 Open the page in a browser.

10 Select random items in the `CheckBoxList`.

11 Click Submit (Try Me).

Apply It

You can set which items are selected at runtime by looping through the list and setting the `Selected` property to `True`.

Looping Through a List Control:

```
For Each item As ListItem In
CheckBoxList1.Items

    If item.Selected Then

        Response.Write(String.Format("The {0}
is checked.<BR>", item.Text))

    Else

Response.Write(String.Format("The {0} is
unchecked.<BR>", item.Text))

    End If

Next
```

In addition to the common formatting properties, such as `ForeColor`, the `CheckBoxList` provides properties that control the `BackColor` and border. The `BackColor` property sets the background color rendered behind the `CheckBoxes` in the list. The `BorderColor`, `BorderWidth`, and `BorderStyle` enable you to define a border to surround your list of `CheckBoxes`. These same properties can also be applied to the `RadioButtonList`.

Defining Formatting Properties for the CheckBoxList:

```
<asp:CheckBoxList ID="CheckBoxList1"
runat="server" BorderColor="Red"
BorderStyle="Double"

  BorderWidth="2" RepeatColumns="3"
RepeatDirection="Vertical">

</asp:CheckBoxList>
```

Collect User Input from RadioButtons

Lists can be displayed in a number of ways in ASP.NET. The `RadioButton` and `RadioButtonList` controls provide the ability to collect either a true-false value or a mutually exclusive value from the user. Both controls inherit from the `ListControl` class, which provides base methods, properties, and events for list-type controls. A `ListControl` contains the `Items` property, which is a collection of `ListItems`. A `ListItem` is a data class that essentially contains a `Value` and a `Text` property that is used by the `List` controls. If no `Value` is specified, then the value is assumed to be the `Text` property.

Data for both controls can either be set through the `DataSource` and `Databind` methods, in the page design, or at runtime. The `DataValueField` property sets the name of the field in the data source to be used in setting the value for each item in the list. The `DataTextField` property sets the name of the field in the data source to

be used in setting the text for each item in the list. Items can also be defined at design time by adding `ListItems` in the markup. Structure can be applied to your `Text` using the `DataTextFormatString`.

Indicating or discovering which items are selected in the `ListBox` can be done by looping or iterating through the `Item` collection and checking the `Selected` property of the item. The `DropDown` list does not allow multiple selections to be made, so it provides three methods to get the selection: `SelectedIndex`, `SelectedValue`, and `SelectedItem`.

The `SelectedIndex` gets the index-selected item, but not the actual values of the item. The returned index can be used against the `Items` collection to get the actual `ListItem`: ddl.Items(ddl.selectedIndex). The `SelectedValue` returns the value for the selected `Item` and is useful because it is often used as an index in the `DataSource`. Direct access is provided with the `SelectedItem` property.

Collect User Input from RadioButtons

① Create a new Web page.

② Add a `RadioButton` control.

③ Add a `Button` control to the right of the `RadioButton`.

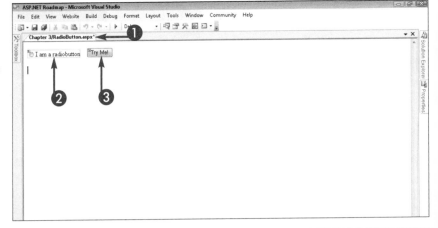

④ Add a `RadioButtonList` below the `RadioButton`.

⑤ Add a `Button` control below the `RadioButtonList`.

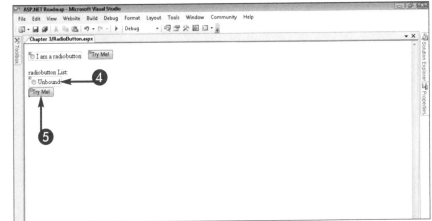

6 Change to code-behind and add a method to bind an array of choices to the RadioButtonList.

7 Add an event handler for the RadioButton button to display the selection made in the RadioButton.

8 Add an event handler for the RadioButtonList button to display the selection made in the RadioButtonList.

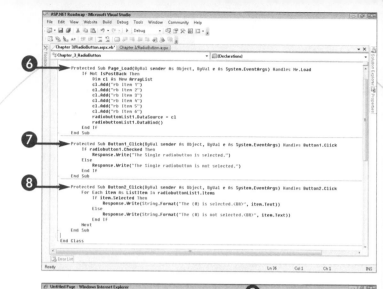

9 Open the page in a browser.

10 Make selections in either the RadioButton or RadioButtonList.

11 Click the button for each RadioButton control to echo your selection.

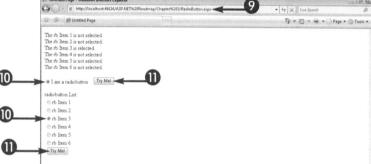

Apply It

You can create an event handler to catch each time the user selects one of the RadioButtons in the list. You do this by setting the AutoPostback property to true and creating an event handler for the RadioButtonList.

SelectedIndexChanged Event Handler for the RadioButtonList:
```
Protected Sub radiobuttonList1_SelectedIndexChanged(ByVal sender As Object, ByVal e As
System.EventArgs) Handles radiobuttonList1.SelectedIndexChanged
    'Process the event
End Sub
```

Display a Date with the Calendar Control

The Calendar control allows you to display dates in a monthly grid format, familiar to most people on wall or desk calendars. It allows users to page through months and select dates. The layout can be declaratively defined for different parts of the calendar, including the header, title, and individual days. You can also programmatically control formatting options and content at runtime.

The Calendar control displays the days one month at a time, in a six-week period. Each cell in the calendar is clickable and raises an event that can be handled on the server. As each cell in the calendar grid is being rendered a DayRender event is fired. This event can be intercepted to manipulate the content of the day.

The DayRender event handler accepts two parameters: source and DayRenderEventArgs. The DayRender EventArgs object contains properties for the date being

rendered and the cell being rendered. You can use these properties to manipulate what is displayed in the cell for that day as well as the formatting of the cell, such as background color and font size. For example, you could display Mondays as a different background color.

A Calendar control can be displayed in any dimensions you need; the day cells scale to fit the desired dimensions. This can be useful if you display a calendar in an Outlook format where you might list appointments, events, or to-do items on each day.

The current month may not always be what you want to display. You can change the month the calendar displays by setting the SelectedDate property with a valid DateTime. You may also use the SelectedDates property to define a set of dates with a SelectedDateCollection. The SelectedDateCollection is just as the name implies, a collection of DateTime objects representing dates to select on the Calendar control.

Display a Date with the Calendar Control

1. Create a new Web page.

2. Add a Calendar control to the page.

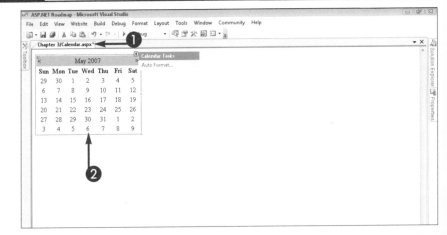

3. Switch to code-behind.

4. Add an event handler for the DayRender event of the calendar.

5. Insert code to render Mondays with a light-blue background.

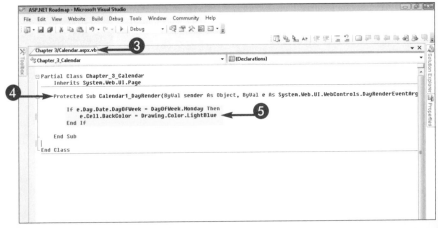

6 Add a `SelectedIndexChanged` event handler.

7 Add code to echo the date selected to the page.

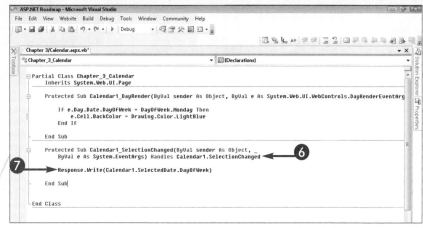

8 Open the page in a browser.

9 Click a day in the calendar.

● The date you select is echoed at the top of the page.

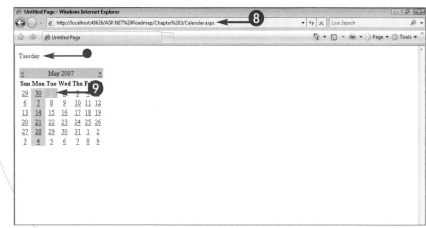

You can add special formatting to a day cell by adding controls to the day cell's control collection or by adding the appropriate HTML to the cell's `Text` property. This is all done in the `DayRender` event handler.

Add a Weather Indicator Icon and Link to a Detailed Forecast:

```
Protected Sub Calendar1_DayRender(ByVal sender As Object, _
ByVal e As System.Web.UI.WebControls.DayRenderEventArgs) _
Handles Calendar1.DayRender
 If e.Day.Date.DayOfWeek = DayOfWeek.Monday Then
   Dim hWeather As New HyperLink
   hWeather.ImageUrl = "~/images/sunny.gif"
   hWeather.NavigateUrl = "~/forecast.aspx?day=" & _
e.Day.Date.ToShortDateString
   e.Cell.Controls.Add(hWeather)
 End If
End Sub
```

Apply an
AutoFormat Style

The Calendar control provides a variety of formatting options that allow you to create a style to match your Web site's theme. You can apply one of the predefined styles by selecting the AutoFormat option from the control's SmartTag, define the style declaratively, or at runtime. The AutoFormat options give you a choice of six predefined styles. They can be used as a good starting point to create your own styles, too.

The Calendar control is a template control that has several style properties of TableItemStyle. A TableItemStyle is a class that inherits from the Style class and allows you to define settings such as colors, fonts, height, width, alignment, and borders. The Calendar control contains eight TableItemStyle properties to control how the calendar is rendered on the page. You can define the style for your calendar declaratively, at runtime, or through a theme.

In addition to providing styles for each template in the calendar there are several properties that can be set to control aspects of the calendar's formatting. The ShowGridLines property turns the grid lines of the table on or off. The ShowTitle property turns the calendar title or header row of the calendar off. The TitleFormat property is an enum allowing you to define if the calendar title is displayed as just the month (Month) or both the month and year (MonthYear).

You can also turn the display of the days of the week on or off with the ShowDayHeader property. The DayNameFormat property allows you to control how the day is rendered.

The ShowPrevNextMonth property controls the display of the links to the adjacent months in the title row. The NextPrevFormat is an enum property defining how the adjacent months are displayed: the full month, short month, or custom text. The custom text is set through the NextMonthText and PrevMonthText properties.

Apply an AutoFormat Style

① Create a new Web age.

② Add a Calendar control.

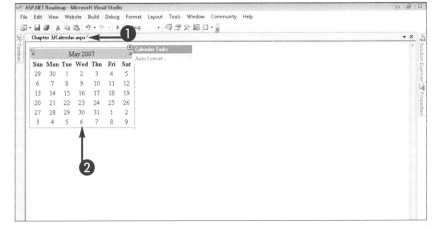

③ Click the SmartTag.

④ Select AutoFormat to display the AutoFormat dialog box.

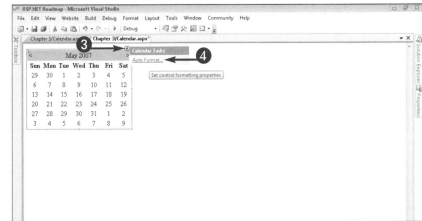

⑤ Select the style you want to apply.

⑥ Click OK.

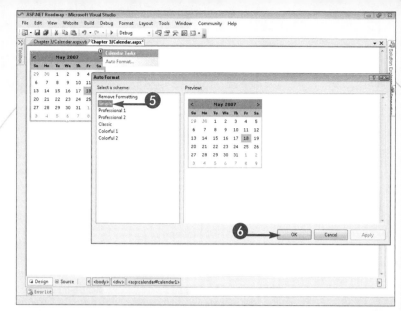

⑦ Open the page in a browser to view the style formatting.

Note: *If you review the declarative tag definition for the* Calendar *control you notice the AutoFormat Wizard completed the style sections to control the formatting of the calendar.*

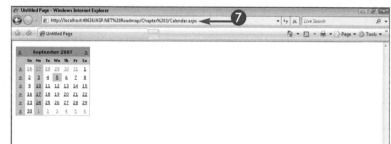

Extra

The Calendar control has several public style properties that give the developer easy access to formatting the display of the calendar. Using these styles makes it integrate with the overall theme of the Web site. The following style classes are available in the Calendar control.

STYLE	STYLE DESCRIPTION
DayHeaderStyle	Sets the style for the days of the week header
OtherMonthDayStyle	Sets the style for the days not in the month being shown
SelectedDayStyle	Sets the style for selected days
SelectorStyle	Sets the style for the week and month selector columns
TodayDayStyle	Sets the style for the current day
WeekendDayStyle	Sets the style for Saturday and Sunday
TitleStyle	Sets the style for the calendar title
NextPrevStyle	Sets the style for the next/previous month pager

Select a Date in the Calendar Control

The `Calendar` control is event driven and has a click event associated with each cell in the grid. When a user clicks a cell in the calendar the `SelectionChanged` event is fired. It has two parameters: sender as an `Object` and e as an `EventArgs`. You can access the control itself to retrieve the selected dates as well as any other property of the control.

A user can select multiple days, unless you specify differently. The `SelectionMode` property is an enum of type `CalendarSelectionMode`. This enum has four choices: Day, DayWeek, DayWeekMonth, and None. Day means only a single day may be selected. DayWeek means either a single day or an entire week may be selected. DayWeekMonth allows day, week, or an entire month to be selected. None means date selection is not permitted.

There are two properties that give you access to the selected date(s): `SelectedDate` and `SelectedDates`.

The `SelectedDate` property is a wrap around the `SelectedDates` collection, giving you direct access to the first date in the collection. When you set the `SelectedDate` property it actually sets the range of the `SelectedDates` collection to just that single day.

The `SelectedDates` property is `SelectedDatesCollection`, which is a specialized collection that implements `ICollection` and `IEnumerable`, plus adds some custom methods. The `SetRange` method allows you to select a series of consecutive dates by specifying the `FromDate` and the `ToDate`. It clears any previous members of the collection to set the range. You can also add a series of scattered dates using the `Add` method for each date. A date can be removed from the collection using the `RemoveDate` method. Because `SelectedDatesCollection` has an `Item` property that can be indexed, you can access each date in the collection.

Select a Date in the Calendar Control

① Create a new Web page.

② Add a `Calendar` control.

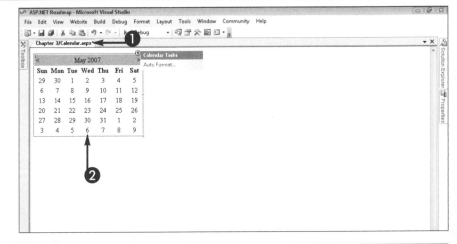

③ Change the `SelectionMode` property to `DayWeek`.

Arrows appear on the left side of the calendar.

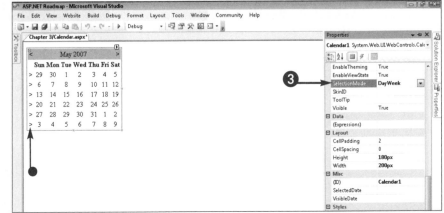

4 Open the page in a browser.

5 Click one of the arrows to select an entire week.

The entire row for the week is highlighted.

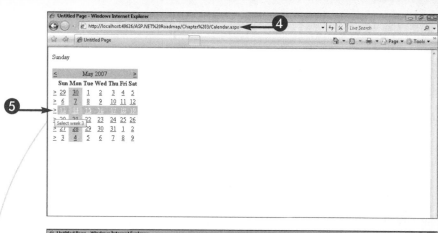

Click a single date in the calendar.

The single day selected is highlighted.

Extra

When a user selects a date, a week, and so on, by clicking on the calendar, a server-side event is raised — `SelectionChanged`. This event has the standard event handler signature of a `Sender` and an `EventArgs` parameter. You will not need to use either of these parameters to execute a typical response to the user selection. Instead, you can call the `SelectedDate` property of the `Calendar` control.

`SelectedDate` is a `DateTime` value that returns the `DateTime.MinValue` if no date is selected. This is important to note so you can check it when you use this value. If you choose a multiple date selection the `SelectedDate` returns the first date in the collection of selected days. Because the `SelectedDate` is a `DateTime` type you have access to all the methods and properties of a date class.

Write the Selected Day to the Browser:
```
Response.Write(Calendar1.SelectedDate.DayOfWeek)
```

Group Controls with the Panel Control

The `Panel` control is a container that is designed to hold controls and static text formatted with HTML. Commonly, the `Panel` is used to manage the display of the grouped controls by setting the `Panel`'s `Visible` property to `True` or `False`. However, there are many other purposes for using a `Panel`, such as setting a default button for the grouped controls or controlling the background and regional scrolling.

The `DefaultButton` property handles the identification of the `Button` control to be used as the default submit mechanism when focus is on a control in the `Panel`. Using the `DefaultButton` on the `Panel` allows the user to press Enter to submit the form.

Some controls, such as a `TreeView`, do not have built-in scrollbars, or a group of controls may need collective scrolling capabilities. The `Panel` offers an insulated container for these controls to be scrolled as needed. You must set the `Height` and `Width` constraints for the `Panel` and configure the `ScrollBars` property.

The `ScrollBars` property is an enumeration with the options of `None`, `Horizontal`, `Vertical`, `Both`, and `Auto`. The first four are self-explanatory; choosing `Auto` lets the `Panel` decide which scrollbars are needed, including displaying no scrollbar.

The background color can be set with the `BackColor` property or a background image set using the `BackImageURL` property. The `BackColor` property gets and sets a `Color` object. This can either be a name or the RGB HEX code for the desired color. The `BackImageURL` property references a URL to an image for the `Panel` background. The image is tiled if it is smaller than the dimensions of the panel. The rendering direction of the `Panel` can be changed by setting the `Direction` property. The choices are `NotSet` (default), `RightToLeft`, and `LeftToRight`. This is useful for sites that target different languages.

Group Controls with the Panel Control

① Create a new Web page.

② Add a `Panel` control.

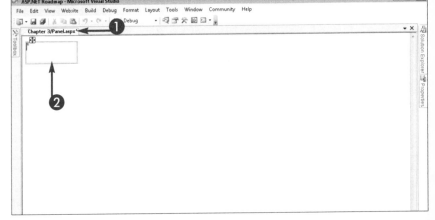

③ Add a `TextBox` and two `Button` controls to the `Panel`. Label the buttons Submit and Hide.

④ Add another `Button` outside the `Panel` labeled Show.

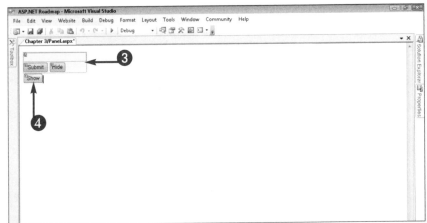

5. Add `click` event handlers to each button.

6. Add the code to the Submit button `click` event to echo the value of the TextBox.

7. Add code to the click event handlers to show and hide the external button and panel accordingly.

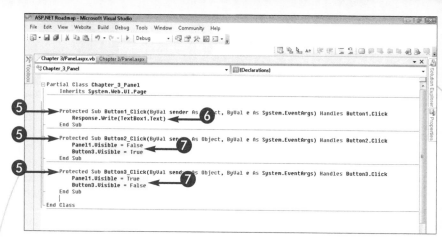

8. Open the page in a Web browser.

- You can click each button to change the background color of the panel.

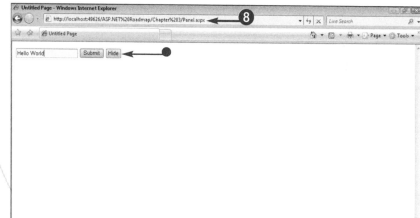

Extra

The `Panel` control is also useful to format a group of controls or text in one spot. The `Panel` control exposes all the standard formatting properties, such as `Font-Bold` and `HorizontalAlign`. These properties cascade to the child controls and any text contained in the `Panel`.

Formatting Demonstration Using Plain Text:

```
<asp:Panel ID="Panel1" runat="server" Height="50px" Width="125px" BackColor="#FFC0C0"
ForeColor="DarkRed" Font-Bold="true" Font-Size="Medium" HorizontalAlign="Justify">
Lorem ipsum dolor sit amet, consectetuer adipiscing elit......</asp:Panel>
```

Load Controls Dynamically into a PlaceHolder

Sometimes you need to create controls at runtime for your page. The `PlaceHolder` control offers you a structured place to inject controls created dynamically into the page. The `Panel` offers similar functionality, but with more overhead and features.

Controls can be added dynamically by calling the `Add` method on the `Controls` property. The `Controls` property is a collection of all the child controls in the `PlaceHolder`. The `Add` method accepts a control object as its only parameter, MyPanel.Controls.Add(myImage).

The `PlaceHolder` control offers no direct way to control the layout or formatting of the injected controls. You can inject HTML controls that form a table or `Literals` with HTML markup that dynamically builds your layout as

you inject controls. This can be a very complicated process to manage.

You can add controls to the `PlaceHolder` control that have event handlers. You need to assign the event handler for the control before it is added to the `PlaceHolder` control collection. You can assign a method to handle an event with the `AddHandler` statement in VB.NET or by assigning a new `EventHandler` delegate in C#.

The `AddHandler` statement accepts a control's event name and the `AddressOf` the method you want to be executed when the event is raised. In C#, you simply assign the method to a new `EventHandler` event with the `+=` operator.

Load Controls Dynamically into a PlaceHolder

① Create a new Web page.

② Add a `PlaceHolder` control to the page.

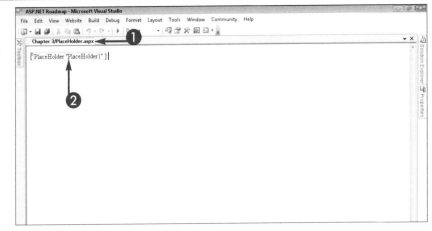

③ Declare a `TextBox` control and a `Button` control.

④ Write the code to inject the `TextBox` control and `Button` control.

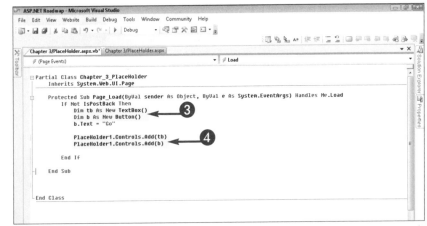

⑤ Add an event handler for the button Click event.

⑥ Create a Click event handler to echo the value of the TextBox.

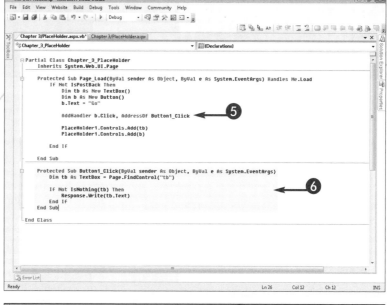

⑦ Open the page in a browser to see the injected controls.

Apply It

The AddHandler statement specifies an event handler that will handle an event. AddHandler along with RemoveHandler allow dynamically adding, removing, and changing the handler associated with an event. AddHandler takes two arguments: the name of an event from an event sender such as a control, and an expression that evaluates to a delegate.

Assign a Button's Click Event Handler Before Adding It to a PlaceHolder:
```
AddHandler b.Click, AddressOf Button1_Click
PlaceHolder1.Controls.Add(b)
```

In C#:
```
b.Click += new EventHandler(Button1_Click);
PlaceHolder1.Controls.Add(b);
```

Set the DefaultButton and DefaultFocus of a Page

A complaint of many Web site users is the result of discrepancies between the Web medium and a traditional desktop application. A difference is setting the initial focus to the first input control on a form and allowing the user to press Enter to submit the form. Another common issue is the default control when a form is loaded.

Over the history of ASP.NET, many developers have created some custom JavaScript solutions for these features. ASP.NET has added properties to the Form and Panel objects to allow more programmatic control over these features.

Both the Form (HtmlForm) control and the Panel control have a DefaultButton property that gets and sets a string that represents the ID of the button for the default submission action of the Form or Panel. If you wanted

Button1 to handle the user pressing Enter, you would set Page.Form.DefaultButton = Button1.UniqueId. This generates some client-side JavaScript that is included when the page is rendered to manage this setting.

Similarly, DefaultFocus is a property available on the Form object to define which control is the initial focus when the page is rendered in the browser. Unfortunately, this is not available in the Panel control because the form could contain several Panels and therefore might cause conflicts between panels.

The use of these two properties can go a long way to enhance the user experience of your Web site. A user does not necessarily need to use the mouse to complete a form and submit it. A typical user would simply start entering information in the fields and press Tab to go to the next field. When done, the user can press Enter and submit the form.

Set the DefaultButton and DefaultFocus of a Page

1 Create a new Web page.

2 Add a TextBox to the page.

3 Add a button to the page.

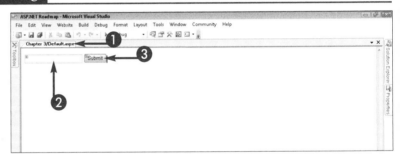

4 Click the Source tab to switch to Source view.

5 Set the DefaultButton to Button2 in the Form tag.

6 Set the DefaultFocus to TextBox2 in the Form tag.

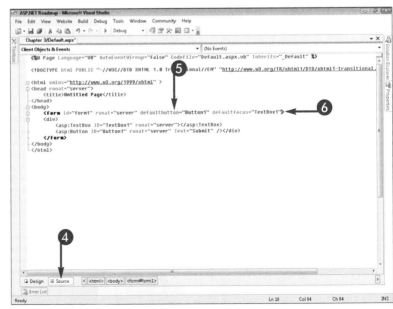

⑦ Switch to the code-behind file.

⑧ Add code to the Page load handler to set the DefaultButton and DefaultFocus controls.

⑨ Add a `Click` event handler for the `Button` control to echo the value of the TextBox.

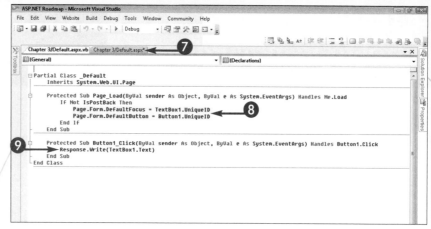

⑩ Open the page in a browser.

⑪ Type a value in the TextBox and press Enter.

● The value of the TextBox is echoed on the page.

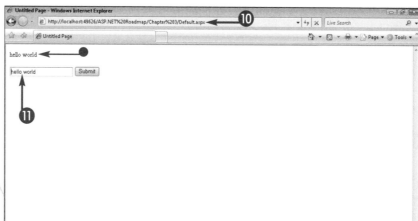

Extra

A Web form can only have one default button by definition and an ASP.NET page can only have one form present on the page. There are sometimes scenarios where you might want the page to be submitted by pressing Enter, but not by the default button specified. The Panel control can offer a solution to this problem through the DefaultButton property.

The DefaultButton property is a string that accepts the ID of the button control that gets clicked when the Panel has focus and the user presses Enter. The DefaultButton can be any control that implements the IButtonControl interface.

Another technique of changing the DefaultButton behavior of a page is to set the choice as the user sets focus on different input controls on the page. An example might be a search form for a site that sells both new and used items. There might be two unique forms to perform the selected search because the criteria are unique.

Use the BulletedList Control to Itemize Points

Organization of information in a document is often done as a list of bulleted points. A bulleted list in HTML is created with a `<UL>` tag and an `<LI>` tag for each item in the list. ASP.NET 2.0 comes with a very flexible Web control, the `BulletedList` control, which allows you to bind a `DataSource` and render the list in any number of ways.

You can provide a `DataSource`, such as a `Dataset`, `Generic`, or `Array` list, or hand-code each item as a `ListItem`. You can also insert and remove items from the list as with any `ListControl` like a `DropDownList`. The `BulletedList` control provides a `DataTextField` and a `DataValueField` to specify the corresponding field names from the `DataSource`. The `DataTextField` provides the actual text that is displayed in the list. The `DataValueField` specifies the data stored in the value field of the `ListItem`. The `DataTextFormatString`

property allows you to specify a format to be used to display the data, such as a date or currency.

The `BulletStyle` property accepts an enum `BulletStyle` that specifies the type of item prefix. The `BulletStyle` enum has ten choices. Details are in the table at the end of the section.

In addition to defining the `BulletStyle` and `DisplayMode`, you can also designate the `First BulletNumber` of the list. If you set this property, you can control what number or letter the list begins with. For example, if you designate 5 as the `FirstBullet Number` the list begins numbering from 5 until it reaches the last item in the list. Bullets can have custom images by setting the `BulletedStyle` to `CustomImage`. The `BulletImageURL` property needs to point to the image you want to use as your bullet. Because this is a server control, the root of the URL can be set to '~/{Image Path}' for any image within the Web site.

Use the BulletedList Control to Itemize Points

① Create a new Web form.

② Add a `BulletedList` control to the form.

③ Add a set of Items through the ListItem Collection Editor.

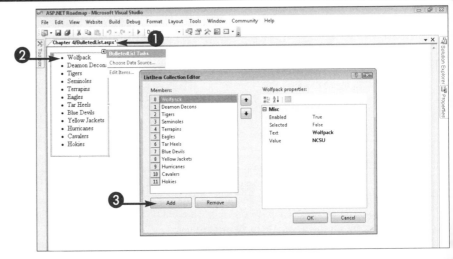

④ Set the `BulletStyle` to Numbered.

⑤ Set the FirstBulletNumber to 5.

The first number in the list is now 5 instead of 1.

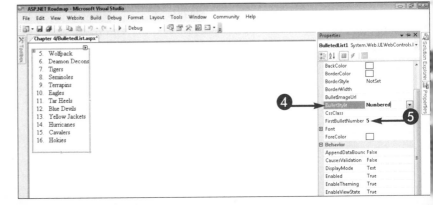

6 Set the BulletStyle to CustomImage.

7 Select `CustomImage` from available images.

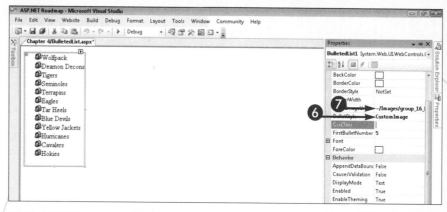

8 Open the Web page in a browser to view the customized bulleted list.

● The Items added in step 3 are displayed with the custom icons.

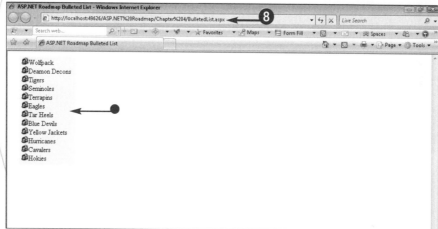

Extra

The `BulletedList` control accepts various `BulletedStyles` to control what type of bullet is displayed in the list. These are the different selections and a description of the corresponding bullet.

BULLETEDSTYLE	DESCRIPTION
NotSet	This leaves the prefix up to the rendering browser.
Numbered	The bullet style is a number (1, 2, 3, and so on).
LowerAlpha	The bullet style is a lowercase letter (a, b, c, and so on).
UpperAlpha	The bullet style is an uppercase letter (A, B, C, and so on).
LowerRoman	The bullet style is a lowercase Roman numeral (i, ii, iii, and so on).
UpperRoman	The bullet style is an uppercase Roman numeral (I, II, III, and so on).
Disc	The bullet style is a filled circle shape.
Circle	The bullet style is an empty circle shape.
Square	The bullet style is a filled square shape.
CustomImage	The bullet style is a custom image.

Add Links to the BulletedList Control

The default display mode of the `BulletedList` is plain text. You can change the display mode of the `BulletedList` control by setting the `DisplayMode` to `LinkButton` or `Hyperlink` to render each item as the corresponding control. This makes the list become active by displaying each item as a hyperlink that links directly to a destination page or causes a form post-back.

If you need a list with links that cause some sort of logic to be executed on the page when the user selects the item, the `LinkButton` should be selected. The `LinkButton` causes the form to be posted back to the server, passing the `Value` property back to the server. You must designate the `Click` event handler by setting the `OnClick` property to the name of the event that handles the event. You can do this automatically by double-clicking the `BulletedList` control in the design view. The designated method accepts two parameters: an `Object` and `BulletedListEventArgs`. The `Object` parameter is a reference to the actual `BulletedList` control and should be cast to a `BulletedList` to access its properties. The `BulletedListEventArgs` contains one property of interest, the `Index` property. Use the `Index` property to access the actual `LinkButton` or bulleted item that was clicked in the list.

Setting the `DisplayMode` to `Hyperlink` renders a series of `Hyperlink`s that provides a navigation or anchor link to a URL. Each item in the list needs to have the `Value` property set to the destination URL. If you want the destination URLs to be opened in a new browser window, designate the `Target` property to the name of the window in the `BulletedList`.

Add Links to the BulletedList Control

① Create a new Web page and add a `BulletedList` control.

② Add some items to the list.

③ Change the DisplayMode to LinkButton.

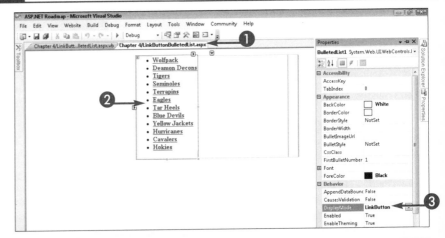

④ Create a `Click` event handler with the `Object` and `BulletedListEventArgs` parameters.

⑤ Add a `Response.Write` call to the event handler to echo the text of the `ListItem` selected.

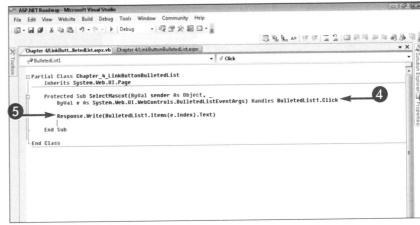

6 Add a New `BulletedList` control to the page.

7 Add some items to the list.

8 Change the DisplayMode to HyperLink.

9 Set the `Value` property of each item to the destination URL.

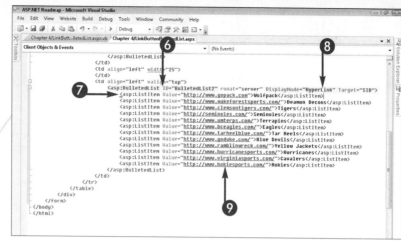

10 Open the Web page in a browser to view the active bulleted lists.

● You can click the items in the list to see the results.

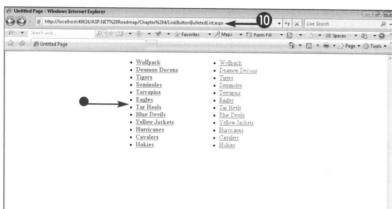

Apply It

The standard formatting properties do not seem to affect the display of the items in the `BulletedList` control. Therefore, the `LinkButton` and `HyperLink` controls display with the standard HTML anchor colors of blue and purple. To control these colors you should use style sheet settings that cascade to the controls. Note that anchor styles should be set for `link`, `visited`, `active`, and `hover` states.

Style Sheet Class for Anchor Tag in a BulletedList:
```
a.BulletedListAnchor:visited a.BulletedListAnchor:hover a.BulletedListAnchor:link
a.BulletedListAnchor:active
{
    font-weight: bold;
    color: #0033ff;
}
```

Apply the Style Class to the BulletedList Element:
```
<asp:BulletedList CssClass="BulletedListAnchor"
```

Hide Your Data in the HiddenField Control

Hidden input tags such as `<Input type="Hidden">` have long been a technique to maintain state values across a Web site. Hidden input tags are not rendered in the browser, but are viewable in the page's source and therefore not a secure technique to store persistent values. However, they can be very useful to the Web application developer when trying to maintain values across post-backs or sessions. Hidden tags are often used in place of a `Session State` or `ViewState` variable, especially when one or both of these features are turned off.

ASP.NET 2.0 introduces a `HiddenField` Web control that encapsulates this functionality and adds a `ValueChanged` event handler. The value of a `HiddenField` control can be set like any Web control attribute in the design (declarative) or in the code-behind (runtime).

The `HiddenField` control has one unique property, `Value`, which represents a `String`. It also has one unique event, `ValueChanged`, which is fired if the `Value` is changed while rendered in the browser. The `HiddenField` control does not cause a post-back to the browser when the value is changed; instead, the `ValueChanged` event is fired when the page is posted back to the server.

The `HiddenField` control's value can be manipulated through JavaScript as input is collected from the user. Because the `Value` is viewable to hackers in the page's source, they may also try to manipulate your site by changing the value of the control and posting it back to the server. This is why the `ValueChanged` event fires when the page is posted back to the server, so you can validate the Value and perform any necessary logic. Here is an example of a `HiddenField` tag as it is sent to the Browser:

```
<input type="hidden" name="HiddenField1"
id="HiddenField1" value="Fresh Load" />
```

Hide Your Data in the HiddenField Control

① Create a new Web page on the site.

② Add a `HiddenField` control from the ToolBox.

③ Add a Label to the page.

④ Clear the default label text.

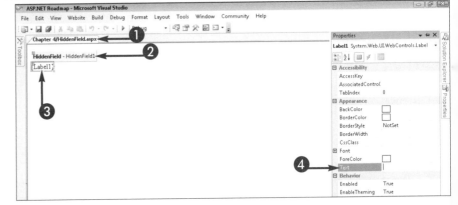

⑤ Add a button to the page.

Note: *You will not need to add code for a* `Click` *event handler for this example.*

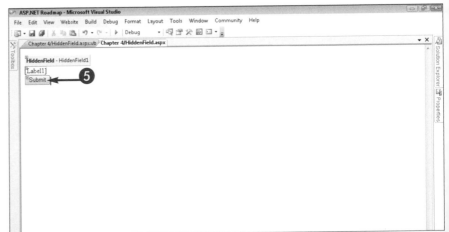

⑥ Add code to set the value of the `HiddenField` based on the `IsPostBack` value.

⑦ Set the label's text property to the value of the `HiddenField`.

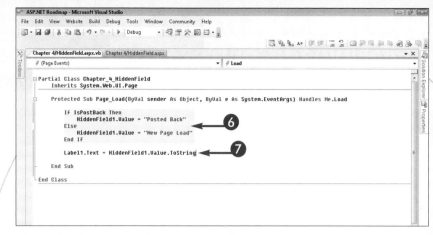

⑧ View the page in a browser and then click the button.

⑨ Click the button to cause the page to post-back to the server.

New Page Load appears when the page is first loaded and Posted Back each time you click the button.

Note: *You can view the source of the page in the browser to see the hidden input tag created by the* `HiddenField` *control.*

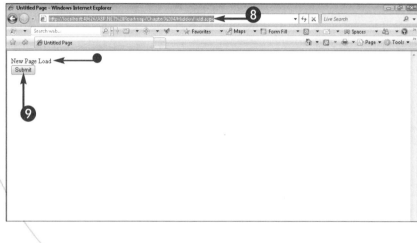

Apply It

Manipulating the value of a `HiddenField` control can be done with JavaScript as the user interacts with the controls on the page. The following is some example code showing how the value can be changed with JavaScript. The function needs to be called when the value needs to be changed and a value passed to set the value of the `HiddenField`.

Example:
```
<script type="text/javascript">
<!--
function SetHiddenFieldValue(value)
{
Form1.HiddenField1.value = value;
} -->
</script>
```

Upload Files with the FileUpload Control

Uploading files through a Web page is a common task many sites need to accomplish. Previous versions of ASP.NET have provided a standard HTML control, but it required a little extra work to define the MIME type of the form. ASP.NET 2.0 provides a FileUpload Web control that handles this for you and provides a few extra helper methods previously not available.

There are five public properties in the FileUpload control: FileBytes, FileContent, FileName, HasFile, and PostedFile. FileBytes returns an array of bytes that represent the file being uploaded. FileContent is a stream of the posted file. The FileName property is the name of the file, minus the path being posted. The HasFile property is a Boolean that indicates if there was a file entered into the control before the form was submitted.

The PostedFile property is the most important because it provides direct access to the file being posted as an HttpPostedFile. An HttpPostedFile is very similar to a normal File except it represents a file that has been posted through the browser. It has four properties and one method available to use. The four properties are FileName, InputStream, ContentLength, and ContentType. The first two are similar to the FileName and FileContent properties of the FileUpload control. The ContentLength property is the size of the posted file in bytes. The ContentType returns the MIME type of the file being posted. The method is SaveAs.

To save a file you need to have permission on the server for the ASPNET user account to write to the folder. To save a file you call the SaveAs method, passing it the full path to the file as you want to call it on the server. The nice thing is you do not have to retain the file name uploaded by the user and can rename the file to fit your naming conventions.

Upload Files with the FileUpload Control

1 Create a new Web page and add a FileUpload Web control.

2 Add an Upload File button to the Web page.

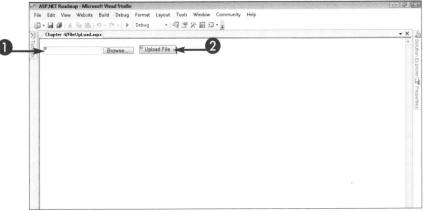

3 Add a ButtonClick event handler.

4 Add code to check the FileUpload control for the presence of a new file (HasFile property).

5 Add code to echo the file name and file size to the browser.

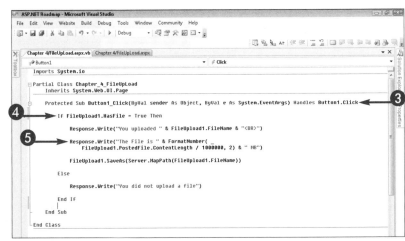

6 Open the page in a browser.

7 Click Browse to open the FileOpen dialog box and designate a file to upload.

Note: *Before you can execute this example you must have proper directory permissions set up for the ASPNET or Interactive user.*

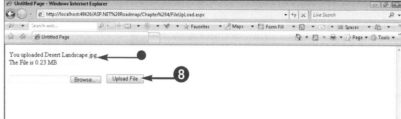

8 Click Upload File to upload the selected file to the server.

● If you upload a file the file name and its size in megabytes appear at the top of the page.

Extra

A special note about file sizes: For security reasons, the default maximum file size that you can upload in ASP.NET is 4MB. This is a pseudo-arbitrary value chosen to allow the majority of file uploads to occur. The limit was set in an effort to thwart a common Denial of Service (DOS) attack where extremely large files are uploaded to the server and overrun its capacity. This value may be overridden in the Machine.Config or the Web.Config files by changing the value of the maxRequestLength attribute.

Similarly, files that are over 256K are buffered to disk and not memory. This setting can also be adjusted in the config files by changing the requestLengthDiskThreshold attribute. Fine-tuning these values can help your overall site performance, but be mindful of the potential security risks.

Set the maxRequestLength and requestLengthDiskThreshold limits:

```
<httpRuntime maxRequestLength ="10000" requestLengthDiskThreshold ="512"/>
```

Control Visibility with the MultiView and View Controls

Creating forms that display content and controls based on user or application data is common among desktop and Web applications. The MultiView helps you organize this task by managing a collection of View controls. A View control is a container for a group of controls. Views can be rendered based on any type of user input you define, such as a QueryString parameter, user identity, user profile, or user action.

Only one View can be displayed at a time. The active View is set by the ActiveViewIndex property or the SetActiveView method. If the ActiveViewIndex is not set then no views are rendered. The ActiveViewIndex may be set declaratively in the control definition, ActiveViewIndex="0", or it can be set at runtime. The SetActiveView method takes a View control instance as its only property, which makes it more feasible to use the ActiveViewIndex property in most cases.

A View is simply a content template and the MultiView contains a collection of these views to display content as needed. A content template is simply a container for HTML markup and controls. You can use Visual Studio to define the content layout of a View in Design mode or in Source mode. If you are in Design mode you can simply point the cursor to the View you want to edit and lay out your content as if it were a base ASP.NET page. You can add controls and HTML markup directly in Source view.

You can add a Button, LinkButton, or ImageButton to each view to guide the user through the MultiView control. You can either handle the logic in the click event handler of each button or set the button's CommandName property to one of the event handlers of the MultiView. Following is an example of how to set a button's CommandName to the NextView.

```
<asp:Button id="Page1Next" Text = "Next"
CommandName="NextView" runat= "Server"/>
```

Control Visibility with the MultiView and View Controls

1 Create a new Web page.

2 Add a MultiView control.

3 Add two View controls to the MultiView by dragging them from the Toolbox onto the Multiview added in Step 2.

4 Add a button to each of the Views and set the button text to View 2 and View 1 in the opposite Views.

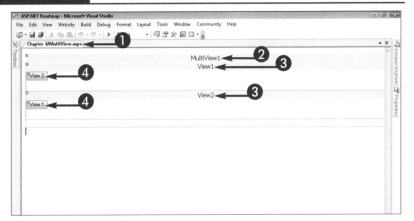

5 Add Click event handlers for each button.

6 Add code to each click event handler to display the opposite View.

7 Add code to the Page_Load event handler to display the first view.

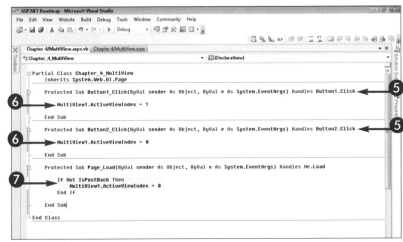

8 Load the page in a browser.

8

9 Click the visible button to load the other view.

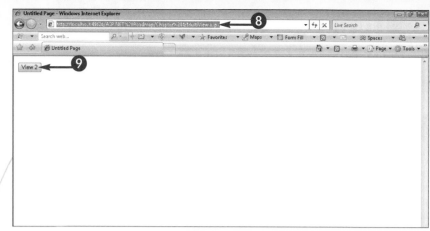

9

View 2 ←⑨

10 Repeat step **9** to see the other view.

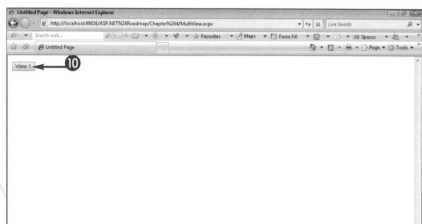

View 1 ←⑩

Extra

An interesting use of the MultiView control might be to display different views of the same information. An example might be to optimize one View that contains more graphics and styling attributes for browser. Another View could be optimized for printed and more stripped-down versions of the content.

Another common problem some developers encounter is the use of validation controls in the MultiView. If you have a set of validation controls on each of the Views in the MultiView the client-side validation tries to execute each of the validation controls on every View in the collection. This can be overcome by defining a separate validation group for each view. This isolates each group into its own client-side validation routine.

Another common use of the MultiView control is to simulate a Tabbed dialog. This can be achieved by adding either a Menu control or a series of buttons above the MultiView and controlling the display of each View in the click event of the button or by setting the value of each menu item to the corresponding View and leaving the NavigationURL empty. The ActiveViewIndex can then be set in the MenuItemClick event handler.

Step Through a Process with the Wizard Control

Often there is a process flow that users need to be guided through, or large forms that would be easier to complete if broken into smaller steps. The Wizard control helps us develop a step-by-step process that guides a user through a logical process. It is flexible enough to allow for nonlinear flow as well. For example, you can skip steps or allow a user to return and change information in a previous step. The state values of the Wizard are maintained across the entire process and not stored until you program it to be stored.

A common use of the Wizard control is a structured survey, checkout, or registration. Unlike the MultiView control, the Wizard control provides the ability to develop a logic flow to turning views on and off as the user enters information.

Each WizardStep has a StepType property that determines the type of navigation displayed to the user.

The options are Auto, Complete, Finish, Start and Step. Auto lets the Wizard control determine what type of step it is based on the order in the wizard. Complete is the last step displayed and no buttons are rendered. Finish is the last data collection step and the Finish and Previous buttons are displayed. Start is the first step displayed and the Previous button is not rendered. Step is a normal step in the process and displays both the Previous and Next buttons.

If you want to let the user know where he or she is in the wizard process, you can display the steps by setting the SideBarEnabled property to true, which is the default setting. The Sidebar navigation allows the user to jump to the different steps of the wizard.

The FinishDestinationPageURL designates the URL or page the user is directed to when clicking Finish. The default is an empty string and stays on the page with the wizard.

Step Through a Process with the Wizard Control

① Create a new Web page.

② Place a Wizard control on the Web page.

③ Add steps to the wizard in the Properties window.

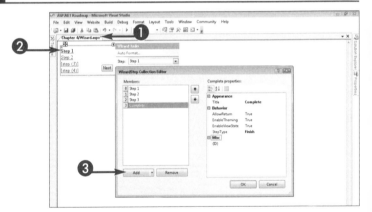

④ Click the Source tab to switch to Source View.

⑤ Add a TextBox to each wizard step.

⑥ Add a label to the final step for each of the previous steps.

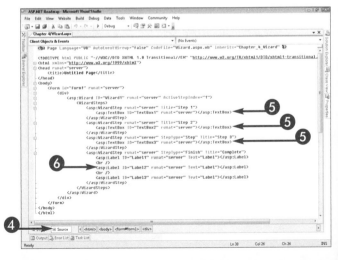

7 Add code to the `NextButtonClick` and `FinishButton Click` event handlers to set the label's text values from the TextBoxes.

Note: *The labels will be used to echo the values entered in the regular steps.*

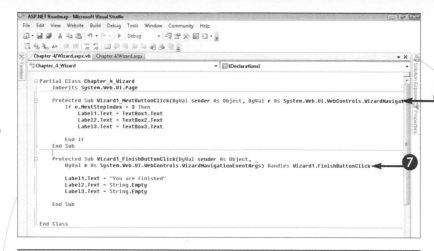

8 Open the page in a browser.

9 Step through the wizard, typing values in the TextBoxes.

10 Repeat step **9** until you reach the final step.

Note: *When you reach the final step in the wizard, you should see the values entered in the previous steps.*

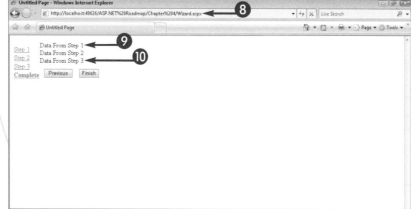

Extra

Some wizard steps need to be forward only, meaning once the user makes a selection he or she cannot navigate back to the previous step again. You can designate this behavior for each step in the wizard by setting the `AllowReturn` property of the individual `WizardStep` to `True` or `False`. If the `DisplaySideBar` property of the wizard is set to `True`, the button for the step is displayed; but if the `AllowReturn` is set to `False` for the step, the `SideBar` navigation action is ignored.

One scenario in which you might want to restrict the user from returning to a step is where the information entered by the user is persisted between steps. A common example of this might be a user registration for an e-commerce site. Here you might guide the user through the checkout process, storing information such as registration in step one, payment in step two, shipping in a separate step, and so on. Each subsequent step relies on the data in a previous step being present. You would also need to handle abandoned carts and sessions. Restricting the user path with the `AllowReturn` property helps keep a controlled process.

Format the Wizard Control

The `Wizard` control contains a collection of `WizardSteps`, which are templates of the controls and layout for each step. The control is flexible enough to allow you to fully customize the look of the controls and styles of the `Wizard` through style templates and properties. The `Wizard` control has 11 style properties that manage a `Style` or `TableStyle` for different templates in the `Wizard`.

As with all controls in ASP.NET you can also assign a style sheet class to each of the style properties, individual controls, and HTML tags in a template. This gives you granular control over how each element in the wizard appears to the user. In many cases, using style sheets and themes is the best way to make managing the overall look of a site easier.

All the style properties are available at runtime and can be changed each time code is executed. For example, you may want to change the wizard's appearance on each step to visually indicate to the user where he or she is or a special circumstance based on the user's input.

Many of the style properties have values that are enums available in the System.Drawing namespace. For example, all the color properties are System.Drawing.Color enum values, which means you can directly set the property from the enum.

Other properties directly represent another object, such as any `Font` property. You can directly access the public properties of the `Font` class from each style, such as Wizard1.HeaderStyle.Font.Bold.

The `System.Web.UI.WebControls` namespace has its own useful enum objects, like `VerticalAlign` and `HorizontalAlign`. These enums can be directly called to set alignment properties of the `Wizard` control.

Format the Wizard Control

① Create a new Web page.

② Place a `Wizard` on the Web page.

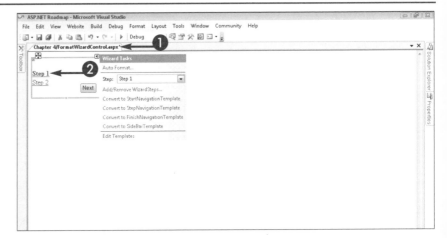

③ Click the Smart Tag located in the upper-right corner of the wizard.

Note: *The Smart Tag is designated by a tiny arrow pointing to the right.*

④ Click the Auto Format link to display the Auto Format dialog box.

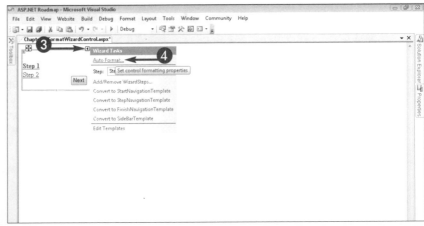

⑤ Select any of the formats listed.

⑥ Click OK.

⑦ Open the page in a browser to see your changes.

Note: *You can review the changes applied by the Auto Format either in the control Properties window or in Design view. This will give you an idea as to how you can adjust the settings for your own choices.*

Extra

The wizard control accepts several styles to format the individual templates in the control.

STYLE	DESCRIPTION
Step Style	Applies to the WizardStep section of the control.
HeaderStyle	Applies to the header section of the control.
SideBarStyle	Applies to the area where the SideBar is displayed.
SideBarButtonStyle	Applies to the buttons contained within the SideBar.
NavigationStyle	Applies to all areas of the control where the Navigation buttons are displayed.
NavigationButtonStyle	Applies to all navigation buttons in the navigation area. These styles are merged with specific styles set on individual navigation buttons. In the event of conflict the more specific style is applied.
StartNextButtonStyle	The next button on steps of StepType=Start.
StepNextButtonStyle	The next button on steps of StepType=Step.
StepPreviousButtonStyle	The previous button on steps of StepType=Step.
FinishPreviousButtonStyle	The previous button on steps of StepType=Finish.
CancelButtonStyle	The cancel button.

Create an Image Map

I mage maps are a common way to hot-link portions of an image to different locations. An image map is an HTML tag that allows you to define regions in an image and associate those regions to corresponding URLs or anchors. ASP.NET 2.0 added a new Web control, ImageMap, to encapsulate this functionality as a server-side control. The ImageMap control is simply an Image control to which you add HotSpots that define the regions and corresponding destinations.

A HotSpot is actually a base class that cannot be directly used, but you define your image map region with a CircleHotSpot, RectangleHotSpot, or PolygonHotSpot. Each hot spot has a HotSpotMode property that can be set to NotSet, Inactive, Navigate, or Postback. You can also set the HotSpotMode in the ImageMap itself, but if you set a different value in the HotSpots, it will override the action for that HotSpot.

For example, if you define the HotSpotMode to Postback at the ImageMap level, but define a HotSpot with Navigate and the NavigateURL, it will simply open the NavigationURL in the browser.

If you set the HotSpotMode to Navigate you will need to set the NavigateURL property of the HotSpot to the destination location. If you specify PostBack mode you will need to define a Click event handler and the PostBackValue of the HotSpot. The PostBackValue is passed in the ImageMapEventArgs to the click event handler and can be used to perform server-side logic.

Specifying Inactive for the HotSpotMode causes the HotSpot to not have any behavior when clicked. You can use this mode to define a region as part of a larger, more complex region. Setting the HotSpotMode to NotSet causes the hotspot to perform the default behavior, either inheriting from the ImageMap control or choosing the default setting of Navigate.

Create an Image Map

①　Create a new Web page.

②　Add an ImageMap control to a Web page.

③　Add an image to the ImageMap.

④　Click OK.

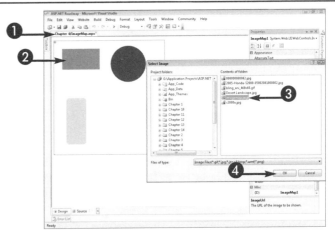

⑤　Click the Collections button in the HotSpot field of the ImageMap Properties page.

⑥　Define a rectangular HotSpot for the rectangle in the top left corner.

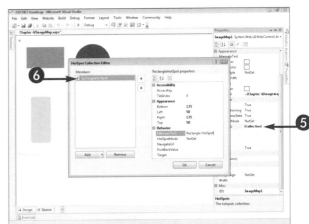

⑦ Define a circular `HotSpot` for the circle in the top right corner.

⑧ Repeat creating `HotSpots` for the rounded rectangle and the polygon.

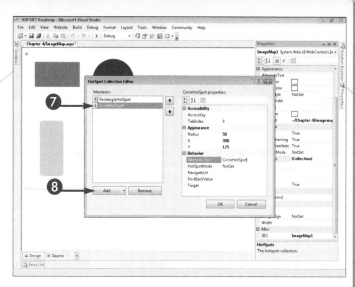

⑨ Open the page in a browser to view the `ImageMap`.

● If you have set the Alternate text property of the `HotSpots`, you can roll over them to see the value.

Note: *If you have set the navigation to a URL, you can click the `HotSpot` and be redirected to the destination. Similarly, if you have set the navigation to PostBack, the page will submit to the server.*

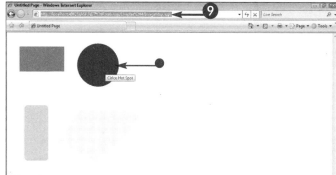

Extra

Each of the `HotSpots` defines different types of regions, each corresponding to its name. The `CircleHotSpot` defines its region with a `Radius`, and `X` and `Y` properties. The `X` and `Y` properties define the coordinates for the center of the circle. The `Radius` defines the radius of the circle that is used to calculate the perimeter of the circle. The `RectangleHotSpot` takes four integers that define the coordinates for each corner of a rectangle: `Top`, `Bottom`, `Left`, and `Right`. The `PolygonHotSpot` takes a coordinates string that defines the x and y points for each vertex of the polygon. The string is a comma-separated series of integers that is an x followed by the corresponding y coordinate.

Apply It

You can add a `HotSpot` programmatically at runtime. This gives you the flexibility to create an image map dynamically.

Example:
```
Dim rhs As New RectangleHotSpot()
rhs.Bottom = 100
rhs.Left = 0
rhs.Top = 0
rhs.Right = 100
rhs.NavigateUrl = "destination.aspx"
ImageMap1.HotSpots.Add(rhs)
```

Avoid Caching Content with the Substitution Control

Building high-performance ASP.NET Web sites requires at least one or more forms of caching, such as `OutputCache`. When a page is cached, the entire rendered content of the page is placed into memory for the specified time period. Sometimes this is not desirable for the entire page and small portions of the page may need to remain dynamic.

For example, a page listing products on an e-commerce site should be cached for a long period of time. A portion of the page may contain a time-sensitive or targeted promotion, or maybe shopping cart information. This section should not be cached because it might be more dynamic. In addition, it may not be optimal to cache a version of the entire page for each individual user because a small portion of the page may be driven by his or her account. The `Substitution` control was designed for just this situation.

You can think of the `Substitution` control as a literal control that cannot be cached. It has one property, `MethodName`. `MethodName` defines the name of a callback method that returns the text to display in the control. A callback method is a shared or static method that is executed as an event or thread handler. The callback method for the `Substitution` control takes one parameter, an `httpContext`.

The callback method can do anything you need to do and you are not required to use the `Context` parameter. The only requirement is to return a string that is displayed in the control. If you return an HTML-formatted string, it is rendered just like it would be with the `Literal` control, so you would see it in its marked-up form.

Avoid Caching Content with the Substitution Control

① Create a new Web page and add a `Substitution` control to the page.

② Add a button to the page.

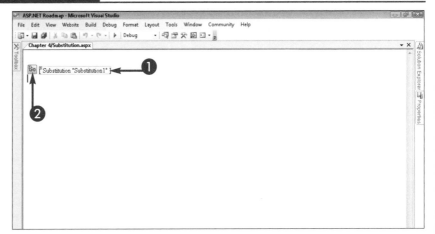

③ Define the `OutputCache` page directive to 60 seconds.

④ Assign the SubstitutionControl callback MethodName.

5 Write the current time when the page is loaded or reloaded in the `Page_Load` event handler.

6 Create a Shared callback function to return the current time to the `Substitution` control.

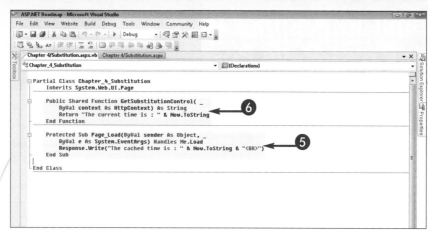

7 Open the Web page in a browser.

8 Click the button to cause the time in the substitution control to update.

● The time on the page updates every 60 seconds, but the `Substitution` control remains the same every time the page is loaded.

Extra

The `Substitution` control only renders textual content exactly how the callback method sends it. Often you need to avoid caching a section of a page with one or more controls contained within it, like a shopping cart window on a cached catalog page. In this case, it would be a good practice to use a user control (.ascx file) and set its `OutputCache` duration property to 1. This gives you the flexibility to cache truly static content, while dynamically controlling the small portion that needs to change upon each page load. The `OutputCache Duration` property cannot be 0, so setting it to 1 second will typically suffice to avoid any major caching issues.

```
<%@ OutputCache Duration="1"%>
```

Submit to Another Page with Cross-Page Post

hen the Web was first defined, form tags were used to group input controls together that send user-supplied data back to the server. The form tag has `Action` and `Method` attributes that define what URL accepts the form information and how it is sent. The reason the `Action` attribute was defined is because HTML pages are by nature static, and in order for form data to be processed in the early days, programmers often relied on CGI-Bin and ISAPI DLLs to process input.

When ASP.NET was introduced, every ASP.NET page included a form tag that by default posts back to itself. This is fine for most cases, but occasionally you may need to submit to another page on the site. In the first two versions of ASP.NET, this was not feasible because of the architecture of ASP.NET. In ASP.NET 2.0 this has changed, and you can designate the target URL for each

input control (anything that implements the `IButton` interface) on the form by designating the `PostBackURL`.

When an input control is executed by the user with a `PostBackURL` defined, the page is posted to that URL and can be processed, much like the original CGI-Bin applications offered. Situations where this might come in handy are a global search box on a site or a multistep wizard. You can verify a `Cross-Page Postback` has occurred by checking the `PreviousPage.IsCrossPagePostBack` property to see if it is `True`.

To access the controls of the originating page you access the `PreviousPage` property, then access the specific control values needed. You use the `FindControl` method to get a reference to the control you want to work with and cast it to a local variable. After you have a reference to the control on the previous page you can use it like you normally would.

Submit to Another Page with Cross-Page Post

Note: *This example will not do a search; it simply echoes the search term.*

① Create a new Web page.

② Add a `TextBox` control and a button to the page.

③ Set the button text to Post.

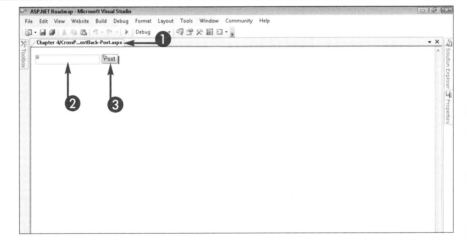

④ Set the `PostBackURL` of the button control to `"~/results.aspx"`.

⑤ Create a new ASP.NET page and name it `"results.aspx"`.

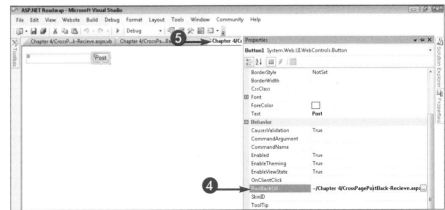

⑥ Add code to the results page to access the search TextBox.

⑦ Echo the value of the search box's text with a Response.Write.

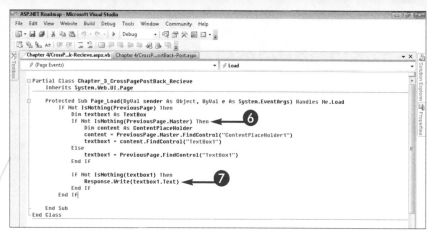

⑧ Load the first page in a browser.

⑨ Type a search term and click Post.

The search term is echoed on the results page, and the results page echoes the search term you typed.

Apply It

If you are using a Master page on the initial page in a Cross Page Post Back that has the submit button in a ContentPlaceHolder, you will need to reference the control a little differently. You must first get a reference to the ContentPlaceHolder, then the control with the value you need.

Get a Reference to a Control from a PreviousPage:

```
Public Function GetPreviousPageControl(ByVal sPPC As String) As Control
  If Not IsNothing(PreviousPage) Then
  If Not IsNothing(PreviousPage.Master) Then
   Dim content As ContentPlaceHolder
   content = PreviousPage.Master.FindControl("ContentPlaceHolder1")
   Return content.FindControl(sPPC)
  Else
   Return PreviousPage.FindControl(sPPC)
  End If
  End If
  Return Nothing
End Function
```

Require Input with the RequiredFieldValidator

Web forms often need to ensure that data is entered into specific fields by the user. The RequiredFieldValidator provides client-side validation that the user has entered or selected data in a control. The RequiredFieldValidator checks to see if the value of the control has changed from the InitialValue property. If it has not, then the RequiredFieldValidator fails and displays the ErrorMessage to the user. Each control on the page that requires input from the user must have its own RequiredFieldValidator.

The RequiredFieldValidator has one property, ControlToValidate, that must be configured, and several properties that should be configured to use properly. The ControlToValidate property is a text field that contains the ID of the control the RequiredFieldValidator validates. The

ErrorMessage property is the text message that appears when the validation fails.

The InitialValue property contains the default value the control being validated has when the page is loaded, maybe some instructions or an example value. By default, this property is empty, which is typical for a TextBox. If this property is set, the RequiredFieldValidator control looks for the value of the control to change. The InitialValue property must be set in order to properly validate list controls, such as the DropDownListBox.

An interesting problem occurs when the InitialValue is set in the RequiredValidator of a TextBox control. The user can simply erase the default value and submit a blank TextBox. This can happen because the initial value has been changed. Ironically, this is an empty value. The work-around for this problem is to add a second RequiredFieldValidator to the page for the TextBox. This time the InitialValue property is not set.

Require Input with the RequiredFieldValidator

1 Create a new Web page with a TextBox, DropDownListbox, two Labels, and a Button control.

2 Set the Text property for the TextBox to "Hello World".

3 Add an item to the DropDownList's Items collection using "----" for the Text and Value properties.

4 Add the corresponding RequiredFieldValidators with ErrorMessages.

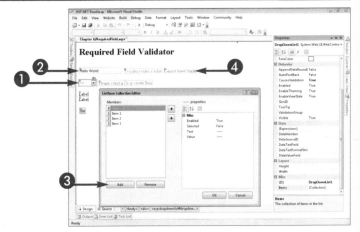

5 Set the InitialValue property for RequiredFieldValidator1 and RequiredFieldValidator3 to "Hello World" and "----", respectively.

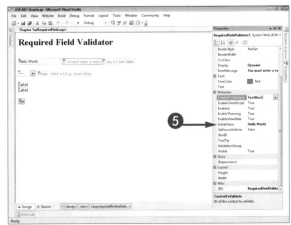

6 Open the page in a browser.

7 Click Go.

● The initial values of the two controls echoed and the validation messages appear on the page.

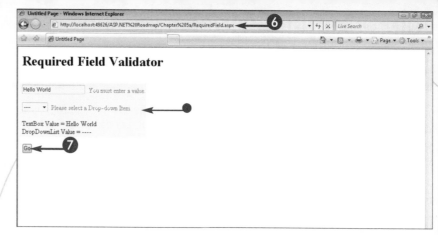

8 Type a new value in the TextBox.

9 Select a value in the DropDownList.

10 Click Go.

The form is submitted.

Extra

Some controls have an `AutoPostback` property to enable automatic post-backs to the server when the control value changes. These include the `TextBox`, `DropDownList`, `RadioButtonList`, and `CheckBoxList`. These controls may have server-side methods that process the values entered and redisplay the page with a new set of controls or values based on the entered values or selection. These controls have a property, `CausesValidation`, which can be set to `false` to turn page validation off upon post-back for that control. If this property is set to `false` the control is still validated when the form is submitted.

A common scenario might be a form with a `DropDownList` of countries where, depending on the selection the user makes, another `DropDownList` displays either U.S. states, Canadian provinces, or a simple `TextBox` requesting their region. You would set the country `DropDownList`'s `CausesValidation` property to `false` and create a handler method on the server that displays the appropriate control with any selection data based on the country. By setting the `CausesValidation` property to `false`, no validation will be performed when the control causes a post-back.

Compare Inputs with the CompareValidator

The CompareValidator control allows you to compare one or more values between user controls or a default value to ensure they match, are different, match an equivalency rule, or contain a specific data type. The most common usage of the CompareValidator is a registration form where the password is requested twice.

The CompareValidator has several properties that may be used to specify the type of comparison being done. ControlToCompare is the ID of the control the ControlToValidate is to be validated against. For example, the first password TextBox would be the ControlToCompare and second password TextBox would be the ControlToValidate. Conversely, the CompareValidator can be used to ensure two controls have unique values entered between them. To accomplish this, set the Operator property to NotEqual.

The Operator property is an Enum specifying the type of comparison being done and can be equal, notequal, lessthan, lessthanequal, greaterthan, greater thanequal, or datatypecheck. The first four value choices are used to check for an equivalency type value.

DataTypeCheck is used to ensure the value of the control is of a specified type, such as String, Integer, Double, Date, or Currency. This is useful for forms where users enter values that can be in any number of acceptable formats, such as a date.

The CompareValidator provides more flexibility than comparing two control values, because it can compare a control value to a constant value. You may want the user to enter a number less than a target number for an age requirement or an income level. To do so, leave the ControlToValidate empty and set the ValueToCompare property to the desired target number and the Operator to the required setting, such as LessThan.

Compare Inputs with the CompareValidator

① Create a new Web page.

② Add a TextBox to capture the user's age and another for comparison.

③ Add a CompareValidator.

④ Set the ControlToValidate property to the first TextBox and the ControltoCompare property to the second TextBox.

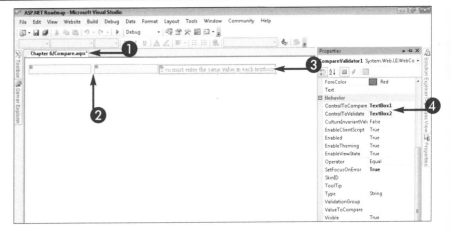

⑤ Add a CompareValidator.

⑥ Configure this validator to ensure the age entered in the first TextBox is less than 66 by setting the ValueToCompare property to 66.

⑦ Set the Operator to LessThan.

⑧ Set the Type to Integer to help with the validation.

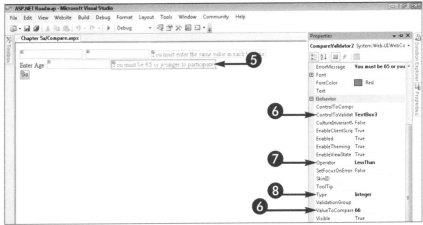

⑨ Open the page in a browser.

⑩ Type invalid data in the fields and submit the form by clicking Go.

● The error messages are displayed.

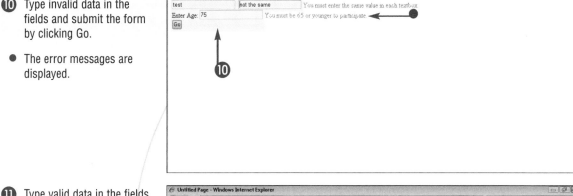

⑪ Type valid data in the fields and submit the form by clicking Go.

Good data allows you to submit the form to the server.

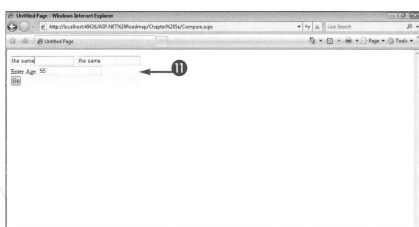

Extra

Improper data is one of the most common errors users make when completing a form. For example, a form may be expecting a date value, but the user may enter a string like Late May or Spring. If the form is submitted with these values an Exception is often thrown when the application tries to process this value as a date. Using a `Validator` like the `CompareValidator` helps eliminate this problem and lets the user know what type of data is expected.

Another common solution to ensure properly formatted data is to create a custom control that has built-in validation or a value mask. There are many third-party controls that make formatting data much easier. Commonly, these controls might format currencies, integers, phone numbers, and dates. The validation for formatting is done with client-side `JavaScript` and typically a `Regular Expression` to validate the data.

Having properly validated data goes a long way in reducing the number of exceptions an application can throw as well as helping users understand what is required to submit a form. Informing the user about the proper data expectations goes a long way for a rich user experience and reduces the amount of errors in an application.

Specify a Range with the RangeValidator

The RangeValidator control works like the CompareValidator, but instead of comparing to a single value, it verifies a value is within a specific range. The RangeValidator control can be used to validate numeric values, strings and dates. For example you can verify an age is within the 18-34 demographic, or a currency value is within an expected range. In addition to the standard validator control properties the RangeValidator has three unique properties: MinimumValue, MaximumValue, and Type.

The MinimumValue and MaximumValue properties specify the limits of the range that needs to be validated. For example a MinimumValue = 18 and a MaximumValue of 34 checks if the number entered is within that age group. The Type property defines what type of data is being validated by the control. The choices are String, Integer,

Double, Date, and Currency. This provides a targeted flexibility that should be useful in most situations.

The RangeValidator does not check to ensure a value is entered in the control being validated and will allow empty values. You must add a RequiredFieldValidator if a field is required to be submitted.

Validating a date is within a specific range can be done by setting the Type property to Date and specifying the MinimumValue and MaximumValue to specific dates you want the entered date limited to.

When comparing strings, the RangeValidator uses the String.Compare method under the hood to perform validation. This will do a culture-sensitive compare to verify the test being validated is alphabetically within the specified range. For example, you want only cities that start with the letter C. You would set the MinimumValue property to C and the MaximumValue property to D. Anything not starting with the letter C causes the validation to fail.

Specify a Range with the RangeValidator

① Create a new Web page.

② Add two TextBox controls, one to ask the person's age and the other to ask for today's date.

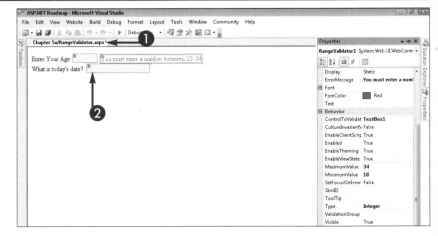

③ Add a Calendar control to help users enter the date.

Note: *You will have to add code to the Calendar's* SelectionChanged *event handler to set the TextBox.*

④ Add RangeValidator controls to check the data being entered.

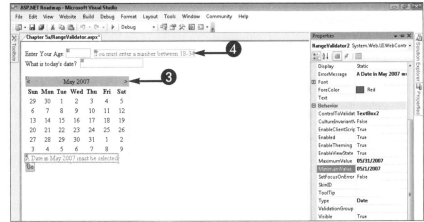

⑤ Load the page in a browser.

⑥ Type an invalid date in the TextBoxes and submit the form.

● Entering data outside the expected range causes the RangeValidators to display error messages.

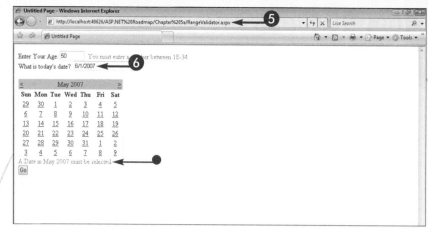

⑦ Type valid data in the fields.

⑧ Submit the form by clicking Go.

Data within the accepted range allows the form to be submitted.

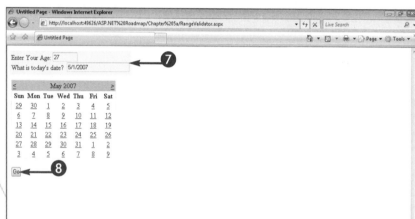

Extra

Often data must be entered within a desired range, but also in proper format. For example, specifying a date range might also need a RegularExpressionValidator or a CompareValidator to ensure the data was entered in a proper format. You can combine validation controls to validate each form element in multiple ways without causing conflicts. In some cases, however, this may cause multiple messages to display for the same control, so it may take some testing to properly decide what controls need to be used on a particular form.

There is no limit to the number of validation controls you can place on a form, nor are their any limitations as to what combination of validators are used. For example, you might need to verify a value is within a specified range, using the RangeValidator, and entered, using the RequiredFieldValidator. If your validation becomes very complex you may want to consider consolidating validation rules into custom methods and use the CustomValidator control. Deciding on the best validation solution can take some trial and error, but goes a long way in providing an optimal user experience and reducing exceptions.

Create Custom Validation with the RegularExpressionValidator

The most flexible of the validation controls is the RegularExpressionValidator control. This control enables you to specify a regular expression pattern that is used to match the data of the control being validated. If you are not familiar with regular expressions, they are a powerful set of textual expressions to match patterns of text. For example, a common regular expression for a U.S. phone number would look like this:

`((\(\d{3}\) ?)|(\d{3}-))?\d{3}-\d{4}`.

The RegularExpressionValidator is much like the RequiredFieldValidator control with one additional property: ValidationExpression. This property gets and sets the regular expression to be used for validation. You can enter any expression you want or choose from the examples that come with the control, including U.S., French, German, and other local phone numbers, postal codes, and e-mail address.

The ValidationExpression property designer has a Regular Expression Editor that is used to either select a prebuilt expression or add your own custom expression. Thoroughly test each expression to ensure it meets your needs. Regular expressions in .NET can be slightly different than expressions for other languages and therefore may not translate correctly and require minor alterations.

Validation is done both client side and server side, unless the browser does not support client-side validation. Client-side validation may also be turned off by setting the EnableClientScript property to false. The regular expression libraries being used on the client and server are slightly different. The client-side library uses JScript validation, while the server uses the RegEx class. JScript regular expressions should be used because they will work for both. Also you should note that validation will succeed if the control is empty.

Create Custom Validation with the RegularExpressionValidator

① Create a new Web page requesting a phone number, U.S. postal code, and an e-mail address.

② Add RegularExpressionValidators for each control.

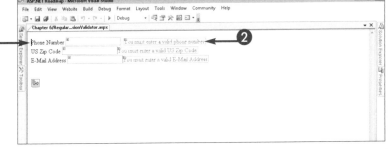

③ Add the regular expressions for each RegularExpressionValidator.

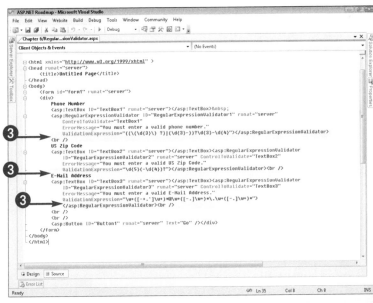

④ Load the page in a browser.

⑤ Type invalid data in the form.

⑥ Click Go.

● An error message appears.

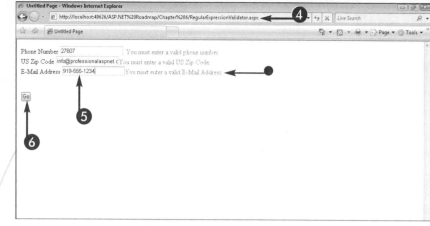

⑦ Type valid data in the fields and submit the form by clicking Go.

Properly formatted data means the form can be submitted.

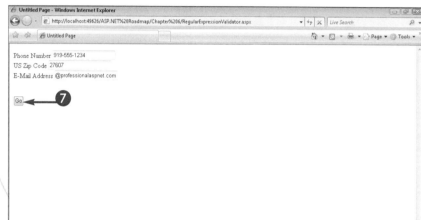

Extra

The RegEx class in the .NET framework provides static methods that can use regular expressions to match patterns in text. It is one of the most powerful and efficient classes available to a .NET programmer. It can be used to find collections of texts, such as all the URLs in a document, or even replace all the text in a string that fits a defined pattern, such as e-mail with a masked version to misdirect e-mail harvesters.

Common Regular Expressions in .NET:

EXPRESSION NAME	EXPRESSION
US Phone Number	((\(\d{3}\) ?)|(\d{3}-))?\d{3}-\d{4}
US Zip Code	\d{5}(-\d{4})?
E-Mail Address	\w+([-+.']\w+)*@\w+([-.]\w+)*\.\w+([-.]\w+)*

Custom Validation with the CustomValidator

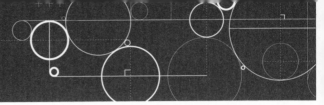

Sometimes a form requires some very complex validation. The number of validation controls needed would be too many to practically manage or might not provide a way to perform the necessary validation. The CustomValidator control offers you the ability to define client-side and server-side validation methods. This is unique from the other validation controls because the validation is not being performed within the control, but rather the control allows you to specify your own external methods to perform validation.

You create a server-side validation method by creating a handler for the ServerValidate event of the CustomValidator control. The validation method is a subroutine (VB) or a Void function (C#) that accepts two parameters, Object and ServerValidateEventArgs. The same method definition is required for both server-side and client-side validation functions. The Object parameter is a reference to the control being validated. The ServerValidateEventArgs parameter is a class that contains two properties: Value and IsValid. It is passed by reference, meaning it will be available to the calling method with any values you may change. The Value property is a string with the value of the control being validated. The IsValid property is set to either true or false depending on the outcome of your validation routine.

The client-side validation method is defined the same way. You set the ClientValidationFunction property of the CustomValidator to the name of the client-side validation method. Be careful to write your validation method in a language the browser supports. You should always include a server-side validation method when you are performing client-side validation. Hackers often take a Web page's source code and remove the client-side validation routines and submit invalid data to the site. Having a server-side equivalent of a validation method ensures the data entered is valid.

Custom Validation with the CustomValidator

① Create a new Web page with TextBoxes asking for user input.

② Add corresponding custom validators.

Note: The first validator is server-side only.

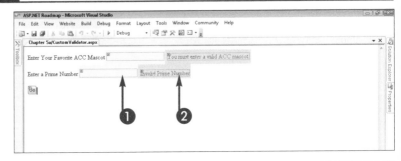

③ Create the client-side validation method to check for a prime number.

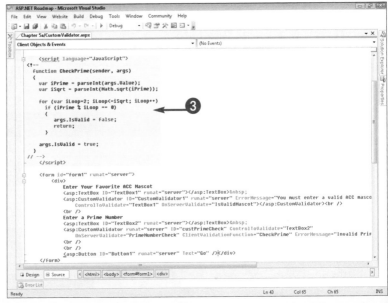

Note: *The prime number validator has both client- and server-side methods.*

④ Create both client-side and server-side validation methods to validate the mascots.

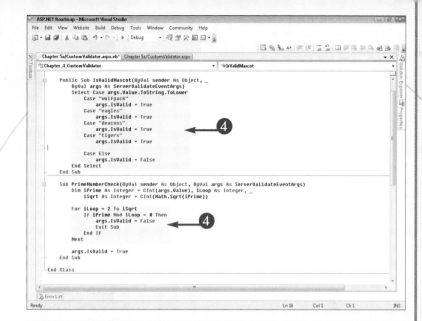

⑤ Load the page in a browser.

Entering invalid data in the first TextBox does not display the error message until the form is submitted. Because the prime number validator has a client-side method, it is checked before post-back.

● Bruins is not a valid ACC mascot and the server-side validation method has caused the error message to be displayed. Entering a valid ACC mascot allows the form to be submitted.

● Entering a prime number, such as 7, allows the form to be submitted.

Extra

A `CustomValildator` is ideal to use when validation depends on values from multiple controls meeting your requirements. For example, you may have logic that only accepts values within a range that may slide depending on the value entered in another control. A loan application would be a good example. A person's income or credit score may allow him or her to have more or less debt or a person's target heart rate may fluctuate with age in a health-related form.

In these cases, you define a validation method that takes into account each of the control values you need to perform validation. Set the `ControltoValidate` property to empty or not set. When validation is performed the `Value` property is an empty string. You must programmatically reference the controls you need to validate against.

Similarly, some controls cannot be directly validated with the `CustomValidator`, like the `CheckBox` control. You set the `ControltoValidate` property to empty and programmatically perform validation on the `CheckBox`.

Summarize Error Messages with the ValidationSummary Control

Large forms can have many fields that require some form of validation. This can cause the display of the form to become cluttered and hard to decipher for users that make many mistakes or have scrolled a long form to the bottom. The `ValidationSummary` control provides a way to report errors in an organized manner. The `ValidationSummary` does not perform any validation, but works with all the validation controls on a form to display their messages in one or more summarized methods.

Error messages can be presented as a list, bulleted list, or paragraph. The `DisplayMode` property can be set to `List`, `BulletedList`, or `SingleParagraph`.

The `ValidationSummary` can be set to display a JavaScript alert message with all the error messages on the page by setting the `ShowMessagebox` property to `true`. This is sure to get the attention of even the most confident user.

A nice feature of the `SummaryValidation` control is the ability to leverage the `Text` property of each validation control. By default, the `ErrorMessages` are displayed in both the `ValidationSummary` control and each validation control that is not properly validated. You may not want the error messages to be displayed more than once on the page. This can be changed by setting the `Text` property of each validation control. Typically, you would place an asterisk (*) or another character that indicates an error with the field.

You can also enter a string for the `HeaderText` property. This is displayed above the `ErrorMessages` and is useful to let the user know why the `ErrorMessages` have been displayed. You can also place multiple `Validation Summary` controls on a page. This might come in handy when you have a very large form and want to display an error summary at the top and bottom of the page.

Summarize Error Messages with the ValidationSummary Control

① Create a new Web page and add two `TextBoxes`.

② Add `RequiredField Validators` for each `TextBox` and enter the `ErrorMessage` for each.

③ Add a `ValidationSummary` control to the page.

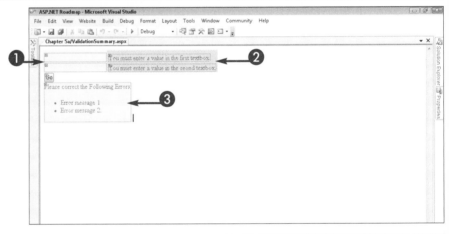

④ Configure the properties of the `ValidationSummary` to display a bulleted list and show an alert `MessageBox`.

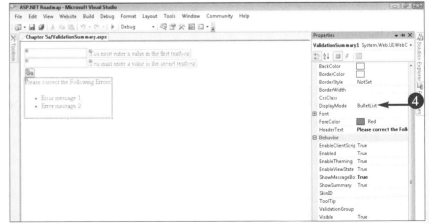

⑤ Load the page in a browser.

⑥ Type valid data in the fields and submit the form by clicking Go.

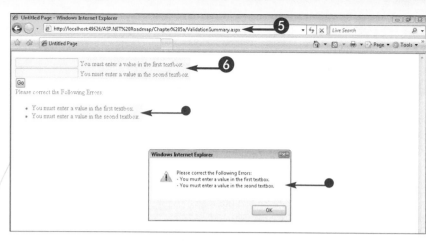

● See the error messages handled by the `ValidationSummary` control and the JavaScript `AlertMessageBox`.

Error messages are displayed for each invalid validator control as well as the `ValidationSummary` control.

⑦ Type valid data in each TextBox and click Go to submit the form.

A clean form appears once valid data is submitted.

Extra

One of the most important aspects of any Web site is how it looks to the end user. Just about every Web and HTML control in the ASP.NET library offers style properties, such as `ForeColor`, `Bold`, `Italics`, and so on. The validation controls are no different, and these properties should be considered when defining your validation controls.

Typically, error messages are displayed in red, but this is not an absolute rule. Error messages can be in any font, color, or size you want. The `ValidationSummary` control offers a variety of display options with a way to list the errors in three fashions with the `DisplayMode`, `ShowMessageBox`, and `ShowSummary` properties. It also provides you with a means to define a header with the `HeaderText` property. A style can be applied either as a class or inline with the `CssClass` and `Style` properties.

All the validation controls provide a rich set of style properties that you should consider when designing your pages. You can even make your error messages vary by applying different styles based on severity, error type, or any other rule you may define.

Display Data in the GridView Control

The `GridView` is the easiest to use of all the tabular data controls because it can automatically bind and display data by nothing more than dragging the control onto a page and binding it to a valid data source. The main drawback is it produces a lot of client-side code and a bloated `ViewState`. You can customize almost every aspect of the `GridView` and make a rich user experience for interacting with your data.

Setting `AutoGenerateColumns` to true, which is the default setting, causes the `GridView` to display the data in all the fields in the `DataSource`. This is great to prove you have connected to the right set of data, but not a valid solution to most real-world requirements. The `GridView` has a Fields dialog box you can display by choosing Edit Columns from the `SmartTag` menu or by selecting the `Columns` property in the Properties window.

The Fields dialog box displays a list of available column types in the top left. Select the field type you want to bind to the `GridView` by double-clicking it or clicking Add. This gives you access to a series of properties that define how the field renders. The most important properties are the `DataField`, the name of the field to be bound, and the `DataFormatString`. `DataFormatString` controls how the data is formatted when it is displayed. Field types include a `BoundField`, `CheckBoxField`, `HyperlinkField`, `ImageField`, and `ButtonField`. Each of these field types has different properties and offers a varying user interface.

An alternative way to control how data is bound to the grid is to use a `TemplateField`. The `TemplateField` gives you the most flexibility because it gives you a canvas to display anything you could add to an ASP.NET Web page. The drawback is it requires more coding to bind data to the `GridView`.

Display Data in the GridView Control

1. Create a new Web page.

2. Add a `GridView` control.

3. Add an `SQLDataSource` control.

4. Set the `GridView`'s `DataSource` to the `SQLDataSource` control.

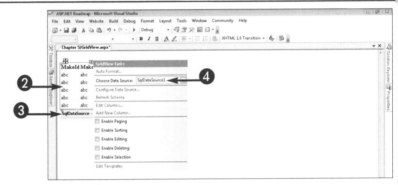

5. Click the Source tab to switch to Source view.

6. Configure the `SQLDataSource`'s Select statement to retrieve a list of car makes from the database.

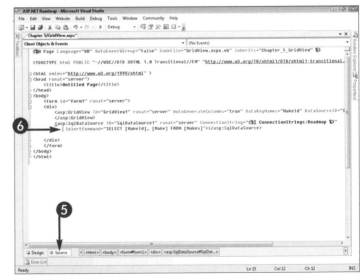

⑦ Switch back to Design view.

⑧ Open the GridView's Smart Tag and select Edit Columns.

⑨ Deselect the Auto-generate fields option.

⑩ Add a BoundField for the Make field.

⑪ Set the HeaderText property of the BoundField to Make.

⑫ Click OK.

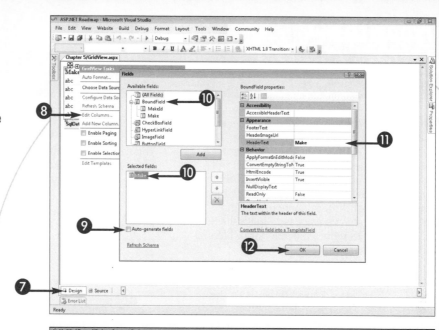

⑬ Open the page in a browser.

● A list of the car makes available in the database appears.

Apply It

The DataFormatString property for a field can be extremely useful in defining how your data is displayed to the end user. Dates often need special formatting. For example, a date is typically stored in the database as a date and time. But more often than not you need to only display the date of a record, not the actual time, or maybe just the time. To use the DataFormatString, you must set the HTMLEncode property to false. This is because the value of the field is HTMLEncoded before the formatting is applied, causing some data types to not have any formatting applied.

Apply a DataFormatString and HtmlEncode to a BoundField:

```
<asp:BoundField DataField="DateSubmitted" HeaderText="DateSubmitted" ReadOnly="True"
DataFormatString="{0:d}" HtmlEncode="false" SortExpression="DateSubmitted" />
```

Format the GridView Control

The `GridView` control offers many ways to format the control for a richer user experience. The problem with many of these formatting features of the `GridView` is they produce bloated code, but provide an easy interface to apply formatting. So just like deciding if you will use the `GridView` as a production control you must weigh how to apply formatting. Fortunately, you can always use Cascading Style Sheets, which go a long way to reduce the amount of bloated code that is sent to a browser.

The `CssClass` property manages the Cascading Style Sheet class used at the global level by the `GridView`. The rules defined in this class are used throughout the control unless a more localized rule is applied.

The `GridLines` property enables you to display lines surrounding the cells of the `GridView`. `ShowFooter` and `ShowHeader` control the display of the two corresponding

templates. `SkinId` is used to specify which `Skin` is applied to the control and may be set at runtime.

You can quickly apply a predefined style to a `GrideView` by selecting Auto Format from the `SmartTag` menu, but these typically do not meet your application requirements.

There are nine style properties in the `GridView`, one for each template type. The styles are `AlternatingRowStyle`, `BorderStyle`, `EditRowStyle`, `EmptyDataRowStyle`, `FooterStyle`, `HeaderStyle`, `PagerStyle`, `RowStyle`, and `SelectedRowStyle`. Each of these style properties is a `TableItemStyle`. A `TableItemStyle` is a class that inherits the `Style` property and offers access to some extra properties that are useful in defining alignment and wrapping. The base `Style` class gives you more properties to manage fonts, colors, borders, and more.

Format the GridView Control

① Open a Web page with a bound GridView.

② Open the Smart Tag menu and select Auto Format.

③ Select one of the predefined schemes.

④ Click Apply.

This example uses Professional.

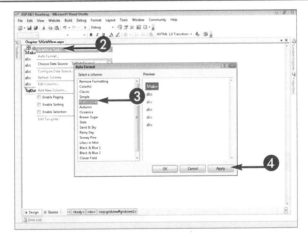

⑤ Open the Properties window for the GridView.

⑥ Set the HeaderStyle Font size to Small.

⑦ Set the HeaderStyle Font Bold to True.

⑧ Set the HeaderStyle Font names to Georgia and Arial.

⑨ Click OK.

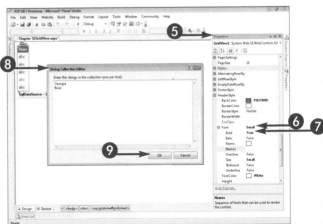

⑩ Set the FooterStyle Font Size to X-Small.

⑪ Set the FooterStyle Font Height to 14px.

⑫ Set the FooterStyle Font Name to Georgia.

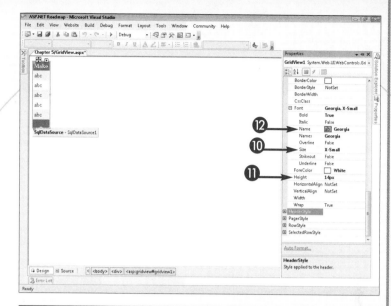

⑬ Open the page in a browser.

● The formatting is applied to the GridView.

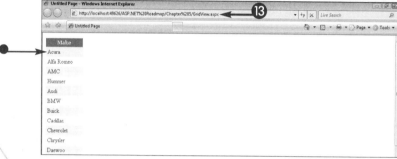

Apply It

You can customize the setting either through the Properties window or in the editor's source view. The `AutoFormat` declaratively applies formatting settings to the various `GridView` style properties. You can adjust these settings as needed. All the `TableStyleItem` properties are also declaratively available in the `GridView` tag definition. The format to access these properties is the stylename-propertyname, for example `HeaderStyle-BackColor="Blue"`. To allow better organization, each of the `TableStyleItems` can also be a child element to the `GridView` definition.

Style Property Settings:
```
<RowStyle BackColor="#F7F6F3" ForeColor="#333333" />
<AlternatingRowStyle BackColor="#FFFFFF" ForeColor="#000000" Font-Bold="true"/>
<FooterStyle BackColor="#5D7B9D" Font-Bold="True"
 Font-Names="Georgia" Font-Size="X-Small"
 ForeColor="White" Height="14px" />
```

Page the GridView Control

The `GridView` offers several out-of-the-box features, such as built-in paging, that make it easy to quickly build interactive tabular data interfaces. To enable paging in a `GridView`, set the `AllowPaging` property to True. The `PageSize` property gets and sets the number of rows displayed in each page of the `GridView`.

The next step is defining the type and style of pager displayed in the `GridView`. You can choose from a series of numeric or textual pagers. The `PagerSettings` property is a reference to a `PagerSettings` object. The `PagerSettings.Mode` property is an enumeration property that defines the type of pager used. It has the options of `NextPrevious`, `Numeric`, `NextPreviousFirstLast`, and `NumericFirstLast`. You can also designate images or the characters used for navigation.

The `PagerStyle` property allows you to control the display of the pager's text and background properties. You may also add customized text to the pager with the `FirstPageText`, `LastPageText`, `NextPageText`, and `PreviousPageText` properties. These properties override the default display of the paging text with the value passed to them. The value may be a formatted string where {0} will be substituted with the actual page number.

If you are binding to a `DataSourceControl`, the paging mechanism is automatically handled for you. If you are not binding to a `DataSourceControl`, you must handle the `PageIndexChanging` event in your code. This event handler has two parameters: an object and a `GridViewPageEventArgs`. The `GridViewPageEventArgs` has a `NewPageIndex` property that indicates what page number is being requested. You must set the `PageIndex` property of the `GridView` to the `NewPageIndex` value and call the `GridView`'s `DataBind` method to cause the grid to display the new records.

Page the GridView Control

① Open a Web page with a bound `GridView` control.

② Click the Smart Tag menu.

③ Select the Enable Paging option.

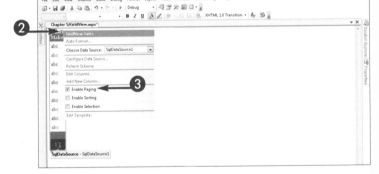

④ Open the GridView's Properties window.

⑤ Set the Paging Mode property to NextPreviousFirstLast.

⑥ Set the PageButtonCount to 5.

⑦ Set the PageSize to 5.

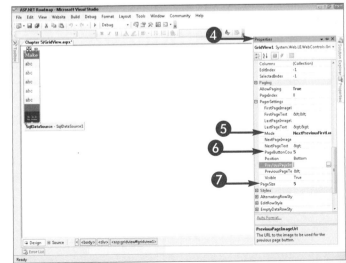

8 Expand the Pager Style section.

9 Set the Font size to XX-Small.

10 Set HorizontalAlign to Center.

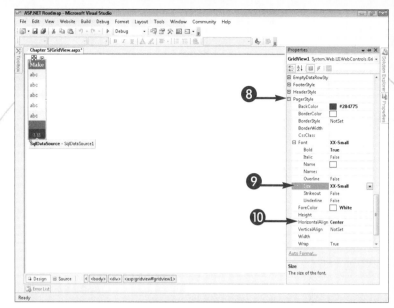

11 Open the page in a browser.

12 Click the various arrows to page through the records.

The records change as you page through the results.

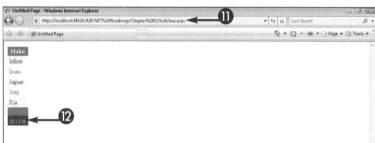

Apply It

The `EnableSortingAndPagingCallbacks` property can be set to `true` to enable client-side callbacks to permit sorting and paging functionality in the `GridView`. If this is set to `true` then the sorting and paging mechanisms will not cause a full post-back to the server, but rather use AJAX to call a service to perform the actions. Some browsers do not support this type of interaction, and you should always call the `SupportsCallback` property before enabling this feature. You also cannot use this feature if you use any of the `Commandfields`, such as an Edit button in the `GridView`. You may also want to visually indicate to the user his or her request is being processed because large datasets require more processing and time to complete.

Setting Up AJAX Support in the GridView:
```
GridView1.EnableSortingAndPagingCallbacks = GridView1.SupportsCallback
```

Sort the GridView Control

A key feature to any enhanced user experience is the ability to sort data by specific columns. The `GridView` has built-in sorting functionality that can be turned on or off for each column displayed. The `AllowSorting` property of the `GridView` must be set to `true` to enable sorting for the grid. By setting the `AllowSorting` property to `true`, each column heading is turned into a hyperlink that can be clicked to sort the data.

Sorting in the `GridView` is much improved over the `DataGrid`'s implementation of sorting. In the `DataGrid` you were responsible for handling the sorting mechanism in your code. The `GridView` automatically manages the sorting routine for you. Also, the default mechanism supports ascending and descending sorting orders by simply continuously clicking on the header links.

Each field has a `SortExpression` property that defines a sort expression. Typically this is the field name for the column, but it may contain multiple field names and directional syntax. If you do not define the `SortExpression` for a field, sorting is not enabled for that column and the header is not rendered as a hyperlink.

The `GridView` has a sort direction property that indicates which direction, `Ascending` or `Descending`, the data is being sorted. You can use this in the `Sorting` and `Sorted` event handlers to manually manage the sorting mechanism for the `GridView`.

The `GridView` fires the `Sorting` event when the user causes a sort operation to be executed. This gives you the ability to intercept the call to sort the data, manipulate the sort expression, or cancel the call altogether. One of the parameters passed by the event is a `GridViewSortEventArgs` object. This object contains the `SortExpression` that is used to perform the sort operation. You may manipulate this value however you want.

Sort the GridView Control

① Open a Web page with a bound `GridView` control.

② Click the Smart Tag menu.

③ Select the Enable Sorting option.

④ Click the Smart Tag menu and select Edit Columns.

⑤ Ensure the SortExpression for the Make BoundField is set to Make.

⑥ Click OK.

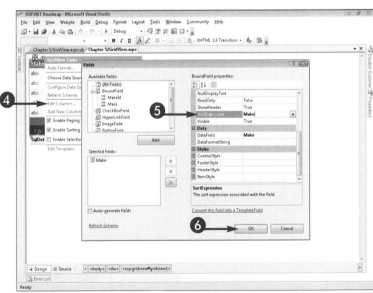

7 Switch to code-behind and add an event handler for the `GridView`'s `Sorting` event.

8 Add code to prevent a sort from occurring when the `GridView` is displaying the last page in the list.

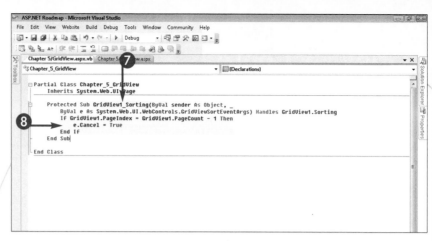

9 Open the page in a browser.

10 Click the Make column header to sort the list.

11 Page through to the last page in the list and select the header.

The order of the list alternates between ascending and descending order. On the last page the sort order does not change when selected.

Apply It

Visually indicating to the user what direction data is being sorted is very useful in making a rich user experience. The `GridView` does not support this out of the box, but can easily be added by checking the `SortDirection` property of the `GridView`. The `SortDirection` property indicates whether the column is being sorted in an `Ascending` or `Descending` order.

Add Sort Direction Images to the GridView Header:

```
Sub CustomersGridView_DataBound(ByVal sender As Object, ByVal e As EventArgs)
  Dim headerRow As GridViewRow = CustomersGridView.HeaderRow
  dim sortImage as new Image()
  Select Case GridView1.SortDirection
    Case SortDirection.Ascending
      sortImage.ImageUrl = "~/down.gif"
    Case SortDirection.Descending
      sortImage.ImageUrl = "~/up.gif"
  end Select
headerRow.Cells(columnIndex).Controls.Add(sortImage)
```

Edit a Record in the GridView Control

The `GridView` offers users the ability to edit records within the control. There are two ways to enable a `Button` to initiate the editing of a record: setting the `AutoGenerateEditButton` property to `true` or adding a `CommandField` to the columns collection and setting the `ShowEditButton` property to `true`. Additionally, you can add a `TemplateField` containing a `Button` control that is designated to initiate an edit operation through the `CommandName` property.

The `CommandField` has several properties that allow you to define the type of button displayed and specific formatting characteristics of that button, such as color and font size. The `ButtonType` property can be set to a `Button`, `Link`, or `Image`. When using an `ImageButton` you can use the `EditImageURL` to set the image to be used in the button. For a `Button` or `LinkButton` you can set the `EditText` property to control the text displayed on the button.

If you are using a `DataSourceControl`, such as an `SQLDataSource`, you need to define the `UpdateCommand` property of the `DataSourceControl`. By using a `DataSourceControl` you can enable the entire edit process without writing a single line of code. If you are not using `AutoGenerateColumns` you must also set the `DataKeyNames` property to the names of the primary key fields.

When a user clicks the Edit button the row is automatically switched to an Edit mode where appropriate Web controls are displayed allowing the user to change the record as needed. `Update` and `Cancel` buttons are also displayed in place of the `CommandField` buttons. The `Update` button attempts to update the record with any changes made by the user. The `Cancel` button stops the operation and returns to the previous state.

Edit a Record in the GridView Control

1. Open a Web page with a bound `GridView` control.

2. Open the GridView's Smart Tag menu.

3. Select Edit Columns.

4. Add an Edit, Update, Cancel CommandField button.

5. Click OK.

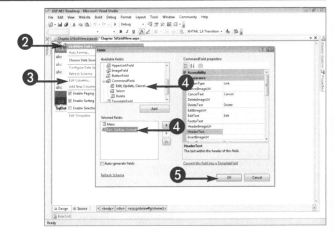

6. Open the SQLDataSource's Command and Parameter Editor for the UpdateCommand property.

7. Add an UpdateCommand.

8. Click Refresh Parameters.

9. Click OK.

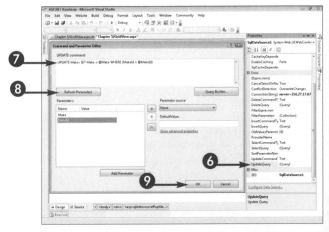

⑩ Open the page in a browser.

⑪ Click the Edit button on a row.

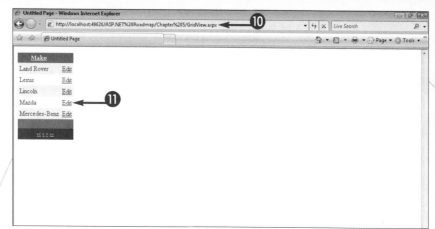

⑫ Type a new value and click Update.

The new value appears in the list.

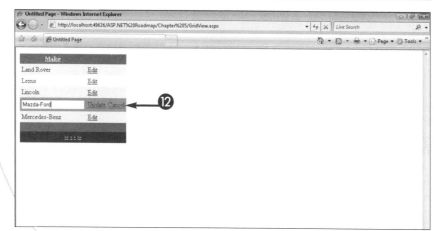

Extra

Inline row editing may also be used with a `TemplateField`. A `TemplateField` column may contain any of several templates, including an `EditItemTemplate`. In the `EditItemTemplate` you can lay out any set of controls you need to collect the information from the user to update a record.

You need to create an event handler for the `GridView`'s `RowEditing` event. In this event, you can access the control in the `EditItemTemplate` and set it to an initial value. Similarly, you need to create a handler for the `RowUpdating` event to set the new values for each field. In both cases you can access the Web controls in the `EditItemTemplate` by calling the `FindControl` method of the `GridViewRow` being updated.

You may also need to invoke the Edit mode from a `TemplateField` with a `Button` control. You will need to set the `CommandArgument` to the primary key of the record and the `CommandName` property to Edit.

Example:

```
Dim btnDelete As Button =
e.Item.FindControl("btnDelete")

btnDelete.CommandArgument =
DataList1.DataKeys(e.Item.ItemIndex)
btnDelete.CommandName = "Delete"
```

Delete a Record in the GridView Control

Deleting a record in the GridView can easily be done by setting the AutoGenerateDelete to true and assigning the DeleteCommand of an associated DataSource. You must also make sure the DataKeyNames is defined with the primary keys for the record's table. Clicking the Delete button on a record in the GridView executes the delete command.

You are not required to use the DataKeyNames value as the criteria to indicate the record to be deleted. The DataSourceControl allows you to define parameters to be used in a delete operation, for example, deleting a list of shopping cart records for a customer by the CustomerId. In this case, you define your delete command to delete records based on the CustomerId and create a corresponding delete parameter in the DataSourceControl.

You should always check for errors when a record is deleted. The GridView's RowDelete event passes a GridViewDeletedEventArgs that contains an exception property that can be processed. The DataSourceControl has a similar feature in its delete event handler.

You may also create your own row templates that include a Delete button. In these cases, you will want to create custom routines in the GirdView's RowDeleting event handler. To cause this to happen with a custom template the Delete button needs to have its CommandName designated as Delete. You may also create a special name but will need to process it through the GridView's Command event handler.

You can cancel the delete operation in the RowDeleting event handler if your criteria for a proper delete are not met. You can do this by setting the GridViewDeleteEventArgs.Cancel property to true. You can also alter the Keys and Values collection before the actual delete operation is processed.

Delete a Record in the GridView Control

1 Open a Web page with a bound GridView control.

2 Click the GridView's Smart Tag menu and select Edit Columns.

3 Add a Delete CommandField button.

4 Click OK.

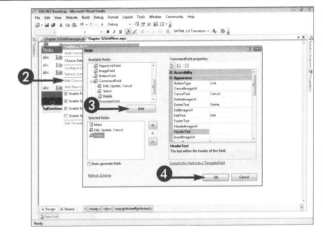

5 Open the SQLDataSource's Command and Parameter Editor for the DeleteCommand property.

6 Add a DeleteCommand.

7 Click Refresh Parameters.

8 Click OK.

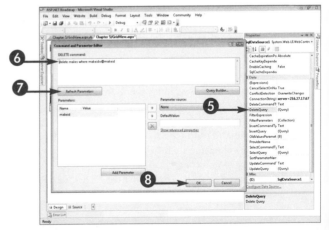

9 Open the page in a browser.

10 Click Delete on a row.

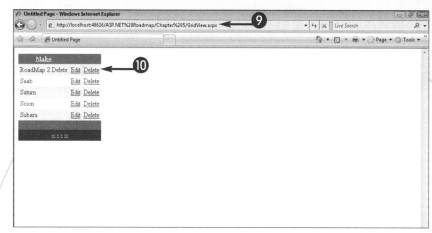

● The selected record is removed from the list.

Apply It

Before you let a user delete a record from the database, provide a prompt just to make certain that is what he or she wants to do. A good way to do this is to display an alert dialog box through JavaScript. Fortunately, ASP.NET button controls have a convenient way to add JavaScript to client-side event handlers through the `Attributes` collection.

A common way to add this JavaScript is in the `RowDataBind` event handler. Here you can get a reference to the Delete button and add the JavaScript to display a warning dialog box to the user.

Add a Confirmation Dialog to a Delete Button:
```
Protected Sub GridView1_RowDataBound(ByVal sender As Object, _
 ByVal e As System.Web.UI.WebControls.GridViewRowEventArgs) Handles GridView1.RowDataBound

 If e.Row.RowType = DataControlRowType.DataRow Then
  Dim btnDelete As ImageButton = CType(e.Row.FindControl("btnDelete"), ImageButton)
  btnDelete.Attributes.Add("onclick", _
 "return confirm('Warning: This will delete the Item from the database.')")
end sub
```

Bind Data to the Repeater Control

The simplest, but most flexible of the Data controls is the `Repeater`. It provides the ability to echo data-driven tables through a series of templates. Control templates are a way to define the layout of data in the control. Data can be bound at runtime in the `ItemDataBound` event or through inline data references.

The `Repeater` control provides five row template choices: `Header`, `Item`, `AlternatingItem`, `Separator`, and `Footer`. Each defines a section of the `Repeater` to lay out the data. The only required template is the `ItemTemplate`, but using the other templates helps make a richer layout.

A template is declared in the design-time code (HTML) with an open and close tag: <ItemTemplate> {Some Content Here} </ItemTemplate>. Inside the template tags you lay out HTML markup and Web controls as you would normally on a Web page. You can access controls

in the `ItemDataBind` event in the page's runtime code through reflection.

As each row from the `DataSource` is bound to the `Repeater` an `ItemDataBind` event is fired. You can define a handler for this event in your page to bind data to controls as needed. This event handler passes a `RepeaterItemEventArgs` parameter that includes an `Item` property that represents the row being bound.

You can see which template type is being bound by checking the `e.Item.ItemType` property, which indicates the type of row being bound, such as a `Header` or `Item` template. After you know the row type you can create an instance of any controls on the row and bind the data to them as needed. The `e.Item.DataItem` is a reference to the record or object being bound to the row. This object can be cast to any custom object you may be binding or a `DataRowView` if you are using one of the common data items such as a `DataSet`.

Bind Data to the Repeater Control

① Create a new Web page.

② Add a `Repeater` control.

③ Add an `SQLDataSource` control.

④ Set the Repeater's DataSource to the `SQLDataSource` control.

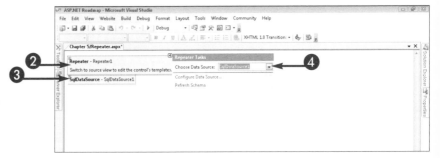

⑤ Click the Source tab to switch to Source view.

⑥ Configure the SQLDataSource's `Select` statement to retrieve a list of car makes from the database.

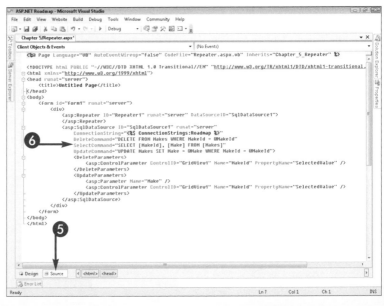

7 Add a `HeaderTemplate` with a `Table` tag and `Header` row.

8 Add an `ItemTemplate` with a table row definition to display the `MakeId` and `Make`.

9 Add an `AlternatingItemTemplate` with a table row definition to display the `MakeId` and `Make`.

10 Add a `FooterTemplate` with a closing `Table` tag.

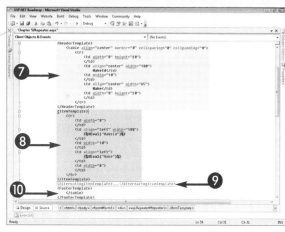

11 Open the page in a browser.

● The entire list of MakeIds and Makes appears in the browser.

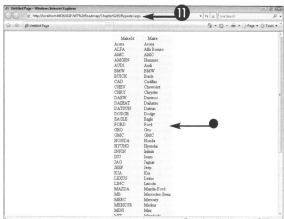

Apply It

Data can be displayed in a template through inline coding, which means a design-time reference to the field is included. An inline reference takes the form of <% =Container.Item("FieldName")%> or <% =Eval("FieldName")%>, where FieldName represents the name of the field in the record being displayed.

Often advanced developers bind values to control at runtime in the `ItemDataBound` event handler. In this event handler, you can use reflection to create an instance of each control on the row being bound. This gives you more flexibility as to how data is bound to controls and ultimately presented to the end user.

Bind Data Values at Run-Time in the Repeater:

```
Protected Sub Repeater1_ItemDataBound(ByVal sender As Object, _
  ByVal e As System.Web.UI.WebControls.RepeaterItemEventArgs) Handles Repeater1.ItemDataBound
   If e.Item.ItemType = ListItemType.Footer Then
     Dim ltlFirstName As Literal = e.Item.FindControl("ltlFirstName")
     Dim dv As DataRowView = e.Item.DataItem
     If Not IsNothing(ltlFirstName) Then
      ltlFirstName.Text = dv("FirstName").ToString
     End If
   End If
End Sub
```

Format the Repeater Control

Because the `Repeater` is the lightest of the data controls it offers no style properties to apply to any of the templates. You format the look and feel of the `Repeater` by applying traditional HTML and style sheet formatting to the elements that define the layout of the data.

By default, the `Repeater` control displays data horizontally, which is often not the desired behavior. The `Header` and `Footer` templates offer a way to define either a `Table` (<TABLE>), `List` (<UL> or <OL>), or other container type to manage how the data is displayed. The `HeaderTemplate` contains the opening tag of the container, <TABLE>, and the `FooterTemplate` contains the closing tag, </TABLE>.

You may also want to add a table row to each of these templates to create a header and footer row for the list. For example, you could create column headings for each

column. The footer could be used to display summary data or even a pager.

The `ItemTemplate` and `AlternatingItemTemplate` each could have a table row, <TR>, and corresponding table cells, <TD>, defined to lay out the actual data in the `Repeater`. HTML attributes and styles can be applied to them as well. An example would be to set the background colors differently for alternating rows.

A common use of the `AlternatingItemTemplate` is to display a slightly different-shade background color. When you have a white background defined for the `ItemTemplate` you might define `WhiteSmoke` or `Gainsboro` as the background for each alternating row. This gives you some stylistic separation with minimal effort.

Any controls placed in a template can also have their properties and styles set just like you would if they were on the page normally.

Format the Repeater Control

① Open a Web page with a bound `Repeater` control.

② Click the Design tab to switch to Design view.

③ Add a `Style` tag to the page header.

④ Insert style sheet definitions for the HTML tag and Header class that defines how the font and background should render.

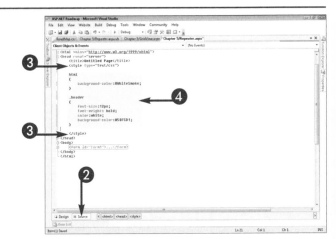

⑤ Add a style sheet tag for `Item` class that defines how the font and background should render.

⑥ Add a style sheet tag for `AlternatingItem` class that defines how the font and background should render.

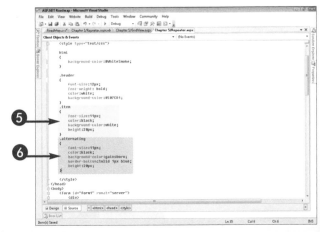

126

7 Apply the Header style class to the header row in the table.

8 Apply the Item style class to the ItemTemplate row in the table.

9 Apply the AlternatingItem style class to the AlternatingItem Template row in the table.

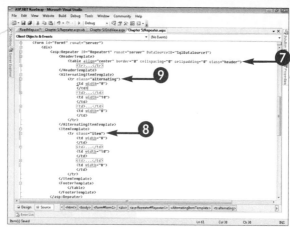

10 Open the page in the browser.

● The same list of MakeIds and Makes appears with the style sheet definitions applied.

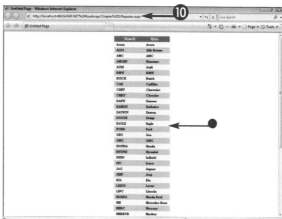

Extra

By default, the Repeater displays records horizontally. Often data needs to be displayed in a vertical fashion, which is where the header and footer templates come in handy. A simple example would be defining a bulleted list with the <UL> tag. The <UL> open tag would be placed in the HeaderTemplate and the </UL> in the footer. The list item tags (<LI> & </LI>) with the value would be placed in the ItemTemplate and optionally the AlternatingItemTemplate. This renders a vertical bulleted list in the Repeater control.

You can use a similar technique with a table, with the table declaration tag in the header and the closing tag in the footer. Each ItemTemplate has a table row definition (<TR><TD>{Content Here}</TD></TR>). The nice thing about the Repeater control is its simple flexibility for layout control and minimal markup footprint.

Display Data with the DataList Control

Like the `Repeater`, the `DataList` control provides an easy way to display tabular data, but with the ability to display multiple items in a row. You can define how many columns are displayed in each row and the direction and flow of data items. The display of the data templates can be set to either horizontal or vertical through the `RepeatDirection` property. `RepeatLayout` allows you to specify whether data is displayed in a tabular or layout format using SPAN tags.

The `DataList` formats the way it displays data through templates, which are sections of predefined markup that are either displayed in the header or footer, or repeated in the `DataList` as each row is bound and rendered. The `DataList` can have an `ItemTemplate`, `AlternatingItemTemplate`, `FooterTemplate`, `HeaderTemplate`, `SeparatorTemplate`, `EditItemTemplate`, or `SelectedItemTemplate`. You

must include an `ItemTemplate` to bind data or nothing will be displayed; all other templates are optional. An `AlternatingItemTemplate` gives you a way to change the display of items on alternating records. For example, you may want a different background or chiral data layout to distinguish items. The header and footer templates offer ways to dress up your table and provide more information to the user. The `SeparatorTemplate` is the space between records on the same row. The `SelectedItemTemplate` is a special template to control the visual display of a selected record.

A template contains HTML markup and can contain any ASP.NET Web control and inline markup. Data can be bound to Web controls either through inline markup or in the `ItemDataBound` event handler. In this handler, you can use reflection to get an instance of each Web control in the template and an instance of the data item being bound and have explicit control over how the data is bound to the control.

Display Data with the DataList Control

① Create a new Web page.

② Add a `DataList` control.

③ Add an `SQLDataSource` control.

④ Set the DataList's DataSource to the `SQLDataSource` control.

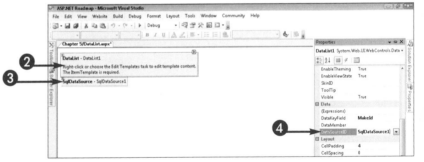

⑤ Add a `HeaderTemplate` with a table tag.

⑥ Add an `ItemTemplate` with a table row definition to display the `Make`.

⑦ Add an `AlternatingItemTemplate` with a table row definition to display the `Make`.

⑧ Add a `FooterTemplate` with a closing table tag.

⑨ Set the `RepeatColumns` property to 3.

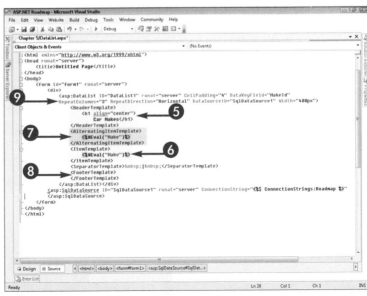

⑩ Configure the SQLDataSource's `SelectCommand` to retrieve a list of car makes from the database.

⑪ Configure the SQLDataSource's `UpdateCommand` to update a car make from the database.

⑫ Configure the SQLDataSource's `DeleteCommand` to delete a car make from the database.

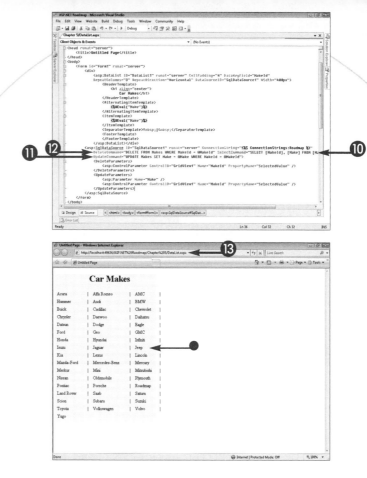

⑬ Open the page in a browser.

● The full list of car makes appears in three-column format.

Apply It

Binding data and formatting to Web controls in a `DataList` control at runtime is a common way to control the presentation of the data in the browser. To do this, define your content layout in the appropriate template in the `DataList` declaration in the pages layout. This can be done either in Design or Source view. If you are in Design view, you can right-click the `DataList` control and select Edit Templates. This displays a list of views from which you can add controls and formatting like you would for the page.

To access the controls for each item, declare an event handler for the `ItemDataBound` event and use reflection, the `FindControl` method, to gain access to the controls and the `DataItem` being bound to the cell.

Use Reflection to Bind Data to Controls in the DataList:

```
Protected Sub DataList1_ItemDataBound(ByVal sender As Object, _
 ByVal e As System.Web.UI.WebControls.DataListItemEventArgs) Handles DataList1.ItemDataBound
 If e.Item.ItemType = ListItemType.AlternatingItem Or _
  e.Item.ItemType = ListItemType.Item Then
  Dim ltlMake As Literal = e.Item.FindControl("ltlMake")
  Dim dv As DataRowView = e.Item.DataItem
  ltlMake.Text = dv("Make")
 End If
End Sub
```

Format the DataList Control

The `DataList` control can be formatted either manually like the `Repeater` or through style properties for each template. You can quickly apply a predefined style to a `DataList` by selecting Auto Format from the Smart Tag menu, but these typically do not meet your application requirements. Cascading Style Sheet rules may also be applied to each template's corresponding style object.

You can access style properties through the properties window for the `DataList`. You can set the values for any property you need to format your template through the properties designer interface. If you feel more comfortable defining your properties in the markup you can also define the properties of each style in the Source view of the page.

The `GridLines` property enables you to display lines surrounding the cells of the `DataList`. `ShowFooter` and `ShowHeader` control the display of the two corresponding templates. `SkinId` is used to specify which `Skin` is applied to the control and may be set at runtime.

There are seven style properties in the `DataList`, one for each template type. The styles classes are `AlternatingItemStyle`, `EditItemStyle`, `FooterStyle`, `HeaderStyle`, `ItemStyle`, `SelectedItemStyle`, and `SeparatorStyle`. Each of these style properties is a `TableItemStyle`. A `TableItemStyle` is a class that inherits the `Style` property and offers access to some extra properties that are useful in defining alignment and wrapping. The base `Style` class gives you more properties to manage fonts, colors, borders, and more.

Format the DataList Control

① Open a Web page with a bound `DataList` control.

② Click the Smart Tag menu and select Auto Format.

③ Select one of the predefined schemes.

In this example, Classic is selected.

④ Click Apply.

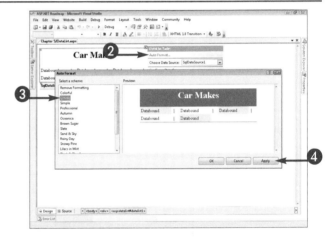

⑤ Add style rules for various elements of the DataList.

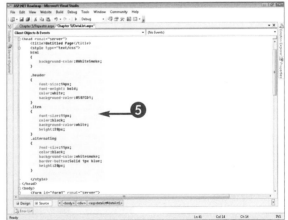

6 Adjust the `HeaderStyle` definition to use the Header Style rule as the `CssClass`.

7 Adjust the `AlternatingItemStyle` definition to use the Header Style rule as the `CssClass`.

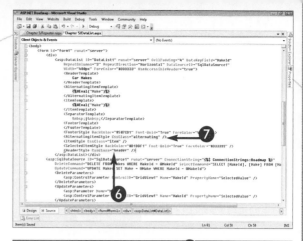

8 Open the page in a browser.

● The style formatting is applied to the list.

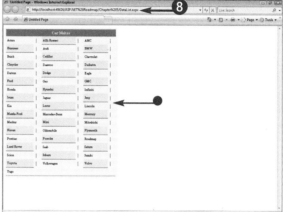

Apply It

Using Cascading Style Sheets has become the preferred method to apply formatting to Web pages. You can create style sheet rules in either an inline style definition or a style sheet file. The more efficient method is to define all styles in a stand-alone file because it will be downloaded the first time a user accesses it and be cached for a period thereafter.

Style rules may be defined for specific HTML elements or may be a custom-defined rule. In the case of HTML elements the rule's name simply matches the element name. A custom rule is indicated with a `RuleName` and is applied to the style classes in the `CssClass` property.

Sample Style Sheet Settings and Assignment:

```
<style type="text/css">
    .footer
    {
        font-size:18px;
        letter-spacing:15px;
    }
</style>

FooterStyle-CssClass="footer"
```

Page the DataList Control

O ne of the most asked questions about using the DataList control is how to page through long sets of data. An easy way is to leverage the PagedDataSource to manage the actual data bound to the DataList. You can also leverage the FooterTemplate or even the HeaderTemplate to add controls or links to manage the paging interface.

The PagedDataSource is a special collection that manages paging-related properties of a data-bound control. The PagedDataSource is actually bound to a datasource, such as a DataSet or custom collection that implements IEnumerable. It has properties to specify the page size, DataSource, and if paging is allowed. Several properties are read-only, such as PageCount, IsLastPage, IsFirstPage, Count, and CurrentPageIndex.

To implement a basic paging mechanism in the DataList control you can add a couple of buttons to the

FooterTemplate: one for the previous page and one for the next page. The buttons need to specify the CommandArgument as the page index. You also need to set the CommandName to indicate the action, for example Prev and Next. This can be processed in the DataList's Command event handler to invoke the paging of the data.

Depending on the direction the user selects, you can page the data forward or backward by incrementing or decrementing the CurrentPageIndex of the PagedDataSource object and calling the method to bind the data. You should also check to see if the new page index is the first or last page in the PagedDataSet and hide or display the buttons accordingly. You can show it again when the CurrentPageIndex is greater than the first page. The method used for binding binds the actual data source to the PagedDataSource and then the PagedDataSource to the DataList control.

Page the DataList Control

① Open a Web page with a bound DataList control.

② Add a Button control and set the Text to < Prev and the CommandArgument to Prev.

③ Add a Button control and set the Text to Next > and the CommandArgument to Next.

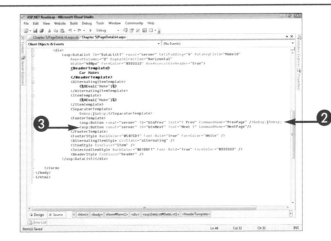

④ Switch to code-behind and add code to declare a PagedDataSource and initialize.

⑤ Create a BindData method to bind the data to the PagedDataSource object.

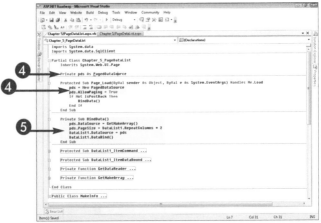

6 Create a `Command` event handler for the `DataList` control.

7 Add code to manage the `CommandArgument`.

8 Add code to page the `PagedDataSource` object backward for the Next button.

9 Open the page in a browser.

10 Click Next and Previous to navigate through the records.

Apply It

The `PagedDataSource` object should be declared so it is available throughout the page while it is being processed. Typically, you declare it at the page level, and initialize it in the `Load` event. It is also a good idea to cache the actual data source that is bound to the `PagedDataSource`. This optimizes the speed of the page because the data is only retrieved the first time the page loads.

Setting Up the PagedDataSource:

```
Private pds As PagedDataSource

Protected Sub Page_Load(ByVal sender As Object, _
 ByVal e As System.EventArgs) Handles Me.Load
 pds = New PagedDataSource
 pds.AllowPaging = True
 If Not IsPostBack Then
  BindData()
 End If
End Sub
```

Bind a Record to the DetailsView

The `DetailsView` control is much like a `GridView`, but it only displays one record at a time. The control offers the ability to view, edit, insert, and delete a record. The `DetailsView` can be paged between records in its associated data source. It is often used in a master-details scenario in conjunction with another data control such as the `GridView`, but it can stand alone. The selected record of the master control determines which record is displayed in the `DetailsView`.

The `DetailsView` offers an editing interface that can be invoked through the `AutoGenerateEditButton` or `CommandField.ShowEditButton` properties. The `DetailsView` also has `AutoGenerateDelete` and `AutoGenerateInsert` button properties to invoke these operations.

You must use a data source that has an update mechanism defined, such as a defined `UpdateCommand`

in an `SQLDataSource` to perform an update operation. Similarly, you must have an insert and delete mechanism defined for those operations for work as well. You may need to define any needed parameters in your data source for each operation, too.

If you use the `DetailsView` in a master-details scenario, remember to rebind the master control after you perform an edit, update, or delete operation. This can be done in the `DetailsView ItemUpdated` event handler. You should call the `DataBind` method of the master data control.

You can use the `DetailsView` to display information from any data source you need. For example, a `GridView` may display a series of car models, while the `DetailsView` displays information about the make of the car. This can occur because the master data control and the `DetailsView` are bound to separate data sources. The master control needs to pass a filter parameter to the `DetailsView` to display the appropriate record.

Bind a Record to the DetailsView

① Create a new Web page.

② Add an `SQLDataSource` to the page.

③ Configure the `SQLDataSource` to connect to the Makes table in the ASP.NET Roadmap database.

④ Set the `SQLDataSources` Select and Update commands.

Note: The ASP.NET Roadmap database is provided with the book's source code.

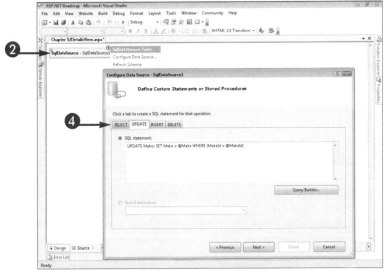

⑤ Add a `DetailsView` to the page.

⑥ Set the data source to the `SQLDataSource` added in step **2**.

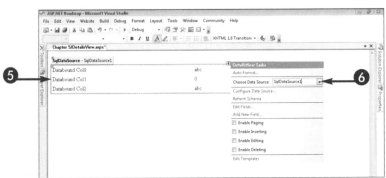

7 Set the `AllowPaging` property to true.

8 Set the `AutoGenerateEdit Button` to true.

9 Set the `AutoGenerate InsertButton` to true.

10 Set the `AutoGenerate DeleteButton` to true.

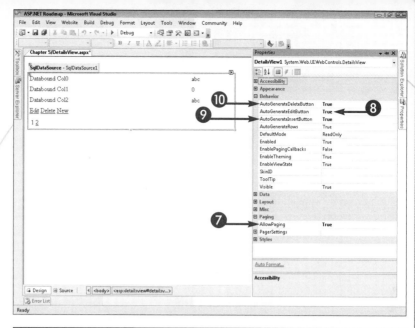

11 Open the page in a browser.

12 Page through the records to see the records bound to the DetailsView.

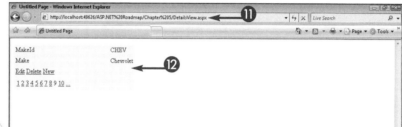

Apply It

By default, the `DetailsView` `DefaultMode` property is set to `ReadOnly`. This means the record is presented to the user as a series of text rendered to the browser, with no means for user input. This mode is the state the control is returned to after an insert, update, or delete operation is performed. It can be set to either `Insert`, `Edit`, or `ReadOnly`. This property may also be defined at runtime.

Set the Current Mode in the DetailsView:
```
DetailsView1.ChangeMode(DetailsViewMode
.ReadOnly)
```

The `DetailsView` can be set to allow paging by setting the `AllowPaging` property to `true`. There are two events that can be handled during the paging operation: `PageIndexedChanging` and `PageIndexChanged`. This gives you the ability to perform some logic when the page changes; for example, setting the `DedaultMode` to `ReadOnly`.

Use the PageIndexChanged Event to Set the Mode of the DetailsView:
```
Protected Sub DetailsView1_PageIndexChanged
(ByVal sender As Object, ByVal e As System
.EventArgs) Handles DetailsView1
.PageIndexChanged

 DetailsView1.ChangeMode(DetailsViewMode
.ReadOnly)

End Sub
```

Format the DetailsView

The `DetailsView` has many properties and accepts style sheet classes to easily apply custom formatting to the control. You can quickly apply a predefined style to a `DetailsView` by selecting Auto Format from the Smart Tag menu, but these typically do not meet your application requirements. Cascading Style Sheet rules may also be applied to each template's corresponding style object.

You can access style properties through the Properties window for the `DetailsView`. You can set the values for any property you need to format your template through the Properties designer interface. If you feel more comfortable defining your properties in the markup you can also define the properties of the each style in the Source view of the page.

The `GridLines` property enables you to display lines surrounding the cells of the `DataList`. `ShowFooter` and

`ShowHeader` control the display of the two corresponding templates. `SkinId` is used to specify which `Skin` is applied to the control and may be set at runtime.

There are 11 style properties in the `DetailsView`, one for each template type. The Style classes are `AlternatingItemStyle`, `CommandRowStyle`, `EditItemStyle`, `EmptyDataRowStyle`, `FieldHeaderStyle`, `FooterStyle`, `HeaderStyle`, `InsertRowStyle`, `PagerStyle`, `SelectedItemStyle`, and `RowStyle`.

Each of these style properties is a `TableItemStyle`. A `TableItemStyle` is a class that inherits the `Style` property and offers access to some extra properties that are useful in defining alignment and wrapping. The base Style class gives you more properties to manage fonts, colors, borders, and more.

Format the DetailsView

① Open a Web page with a bound `DetailsView`.

② Click the Smart Tag menu and select Auto Format.

③ Select one of the predefined schemes.

In this example, Professional is selected.

④ Click Apply.

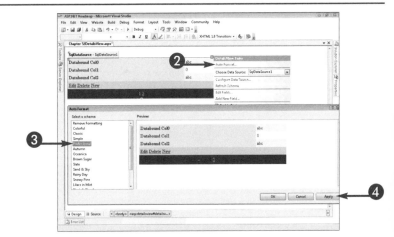

⑤ Open the Properties window for the `DetailsView`.

⑥ Set the `PagerStyle` Font size to X-Small.

⑦ Set the `PagerStyle` Font Bold to True.

⑧ Set the `PagerStyle` `HorizontalAlign` property to Right.

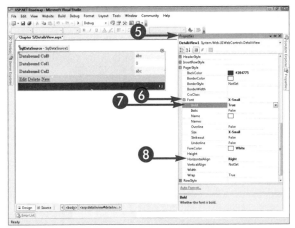

⑨ Set the `CommandRowStyle` Font Size to X-Small.

⑩ Set the `CommandRowStyle` Font Bold to True.

⑪ Set the `CommandRowStyle` HorizontalAlign property to Right.

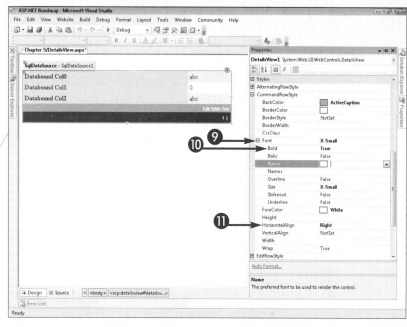

⑫ Open the page in a browser.

● The style formatting is applied to the `DetailsView`.

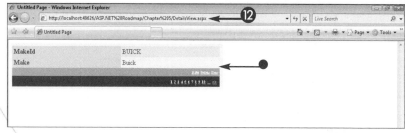

Apply It

It is very common to apply formatting rules to a control at runtime. You can apply formatting rules at any point in the page processing pipeline after the control is initialized in the page's `Init` event. Each of the style properties can be set at runtime by calling them directly. The style properties are read-only, but you can set the individual properties of the style classes directly.

TableStyle Settings:
```
DetailsView1.RowStyle.ForeColor = System.Drawing.Color.Tomato
DetailsView1.RowStyle.BackColor = System.Drawing.Color.Sienna
DetailsView1.RowStyle.BorderWidth = Unit.Pixel(1)
DetailsView1.RowStyle.BorderStyle = BorderStyle.Dotted
DetailsView1.RowStyle.BorderColor = System.Drawing.Color.Red
DetailsView1.AlternatingRowStyle.CssClass = "AtlRow"
```

Edit and Insert a Record with the DetailsView

The `DetailsView` has the ability to let the user insert new records or edit existing records. If you are using a `DataSourceControl` you must have the corresponding `Update` and `Insert` commands defined, as well as the corresponding parameters. You also need to have the `DataKeyNames` value defined in the `DetailsView` control or you will experience errors.

The `DetailsView` `AutoGenerateEditButton` property should be set to `true` for the `Edit` button to automatically be displayed as each record is rendered in the browser. This button is automatically wired to the `DetailsView` command pipeline and causes the control to switch to Update mode. This causes the `ModeChanging` event to fire and the `EventArgs` parameter has a `NewMode` value of `Edit`. When the edit interface is generated there are appropriate controls, such as `TextBoxes` and `Checkboxes`, displayed for each field. There will also be

`Update` and `Cancel` buttons. By default, these are `LinkButtons` but may be set to a regular button or an `ImageButton`. Choosing the `Update` button causes the `Update` command to execute with the entered changes. Selecting the `Cancel` button causes the control to revert to read-only mode, and no changes are applied.

Similarly, setting the `AutoGenerateInsertButton` property to `true` causes a New button control to be rendered, again as a `LinkButton` by default. This causes the `ModeChanging` event to fire and the `EventArgs` parameter has a `NewMode` value of `Insert`. When the user selects the New button, the same interface is displayed as the Edit interface, except this time with empty controls. After entering the data for the new record, you can click Insert to add the new record to the database. If you want to cancel the operation, click Cancel.

Edit and Insert a Record with the DetailsView

① Open a Web page with a bound `DetailsView`.

② Click the Smart Tag menu and select the Enable Editing option.

③ Click the Smart Tag menu again and select the Enable Inserting option.

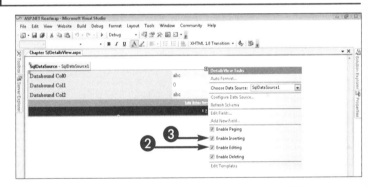

④ Click the Source tab to switch to Source view.

⑤ Add an `SQLCommand` to `Update` a record.

⑥ Add an `SQLCommand` to `Insert` a record.

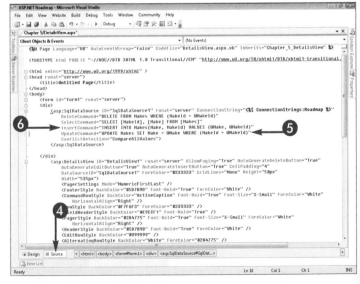

7 Open the page in a browser.

8 Select a record to update.

9 Make some changes.

10 Click Update to save the record.

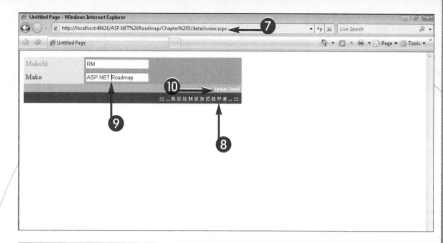

11 Click the Insert link.

12 Add a new record.

The new record displays.

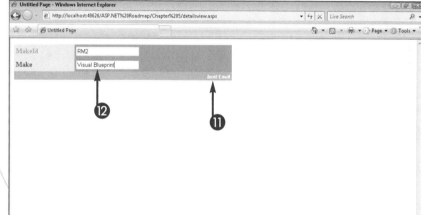

Apply It

Dealing with concurrency is a common problem faced by most multiclient data-oriented applications. The problem is when two users almost simultaneously update the same record, how do you determine which modification is finally accepted? The solution is by using the DataSourceControl's ConflictDetection property. The choices are CompareAllValues and OverRightChanges.

OverRightChanges is the default setting, which tells the control to let the last user's changes be the final changes. If you set it to CompareAllValues it tracks the original values against the changes that have been made. It does not let a user update a record that has been updated since opening the record.

The SQLDataSource control modifies the UpdateCommand to perform a comparison with the original values before updating the record.

Set the Conflict Resolution Choice:
```
pdateCommand="UPDATE Makes SET Make = @Make WHERE (MakeId = @MakeId)"
ConflictDetection="CompareAllValues">
```

Bind a Record to the FormView

Like the `DetailsView` and other data controls, you can bind a set of data to a `FormView`, but unlike the `DetailsView` the `FormView` does not have automatic table rendering built in. To display data in the `FormView` you must define your own templates and binding mechanisms.

The `FormView` can be comprised of several item templates: `ItemTemplate`, `EditItemTemplate`, `InsertItemTemplate`, and `EmptyItemTemplate`. Each of these is rendered as needed; the `ItemTemplate` and the `EmptyItemTemplate` are used to display actual records. The `EditItemTemplate` and the `InsertItemTemplate` are used to update existing records and add new records, respectively.

Additional templates may be defined for the `HeaderTemplate`, `FooterTemplate`, and `PagerTemplate`. Each of these templates can be used to define supporting information to be displayed to users

about records they are viewing. You may want to use these templates to display extra information about the record.

The `FormView` can be used to `View`, `Page`, `Edit`, `Insert`, or `Delete` records. Because the `FormView` is built using templates it is also easier to implement data validation controls.

Controls may be bound to fields in the data source using the `Eval` method. The `Eval` method offers a couple of overloads: the first accepts a field name, and the second adds a data formatting expression. The syntax to use the `Eval` method to perform inline binding is `<%#Eval("FieldName", "FormatExpression")%>`. The `Eval` method is used for one-way binding.

When you are binding a record to a web control you would use the `Bind` method in a similar fashion, `<%#Bind("FieldName")%>`. The `Bind` method is used for two-way or updatable binding operations. It does not support the formatting expression.

Bind a Record to the FormView

1. Create a new Web page.

2. Add a `FormView` control.

3. Add an `SQLDataSource` control.

4. Set the FormView's DataSource to the `SQLDataSource` control.

5. Click the Source tab to switch to Source view.

6. Configure the `SQLDataSource`'s `Select` statement to retrieve a list of car makes from the database.

7. Configure the `SQLDataSource`'s `UpdateCommand` to `Update` a car make from the database.

8. Configure the `SQLDataSource`'s `DeleteCommand` to delete a car make from the database.

9. Configure the `SQLDataSource`'s `InsertCommand` to add a car make to the database.

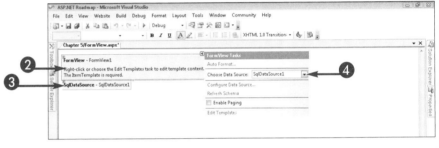

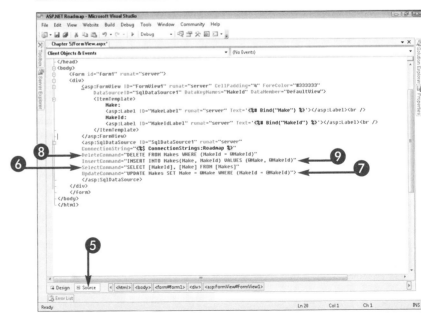

⑩ Open the Properties window for the FormView.

⑪ Set the AllowPaging property to True.

⑫ Set the Pager Mode to Numeric.

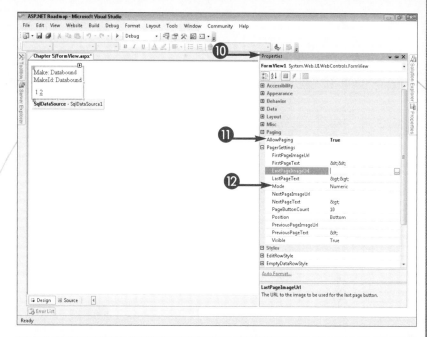

⑬ Open the page in a browser.

● The records appear one at a time on the page with the page numbers listed below.

Apply It

To enable paging through records set AllowPaging to True. This automatically displays a pager at the bottom of the FormView that allows the user to scroll through the records. There are several properties available to format the way the Pager is displayed, or you can create a custom template with the PagerTemplate.

You may add any combinations of Web controls and HTML you want in the PagerTemplate. Any Button control that posts back to the server should have the CommandName and CommandArgument defined. The CommandName should be set to Page, while the CommandArgument may be anything you need.

Define LinkButtons for a Simple Custom Pager:

```
<PagerTemplate>
    <asp:LinkButton ID="LinkButton1" runat="server"
    CommandArgument="Prev" CommandName="Page">< Prev</asp:LinkButton>
    <asp:LinkButton ID="LinkButton2" runat="server" CommandArgument="Next"
    CommandName="Page" Height="20px">Next ></asp:LinkButton>
</PagerTemplate>
```

Edit and Insert a Record with the FormView

The `FormView` has the ability to let the user insert new records or edit existing records. If you are using a `DataSourceControl` you must have the corresponding `Update` and `Insert` commands defined, as well as the corresponding parameters. You will also need to have the `DataKeyNames` value defined in the `FormView` control or you will experience errors.

The `FormView`'s `ItemTemplate` needs to have a `Button` control added to invoke the `Edit` mode. This button can be any control that inherits from `Button`. Set the `CommandName` property to Edit in order for the update interface to be displayed for the record. This causes the `ModeChanging` event to fire and the `EventArgs` parameter will have a `NewMode` value of `Edit`. The `EditItemTemplate` is rendered, and it should contain appropriate controls defined such as `TextBoxes` and `Checkboxes` displayed for each field. It should also

contain `Update` and `Cancel` buttons. They may be set to a regular `Button`, a `LinkButton`, or an `ImageButton`. Their `CommandName` arguments should be set to `Update` and `Cancel`, respectively. Choosing the `Update` button causes the `Update` command to execute with the entered changes. Selecting the `Cancel` button causes the control to revert to read-only mode, and no changes are applied.

Similarly, adding a `Button` with the new `CommandName` causes the `InsertItemTemplate` to be displayed. This causes the `ModeChanging` event to fire and the `EventArgs` parameter will have a `NewMode` value of `Insert`. When the user selects the `New` button the same interface is displayed, which should resemble the `EditItemTemplate`, except this time with empty controls. After entering the data for the new record the user can click Insert to add the new record to the database. He or she can click Cancel to cancel the operation.

Edit and Insert a Record with the FormView

① Open a Web page with a bound `FormView`.

② Add an `EditItemTemplate` to the `FormView`.

③ Add controls to collect the appropriate values from the user.

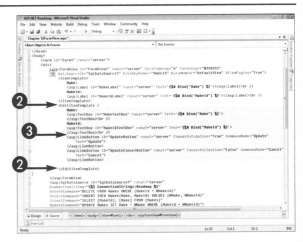

④ Add an `InsertItemTemplate` to the `FormView`.

⑤ Add controls to collect the appropriate values from the user.

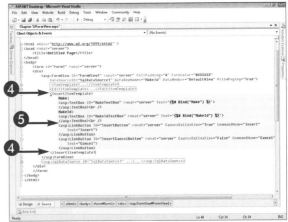

6 Add a `LinkButton` to the `ItemTemplate` to invoke Insert mode.

7 Add a `LinkButton` to the `ItemTemplate` to invoke Edit mode.

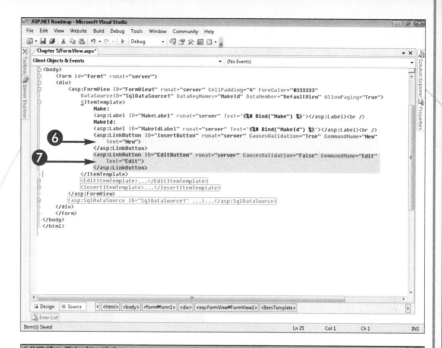

8 Open the page in a browser.

9 Click Edit for one of the records.

10 Type new values for the record.

11 Click Update to apply the changes.

The updates are displayed in the FormView.

Apply It

To add the ability to delete a record from the database, you will need to define a `Button` control with its `CommandName` set to `Delete`. This causes the `ItemDeleting` event to fire. If you are using a `DataSourceControl`, you need to set the `DeleteCommand` to a valid delete query. If you are using a custom business object or using custom code to process the delete request, you can do so in the `ItemDeleting` event handler.

It is also a good idea to prompt the user to confirm the request to delete a record before it is cleared from the database. This can be done by adding some simple JavaScript to the button's `OnClientClick` property.

Add a Confirmation Dialog to the Delete Button:

```
<asp:LinkButton
  id="lnkDelete"
  Text="Delete Make"
  CommandName="Delete"
  OnClientClick="return confirm('Really, Do you want to delete this Make?');"
  Runat="server" />
```

Introduction to the Membership Provider

Validating users to a Web site is a common need for just about every modern Web site. The ASP.NET Membership provider offers a built-in set of classes or interfaces to store user credentials and provide a reasonably secure means to authenticate users. The membership provider offers a set of classes you can manually use to manage user authentication, credentials and role membership, or utilize a set of Web controls built into the ASP.NET 2.0 framework.

A benefit of using the provider model is it allows you to create a custom provider to manage membership for your site based on an existing user system or custom data store. This means you can create your Web application and change the way you store and manage user accounts and authentication without having to change any code in your application. The provider model provides an abstracted architecture that defines a set of base classes and method signatures that are replicated in any custom provider classes. Custom providers are activated by changing the configuration settings in the site's web.config file.

ASP.NET 2.0 ships with two membership providers — one for SQL Server and a second for Active Directory. A custom provider implements the membership provider methods, but manages the logic to interact with a different data store, such as Oracle or a custom data schema.

Custom Membership Providers

The built-in membership providers can be extended or completely bypassed for a custom provider. You implement a custom provider by configuring the site to use the custom provider in the web.config file. After you configure the custom provider, the membership classes implement the custom version instead of the previous provider. This makes it easy to write your application and change the provider used to manage user accounts and authentication.

A custom membership provider must have a membership class that inherits and implements member methods of the `MemberShipProvider` class. These include properties and methods to manage password rules, credentials, and authentication routines. You can quickly have Visual Studio create empty stubs for the required methods and properties by defining your membership class inheriting from the `MemberShipProvider` abstract and pressing Enter at the end of the inherits line. Visual Studio automatically creates the stubs for you and you can then begin to write your custom code for each member.

Custom members of your membership provider can be invoked through the `Provider` or `Providers` property of the `Membership` class. The way to code this command is to cast the `Membership.Provider` to an instance of your custom class, for example:

```
Dim p As MyCustomProvider = CType
(Membership.Provider, MyCustomProvider)

dim cui as MyCustomUserInfo =
p.GetCustomUserInfo(username)
```

The membership provider allows you to define an application name in the configuration section. This allows you to use the same membership data store, such as an SQL database, for multiple applications. Each entry in the database will be associated with the application that stored the record. An example of this is a Web portal that provides multiple sites from one SQL database. The membership provider being used should utilize this setting automatically, and there is no need to pass this parameter in any of the calls you make to the Membership system. Make sure you have the same application name configured in both the Membership and role provider sections of your web.config file or you will run into problems with duplicate entries.

ASP.NET Membership Classes and Interfaces

There are several supporting classes available with the membership provider that provide supporting functionality. The `MembershipProviderCollection` manages a collection of all the available providers. The `MembershipUser Collection` stores references to `MembershipUser` objects. The `MembershipCreateStatus` provides descriptive values for success or failure when creating a new membership user.

The `MembershipCreateUserException` defines the exception thrown if a user cannot be created. A `Membership CreateStatus` enumeration value describing the reason for the exception is available through the `StatusCode` property. The `MembershipPasswordFormat` specifies the possible password storage formats used by the membership providers included with ASP.NET (Clear, Hashed, Encrypted).

The Membership Class

The Membership class acts as the global manager of the membership provider system. It provides the core methods any ASP.NET application can call to interact with the membership data store: SQL Server, for example.

METHOD	DESCRIPTION
CreateUser	Creates a new user
DeleteUser	Deletes a user
UpdateUser	Updates a user with new information
GetAllUsers	Returns a list of users
FindUsersByEmail	Finds a user by name or e-mail
ValidateUser	Validates (authenticates) a user
GetNumberOfUsersOnline	Gets the number of users online
FindUsersByName	Searches for users by username
EnablePasswordRetrieval	Indicates if password retrieval is enabled
EnablePasswordReset	Indicates is password reset is enabled

The MembershipUser Class

The MembershipUser class encapsulates the properties that define a site member and several shared utility methods to manage specific aspects of a member. The ChangePassword method allows the member's password to be changed to a new value. The GetPassword method returns the member's password. The ResetPassword changes the password to a randomly generated password. The Unlock method unlocks a user that has violated the site's invalid login attempt rules.

METHOD	DESCRIPTION
GetPassword	Gets the user's password
ChangePassword	Changes the password
IsOnline	Determines whether the user is online
IsApproved	Determines whether the user can be authenticated
LastActivityDate	Returns the date for last activity, login, and password change
UnLockUser	Unlocks a user
ResetPassword	Resets the user's password

The SQLMembershipProvider Class

The SQLMembershipProvider class encapsulates the functionality of a membership provider to work with a back-end SQL Server database. The provider depends on having a pre-defined table structure and set of stored procedures. Fortunately the aspnet_sql utility application provides a simple wizard to set these up for developers.

The needed stored procedures along with the SQLMembershipProvider methods and properties provide the needed support to ensure proper variable validation and return values. Since the provider is built on SQL Server the stored procedures can be customized to meet your particular needs.

The ActiveMembershipProvider Class

The ActiveMembershipProvider class defines how the membership provider interacts with the Active Directory system. You should take care to check the permissions for the account being used by ASP.NET that is has proper permissions to interact with the Active Directory to retrieve and change values for accounts. Some membership provider methods, such as GetNumberOfUserOnline and GetPassword are not supported by the ActiveMembershipProvider.

Configure the ASP.NET Membership Provider

The membership provider in ASP.NET is configured in the application's web.config file or on the server in the machine.config. The Membership element in the System.Web section of the config file is where the membership provider settings for an application can be customized. You can do this by either manually editing the config file or using the Web Site Administration tool.

The Web Site Administration tool is a Web interface to manage common tasks in the web.config file. If you do not have Visual Studio or feel a little intimidated editing XML configuration settings by hand, try this tool first. The Web Site Administration tool can be accessed by clicking the Configuration button at the top of the Solution Explorer window. You must be logged in with Read/Write permissions on the web.config file for the site.

The membership provider allows you to configure several settings in the membership section of the config file. The membership section is a child section of the system.web section. You can set the defaultProvider and the userIsOnlineTimeWindow settings at the top level. Inside the membership section you can add additional providers in the providers child section. Here you can clear, remove, and add providers as you would with any web.config section.

Inside the add tag you can set each of the membership provider attributes that need to be set for the specific provider. These include settings for password requirements, unique e-mail, and application name. Each provider type may have custom attributes that can be defined, so be sure to check with the documentation of the provider to see what is available and required. For example, the SQL Membership provider also allows a connectionstring property.

Configure the ASP.NET Membership Provider

① Open the Web site's web.config file.

② Add a membership element to the system.web section.

③ Add a providers element to the membership section.

④ Add a remove element with the name attribute of AspNetSQLMembershipProvider.

⑤ Add an add element to the providers section.

⑥ Set the Name attribute to RoadmapMembershipProvider.

⑦ Set the type to System.Web.Security.SQLMembership Provider with the corresponding assembly identifiers.

Note: *When declaring an assembly or library type there can be quite a few attributes to add. It is a good idea to find an example and copy it for reference.*

⑧ Configure the remaining membership provider attributes according to your desired setup.

⑨ Set the defaultProvider attribute of the membership element to RoadmapMembershipProvider.

⑩ Set the userIsOnlineTimeWindow attribute to 15.

The membership provider is now configured to use the custom settings.

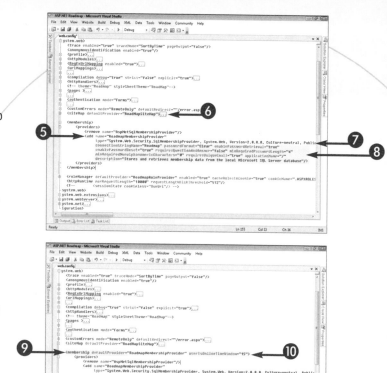

Most ASP.NET Web sites use Forms authentication to verify user credentials. Forms authentication works with the membership service, but must be configured in the config file as well. Inside the system.web section, a site needs to have an authentication section with the mode set to Forms. Other options are Passport, Windows, and None. This is the minimum needed to configure the site to use the membership service for authentication.

The authentication section can have another child section — forms. This section has several possible attributes including name, loginURL, protection, timeout, path, requireSSL, and sliding expiration. The name specifies the cookie name used for authentication. The loginURL specifies the page users are directed to if they are not authenticated for the requested page.

The timeout attribute specifies the amount of minutes in which a user's session expires; the default is 30 minutes. If you use the slidingexpiration setting, a user's session timeout resets each time he or she requests a new page. In ASP.NET 1.0 the default slidingexpiration setting was True, but for 2.0 its default is False. This is a common mistake many 2.0 sites make when setting up authentication.

Configure the SQLMembership Provider

Before you can use the SQL Membership provider in your Web site, its SQL Server database must be configured to use the membership provider, meaning it needs to have the proper tables, stored procedures, and other required objects and permissions set. The easiest way to do this is to run the ASP.NET SQL Server Setup Wizard, aspnet_regsql.exe. This is actually a command-line tool. When you execute it without any command-line switches it launches a visual wizard that steps you through the setup process to add the SQL membership provider tables and accompanying stored procedures. It is located in the %WINDOWS%\Microsoft.NET\Framework\<Version> folder.

The wizard guides you through five screens, gathering input from you to connect to the target database and determining if you want to add the provider or remove it. The wizard's third screen requires you to enter the

connection information to the SQL Server and the database you want to configure. The second screen can be used to indicate whether you want to remove the membership system from an existing database. The remaining screens are either informational or conformational and require no direct input.

The wizard actually runs an SQL script — %WINDOWS%\Microsoft.NET\Framework\<Version>\InstallCommon.sql — with a slight modification. By default, this script attempts to install the membership system in a database by the name of aspnetdb. The wizard replaces the name of the database to match the one being configured.

The InstallCommon.sql script installs the entire membership system, including Membership, Roles, Personalization, and so on. There are more specific scripts available in the same folder that install individual pieces of the membership-related services. If the database specified in the script does not exist, the script creates the database.

Configure the SQLMembership Provider

① Open the aspnet_regsql utility from the command-line utlity.

② Click the Configure SQL Server for application services option.

③ Click Next.

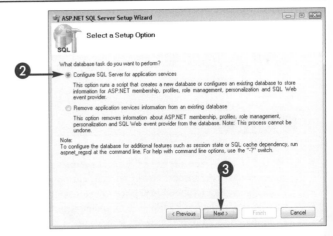

④ Enter the Name or Address of the SQL server you wish to configure.

Note: *If your server requires SQL server authentication you need to select that radio button and enter your credentials.*

⑤ Enter the Database name.

⑥ Click Next.

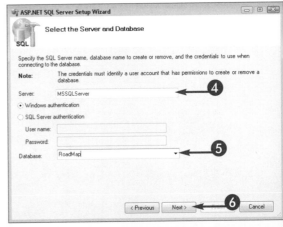

7 Verify your settings are correct.

8 Click Next when the connections settings are correct.

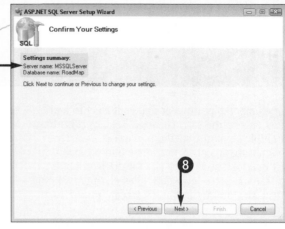

9 After the SQL Server Setup Wizard is complete, click the Finish button.

This `aspnet_regsql.exe` utility may also be used to configure several other aspects of ASP.NET in an SQL server. You can install any of these options from the command line by utilizing switches on the utility. For a complete list, run the utility with the -? Option. The utility may be used to install or remove the following services: Membership, Roles, Profiles, Personalization, SQL Dependencies, and SQL Web Event Provider.

A SQL dependency is a relationship between the Web application and data in the database. Typically they are used in conjunction with cached data, such as a product catalog, that does not change very often. The dependency alerts the application there is a new record in the table and if configured to do so, deletes the cached records forcing an update with the new records.

Configure an SQL Dependency for a Site Map:
```
aspnet_regsql -S localhost -E -d SiteMapDatabase -ed
aspnet_regsql -S localhost -E -d SiteMapDatabase -t SiteMap -et
```

Add a User

The membership provider makes it easy to add a new user to the site. The `Membership` class has a multiple signature method, `CreateUser`. The minimal signature accepts a username and password and the largest overload accepts values for the username, password, e-mail, secret question, answer, approval, and provideruser key, and returns a `MembershipUser` and the `MembershipCreateStatus`.

The methods available in the `MembershipUser` class allow you to manage the user's password: `ChangePassword`, `ResetPassword`, and `GetPassword`. Another method unlocks a user's account that has been locked by too many invalid login attempts.

If there is a problem creating a new user with the `CreateUser` method, a `MembershipCreateUser Exception` is thrown. Check the `StatusCode` property to determine why the user account could not be created. The `StatusCode` is a `MemberShipCreateUserStatus` enumeration with one of the following values: `InvalidUserName`, `InvalidPassword`, `InvalidEmail`, `InvalidQuestion`, `InvalidAnswer`, `DuplicateEmail`, `DuplicateUserName`, or `UserRejected`, along with a few others related to the provider itself. You can use this value to inform the user what the problem is so that he or she can take the appropriate action to enter the correct criteria.

The membership provider is flexible and can be configured in the site's web.config file to enforce site-specific rules regarding user credentials. Some of the options include requiring a question and answer, password strength, account locking rules, and security features to guard against brute force attacks.

You can also configure if the users can retrieve their passwords or must have them reset. The default settings for the default membership provider are configured in the machine.config file, but can be overridden in the site's web.config file.

Add a User

1. Create a new Web page.

2. Add a TextBox to collect the Username.

3. Add a TextBox to collect the password, and set the `TextMode` property to password.

4. Add a TextBox to collect the user's e-mail address.

5. Add a Submit button.

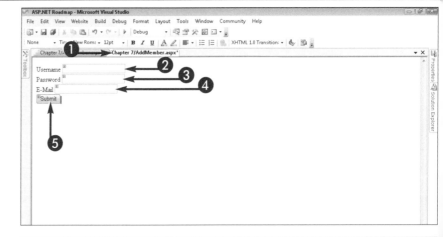

6. Double-click the Button to add a click event handler.

7. Add code to create a new user.

Note: *The Try Catch statement catches a MembershipCreate UserException.*

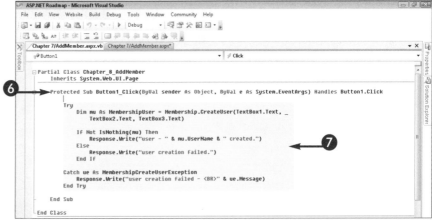

8 Open the page in a browser.

9 Type values in the text boxes to define a new user.

10 Click Submit to create the user.

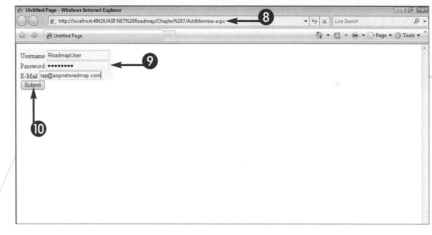

11 View the User created confirmation message.

Note: *If there is an exception creating the user, an error appears at the top of the page.*

Apply It

Enforcing strong passwords is a good security practice even for the smallest organizations. The membership provider provides a configurable setting to apply a RegularExpression to be used to enforce password strength. This can be set through the passwordStrengthRegularExpression attribute of the Add element that defines a membership provider.

Additional attributes may be set to enforce rules to require stronger passwords; for example, MinRequiredPasswordLength and MinRequiredNonAlphanumericCharacters. Both of these attributes are self-explanatory: they require a minimum number of characters for a password and a minimum number of non-alphanumeric characters, such as %, #, & and !, to form a password.

Configure the Membership Provider:

```
<providers>
 <add name="SqlProvider"
 type="System.Web.Security.SqlMembershipProvider"
 connectionStringName="SqlServices"
 requiresQuestionAndAnswer="true"
 minRequiredNonalphanumericCharacters="1"/>
</providers>
```

Update a User

A user account can be updated by changing the values of the `MemberShipUser` object representing the user and submitting that to the `Membership.UpdateUser` method. You can either create an entirely new `MemberShipUser` object or modify one you retrieved for an existing member.

You can update a select number of properties of the `MemberShipUser` class. You can update the `Comment`, `Email`, `IsApproved`, `LastActivityDate`, or `LastLoginDate`. The `Email` property is required and must be unique if the `RequiresUniqueEmail` attribute of the membership provider is set to true.

To update a member's password call the `ChangePassword` method and configure the site to allow password changes. You can also call the `ResetPassword` method to have the member's password set to a new, automatically generated password.

The `UpdateUser` method can throw various exceptions, depending on the provider being used. All can throw an `ArgumentNullException` when the `UserInfo` being passed is null or the e-mail address is empty and the `RequiresUniqueEmail` is set to true.

The `SQLMembershipProvider` may throw an `ArgumentException` if the `UserName` property is an empty string, contains a comma, or is longer than 256 characters. Another cause for this exception would be the e-mail being longer than 256 characters. A `ProviderException` may be thrown if the username does not exist in the database or if the e-mail address exists when the `RequiresUniqueEmail` is true.

The `ActiveDirectoryMembershipProvider` may also throw an `InvalidOperationException` if the `UpdateUser` method is called before the provider is initialized. The `ActiveDirectoryMembership Provider` can use either Active Directory or ADAM, the lightweight version of Active Directory.

Update a User

1. Create a new Web page.

2. Add a TextBox for the Username.

3. Add a TextBox for the New E-Mail address.

4. Add a Submit button.

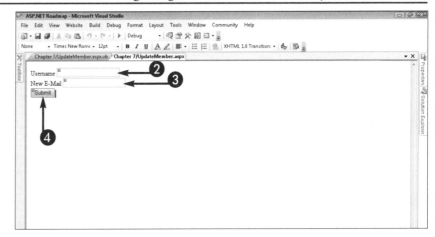

5. Double-click the Submit button to add a click event handler.

6. Add code to update the user's e-mail address.

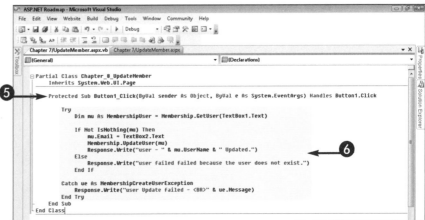

152

7 Open the page in a browser.

8 Type values to identify the user and the new e-mail address.

9 Click Submit.

● View the user update confirmation message.

Apply It

When you create a custom membership provider you may have more fields or properties that can be updated. You must create your own version of a `MemberShip` user to manage any custom data fields in your custom system. You must support the base `UpdateUser` method, but you can declare your own overload to perform your custom update routine. You may choose to either support updates based on the base `MemberShipUser` object or simply throw a `NotSupportedException`.

Custom Version of UpdateUser:

```
Public Overrides Sub UpdateUser(ByVal user As System.Web.Security.MembershipUser)
 Throw New NotSupportedException("Base Membership Method, UpdateUser, Not supported. Please
pass the ExMemberShipUser")
End Sub

Public Overloads Sub UpdateUser(ByVal user As ExMembershipUser)
 'process User Update
End Sub
```

Delete a User

Eventually a user will need to be removed from the site's membership system. A site `Member` may be deleted by calling the `Membership.DeleteUser` method. This method has two overloads. The first just accepts the `UserName` and the second accepts the `Username` and a Boolean indicating if any related data, such as role membership and personalization data, should also be removed from the database. If the delete operation is successful the method returns true; otherwise it returns false.

Depending on how your application is architected you should also make an effort to clean up any legacy, nonmembership, or personalization data associated with this user from the database. If you use the `SQLMember ShipProvider` you can modify the `aspnet_Users_ DeleteUser` stored procedure to add your custom data cleanup routines. This method only deletes users for the application specified in the configured `applicationName`.

If you use the `ActiveDirectoryMembershipProvider` you must have the provider initialized for your application before calling the `DeleteUser` or any other `Membership` methods. If you do not have it initialized, an `InvalidOperationException` is thrown. If there is an error deleting the user, a `COMException` is thrown by the `ActiveDirectoryMembershipProvider`.

Also, note that the username cannot contain a backslash when using Active Directory. The site's user account also needs explicit permission to delete user accounts in the Active Directory for the account being used by the Web site.

The `DeleteUser` method throws an `ArgumentException` if the username provided is empty or contains a comma. It throws an `ArgumentNullException` if the username is a null reference. Always wrap a call to the `DeleteUser` method in a try catch statement and handle the errors appropriately.

Delete a User

① Create a new Web page.

② Add a TextBox to collect the username.

③ Add a Delete button.

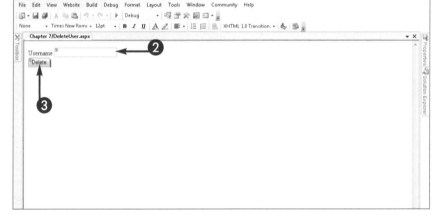

④ Double-click the Delete button to create a click event handler.

⑤ Add code to delete a user.

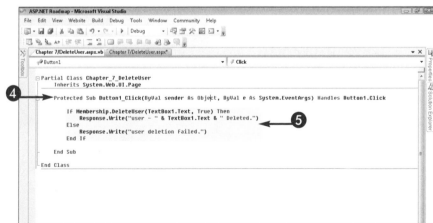

6 Open the Page in a browser.

7 Type the username to delete.

8 Click Delete.

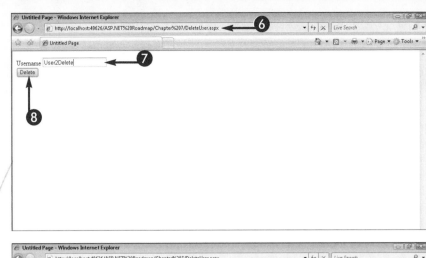

● View the User delete confirmation message.

Apply It

The `SQLMembershipProvider` calls the `aspnet_Users_DeleteUser` stored procedure under the hood. This stored procedure takes four parameters: `ApplicationName`, `UserName`, `TablesToDeleteFrom`, and `NumTablesDeletedFrom` as an `OUTPUT` parameter. The `TablesToDeleteFrom` parameter is an integer that actually represents a bitwise operator that tells the procedure from which tables to delete records. You can use this knowledge to create your own custom delete user method that deletes data from the tables you specify.

Delete the User's Membership and Role Data:
```
Public function DeleteUserFromMembership(UserName as String) as Boolean
 Dim TablesToDeleteFrom as Integer = 1 & 2
 'Call the aspnet_Users_DeleteUser procedure.
 'Use your own SQL connectivity routines to call the procedure.
 '
 '
 '
 Return true
End function
```

Retrieve a User Account

I ndividual user profiles can be retrieved through one of the various overloaded GetUser methods. There are six overloads of the GetUser method that return the currently logged-on user or a user specified by either a special key (ProviderKey) or a username.

The GetUser method returns a MemberShipUser object that represents the user's profile. If there is no user matching the username or ProviderKey it returns null. You should always check to see if the returned MemberShipUser object is null before doing any sort of processing of the MemberShipUser object.

There are two types of Exceptions that can be thrown in the GetUser method: ArgumentNullException and ArgumentException. An ArgumentNullException is thrown when the ProviderKey or username provided is null. The ArgumentException is thrown when the ProviderKey is not a Guid. When you are using the

ActiveDirectoryMembershipProvider the GetUser method can also throw an InvalidOperation Exception if the method is called before the provider is initialized.

The ActiveDirectoryMembershipProvider performs its search from the point specified in the Active Directory connection string. An Active Directory connection string designates the point to start any queries. The Active Directory connection string is specified in the ConnectionStrings element of the web.config file.

There is an optional argument to the GetUser method, userIsOnline, which is a Boolean that indicates the user is currently online if true. This causes the last-activity value to be updated in the user's profile; it also causes the GetNumberOfUsersOnline to be stay updated. Of course, you will want to make sure the user is online before passing a true value to this method.

Retrieve a User Account

1. Create a new Web page.

2. Add a TextBox to collect the username.

3. Add a Retrieve button.

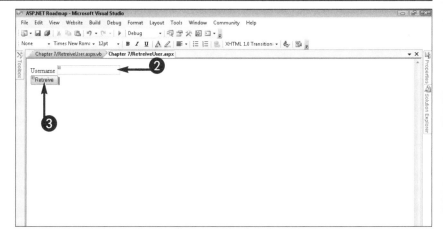

4. Double-Click the Retrieve button to create a click event handler.

5. Add code to retrieve a user.

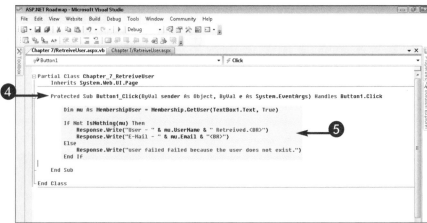

6️⃣ Open the Page in a browser.

7️⃣ Type the username you want to retrieve.

8️⃣ Click Retrieve.

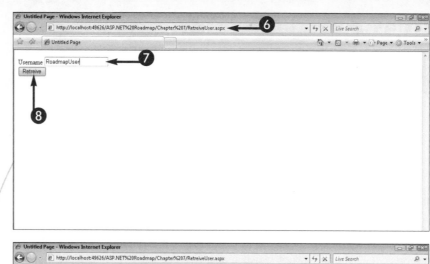

● The retrieved user information appears.

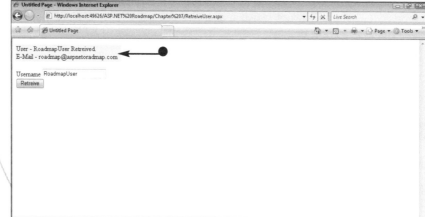

Apply It

The standard `MemberShipUser` object contains some basic information about the user. Most sites, however, need more information associated with the user account. To do this, a good practice is to create your own user class and apply the `MemberShipUser` properties to your class. You can create your own overloaded method that retrieves the membership information from the core `GetUser` method and also retrieves any site-specific data.

Custom User Retrieval Method:
```
Public Function GetMyCustomUser(ByVal username As String) As MyCustomUser
 Dim mu As MembershipUser = Membership.GetUser(TextBox1.Text, True)
 If Not IsNothing(mu) Then
 Dim mcu As New MyCustomUser
 mcu.UserName = mu.UserName
 mcu.Email = mu.Email
 mcu.CurrentShoppingCart = GetUserCartCollection(username)
 mcu.OrderHistory = GetUserOrderHistory(username)
 Return mcu
 Else
 Throw New Exception("The User does not exist.")
 End If
 Return Nothing
End Function
```

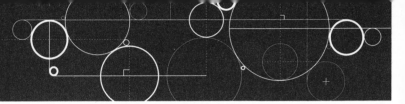

A list of site members can be retrieved by calling the `Member.GetAllUsers` method. This method has two overloads. The first takes no parameters and returns a `MembershipUserCollection` for every member in the site. The second method takes three parameters: `pageindex`, `pageSize`, and `totalRecords`, which is an output parameter.

A `MembershipUserCollection` is a collection of `MembershipUsers` and implements `ICollection` and `IEnumerable`. The `MembershipUserCollection` can be bound to any of the data or list controls such as a `DataList` or `CheckBoxList`. Because it is a collection of `MembershipUser` objects, you can explicitly bind properties such as username to fields or controls in the Data or List controls.

If the site is configured to allow nonunique e-mail addresses, a collection of `MemberShipUser` objects can be obtained by calling the `FindUsersByEmail` method. This method accepts four parameters — `emailToMatch`, `pageIndex`, `pageSize`, and `totalRecords` — as an output variable. The `emailToMatch` parameter is the e-mail address to perform the search. The `pageIndex` and `pageSize` indicate the subset and size of the subset of records to return, which helps when there is a large number of records in the result set. The `totalRecords` parameter actually returns the number of records returned.

Similarly, you can also retrieve a collection of users with the same username. While this may not be a good idea to allow on your site, some sites do allow this as long as the password and/or other values for the profile are unique. The `FindUsersByName` method also accepts the same parameters, except the `emailToMatch` is now `usernameToMatch`. Unfortunately, this method does not allow you to do a wildcard search for a username, so you cannot try to search for users based on a partial match.

Retrieve a List of Users

① Create a new Web page.

② Add a GridView to the page.

③ Click the Smart Tag button and select one of the Auto Format options from the menu.

④ In the Auto Format dialog box, select a scheme.

⑤ Click Apply.

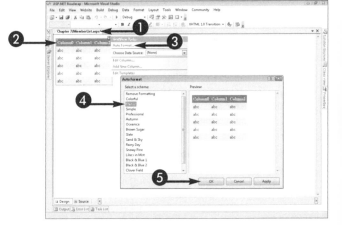

⑥ Switch to Source view.

⑦ Add a `TemplateField` to the GridView.

⑧ Add a `Literal` control to the `ItemTemplate`.

⑨ Set the `HeaderText` of the Field to `User Name`.

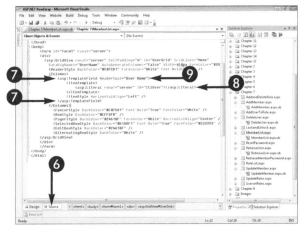

⑩ Switch to code-behind.

⑪ Add code to bind the Membership Users to the GridView.

⑫ Add a RowDataBound event handler to bind the UserName to the Literal control.

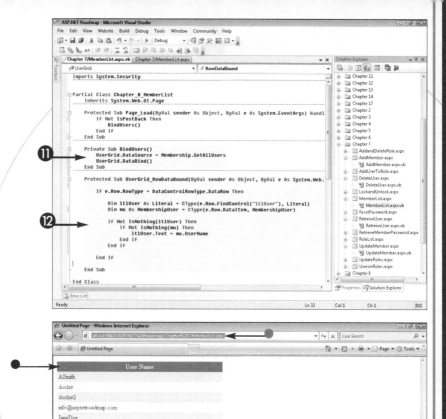

⑬ Open the page in a browser.

● A list of Usernames for the site appears.

The list of users on a site can become quite lengthy. The `RoleProvider` has a `GetUsersInRole` method that returns a list of usernames that belong to the supplied Role.

```
Dim sUser() as string = Roles.GetUsersInRole(sRole)
```

You can also create custom methods and stored procedures to return a smaller subset of users. For example, you can create a custom stored procedure that returns only usernames starting with a letter of the alphabet. Because the `aspnet_Membership_GetAllUsers` source is accessible, it can be used as a model for the custom procedure, `aspnet_Membership_GetAllUsersByLetter`.

Create a Custom Version of GetAllUsers Stored Procedure:
```
CREATE PROCEDURE dbo.aspnet_Membership_GetAllUsersByLetter
  @ApplicationName     nvarchar(256),
  @StartLetter     char(1),
  @PageIndex         int,
  @PageSize          int
AS
BEGIN
```

Add This Line to the Where Clause:
```
AND u.UserName like @StartLetter + '%'
```

Reset a Password

Programmatically resetting a lost password involves a little more programming than just a single method call. First, you must enable password resets in the web.config file. You can then reset the user's password to a new, randomly generated value by calling `Membership.ResetPassword`. This method has two overloads. The first has an empty set of parameters, while the second passes the password question and answer value.

If the Web site is not configured to allow password resets, then a `NotSupportedException` is thrown by the provider. You can configure the `PasswordReset` setting in the web.config file by setting the `enablePasswordReset` attribute of the membership provider definition to True. You can also control if the `Question` and `Answer` check is enabled in the web.config file by setting the `requiresQuestionAndAnswer` attribute.

The password created by the `ResetPassword` method may not meet the criteria outlined by the regular expression in the `PasswordStrengthRegularExpression` property. It will meet the criteria established by the `MinRequired PasswordLength` and `MinRequiredNonAlphanumeric Characters` properties defined in the provider's configuration.

The password is generated by the private method `GeneratePassword` to get the actual password. This method is actually part of the `Membership` class and can be used or overridden by any custom membership provider classes. It uses the `RNGCryptoServiceProvider` class to get a random set of bytes and converts them into a character string. If the user supplies a bad answer or the user account is currently locked the `Membership PasswordException` is thrown.

After the new password is defined and passes all the validation checks it is stored in the membership database as the user's password. The method finally returns the new password so you can either display it or send it to the user.

Reset a Password

① Create a new Web page.

② Add a TextBox to collect the Username.

③ Add a TextBox to collect the old password, and set the `TextMode` property to password.

④ Add a TextBox to collect the new password, and set the `TextMode` property to password.

⑤ Add a Submit button.

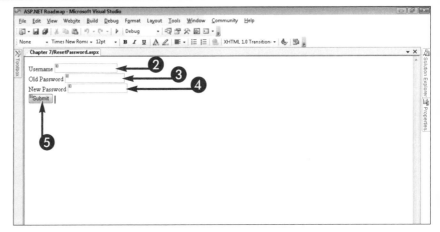

⑥ Double-click the button to add a click event handler.

⑦ Add code to validate that each of the TextBoxes has content.

⑧ Add code to get the `MemberShipUser` object for the designated Username.

⑨ Call the `ChangePassword` method on the `MemberShipUser` object.

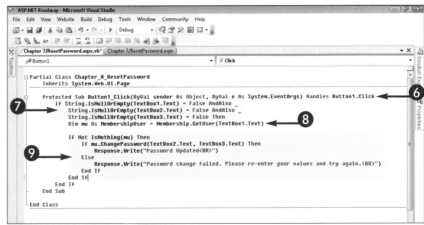

10 Open the page in a browser.

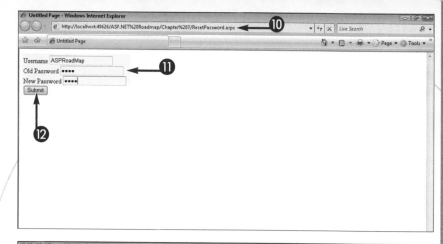

11 Type appropriate values in each of the TextBoxes.

12 Click Submit.

- A message appears indicating the password change was successful.

Apply It

Sometimes you want to give users the ability to reset their own passwords, but they may not know their existing passwords. Many sites offer users unique ways to verify their identities, which enables them to reset their passwords. If you want to control what the new password value is, you can call the ChangePassword method and pass it the result of the ResetPassword method and the new password.

Directly Change the Password to a Known Value:

```
Try
 If mu.ChangePassword(mu.ResetPassword(), TextBox3.Text) Then
 Response.Write("Password Updated<BR>")
 Else
 Response.Write("Password change failed. Please re-enter your values and try again.<BR>")
 End If
Catch empe As MembershipPasswordException
 Response.Write("There is a problem updating your password<BR>")
End Try
```

Retrieve a User Password

Users often forget their username and password for a site because they have so many. Most sites provide a mechanism for users to retrieve their passwords via e-mail or even, rarely, through the browser. Many sites automatically reset passwords before sending it to users and require them to reset it the first time they authenticate.

Enabling users to retrieve their passwords involves several steps. First, enable password retrieval in the web.config file. Then designate if the user is required to type a matching question and answer combination. These settings are made by configuring the enablePassword Retrieval and requiresQuestionAndAnswer attributes of the membership provider element of the web.config file. The Membership object has a read-only EnablePasswordRetrieval property and Requires QuestionAndAnswer property that returns the value of each corresponding setting, either true or false.

After a site is configured, members' passwords can be retrieved by calling the Membership.GetPassword method. You should call the Membership.Enable PasswordRetrieval method to ensure password retrieval is enabled. The GetPassword method takes two parameters: the username and the security question answer.

If the password answer is incorrect, a MembershipPasswordException is thrown by the MembershipProvider. If the site does not require a question and answer combination you can simply type an empty string for that parameter.

The GetPassword method returns the user's password. The MembershipProvider has a private method, UnEncode Password, which first checks to see if the password is stored in a hashed format. If the passwordFormat attribute is set to Hashed the GetPassword method throws an exception. You cannot return hashed passwords through the membership provider.

Retrieve a User Password

① Create a new Web page.

② Add a TextBox to collect the username.

③ Add a Submit button.

④ Double-click the button to add a click event handler.

⑤ Add code to get the MemberShipUser object for the designated Username.

⑥ Create an If statement to verify the MemberShipUser object was retrieved and password retrieval is enabled.

⑦ Add code to echo the password to the browser or display an unavailable message.

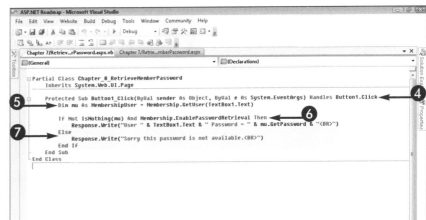

Note: Use caution when passing passwords in plain text across the Internet.

8 Open the page in a browser.

9 Type the Username in the TextBox.

10 Click Submit.

● A password retrieval message appears.

Identity theft has become a common concern for many people and often leads to hesitancy to provide personal information to any online presence. Microsoft released `CardSpace` with Windows Vista and as an add-on to Windows XP to provide a way for users to maintain their identity either with self-issued cards or cards from third-party authentication services.

CardSpace Object Tag for the User to Select:

```
<button type="submit">Click here to sign in with your Information Card</button>
<object type="application/x-informationcard" name="xmlToken">
 <param name="tokenType" value="urn:oasis:names:tc:SAML:1.0:assertion" />
 <param name="requiredClaims" value="http://schemas.xmlsoap.org/ws/2005/05/identity/claims/
givenname http://schemas.xmlsoap.org/ws/2005/05/identity/claims/surname http://schemas
.xmlsoap.org/ws/2005/05/identity/claims/emailaddress http://schemas.xmlsoap.org/ws/2005/
05/identity/claims/privatepersonalidentifier" />
</object>
```

Decrypting a CardSpace Token:

```
Dim xmlToken As String
xmlToken = Request.Params("xmlToken")
If xmlToken = Nothing Or xmlToken.Equals("") Then
 ShowError("Token presented was null")
 Else
 Dim token As Token = New Token(xmlToken)
 email.Text = token.Claims(ClaimTypes.Email)
 uid.Text = token.UniqueID
End If
```

Get the Number of Users Online

Tracking the number of users currently using a Web site is either an interesting little fact to publish on the site or a useful piece of information for a site owner to evaluate the usefulness of the site. One problem with tracking the number of users online is the Web is a stateless medium, meaning a request for a page or resource on the site by a visitor is an instantaneous event and there is no true way to know how long a person stays on the site without some sort of client-side code that is executed when the user navigates away or closes the browser. Another problem occurs when a user "abandons" the computer and leaves the browser on the same URL for hours or even days at a time.

To combat this problem, the membership provider provides a `LastActivityDate` property for each member that is refreshed each time he or she makes a request. The membership provider `GetNumberOfUsersOnline`

method uses the `LastActivityDate` to return the number of users that have been active on the site in the timeframe specified in the `UserIsOnlineTimeWindow`. The `UserIsOnlineTimeWindow` property is defined in the provider's definition section of the web.config file. By default, it is 15 minutes in length. Under the hood, the SQLMembership provider calls the `aspnet_Membership_GetNumberOfUsersOnline` stored procedure to return the number of users on the Web site. This stored procedure automatically returns the number of users within the allowed timeframe for the application based on the current time on the Web server.

The `LastActivityDate` for a user is updated by calling the `GetUser` method or when the `ValidateUser` method is called. You can determine if a user is currently online by calling the `IsOnline` property of the `MembershipUser` object. You should also note the `ActiveDirectoryMembershipProvider` does not support this method.

Get the Number of Users Online

① Create a new Web page.

② Add a `Label` control to the page.

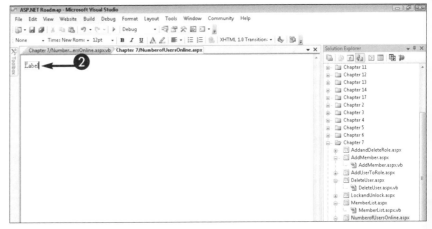

③ Switch to the code-behind page.

④ Add a `Page_Load` event handler.

⑤ Add code to display the number of users currently on the Web site.

You can open the page in a browser to see the current number of users displayed on the site.

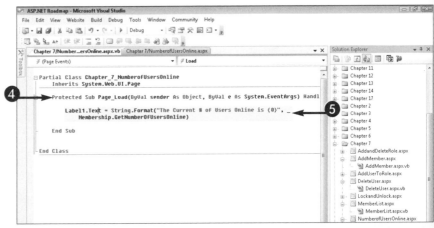

Lock and Unlock a User Account

A user may lock an account by attempting too many invalid login attempts within the specified time period. This means the user's account is completely disabled. A user may also become locked out if he or she types the wrong answer to the question and answer challenge according to the same guidelines. Even an authenticated user may lock his or her account out during a password reset attempt if the answers are not properly supplied. Because this is completely configurable, the attempts and timeframe are up to you and your security policy. The default settings for this feature are five failed attempts in ten minutes. You may completely disable this security feature in the configuration file as well.

You can customize the settings that control when a bad user is locked out of an account in the `add` element of the membership provider. You can set the `maxInvalidPasswordAttempts` attribute to the maximum number of bad passwords or bad password answers allowed. The `passwordAttemptWindow` is the time interval in minutes for entering the number of bad password attempts.

You can still retrieve a user's profile from the membership provider. If the profile is locked out the `IsLockedOut` property returns true. You may also programmatically check the configuration settings from the membership provider by calling the `MaxInvalidPasswordAttempts` and `PasswordAttemptWindow` properties.

If a user account becomes locked, you can manually unlock the account by calling the `MemberShipuser.UnlockUser` method. The method returns a Boolean — `true` if the account is successfully unlocked, or `false` if it is not. Make sure the user meets your security requirements to enable the account to be unlocked again, such as a password reset.

Lock and Unlock a User Account

1 Create a new Web page.

2 Add a TextBox to collect the username.

3 Add a Submit button.

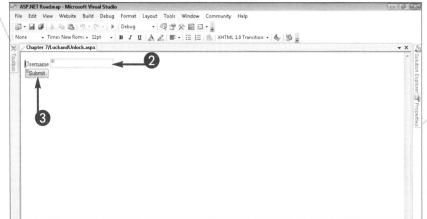

4 Double-click the Submit button to create a click event handler.

5 Add code to unlock the user.

Running the page in a browser and submitting a valid user's name will unlock their account.

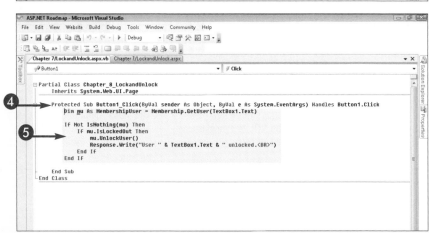

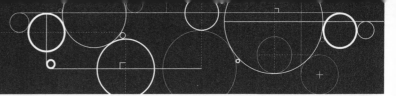

Introduction to Role Management

Authorization or managing access to areas of an ASP.NET site can be done using role management. After you define roles for the site you can assign access rules to different parts of the site. For example, you may have some content only available by subscription or limit site administration to specific members of a company. Utilizing roles is a much more efficient way to manage access than specifying individual members. Role management provides a very easy way to use sets of classes and methods to manage these roles and site members for each role.

Members can belong to multiple roles, and roles can be assigned access to multiple areas on the site. You can even use roles to specify what type of access a member can have to content. For example, you could include logic in the site to allow read-only access to one role, while providing full read-write permissions to another role.

Role Provider Methods

The role provider defines several core methods that every custom role provider must implement. A custom provider does not have to actually implement the functionality of the method, but must have a method signature that matches each of the methods that must be overridden.

METHOD NAME	DESCRIPTION
AddUsersToRoles	Accepts an array of usernames and an array of role names to associate the provided users
CreateRole	Accepts a roleName to create a new role
DeleteRole	Accepts a roleName to delete and a Boolean to indicate if an exception should be thrown if users still belong to the role
FindUsersInRole	Accepts a roleName and a username string pattern to return a list of matching users for the role
GetAllRoles	Returns an array of all the roles in the application
GetRolesForUser	Accepts a username and returns an array of roles the user belongs to
GetUsersInRole	Accepts a roleName and returns an array of usernames associated with the role
IsUserInRole	Accepts a username and a roleName and returns true or false to indicate if the username is associated with the roleName
RemoveUsersFromRoles	Accepts an array of usernames and an array of role names and removes the association between the usernames and the roles
RoleExists	Accepts a roleName and returns true if the role already exists and false if it does not exist

SQLRoleProvider

The SQLRoleProvider class manages interactions with the stored procedures and tables in the SQL Server database designated in the provider's connectionString.

The class manages the interactions with all the stored procedures to manage roles and the user associations with those roles. It implements all the methods of the Role provider.

WindowsTokenRoleProvider

`WindowsTokenRoleProvider` is a read-only provider that provides quick access to the verifying if a user is in a role or users in a role. The only two methods supported by the `WindowsTokenRoleProvider` are `IsUserInRole` and `GetUsersInRole`. All other methods throw a `ProviderException`.

The `WindowsTokenRoleProvider` works best with sites that use Windows authentication and disabled anonymous authentication. The actual roles and role membership would typically be managed by network administrators in a separate application.

Roles Class

The `Roles` class is the actual class used to call the specific provider methods of the role provider. The class actually implements variations of several role provider methods. For example, the `AddUsersToRoles` method has three related methods that can be called to add users to roles: `AddUserToRole`, `AddUserToRoles`, and `AddUsersToRole`. These are logical extensions of the core methods and they actually create the required string arrays as needed to call the core `AddUsersToRoles` method, which is implemented by the provider.

AuthorizationStoreRoleProvider

The `AuthorizationStoreRoleProvider` manages roles either in an XML file or `ActiveDirectory`. It works with both Forms and Windows-based authentication in ASP.NET. Specifying which underlying store type used is by the provider is done by setting the connection string to point to the provider. A connection string to an XML file will look like this: msxml://<path to xml file>. The path may contain the "~" character to specify the root of the Web site. The file must reside in the directory tree of the ASP.NET application. The XML file should be stored in the App_Data folder to ensure the file is secure.

A connection string to an Active Directory store looks like this: msldap://myserver/CN=MyAzManStore,OU=MyOU,DC=MyDomain,DC=MyDC,DC=Com.

Configuring the Role Provider

The default role provider is set up in the machine.config file, but can be overridden in the local web.config file to configure application-specific behavior.

The `roleManager` element is a child node of the system.web element of the configuration file. The `roleManger` element has several attributes that define specific characteristics of the site's role provider. Each site can actually have multiple providers, which are configured by adding provider nodes to the `roleManager` element.

The `defaultProvider` attribute is the name of the default role provider to be used in the Web site. The `enabled` attribute specifies if role management is enabled.

The `cacheRolesInCookie` attribute specifies if the list of roles the user belongs to is cached in a cookie on the user's machine. The `cookieName` attribute designates the name used for the role cookie. The `cookiePath` attribute designates the path to the role cookie. The `cookieRequireSSL` attribute designates if the cookie requires SSL on the server. The `cookieSlidingExpiration` attribute designates if the role cookie timeout will be periodically reset based on user activity. The `createPersistentCookie` attribute specifies if the role cookie expires when the session times out. The `cookieProtection` attribute designates the `CookieProtection` enumeration choice. The `CookieProtection` enumeration values are `All`, `Encryption`, `None`, and `Validation`.

The providers node defines the list of providers that can be used on the site. The add node is used to add a provider to the site.

The `name` attribute defines the name used to identify the provider in the application. The `connectionString` attribute declares the name of the `connectionString` to connect to the data store with the role manager data.

The `applicationName` attribute defines the name this application uses to designate its data. The `type` attribute is the fully qualified name of the role provider being added. The `remove` element removes a named provider from the site.

Add a Role

Arranging members into groups is an important part of managing security in an application. Roles are a way to put site members into groups. They play an important role in managing security for a Web site because it is much easier to manage access to content based on individual roles than individual members. There is no limit to the number of roles a site can have. A role can be added to a site's database by calling the `Role.CreateRole` method.

The `Role.CreateRole` method accepts one parameter, the role name, as a string. If the role already exists, a `ProviderException` is thrown because duplicate roles are not allowed on any site. When a role is added, users can be added to that role immediately by calling the `AddUsersToRoles` method.

The `AddUsersToRoles` method accepts two string arrays. The first contains usernames, and the second contains a

list of roles to which those users belong. Either of the arrays can be just a single item, such as a string array of just a role name. There are three variations of the `AddUsersToRoles` method that may also be used: `AddUserToRole`, `AddUsersToRole`, and `AddUserToRoles`. Each does exactly what its name states — add a single user to a single role, add multiple users to a single role, and add a single user to multiple roles.

The maximum length for the role name is 256 characters. Role names are not case-sensitive. Commas are not allowed in role names. An `ArgumentException` is thrown if the role is an empty string or contains a comma. It is also thrown if the role is longer than 256 characters.

A `ProviderException` is thrown if the role already exists in the database or an unknown error occurs while communicating with the database. An `ArgumentNullException` is thrown if the role is null.

Add a Role

① Create a new Web page.

② Add a TextBox to collect the role name.

③ Add a Submit button.

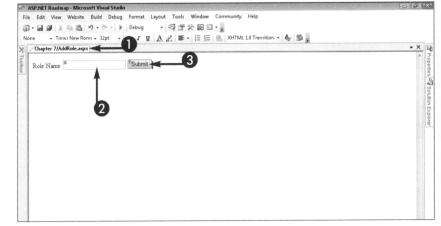

④ Double-click the Submit button to create a click event handler.

⑤ Add code to create a new role and echo a confirmation message.

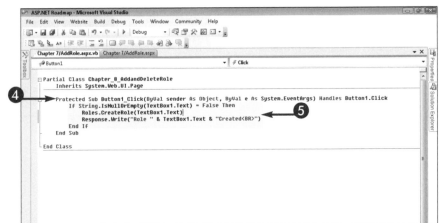

6 Open the page in a browser.

7 Type the name of a new role in the TextBox.

8 Click Submit to add the new role.

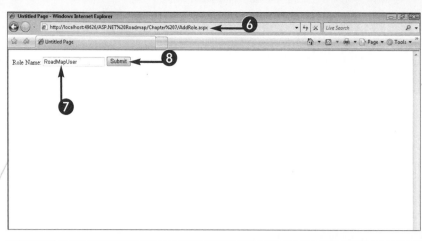

● A message confirming the creation of the Role appears.

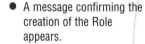

Apply It

Efficiently programming an application can go a long way toward success and ease of maintenance. Typically when a new role is added to a site, existing users are assigned to this role. A good custom method not provided by the core role provider would create a new role and assign an initial list of users to that role. The method would accept a role name and an array of usernames. Overloads and variations could be created to add just one user and accept more parameters to pass the core provider or to perform any custom business logic.

Custom CreateRoleWithUsers Method:

```vb
Public Function CreateRoleWithUsers(ByVal rolename As String, ByVal usernames() As String) As
Boolean
 Try
  Roles.CreateRole(rolename)
  Roles.AddUsersToRole(usernames, rolename)
 Catch ex As Exception
  'Should perform custom error handling here
  Return False
 End Try
 Return True
End Function
```

A Role cannot be directly updated or changed, but rather you must manually create a new role, then migrate any items assigned to or dependant upon the role being changed, such as users belonging to the role to the new role and then delete the old role. The reason this is not offered as a standard method in the role provider is many sites can associate different permissions and objects with a role.

The first step is to create a new role. All users for the role being changed should then be added to the new role. An easy way to accomplish this task is to call the AddUsersToRole method and pass the GetUsersInRole method as the user's parameter; the new role name is passed as the role. The role name being updated is passed to the GetUsersInRole to return a list of the users in that role. Next, users assigned to this role should be deleted by calling the RemoveUsersFromRole

method, passing the old role name as the roleName parameters and the GetUsersInRole method as the user's parameter. Any references to the role name in the application should also be updated to the new role name.

After the AddUsersToRole method is called, any application-specific data associated with the role being changed should be migrated to the new role. It is good to have a custom method available to manage this process for the application data similar to the AddUsersToRole method.

After all associated information is successfully migrated to the new role name the previous role name should be deleted by calling the DeleteRole method. To be on the safe side, indicate to the DeleteRole method to throw an exception if there are any users still associated with this role. In this case, the call to RemoveUsersFromRole should be repeated or some other custom verification routine executed.

Update a Role

① Create a new Web page.

② Add a TextBox for the existing role name.

③ Add a TextBox for the new role name.

④ Add a Submit button.

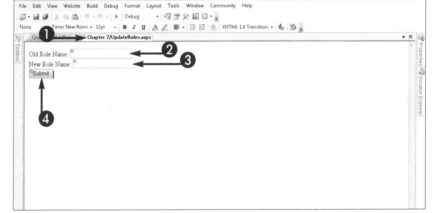

⑤ Double-click the Submit button to create a click event handler.

⑥ Add code to update the role name.

⑦ Add code to echo a confirmation message.

Note: *You must actually create a new role, add the users from the old role name, and delete the old role.*

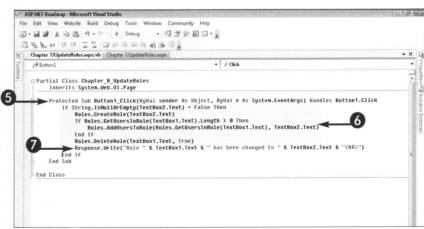

⑧ Open the page in a browser.

⑨ Type the old role name.

⑩ Type the new role name.

⑪ Click Submit.

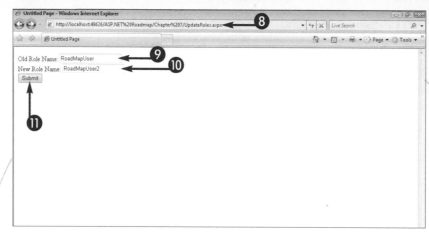

● The confirmation message appears.

Apply It

In object-oriented programming is it a good idea to refactor and abstract methods and common routines to a base location. Because there is no method in the ASP.NET role provider to update or migrate a role name to a new name this is a primary candidate for a custom method. Depending on how the application is architected, this method could exist in a custom role provider class that derives from one of the supplied role providers or possibly in a custom `Page` class or application module. The method would automatically handle all of the steps outlined in this section and could accept as little as one parameter. Overloads could be made to accept additional parameters the provider methods allow, such as throwing an exception when a role is being deleted with users still associated with it.

Custom UpdateRole Method:
```
Public Sub UpdateRole(ByVal oldRoleName As String, ByVal newRoleName As String)
 Roles.CreateRole(newRoleName)
 Roles.AddUsersToRole(Roles.GetUsersInRole(oldRoleName), newRoleName)
 Roles.RemoveUsersFromRole(Roles.GetUsersInRole(oldRoleName), oldRoleName)
 Roles.DeleteRole(oldRoleName)
End Sub
```

Delete a Role

A role can be deleted by calling the `Roles.DeleteRole`, but each application may need to have some custom code and operations performed to clean up any associations to the role first. The `DeleteRole` has two overloads, one that accepts just the role name and a second that accepts the role name and a parameter indicating if an exception should be thrown if users are still assigned to this role.

While the `throwOnPopulatedRole` parameter can be used when set to `true` by the provider to check if users are still assigned to the role, throwing an exception is not really an efficient mechanism to check this state. A call to `GetUsersInRole` can be done before calling the `DeleteRole` method. If any users are returned, a quick call to `RemoveUsersFromRole` can be made. If the `throwOnPopulatedRole` is set to `false`, any users

associated with the role will be deleted. The user accounts are not affected directly, only the association with the role being removed.

The `DeleteRole` method returns `true` if the role is successfully deleted. If the role cannot be deleted it returns `false`.

The `AuthorizationStoreRoleProvider` can throw an `HttpException` if read-access permission is not granted to the file for a file-based policy store. A `FileNotFoundException` is thrown if the file does not exist.

An `ArgumentNullException` is thrown if the `roleName` is a null reference. An `ArgumentException` is thrown if the `roleName` is an empty string, contains a comma, or is longer than 256 characters. A `ProviderException` is thrown if an unknown error occurs while communicating with the database.

Delete a Role

① Create a new Web page.

② Add a TextBox for the role name to delete.

③ Add a Submit button.

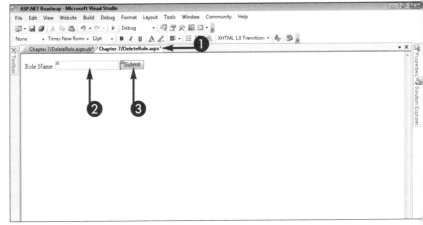

④ Double-click the Submit button to create a click event handler.

⑤ Add code to delete the role.

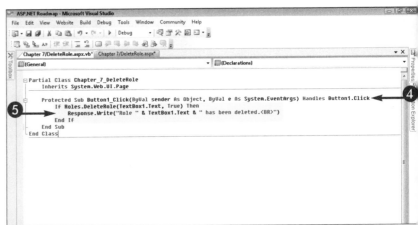

6 Open the page in a browser.

7 Type the name of the role you want to delete.

8 Click Submit.

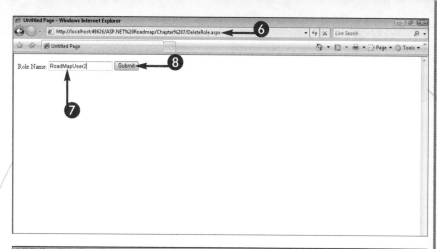

● A confirmation message that the role has been deleted appears.

Apply It

Deleting a role from the Role database can have ripple effects throughout the application. The role provider offers methods to remove any users associated with the role that can be used before actually removing the role from the system. However, any custom application data associated with the role also needs to be cleaned up before the role is removed because this could cause problems going forward with the application.

It is a good idea to create a custom method to execute when a role needs to be removed from the system that will first manage removing associations between custom application data and then users. Finally, it calls the DeleteRole method.

Custom DeleteRole Method:

```
Public Sub DeleteRole(ByVal RoleName As String)
  MyApp.RemoveCustomAppDataFromRole(RoleName)
  Roles.RemoveUsersFromRole(Roles.GetUsersInRole(RoleName), RoleName)
  Roles.DeleteRole(RoleName)
End Sub
```

Retrieve a List of Roles

A list of roles in the application is useful for administration as well as security checks. You can retrieve a full list of current roles for the Web site by calling the `Roles.GetAllRoles` method. This returns a string array of each role name in the site. You can bind this list to any `Data` or `List` control, such as a `Repeater` or `ListBox`. For more advanced management they could be added to a generic list or dictionary.

The string array contains the names of all the roles stored in the data store for a particular application. The `SQLRoleProvider` calls the `aspnet_Roles_GetAllRoles` stored procedure, which retrieves all the roles for the current application. The `GetAllRolesForUser` method also returns a list of role names, but they are filtered for a particular user.

The application is defined in the configuration element for the role provider in the web.config file. The default application name is simply a forward slash (/). The role and membership providers are designed to allow multiple applications to store their users and roles in a common database. Each application has a unique identifier used to designate data from the other application. This can prove useful for scalable portal platforms that service multiple clients on the same site. The role provider manages the application name automatically for the developer so no special code is needed.

A `ProviderException` is thrown if an unknown error occurs while communicating with the database or the application name used is larger than 256 characters in length. For the `AuthorizationStoreRoleProvider` an `HttpException` exception is thrown if read permission is denied on the data file. If the data file cannot be found, a `FileNotFoundException` is thrown. The `WindowsTokenRoleProvider` does not implement the `GetAllRoles` method; if it is called, a `ProviderException` is thrown.

Retrieve a List of Roles

① Create a new Web page.

② Add a GridView to the page and select an AutoFormat.

③ Select one of the AutoFormat options from the AutoText dialog box.

④ Click Apply.

⑤ Click the Design View tab.

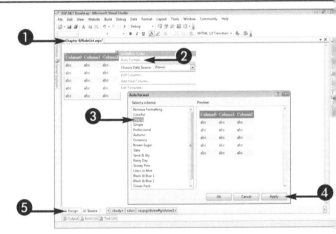

⑥ Add a `TemplateField` to display the role name.

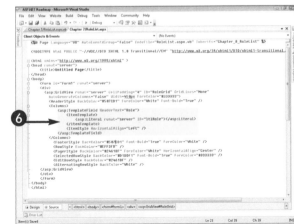

7. Switch to the code-behind file and add code to bind the list of roles to the GridView.

8. Add a `RowDataBound` event handler to bind the role name to the `Literal` in the `TemplateField`.

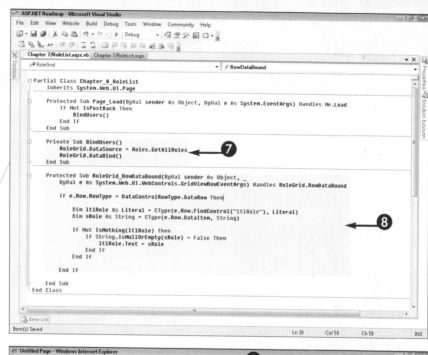

9. Open the page in a browser.

- A list of roles is displayed in the `GridView`.

Apply It

There are no methods or stored procedures available with the standard role provider to provide content for the roleName field. A custom set of store procedures and methods can be created to manage the content of this field and extend the role system.

Role Description Field Stored Procedures:

```
CREATE PROCEDURE [dbo].[aspnet_Roles_RetrieveFullRole]
    @ApplicationID    uniqueidentifier,
    @RoleName         nvarchar(256)
AS
BEGIN
Select [ApplicationId],[RoleId],[RoleName],[LoweredRoleName],[Description]
FROM [dbo].[aspnet_Roles]
  WHERE [ApplicationId] = @ApplicationId and [RoleName] = @RoleName
END
```

Add a User to a Role

Users can be programmatically added to a role at anytime by calling one of several static methods on the `Role` object. A single user can be added to a single role by calling the `AddUserToRole` method, passing the username and the role name. Similarly, a user can be added to multiple roles by calling the `AddUserToRoles` method, passing the username and an array of role names. Multiple users can be added to a single role by calling the `AddUsersToRole` method, passing an array of usernames and the role name.

Under the hood of the role provider the `AddUsersToRoles` method is called by all of the mentioned methods. Each one creates the appropriate string array from the required parameters. The `AddUsersToRoles` method accepts two string arrays. The first contains usernames, and the second contains a list of roles to which those users will belong. Either of the

arrays can be just a single item, such as a string array of just a role name. Each of the calling methods does exactly what its name states: add a single user to a single role, add multiple users to a single role, and add a single user to multiple roles.

The `SQLRoleProvider` actually takes the array of roles and the array of usernames and builds comma-separated strings of each to pass to the `aspnet_UsersInRoles_AddUsersToRoles`-stored procedure. Each of the procedure's parameters allows a 4000-variable character string. So when passing a list of usernames and role names make sure they do not contain more than 4000 characters including delimiting commas.

An `ArgumentException` is thrown if either of the string arrays is empty, contains a comma (,), or contains a duplicate entry. An `ArgumentNullException` is thrown when at least one of the arguments is null. If either one of the roles or usernames is not found, a `ProviderException` is thrown.

Add a User to a Role

① Create a new Web page.

② Add a TextBox for the role.

③ Add a TextBox for the username.

④ Add a Submit button.

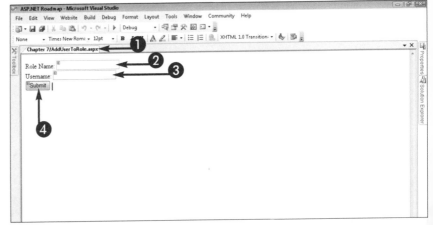

⑤ Double-click the Submit button to create a click event handler.

⑥ Add code to the event handler to add a user to a role and display a confirmation message.

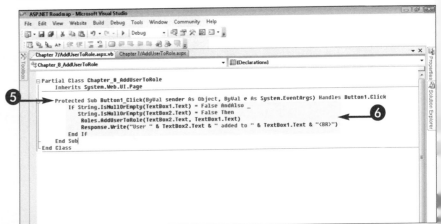

7 Open the page in a browser.

8 Add the role name to the first TextBox.

9 Add the username to the second TextBox.

10 Click Submit to add the user to the role.

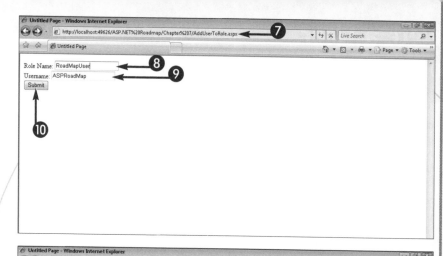

● A confirmation message appears that the user is added to the role.

Apply It

The 4000-character limit on the length of the username and role list is mostly likely enough to accommodate just about any application's needs. But just in case there is the need to add many more users to a role or a user to a large list of roles a custom method is a good idea. This method needs to manage the length of characters being sent to the AddUsersToRoles method by creating smaller arrays and calling the method multiple times.

Handling a Large List of Users to Add to a Role:
```
Public Sub AddLargeUsersToRole(ByVal usernames As String(), ByVal rolename As String)
  Dim mLength As Integer = 0
  Dim tempUserNames As New StringBuilder

  For Each user As String In usernames
   tempUserNames.AppendFormat("{0},", user)
   If mLength >= 3950 Then
    Roles.AddUsersToRole(tempUserNames.ToString.Split(","), rolename)
    tempUserNames = New StringBuilder
   End If
  Next
End Sub
```

Delete a User from a Role

E
ventually, a user will need to be removed from a role or multiple users from multiple roles. The ASP.NET role provider contains several methods to manage this process. They all ultimately call the `RemoveUsersFromRoles` method.

The `RemoveUsersFromRoles` method takes a string array of usernames and a string array of roles as its arguments. The `RemoveUserFromRole` abstracts removing one user from one role, but actually calls the `RemoveUsersFromRoles` method passing an array of one username and another with one role name. The `RemoveUsersFromRole` method works in the same fashion, but works by accepting an array of usernames to remove from one role. The `RemoveUserFromRoles` abstracts removing a user from a set of roles. Each of the abstracted methods check the variables before making the call to the `RemoveUsersFromRoles` method, ensuring the parameters are valid.

Like the `AddUsersToRoles` method in the `SQLRoleProvider`, each array is converted to a comma-separated list of usernames and roles before it is passed to the `aspnet_UsersInRoles_RemoveUsersFromRoles`-stored procedure. So when passing a list of usernames and role names make sure they do not contain more than 4000 characters including delimiting commas.

An `ArgumentException` is thrown if either of the string arrays is empty, contains a comma (,), one of the entries is longer than 256 characters, or contains a duplicate entry. An `ArgumentNullException` is thrown when at least one of the arguments is null. If either one of the roles or usernames is not found a `ProviderException` is thrown. The `ProviderException` is also thrown when one or more of the users is not found to be associated with the role provided.

The `WindowsTokenRoleProvider` does not implement any of the methods to remove a user from a role.

Delete a User from a Role

① Create a new Web page.

② Add a TextBox for the role name.

③ Add a TextBox for the username.

④ Add a Submit button.

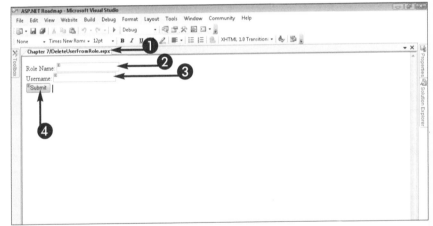

⑤ Double-click the Submit button to create a click event handler.

⑥ Add code to the event handler to remove the user from the role.

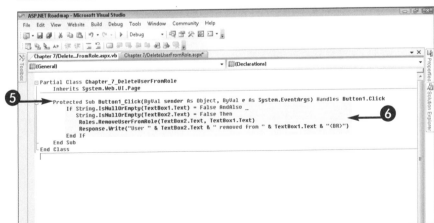

7 Open the page in a browser.

8 Add the role name to the first TextBox.

9 Add the username to the second TextBox.

10 Click Submit to remove the user from the role.

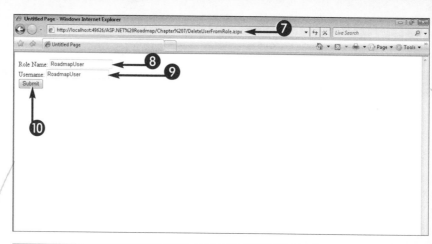

● A confirmation message that the user has been removed from the role appears.

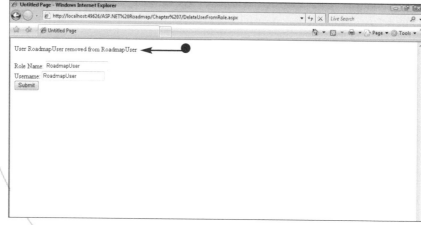

Extra

One of the drawbacks to the way the `RoleProvider` has been designed is that it is not intuitive on how to extend the provider methods. The `Roles` class acts as an interface to the designated provider. It adds methods such as `RemoveUserFromRole` that actually calls the `RemoveUsersFromRoles` method. The `RemoveUsersFromRoles` is implemented by the actual role provider, such as the `SQLRoleProvider`.

Unfortunately the `Roles` class cannot be inherited, meaning you cannot create another class that inherits `Roles` and extends its functionality. A custom class must be created that either calls its own routines, stored procedures, and the underlying provider core methods. To execute methods in the designated provider class the custom class must reference the underlying property and the desired method, `Roles.Provider.CreateRole(roleName)`.

When creating a custom class to manage the role provider the configuration file must be queried to build a collection of available role providers. This collection is used to execute the appropriate methods with the role data store. The `RoleManagerSection` class provides a managed interface to the custom configuration section in the config file that defines the application's role provider setup. By reading this class, the `RoleProvider` collection and other role provider settings can be initialized.

Retrieve Users in a Role

Y ou can retrieve a list of users in a specific role by calling the `Role.GetUsersInRole` method. This method takes one parameter, the role name, to return a filtered list of associated users. The method returns an array of strings with all the usernames associated with the role.

You can also search for users in a role by calling the `FindUsersInRole` method. This method returns a string array of usernames associated with the supplied role name and matches the `usernameToMatch` pattern. The method requires two parameters: the search pattern for the username and the role being queried. In addition to the causes for exceptions listed in the following sections, an `ArgumentException` can also be thrown if the `usernameToMatch` is longer than 256 characters.

An `ArgumentException` is thrown if the role name contains a comma (,) or is longer than 256 characters.

An `ArgumentNullException` is thrown when the role name parameter is null. If role management is not enabled a `ProviderException` is thrown. A `ProviderException` is thrown by the `SQLRoleProvider` if the role name is not found in the role database or there is an error communicating with the SQL Server database.

The `GetUsersInRole` method is not implemented by the `WindowsTokenRoleProvider` and will throw a `ProviderException`. The `AuthorizationStoreRoleProvider` throws an `HttpException` when read access is denied to the file-based policy store. A `ProviderException` is thrown when the configured `applicationName` is not found, the configured `scopeName` is not found, or the authorization-manager runtime is not installed on the server. A `FileNotFoundException` is thrown with the `connectionStringName` attribute references a connection string to a file that does not exist.

Retrieve Users in a Role

① Create a new Web page.

② Add a `DropDownList` control to hold the role list and set the `AutoPostback` property to true.

③ Add a GridView to hold the Usernames.

④ Double-click the `DropDownList` to create a `ChangeEvent` handler.

⑤ Add code to bind the list of roles to the `DropDownList`.

⑥ Add code to bind a list of users for the selected role to the `GridView`.

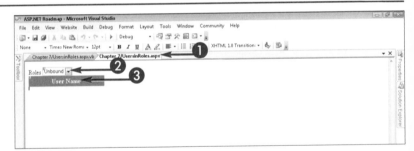

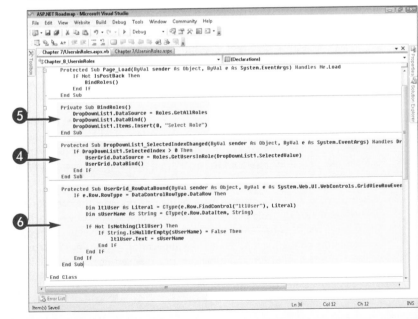

7 Open the page in a browser.

8 Select a new role from the DropDownList.

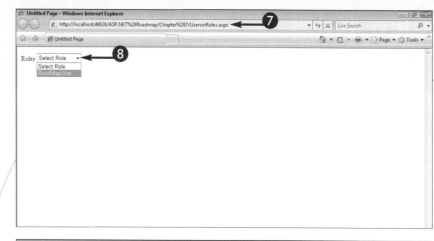

- A list of users assigned to the selected role appears.

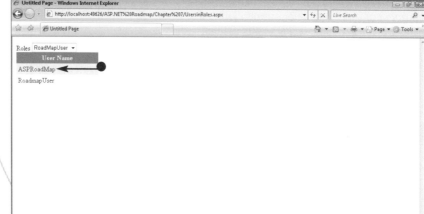

Apply It

Many of the methods related to the role and membership providers accept a string array as one or more of their parameters. Creating a dynamically sized string array cannot be done, but the StringCollection class provides a way for this to be accomplished.

A StringCollection is simply a collection of strings that when needed can be copied to a string array. This is done by calling the CopyTo method of the StringCollection class.

Method to Return a Dynamically Sized String Array:
```
Public Function GetSpecialStringArray() As String()
 Dim sa As New StringCollection
 sa.Add("Welcome")
 sa.Add("to The")
 sa.Add("ASP.NET")
 sa.Add("Roadmap")

 Dim sar As String() = New String(sa.Count - 1) {}
 sa.CopyTo(sar, 0)
 Return sar
End Function
```

Retrieve Roles by User

I t is often useful to retrieve a list of roles to which a user belongs. This list can be used for security checks or added to the user's custom profile for quick access by the application. A list of roles associated with a user can be retrieved by calling the GetRolesForUser method.

The GetRolesForUser method is overloaded and accepts the specific username to retrieve a list of roles or no parameters at all. Call the method with no parameters and it will retrieve a list of the currently authenticated user accounts it is associated with. The GetRolesForUser returns a string array, so many data controls can bind to the role list returned. You can bind the list to any data or List control such as a GridView, Repeater, or DropDownList. When no username is specified, the Roles class calls an internal method to retrieve the current username, GetCurrentUserName. It does this by accessing the current httpContext.User property, which is an IPrinciple object.

An ArgumentException is thrown if the username contains a comma (,) or is longer than 256 characters. An ArgumentNullException is thrown when the username parameter is null. A ProviderException is thrown by the SQLRoleProvider if there is an error communicating with the SQL Server database.

The GetRolesForUser method is not implemented by the WindowsTokenRoleProvider and throws a ProviderException. The AuthorizationStoreRole Provider throws an HttpException when read access is denied to the file-based policy store. A ProviderException is thrown when the configured applicationName is not found, the configured scopeName is not found, or the authorization-manager runtime is not installed on the server. A FileNotFoundException is thrown when the connectionStringName attribute references a connection string to a file that does not exist.

Retrieve Roles by User

① Create a new Web page.

② Add a DropDownList control to list usernames.

③ Set the DropDownList control to AutoPostBack.

④ Add a GridView to hold the usernames.

⑤ Double-click the DropDownList to create a ChangeEvent handler.

⑥ Add code to bind a list of roles for the submitted user to the GridView.

⑦ Add code to bind the usernames to the DropDownList.

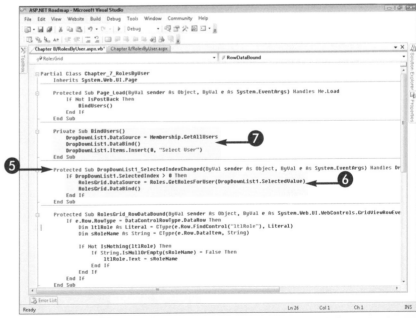

8 Open the page in a browser.

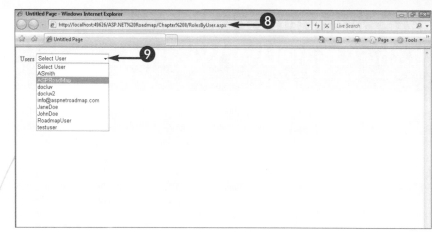

9 Select a user from the DropDownList control.

- A list of assigned roles for the username appears.

Extra

When collecting input from users, typos and capitalization errors are often found. The SQL membership and role providers both contain extra fields in their respective tables that contain a lowercase version of the username and role names.

The reason this is a good idea is to do any filtering against these fields, using a lowercase version of the username or role name submitted by the user. This reduces the chance for errors when querying the data. When a username or role name is added to the database the SQL Server LOWER function is called. This function converts all letters to their lowercase equivalent to ensure a consistent comparison in a where clause.

Create Site Members with the CreateUserWizard

reating a form to manage the creation of a new user with the membership provider can be quickly done with the CreateUserWizard. The wizard automatically creates a series of labels and inputs for each field with the necessary validation. The actual fields being displayed can be controlled through the Web.config file by defining your own custom template and integrated with the Personalization provider. It provides a way for you to not only leverage the membership provider, but store values in your own data store.

The CreateUserWizard automatically handles a minimal set of inputs to identify a user for the site. With no effort on the programmer's part the control displays fields to collect the User Name, Password, Password confirmation, E-Mail address, a Security Question, and corresponding answer. These are the base fields needed to define a user for the ASP.NET Membership provider with no

customization. The control automatically performs data validation when the user clicks Create User.

The UserName and Password fields enable the user to log in to the site later using the Login control. The Login control really authenticates through the membership provider and the login interface configured in the site. The user's e-mail address is collected so you can send login credentials if he or she forgets how to log in to the site. The security question is used to verify the user before those credentials are sent.

After users type valid data in the CreateUserWizard they are presented a confirmation view. This view contains a confirmation message and a Continue button. The confirmation message is set with the CompleteSuccessText property, which takes a string to be displayed. The ContinueDestinationPageUrl is a string property that represents the destination URL users are taken to when they click Continue.

Create Site Members with the CreateUserWizard

1 Add a new Web page to a site that has a membership provider configured.

2 Add a CreateUserWizard to the page from the ToolBox.

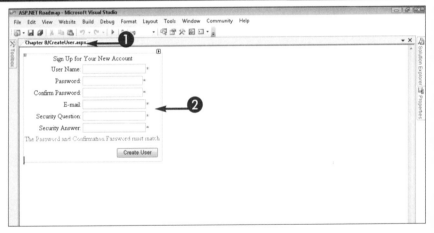

3 Set the CreateUserWizard CompleteSuccessText to Thank you for registering.

4 Set the ContinueDestinationUrl, CancelDestinationURL, and FinishDestinationURL properties to appropriate pages in the site.

Note: The UserProfile.aspx page should be added to your site to fully see how the control works.

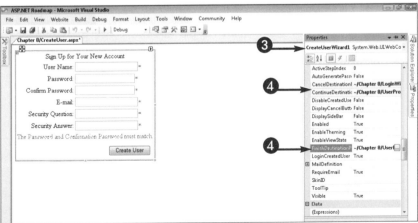

5 Open the page in a browser.

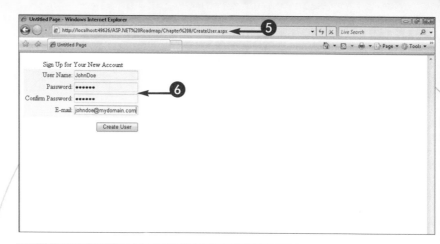

6 Supply information to complete the `CreateUserWizard`.

Note: *If you omit or type invalid data in the `CreateUserWizard`, validation stops the submission.*

7 Submit the registration.

● A message appears informing you that your account has been successfully created.

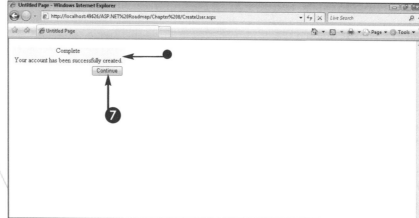

Note: *View the CompleteSuccess Text in the CompleteWizardStep.*

Apply It

The `CreateUserWizard` accepts a password that meets or exceeds the requirements of the site's membership provider settings. The membership provider has a `PasswordStrengthRegularExpression` property that defines a pattern that passwords must comply with. This value is set in the application's Web.config file in the `passwordStrengthRegularExpression` attribute of the membership element. The following setting is an example that requires at least seven characters with at least one being numeric: `passwordStrength RegularExpression=" @\"(?=.{6,})(?=(.*\d){1,})(?=(.*\W){1,})"`.

The `CreateUserWizard` utilizes the membership provider's settings to determine several aspects of the display and actions of the control. If the site has a configured SMTP server the control can send a welcome e-mail message to the new user. The message the user would receive can be set through the `MailDefinition` property. The `MailDefinition` property is an object that contains properties to define an e-mail message such as To, From, or Body and automatically performs a merge on the properties that define the new user. For example, you can merge the username by inserting the `<%Username%>` expression in the body of the e-mail template. It can also disable a new user's account until he or she verifies the request if the `DisableCreatedUser` property is set to True.

Format the CreateUserWizard

The `CreateUserWizard` control gives you the ability to completely customize the style and layout of the control. In addition to formatting the style of the `CreateUserWizard`, you can also define custom fields by defining personalization properties and using the `WizardStep` templates. ASP.NET 2.0 added a new feature, `Personalization`, which allows you to store profile information for each user account. These properties can reflect any type of data and are fully customizable.

The `CreateUserWizard` is built using `WizardStep`s, which are layout templates. A `WizardStep` gives you the ability to define controls and the layout incorporated in each step of the `CreateUserWizard` control. A `WizardStep` template works exactly like a template in a data control, because it allows you to define the HTML markup to control the layout of your controls as well as lets you define what controls are included.

The style for a `WizardStep` can be defined by using the `StepStyle`, which is a `TableStyle` property. The `CreateUserWizard` control also has style properties available to control individual controls and labels automatically displayed in the wizard. These properties let you define the style for each of the navigation buttons, hyperlinks, the `SideBar`, and labels. Each of these properties represents a `Style` class, which is the base class to represent the style of a Web control.

If your registration process needs multiple steps to collect the needed information from the user, you can define multiple steps with the `WizardSteps` element. This element contains the `WizardStep` templates that comprise your registration process. It can contain `WizardStep`, `CreateUserWizardStep`, and `CompleteWizardStep` templates. You do not have to create a custom `WizardStep` for custom properties; these can be incorporated directly into the `CreateUserWizardStep` template.

Format the CreateUserWizard

① Add a new Web page to a site that has a membership provider configured.

② Add a `CreateUserWizard` to the page from the ToolBox.

③ Click the `CreateUserWizard` Smart Tag at the top right corner of the control.

④ Click Auto Format from the `CreateUserWizard` Tasks selections.

⑤ Click Professional from the Select a scheme list.

⑥ Click Apply.

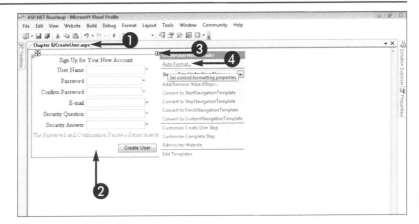

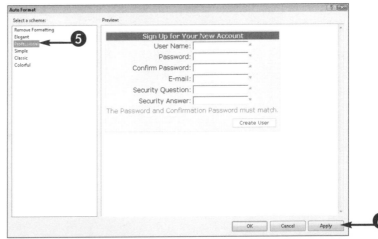

7 Open the page in a browser.

8 Complete the registration.

Note: *The* `CreateUser` *control has some nice formatting.*

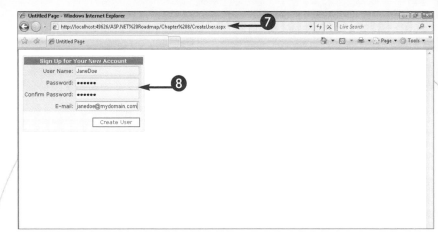

9 Click the Create User button to submit the registration.

● A message appears notifying you that your account has been successfully created.

Note: *The formatting automatically carries over to the Confirmation view.*

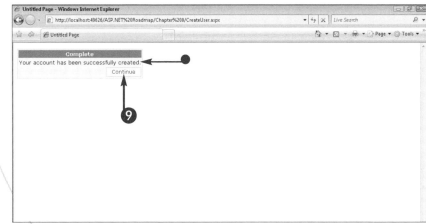

Extra

The nice thing about being able to completely customize the look of the `CreateUserWizard` is you can easily tie it into a custom membership system. When ASP.NET 2.0 introduced the membership provider, many development teams faced the debate over what to do with an existing or customized membership system. Often these systems have been in use for years and have many thousands or more of member profiles stored and managed and have an infrastructure in place to manage the associate data and business logic.

Because many teams want to leverage the great new features of the membership provider and the consistency of the provided membership-related controls, a balanced solution must be made. The `CreateUserWizard` control allows complete customization. Not only can the user interface continue to represent the custom fields required by many applications, but those values can be stored in the existing solution structure.

The `CreatedUser` event fires when the user is added by the control. This event can be handled by your application and allows you to store the values provided by the new registration. This creates a parallel solution that lets the membership provider manage username and password encryption, which is what it does best, and retain the custom attributes as always. This allows existing code bases to easily migrate.

Add a Login Interface with the Login Control

You can quickly build a login page for unauthenticated users with the `Login` control. It is a prebuilt composite control with `Username`, `Password`, and `Validation` controls that communicate directly with the membership provider. The `Login` control may be used without setting any properties to customize behavior or style. It does offer the ability to customize template support as well as granular control over what the control displays.

The `Login` control offers a set of properties that allows you to define messages, label text, validation error messages and if the user's authentication is remembered. The control also provides a link to let the user retrieve a lost password and another link to let a new user register on the site. You can define these two destinations with the `CreateUserUrl` and `PasswordRecoveryURL`.

The `DisplayRememberMe` property is a Boolean that indicates if the `CheckBox` control is displayed so the user

can indicate if he or she wants the site to store the authentication cookie after the session is complete. The `RememberMeText` is a string property that contains the text displayed next to the `RememberMe` check box. The `RememberMeSet` property is a Boolean that indicates if the cookie will persist after the session ends. If the `DisplayRememberMe` is set to `true` and the `RememberMeSet` is `true`, then the check box is initially checked. If `RememberMeSet` is `true` but the `DisplayRememberMe` is `false`, then the cookie persists as soon as the user is authenticated.

The style of the `Login` control can be controlled through several properties. Each element of the control has an associated style, such as the `HyperLinkStyle`, `LabelStyle`, and `TitleTextStyle`. Each of these properties represents a `Style` class that is easy to manage through the `Intellisense` built into Visual Studio.

Add a Login Interface with the Login Control

① Create a new Web page.

② Add a `Login` control to the page.

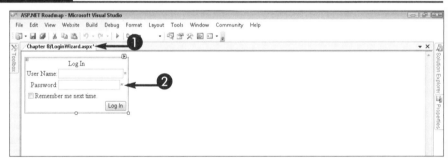

③ Click the Smart Tag and select Auto Format.

④ In the AutoFormat dialog box, select one of the predefined styles.

In this example, Simple is selected.

⑤ Click Apply.

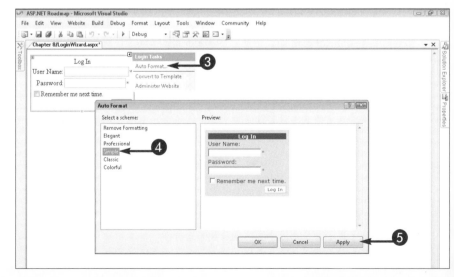

6 Open the page in a browser.

7 Type valid login credentials.

Note: *If you do not already have a user account on the site, review the CreateUserWizard section to learn more.*

8 Submit the `Login` control by clicking the Login button.

- The username appears if the login is successful.

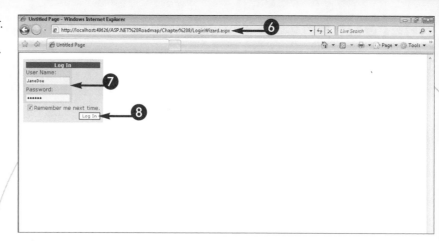

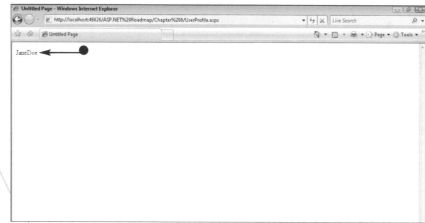

Extra

The `Login` control is fully customizable through layout templates and style properties. Each piece of text has a corresponding text and style property to let you define the formatting and text of the label. If no text is customized, the default values are used, and these values are localized.

If you create a custom layout template, the default settings for `AccessKey` and `TabIndex` are lost. You must define these properties on each control you define in your template.

The `Login` control provides a long list of custom style properties to manage how the control is displayed. Some are `Style` properties, such as `CheckBoxStyle`, `FailureTextStyle`, and `TitleTextStyle`. The `BorderPadding` property is an integer that defines the padding between the cells of the HTML table defining the `Login` control's layout.

The `UserName` and `Password` fields have `RequiredFieldValidators` associated with them. To allow the control to perform validation separate from other controls on the page the `Login` control uses a `Validation Group`, which inherits the `Login` control's ID as a group name. You can customize the group name by using a custom layout template and changing the `Validation Group` name.

Display the User's LoginStatus

When you implement user authentication on a site you generally implement some sort of link or navigation that clues the user where to click to log in or log out, as the case may be. ASP.NET 2.0 provides a control to manage this feature that automatically leverages the Authentication system built into ASP.NET.

The LoginStatus control automatically displays login or logout text, or corresponding images based on the current user's authentication status. This provides the developer with a means to manage how the control is visually represented to the user. To set the text for the control you set the LoginText and LogoutText properties. The default for these properties is Login and Logout, respectively. Alternatively, you can assign images for the two states through the LoginImageURL and the LogoutImageURL. These images can be used to match the theme of the site.

When users click the control they will be automatically redirected to the location of either the login URL or logout URL. The login URL is defined in the site's Web.config file in the authentication section. The LoginStatus has a LogoutPageURL property that takes a string that represents the URL to take the user to logout. You will want this URL to automatically log the user out of the site when it is loaded.

In addition, the LoginStatus control has a LogoutAction property that is a LogoutAction enum. The enum choices are Redirect, RedirectToLoginPage and Refresh. The Redirect option takes the user to the LogoutPostURL. The RedirectToLoginPage option takes the user to the login page defined in the configuration file. The Refresh option simply refreshes the current page, allowing you to use the LoggingOut event handler to manage the user's authentication status.

Display the User's LoginStatus

1 Create a new Web page.

2 Add a LoginStatus control to the page.

3 Set the LogoutPageURL to a page you want to direct users to once they explicitly log out.

Note: Set the LoginPageURL to a page with a Login control or some other interface for authenticating a user.

4 Set the Foreground and Background colors to match your site.

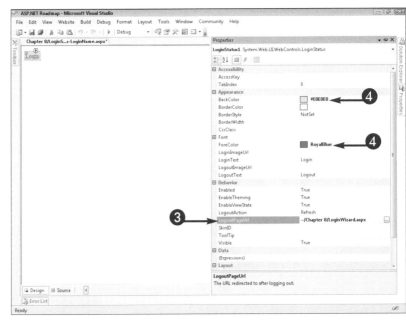

⑤ Open the page in a browser.

The word Login appears on the page formatted according to your style settings.

⑥ Click the Login link and proceed to log in to the site.

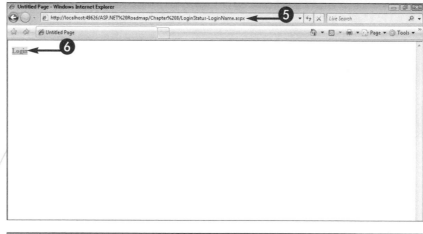

● You are taken to the login page you specified and then back to the page your `LoginStatus` control is on.

Extra

The `LoginStatus` control has two events associated with it — `LoggingOut` and `LoggedOut`. You can build your own handlers for these two methods to handle logic based on these two states.

The `LoggingOut` event handler fires just before the user logs out of the site. Use this event to store any user-related data before it is removed from memory or session state. You can even prompt the user to save data before logging out and even give him or her the option of canceling the operation before logging out. If you inherit from the `LoginStatus` class you will want to override the `OnLoggingOut` method.

The `LoggedOut` event handler is where you should process any cleanup code about the user's account after he or she is logged out. This might include deleting any in-memory objects associated with the account or closing any open database connections and files. If you derive your own class from `LoginStatus` you should override the `OnLoggedOut` method.

Display the User's Name with the LoginName Control

Displaying the user's `UserId` is a common way many Web sites interact with their members to let them know they are authenticated. The `LoginName` control can be used to display the user's `UserId` in an `HTMLEncoded` manner.

If the user has been authenticated, the `UserId` appears in the control; otherwise the control is not rendered at all. Under the hood, the `LoginName` control calls a sealed class, `LoginUtil`. A sealed class means it is not publicly available. The `LoginUtil` class manages access to the current `IPrincipal` object that represents the currently authenticated user. The `Identity` property of the `IPrincipal` returns an instance of an `IIdentity` object. Any `IIdentity` object contains a `Name` property that returns the current username. The `IPrincipal` object can be retrieved at anytime by referencing the current `httpContext` object and referencing the `User` property.

The format of the message can be controlled with the `FormatString` property. `FormatString` accepts a string with a {0} parameter where the `UserId` should be inserted. For example, you could provide a welcome message to the user such as "Welcome back {0}". The {0} is a placeholder for the `UserId` to be inserted and is automatically done by the control. You could also leave the {0} if you do not want to echo the `UserId` out.

The `LoginName` control inherits directly from `WebControl` and carries all the base formatting properties from the base class. This means you have full control over the background color, font styles, and alignment attributes.

The `LoginName`, like the `Menu`, `LoginStatus`, and `LoginView` controls is a good control to place in a `MasterPage` for a site. This is because most pages on the site could use this control, and it is much easier to manage this control in one location rather than in each page.

Display the User's Name with the LoginName Control

1 Create a new Web page.

2 Add a `LoginName` control to the page.

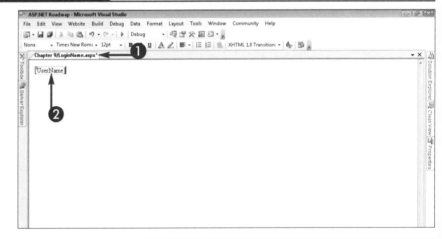

3 Set the `FormatString` property to Welcome {0}.

4 Add a `Login` control to the page.

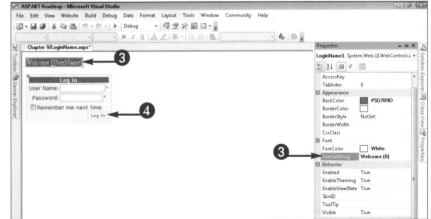

⑤ Open the page in a Web browser.

⑥ Log in with the Login control.

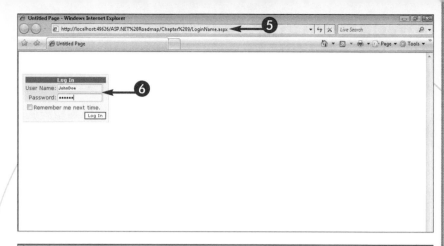

● View the LoginName control displaying your formatted message.

Apply It

Under the hood of the LoginName control the UserName of the authenticated user is passed to a series of methods to produce the actual output on the page. First, the UserName is passed through the httpUtility.HTMLEncode method. The HTMLEncode method is important whenever you echo data entered by a user directly to the browser. When a value is passed through the HTMLEncode method it changes any potentially malicious code to a character equivalent. This means it should be rendered in the browser harmlessly.

To decode any text that has been HTML-encoded you would call the httpUtilty.HTMLDecode method. Both accept one parameter: the string to be processed and a return string value representing the encoded or decoded string.

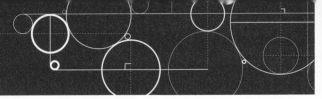

Control Content Access with the LoginView

Displaying targeted information to a user based on authentication can be done with the LoginView control in ASP.NET 2.0. The LoginView control enables you to manage text and controls that are available to a user based on current authentication status. The control consists of an AnonymousTemplate, LoggedInTemplate, and RoleGroups. AnonymousTemplate and LoggedInTemplate are templates where you can place anything you want directly inside of the template definition just like a data control. A RoleGroup is a role or group of roles in the ASP.NET 2.0 membership system.

The AnonymousTemplate displays content you want unauthenticated users to view. This content would be public, nonprotected content that any visitor to the site might see; for example, a sales pitch for a product.

The LoggedInTemplate displays content to an authenticated user. To extend the previous example of an authenticated customer, the site may not need to have a sales pitch for a product he or she already purchased, but displays information related to the account.

Finally, RoleGroup gives you the flexibility to add content based on the user's role membership. Inside the RoleGroup's definition you add individual RoleGroup sections for each role or group of roles for which you want to show additional, targeted information. You can assign a RoleGroup multiple roles to display data; for example, retail customer and wholesale customer. Both have basic customer profile data, but a site Administrator would have different data and controls displayed.

Be careful of the order in which RoleGroups are defined on the page, because the first role a user matches displays as the RoleGroup. Content for a RoleGroup is defined in a ContentTemplate like the Anonymous Template and LoggedInTemplate.

Control Content Access with the LoginView

① Create a new Web page.

② Add a LoginView control to the page.

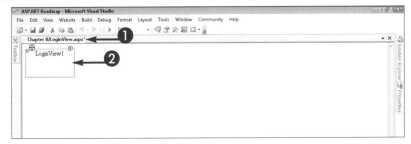

③ Click the Source button to switch to Source view.

④ Add templates for an anonymous and logged-in user.

⑤ Add content for an Admin RoleGroup.

Note: RoleGroups can be added with a wizard in Design view, but templates and the content for a RoleGroup are easier to manage in Source view.

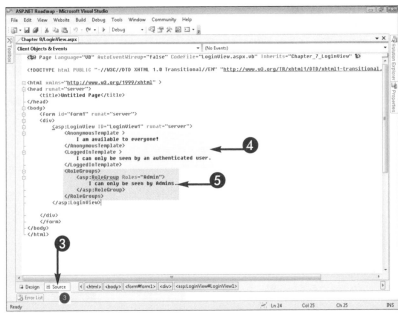

6 Open the page in a browser.

- You will see the content available to any visitor.

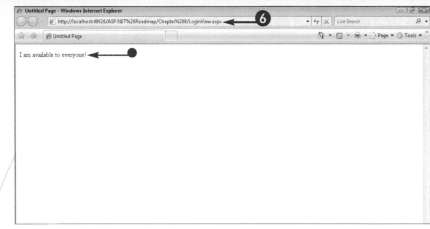

7 Change the user account to see the different content displayed.

Note: To change users, use a page that manages user authentication.

- After logging in the protected content is displayed.

Apply It

The `LoginView` control has a `RoleGroups` property that is a `RoleGroupCollection` value. The `RoleGroupCollection` contains `RoleGroup` objects for each of the `RoleGroups` belonging to the `LoginView`. A `RoleGroup` has two properties, `Roles` which contains a list of `Role` names that can see the content, and a content template. The content template implements `ITemplate` which is an interface to derive content templates from. Each template can contain HTML markup and controls. A `RoleGroup` may be added at runtime and the content template defined at run-time too, instead of at design-time as demonstrated in the visual steps.

Setting a RoleGroup at Runtime:

```
Dim rg As New RoleGroup
rg.Roles = {"Admin", "Vendor", "Manager"}
rg.ContentTemplate = New MyVendorTemplate
LoginView1.RoleGroups.Add(rg)
```

Recover a Lost Password with the PasswordRecovery Control

The `PasswordRecovery` control provides a structured interface for users to retrieve lost passwords. When a user supplies correct authentication information, such as the answer to a question provided at registration, the password is e-mailed. The password may be the original or a new, randomly generated string depending on the configuration of the membership provider on the site. The site must have a membership provider configured for the `PasswordRecovery` control to work.

The `PasswordRecovery` control relies on the mail server to be defined in the site's Web.config file. The <mailsettings> section of the Web.config file is located in the <system.net> section where you can specify information about the SMTP server and default from address.

The `PasswordRecovery` control allows you to define a `MailDefinition` element, which requires a `From` attribute as its minimal configuration. The `From` attribute should be a valid e-mail address you can use to send e-mail from your site. The `MailDefinition` element gives you the ability to customize the e-mail sent to the user.

The `PasswordRecovery` control prompts the user for a username and an answer to the secret question, which was defined when the user registered. If you do not have the `Question` and `Answer` feature of the membership provider turned off, then this feature is not displayed and the recovery e-mail is sent to the user.

You must also change the way the membership provider manages passwords. The actual password is not stored; a hashed version is stored by default. You must change the `PasswordFormat` to `Clear` or `Encrypted` to make it possible for passwords to be sent to the user in a readable format.

Recover a Lost Password with the PasswordRecovery Control

① Create a new Web page.

② Add a `PasswordRecovery` control.

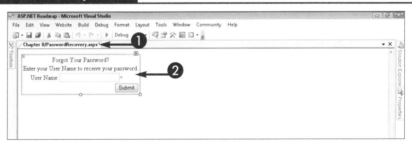

③ Click the Smart Tag button and select Auto Format.

④ In the Auto Format dialog box, select one of the predefined styles in the Select a scheme list.

In this example, Professional is selected.

⑤ Click Apply.

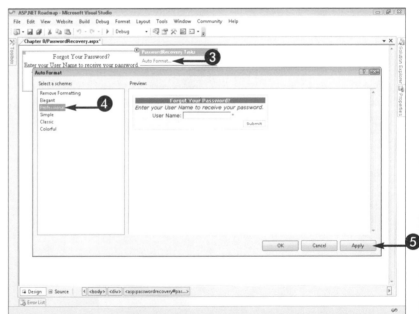

6 Open the page in a browser.

7 Type a valid username in the User Name field.

8 Click Submit to submit the request.

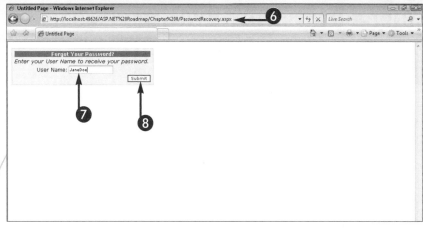

● A note appears indicating an e-mail containing the password has been sent to the user's e-mail.

Note: A valid username must be typed and the site configured to allow password recovery.

Extra

The `PasswordRecovery` control has three states, or views: `UserName`, `Question`, and `Success`. The `UserName` view requests the username from the user. The `Question` view prompts for the answer to a user's secret question. The `Success` view is the final display that lets the user know the e-mail is on the way.

Like many of the other Web controls, the `PasswordRecovery` provides a series of `Style` properties that allow you to define how the control is displayed. An easy way to format the `PasswordRecovery` control is to use the Auto Format feature through the control's Smart Tag. The Smart Tag is a tiny arrow icon located at the top right corner of the control in Visual Studio.

If you want to format the control by hand you can adjust individual styles in the Design view or through the Property dialog box for the control. The Property window gives you a familiar user interface to adjust various properties of each of the style elements, such as Font, Background Color, and Border Color.

`Validation` in the `PasswordRecovery` control is managed with a `ValidationGroup` to isolate its validation from other controls on the page.

Change a Password with the ChangePassword Control

A user may want to change a password on his or her own while corporate policy sometimes requires users to change their passwords occasionally. The `ChangePassword` control provides a complete user interface to manage this process through the configured membership provider.

The control prompts the user to type his or her existing password and the new password twice. The user can click Submit after doing this and the control works through the membership provider to change the password for the account. If the user does not correctly type the password twice, he or she is prompted before clicking Submit to correct the new password. If the change cannot occur or fails, the user is informed of the failure after the attempt to change the password.

A user does not have to be logged on to the site in order to change a password. If the `DisplayUserName` property

is set to `true`, the control displays a User Name textbox to type the account username. The user can type his or her username in the control along with the current password and new password to change the account password. After the password is changed the user is logged in to the site. A user can also change the password of another account by typing the same information; this can be extremely useful for site administration.

There are two views or display states in the `ChangePassword` control: the `ChangePassword` view and the `Success` view. The `ChangePassword` view displays input controls to input the values to set the new password. If there is an error with the change password process an appropriate error message appears in the `ChangePassword` view, which gives the user a chance to correct the error and attempt to change the password again. The `Success` view displays a confirmation message to the user that the account password was successfully changed.

Change a Password with the ChangePassword Control

① Create a new Web page.

② Add a `ChangePassword` control to the page.

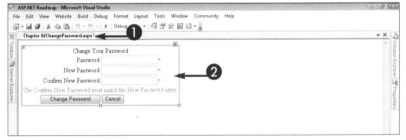

③ Click the Smart Tag button and select Auto Format.

④ In the Auto Format dialog box, select one of the predefined styles in the Select a scheme list.

In this example, Professional is selected.

⑤ Click Apply.

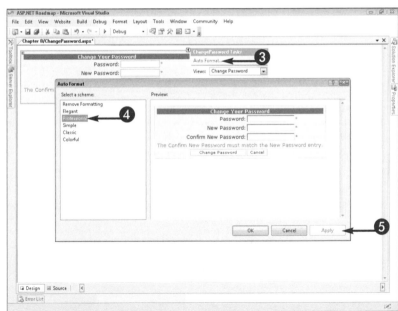

6 Open the page in a browser.

7 Type the current password and then type the new password in the appropriate fields.

8 Click the Change Password button to submit the request.

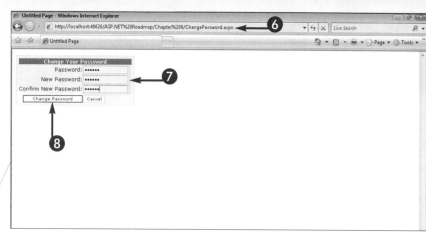

● A confirmation message appears.

Note: *If you entered the information correctly you should see a confirmation message, otherwise you will see an error message.*

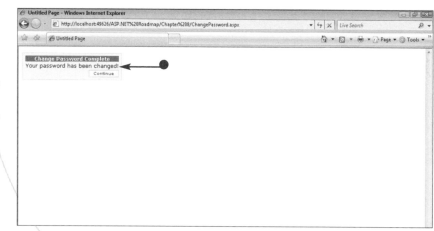

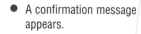

Extra

As security becomes more and more important, many Web sites and enterprises require more complex passwords. It is important to require a password that is complex enough to make it tough for a hacker to guess by using a common dictionary attack. But you must allow the user to set a password that is relatively easy to remember.

Validating a user's password can easily be done by defining a regular expression using the `NewPasswordRegularExpression` property of the `ChangePassword` control. If the user does not enter a new password that meets the `NewPasswordRegularExpression` criteria an error message is displayed that can be set through the `NewPasswordRegularExpressionErrorMessage` property. If a new password is not entered, the text of the `NewPasswordEequiredErrorMessage` is displayed. The following regular expression requires at least eight characters, with at least two numbers and one special character; `@\"(?=.{8,})(?=(.*\d){2,})(?=(.*\W){1,})`.

Additionally, the new password must meet all the criteria of the membership provider's password properties. These include the `MinrequiredPasswordLength`, `MinrequiredNonAlphaNumericCharacters`, and the `PasswordStrengthRegularExpression` properties. These properties can be configured in the site's Web.config file in the membership provider's definition section.

Create a SiteMap

A SiteMap is an XML file with a .sitemap extension that can be used to define the navigation structure for the Web site. The SiteMap automatically works with the default SiteMap provider, XMLSiteMapProvider, and is automatically used by the three navigation controls, SiteMapPath, Menu, and TreeView.

Only one SiteMap element may exist in the file, and it can have only one SiteMapNode element as a child element. But each SiteMapNode may contain unlimited child SiteMapNode elements.

A SiteMapNode has three attributes: Title, Description, and URL. The URL attribute is not required and may be left blank if you want to include a node in the navigation that is not active. One of the flexible features of a SiteMap is that it does not have to mirror the navigation structure of the site. For example, you may have a group of products and individual navigationfor each product, but not a category page. The

URL attribute may start with ~/, which indicates the application root.

The Title attribute specifies the text used in any anchor representing that node. However, this may simply be unlinked text if no URL is defined. The Description attribute supplies the tool tip text and documentation for the node.

The SiteMap element may be extended with custom attributes: for example, values for Keyword and Description Meta tags for each node. You just need to add attributes and text values for each custom property. These values are accessed programmatically from the SiteMapNode class:
SiteMap.CurrentNode("MetaDescription").

A site can have multiple sitemaps. You configure this by setting a SiteMapNode to have a SiteMapFile that references another sitemap file. The SiteMapNode may be localized in the Title and description attributes. To localize the URL property, define separate sitemap files for each language.

Create a SiteMap

① Open the Add New Item dialog box.

② Select SiteMap.

③ Click Add.

④ Replace the top SiteMapNode element values to represent the Web site's home page.

⑤ Repeat this process for the child SiteMapNodes to represent the site's navigational structure.

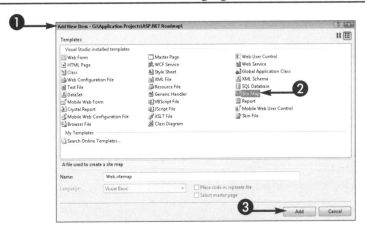

6 Add a new Web page to the site.

7 Add a `SiteMapData Source` control.

8 Add a `TreeView` control.

9 Set the `TreeView`'s data source to the `SiteMapDataSource`.

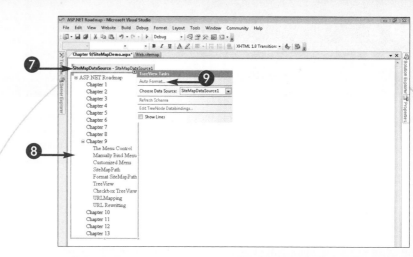

10 Open the page in a browser.

● You can see in the TreeView display that the SiteMap matches what was created in Steps 4 and 5.

Apply It

The `SiteMap` provider allows you to develop your own custom providers. You can even utilize more than one `SiteMap` provider in the same application. The machine.config configures the `XMLSiteMapProvider` by default, but this may be removed or added to in the web.config for each site. The following code demonstrates how to add a custom `SiteMap` provider, `SqlSiteMapProvider`, to the application. The sitemap element is located in the system.web section of the config file.

Configure a Custom Implementation of the SiteMapProvider:

```
<siteMap enabled="true" defaultProvider="AspNetSqlSiteMapProvider">
 <providers>
  <add name="AspNetSqlSiteMapProvider" type="SqlSiteMapProvider" securityTrimmingEnabled="true"
connectionStringName="MySiteDB"/>
 </providers>
</siteMap>
```

Use a SiteMapDataSource

The `SiteMapDataSource` control allows you to declaratively bind sitemap data to controls. It can be bound to `TreeView`, `Menu`, `GridView`, or `DropDownList` controls. The control automatically represents the data from the configured sitemap provider, such as a .sitemap file.

The root node of the sitemap is not necessarily the point the control will provide; you can designate another node to start the navigation from by setting the `StartFrom CurrentNode` to `false` and setting the `Starting NodeURL`. If you want to start the navigation from the current page you would set the `StartFromCurrentNode` to `true` and the `StartingNodeURL` to an empty string.

The `StartingNodeURL` manages the starting node for the `SiteMapDataSource` control. You can set this as the URL of the node to start the navigation hierarchy. The `StartFromCurrentNode` is a Boolean property to let you

designate if navigation starts from the current page or not. The `ShowStartingNode` property allows you to hide the starting node.

You can also set the `StartingNodeOffset` to indicate the number of levels up or down to render nodes in the tree from the current page. For example, you could set the `StartingNodeOffset` to -1 to start the navigation from the parent node down. If the value is positive, the first level of nodes displayed will be n level down from the starting node. The control determines how to choose the nodes to display based on the position of the requested page in the hierarchy. If the current node is not in the hierarchy the `StartingNodeOffset` is ignored.

If there are multiple `SiteMap` providers configured for the site, you can designate which provider to use by setting the `SiteMapProvider` property to the name of the target provider. You can set this programmatically and access a list of available providers through the `System.Web.SiteMap.Providers` collection.

Use a SiteMapDataSource

❶ Open the New Item dialog box.

❷ Select SiteMap.

❸ Click the Add Button.

❹ Replace the top `SiteMapNode` element's values to represent the Web site's home page.

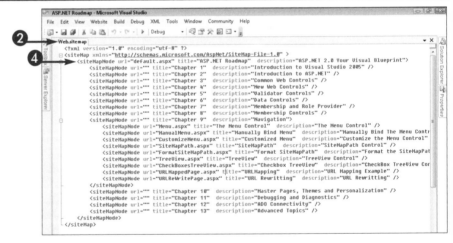

❺ Add a new page to the site named `SiteMapDataSource`.

❻ Click Add.

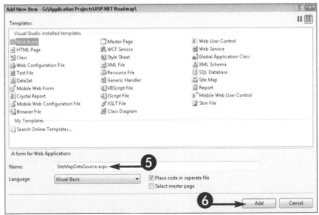

7. Add a `SiteMapdata Source` control.

8. Add a `Menu` control.

9. Set the Menu's data source to the `Site MapDataSource`.

10. Open the page in a browser.

11. Expand the Menu items.

● The nodes from the SiteMap file are displayed.

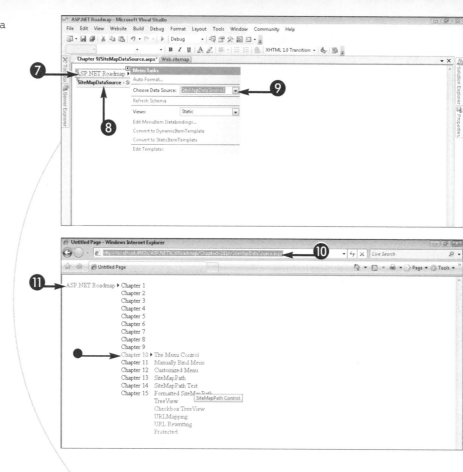

Each `DataSource` control has an associated Helper object, the `DataSourceView`. The `SiteMapData Source` is no different; it has the `SiteMapDataSourceView`. The `SiteMapDataSourceView` is used by control developers and not by a page developer. The `SiteMapDataSourceView` actually wraps the `SiteMapNodeCollection` class, giving you the ability to manipulate the collection.

The main method used to retrieve `SiteMapNodes` is Select, which returns a `SiteMapNodeCollection`.

Use the SiteMapView:
```
Dim siteMapView As SiteMapDataSourceView = _
 CType(siteMapData.GetView(String.Empty), SiteMapDataSourceView)


'Get the SiteMapNodeCollection from the SiteMapDataSourceView
Dim nodes As SiteMapNodeCollection = _
 CType(siteMapView.Select(DataSourceSelectArguments.Empty), _
 SiteMapNodeCollection)
```

A common problem when rendering site navigation is properly protecting site resources from those who are not authorized to view them. A `SiteMap` may have these resources defined in the structure so they can be included in the navigation controls. The sitemap provider is smart enough to protect site resources if security trimming is enabled.

To enable security trimming, the sitemap provider must be configured to do so in the web.config file by setting the `enableSecurityTrimming` attribute to `true`. The sitemap provider is configured at the machine level. To enable security trimming, override that configuration by creating a custom configuration in the site's web.config file.

The `SiteMapNode` element in the `SiteMap` file has a `Roles` attribute that can be used to specify a comma-separated list of allowed user roles. If you have external URLs defined in your sitemap you have to explicitly set

the roles that may access those URLs. You may define specific roles or an asterisk (*) wildcard for anyone to access a URL. If you have nodes without a URL specified, the roles need to be explicitly designated, such as in a subdirectory name.

Security trimming should not be confused with securing a Web site resource. It only prevents the URL from being rendered in a navigation control. To properly secure a Web resource you should configure the security either through ACLS for Windows authentication or through the `location` element with `Forms Authentication`.

The use of security trimming may cause performance degradation for sitemaps over 150 nodes. Because each node performs URL authorization, extra time is needed to perform this operation for each new page request and each node in the sitemap. The `Roles` attribute should be explicitly set for each node in the sitemap, allowing security trimming to bypass URL authorization.

Use Security Trimming

① Create a new Web page.

② Add a `Login` control.

③ Add a `SiteMapData Source` control.

④ Add a `TreeView` control and set the Data Source to the SiteMapDataSource.

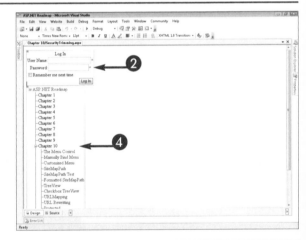

⑤ Open the site's sitemap file.

⑥ Add a `Roles` element to each node with an empty URL and set it to *.

⑦ Set the ProtectedPage.aspx `Roles` attribute to RoadMapUser role.

Note: *You may need to get a list of roles for your site and set any protected pages accordingly.*

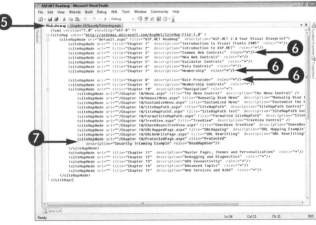

Open the web.config file.

⑨ Enter a custom SiteMap provider section with `securityTrimmingEnabled` set to `true`.

⑩ Add a location tag to allow only RoadMapUsers access to the protected page.

Note: *In the book's example site this is placed in a web.config file for the Chapter 10 folder.*

⑪ Open the page in a browser.

Note: *You should not see the protected page in the TreeView.*

⑫ Log in as a member of the RoadMapUser role.

● The Protected page is listed in the tree.

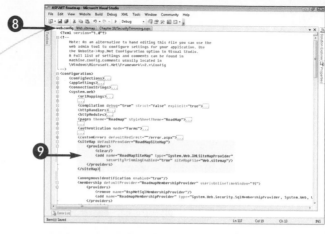

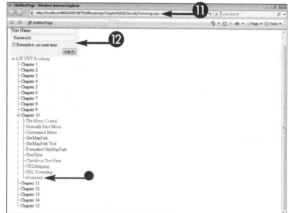

Apply It

Configure authorization rules and roles attributes carefully to prevent the unintended trimming of child site map nodes. In the following structure, you would not want to set tighter restrictions on the Honda node than the individual car nodes. This allows the Honda node to be visible to users when they have permission to view the individual car pages. If Honda had tighter restrictions, the individual car nodes would be hidden.

Example:
```
Cars
    Honda
        Civic
        Accord
        CRV
        Odyssey
```

Use the Menu Control

The Menu control can create either vertical or horizontal menus. You can create menus that are very similar to traditional Windows desktop applications or that span verticals on the left or right of the page with the Menu control. The Menu control is more flexible than the SiteMapPath control because it is not limited to just a SiteMap provider as its data source. You may bind any data source that implements the IHiearchicalDataSource or IHiearchicalEnumarable interfaces. The Menu control may also contain declarative data or have data bound to it at runtime.

The Menu control may have data bound to it declaratively or in the page markup by adding an Items property. The Items property is essentially a template that contains a collection of MenuItem objects. Each MenuItem object may contain child MenuItem objects, producing a menu

that cascades with each parent node. The Menu control may have only one Item tag, but it may have an unlimited number of MenuItem objects.

A MenuItem has several properties that may be set to define the appearance and target of the item in the Menu control. The NavigateURL property specifies the target URL for the menu node; it may be set to an empty string. If NavigateURL is an empty string then the node will not render a link, just the Text. The Text property represents the text displayed in the menu node. The Target property is used to specify the target window or frame in which the NavigateURL is opened.

The ImageURL is used to set the image used in the node instead of the Text property. Similarly, the PopOutImageURL can be used to designate an image used to indicate if the node has a pop-up menu of child nodes. If the Selectable property is set to false, clicking on the node does nothing.

Use the Menu Control

1 Create a new Web page.

2 Add a Menu control.

3 Add a SiteMapData Source control to the page.

4 Set the Menu's data source to the SiteMapDataSource.

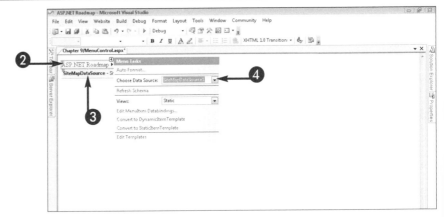

5 Click the Smart Tab button and select AutoFormat.

6 In the Auto Format dialog box, select one of the predefined schemes.

7 Click Apply.

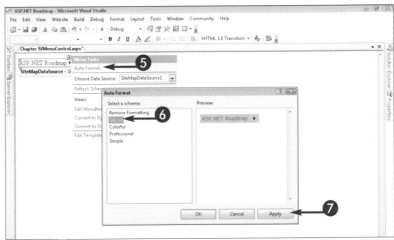

⑧ Open the Menu control's Properties window.

⑨ Set the Orientation to Horizontal.

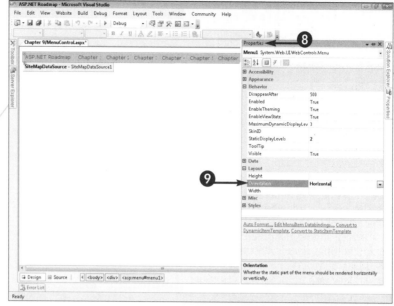

⑩ Open the page in a browser.

⑪ Move your mouse cursor around the menu.

The menu displays submenus with items that you can choose for navigation.

Apply It

Value is a string property of the MenuItem that can be used to store additional data about the node. The Value content is not visually displayed by the Menu control, but is used for supplemental purposes when the MenuItemClick event is raised. If a MenuItem does not have a NavigateURL set and the Selectable property is true, the MenuItemClick event will be raised when the node is selected by the user. This event may be used to process the selection as needed.

Use the Value Property to Perform Custom Logic:

```
Protected Sub Menu1_MenuItemClick(ByVal sender As Object, _
 ByVal e As System.Web.UI.WebControls.MenuEventArgs) _
  Handles Menu1.MenuItemClick
 'Process Selection Here
 Select Case e.Item.Value
  Case "SpecialValue"
    Response.Redirect("specialpage.aspx?sp=" & e.item.value)
 End Select
End Sub
```

Manually Bind the Menu Control

The navigational hierarchy may be set programmatically by manually adding MenuItems to the Items collection of the Menu control. Similarly, MenuItems may be added to the ChildItems collection of a MenuItem to create an organized navigation structure.

Stand-alone nodes may be added directly as a new object to a node collection. If a node has child nodes, you must create an instance of the node and add the child nodes directly to it before adding the parent MenuItem to the Menu control. The child node collection can be managed through the ChildItems property of the MenuItem object. The ChildItems property represents a MenuItemCollection that holds any child nodes for the MenuItem. It functions like any other collection and implements ICollection, IEnumerable, and IStateManager.

When you bind items to the Menu control at runtime you have more control over how each node is displayed. Because you can create a specific instance of each MenuItem you can specifically set each property of the node in the menu. The Text property controls the text displayed in the menu. You can indicate if it is clickable by setting the Selectable property to true or false.

The ImageURL property gets or sets the image that displayed next to the menu item, such as an icon. The PopOutImageURL specifies the image used to indicate the presence of child items. The SeparatorImageURL sets the image displayed below the menu item to separate it from other items.

The NavigationURL property gets or sets the destination of the menu node. You can control the QueryString values at runtime, which is useful when these may vary by user, session, or the URL of the current page. The Target property lets you set the target window or frame for the NavigationURL.

Manually Bind the Menu Control

① Add a new Web page.

② Add a Menu control.

③ Change to code-behind.

④ Add a BindMenu method with code to manually bind nodes to the menu control.

Note: *Stand-alone nodes may be added directly as a new object to the node items. If a node has child items, you must create an instance of the node and add the child nodes directly to it before adding it to the menu control.*

⑤ Open the Menu control's Properties window.

⑥ Set the StaticHover Style's Back Color to #FF8080.

⑦ Set the StaticHoverStyle's BorderStyle to Solid.

⑧ Set the StaticHoverStyle's BoderWidth to 1px.

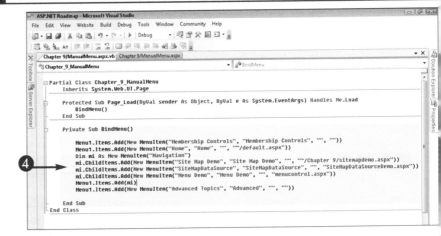

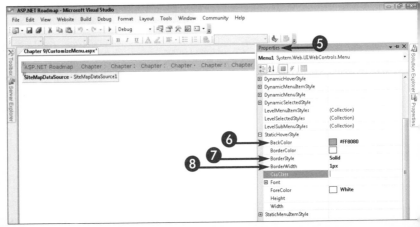

9 Set the ForeColor to #284E98, a dark blue.

10 Set the BackColor to #85C7DE, a light blue.

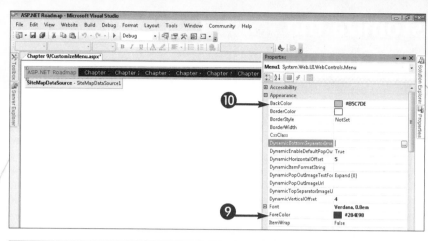

11 Open the page in a browser.

12 Move the mouse over the various menu items.

The various menu items are manually bound to the Menu control.

Apply It

The concept of security trimming or controlling access to pages is configurable when using a SiteMap file. When nodes are manually bound to a Menu control, managing access to nodes must be done by hand. A good way to check for proper authentication is to use the Role Provider to verify a user belongs to a role before adding the node to the Menu control or managing how the node is added to the Menu.

Use the Role.IsUserInRole Method to Verify Access to a URL:
```
If Role.IsUserInRole(Page.Identity, "Admin") then
 Menu1.Items.Add(New MenuItem("Admin", "Admin", "", " ~/admin/default.aspx"))
End if
```

Customize the Menu Control

The Menu control is fully customizable through a rich series of properties, style objects, and the use of Cascading Style Sheets. Some properties affect static menu items, while others are specific to dynamic menu items. The quickest way to apply style formatting to the Menu control is to select a scheme from the Auto Format dialog box, which is available through the control's Smart Tag.

While there are numerous individual properties, the Menu control supports many Style objects that can be used to control specific aspects of the Menu's appearance. There are also several Style object collections available to hold style settings for each progressive child level. The StaticHover Style defines the Style for the appearance of a static menu item when the mouse pointer is positioned over it. The StaticMenuItemStyle defines the Style for the appearance of a static menu item. The StaticMenuStyle defines the Style for the appearance of a static menu. The

StaticSelectedStyle defines the Style for the appearance of a selected static menu item. The Dynamic HoverStyle defines the Style for the appearance of a dynamic menu item when the mouse pointer is positioned over it. The DynamicMenuItemStyle defines the Style for the appearance of a dynamic menu item. The DynamicMenu Style defines the Style for the appearance of a dynamic menu. The DynamicMenuSelectedStyle defines the Style for the appearance of a selected dynamic menu item.

The LevelMenuItemStyles gets a MenuItemStyle Collection object that contains the style settings defining the appearance of menu items based on their level in a Menu control. LevelSelectedStyles gets a MenuItem StyleCollection object that contains the style settings that define the appearance of selected menu items based on their level in a Menu control. The LevelSubMenu Styles gets a MenuItemStyleCollection object that contains the style settings that define the appearance of submenu items based on their level in a Menu control.

Customize the Menu Control

❶ Create a new Web page.

❷ Add a Menu control.

❸ Add a SiteMapDataSource.

❹ Open the Menu control's SmartTag menu and set the Data Source to the SiteMapDataSource.

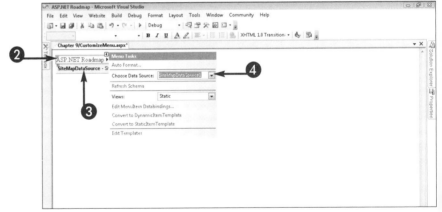

❺ Click the Smart Tag button and select Auto Format from the menu.

❻ Select one of the predefined schemes.

❼ Click Apply.

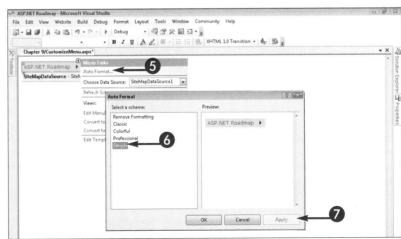

8 Open the Menu control's Properties window.

9 Set the StaticDisplay Levels property to 2.

10 Set the Orientation property to Horizontal.

11 Open the page in a browser.

12 Mouse over the menu items.

The display of each menu item is rendered differently.

Extra

There are many properties that are available to control specific aspects of the Menu control. Some control how the menu is rendered, while others manage commonalities to each MenuItem.

DisappearAfter	The amount of time in milliseconds a dynamic menu is displayed after the user moves the mouse out of the menu.
DynamicPopOutImageURL	Specifies the URL for the image that visually indicates a pop-up menu is available. The default is a triangle.
DynamicVerticalOffset	The number of pixels a dynamic menu is displaced from the parent menu item.
ItemWrap	Indicates if the MenuItem's text should be wrapped.
Orientation	Specifies if the menu is rendered vertically or horizontally.
StatisDisplayLevels	The number of static levels to display.

Use the SiteMapPath Control

The `SiteMapPath` control is used to create a BreadCrumb navigation strip for a Web site. It relies on the presence of a sitemap as part of the Web site. It creates a link for each of the nodes in the hierarchy to the current page. There is a node for each parent URL above the current page, so it shows users where they are in relation to the rest of the site.

The `SiteMapPath` control uses the `Title` attribute of each `SiteMapNode` as the linked text in each node. The `Description` attribute is used as the tool tip for each link displayed by the `SiteMapPath`. The URL attribute is used as the anchor link for each node displayed.

The `SiteMapPath` control can be customized to display custom separators through the `PathSeparator` property. It is used to change the text and HTML displayed between each node. The `PathSeparatorTemplate` can be used to create custom separators, such as special images.

The `PathDirection` property is an enumeration that has two values: `RootToCurrent` and `CurrentToRoot`. The default setting is `RootToCurrent`, which displays the node from the top level down to the current page. The `CurrentToRoot` displays in the reverse order, current page to the top level.

The `ParentLevelsDisplayed` property controls how many levels deep the navigation structure is displayed. It only shows the number of levels up from the current node. This is useful when the site navigation has numerous levels allowing you to reduce the number of levels displayed in the `SiteMapPath`.

The `ShowToolTips` property turns the display of tool tips on or off. The `RenderCurrentNodeAsLink` property allows the current node to be a hyperlink; by default it is plain text. The `SitemapProvider` property specifies which provider to use when more than one provider is defined for the site.

Use the SiteMapPath Control

① Create a new Web page.

② Add a `SiteMapPath` control to the page.

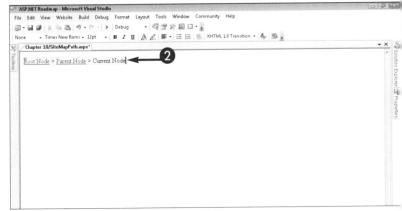

③ Click the Smart Tag button and select Auto Format from the menu.

④ Select one of the predefined schemes.

⑤ Click Apply.

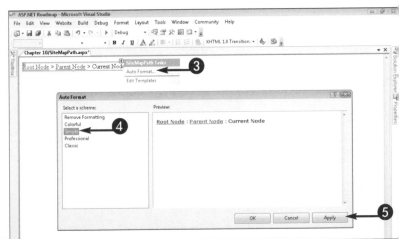

6 Open the page in a browser.

● The path to the current page appears.

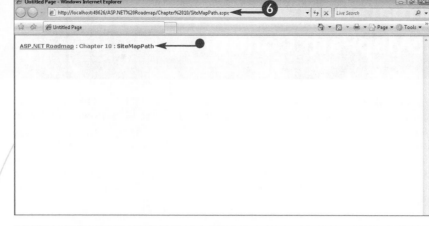

7 Open another page with a `SiteMapPath` control displayed.

● The path changes.

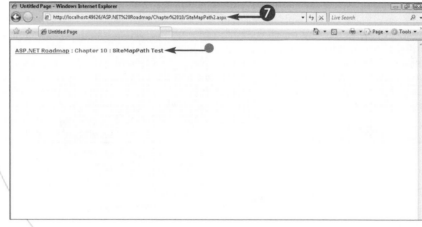

Extra

The `SkipLinkText` property makes the `SiteMapPath` more accessible to screen readers. If this property is set, an invisible image is rendered with the alternate text set. Because it is an invisible image the flow of the page is not disturbed, and it gives the reader an opportunity to skip the text altogether. The default setting makes readers skip this control. If you want to disable that behavior, you can set the property to `String.Empty`.

The value of this property is stored in `ViewState`, so you may want to consider this before adding a lot of information to this property. The value of this property may also be stored in a resource file and localized. Using a `SkipLinkText` property is useful for a site seeking Section 508 compliance for people with visual impairments.

Format the SiteMapPath Control

You can make the `SiteMapPath` control look consistent to your site by utilizing either custom templates or styles. The `SiteMapPath` control has the following style objects that allow you to set the formatting of the control: `CurrentNodeStyle`, `NodeStyle`, `PathSeparatorStyle`, and `RootNodeStyle`. It also has the following corresponding templates: `CurrentNodeTemplate`, `NodeTemplate`, `PathSeparatorTemplate`, and `RootNodeTemplate`.

The `CurrentNodeStyle` applies the formatting style to the current page's node in the path listing. The `NodeStyle` sets the formatting for all the nodes in the list regardless of their position in the list. If the node has an overriding style, such as the `CurrentNodeStyle`, configured, then the two styles are merged for that node. The settings for the current node are used first; any remaining settings from the `NodeStyle` are then applied. The `PathSeparatorStyle` sets the formatting for the separator object. The `RootNodeStyle` sets the formatting of the root node for the site.

The `NodeTemplate` is applied to all nodes in the list. If a `NodeStyle` is defined the template takes precedence. The `CurrentNodeTemplate` defines the layout for the current page's node in the list. The `RootNodeTemplate` defines the layout of the home page for the site and the `PathSeparatorTemplate` defines the layout for the list separators. If you have both a `NodeTemplate` and either a `RootNodeTemplate` or a `CurrentNodeTemplate` defined the `NodeTemplate` is ignored.

When you define a template you are responsible for adding any controls or elements to the template and binding them to the appropriate data. This means you are responsible for providing `Hyperlink` controls or `Labels` or whatever control or HTML elements, and binding the appropriate data to them. You can declaratively bind data from the sitemap data source by using the `Eval` method, `NavigateURL="<%# Eval("URL")%>"`.

Format the SiteMapPath Control

① Create a new Web page.

② Add a `SiteMapPath` control to the page.

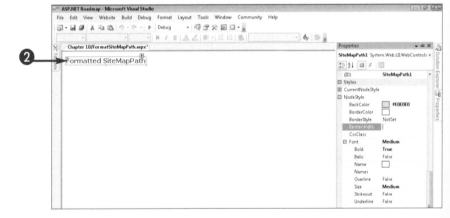

③ Click the Smart Tag button and select Auto Format from the menu.

④ Select one of the predefined schemes.

⑤ Click Apply.

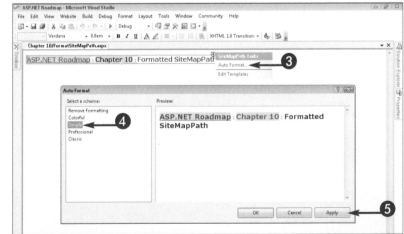

6. Set the `PathSeparator` to a colon (:).

7. Set the `CurrentNode` BackColor to white.

8. Set the `CurrentNode` ForeColor to #333333.

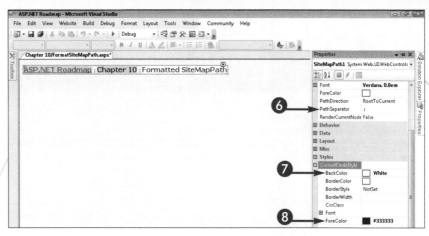

9. Open the page in a browser.

● The different styles are applied to the `SiteMap Path` control with the colon as a path separator.

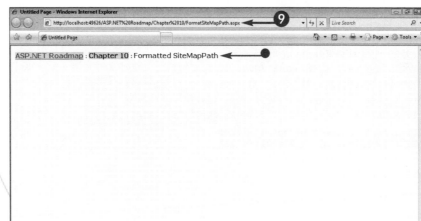

Apply It

You can set formatting at runtime by creating an event handler for the `SiteMapPath`'s `ItemCreated` event. The event passes a `SiteMapNodeItemEventArgs`, which gives you access to the node being rendered and all of its properties.

Set the Formatting Properties for the SiteMapPath at Runtime:

```
Protected Sub SiteMapPath1_ItemCreated(ByVal sender As Object, _
ByVal e As System.Web.UI.WebControls.SiteMapNodeItemEventArgs) Handles SiteMapPath1.ItemCreated
  Select Case e.Item.ItemType
   Case SiteMapNodeItemType.Current
    e.Item.ForeColor = Drawing.Color.Black
    e.Item.BackColor = Drawing.Color.AliceBlue
   Case SiteMapNodeItemType.Root
    e.Item.ForeColor = Drawing.Color.Tomato
    e.Item.BackColor = Drawing.Color.Red
  End Select
End Sub
```

Display Navigation in the TreeView Control

The `TreeView` control displays hierarchical data in an expandable tree structure. You can bind data to the `TreeView` control declaratively, manually, from a `SiteMapDataSource`, or from any data source that implements the `IHierarchicalDataSource`. The `TreeView` control is composed of a series of nested `TreeNode` objects that specify at least a `Text` property.

A `TreeView` control can be built declaratively by adding a <Nodes> template with a series of nested `TreeNodes`. Each `TreeNode` is composed of at least a `Text` property, but may optionally contain a `NavaigateURL` and `Value` property. If the `NavigateURL` property is set to a URL, when the user clicks the link he or she is taken to that location. If this property is left blank the node causes the page to post back to the server.

When the user selects a node in the `TreeView` control that does not have a designated `NavigationURL` value,

the page is posted back to the server and a `SelectedNodeChanged` event is executed. The `Value` property should be used to pass special values back when the user selects a node and it posts back to the server for processing.

You can format the TreeView through several `TreeNodeStyle` objects. The `TreeNodeStyle` class inherits the `Style` class but adds a few more properties specific to the `TreeView` control such as `NodeSpacing` and `ImageURL`. `NodeStyle` represents the general appearance of nodes in the tree. The `HoverNodeStyle` defines the appearance of a node when the mouse hovers over the node. The `LeafNodeStyle` defines the appearance of a leaf node or a node without any children. The `ParentNodeStyle` defines the appearance of a parent node. `SelectedNodeStyle` defines the appearance of the selected node. An easy way to apply formatting is to choose predefined schema from the Auto Format dialog box through the control's `SmartTag`.

Display Navigation in the TreeView Control

① Open the New Item dialog box.

② Select SiteMap.

③ Click Add.

④ Replace the top `SiteMapNode` element's values to represent the Web site's home page.

⑤ Repeat this process for the child `SiteMapNodes` to represent the site's navigational structure.

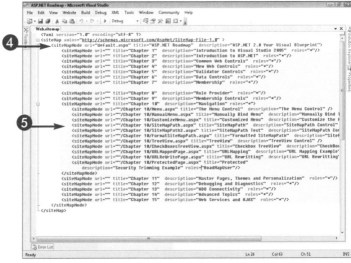

6. Add a new page to the site.

7. Add a `SiteMapDataSource` control.

8. Add a `TreeView` control.

9. Set the `TreeView`'s data source to the `SiteMap DataSource`.

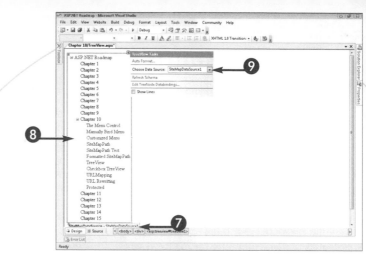

10. Open the page in a browser.

- The `TreeView` displays the SiteMap matching what you created in Steps 4 and 5.

Extra

Another important formatting option for the `TreeView` control is designating the style of lines used to connect the nodes of the tree. You need to set the `ShowLines` property to `true` before lines can be rendered. You can then access the TreeView Line Image Generator tool to designate the types of lines you want in the `TreeView` control. This tool can be accessed either through the `TreeView`'s `SmartTag` or Properties window. You can also click the expand and collapse icons associated with the various nodes in the tree in this dialog box.

Apply It

You can programmatically expand and collapse nodes in the tree. This can be done at the TreeView level or at the node level.

Methods to Collapse and Expand Tree Nodes:
```
TreeView1.Collapse()
TreeView1.ExpandAll()
TreeView1.Nodes(0).Expand()
TreeView1.Nodes(0).CollpaseAll()
```

Display Check Boxes in the TreeView Control

You can display check boxes to the left of nodes in the TreeView by setting the ShowCheckBoxes property to one of the available TreeNodeTypes enumerations. The enumeration options are All, Leaf, None, Parent, and Root.

All causes check boxes to be displayed to the left of each node in the tree, while Leaf causes this only for nodes that have no child nodes. The Parent option will display check boxes only for nodes that have children. The Root option will display a check box only for the Root node. You can set the ShowCheckBoxes property at runtime as well as declaratively.

Checking the state of a check box in the TreeView control can be done by looping through each Node in the CheckedNodes collection. The CheckedNodes collection holds a reference to each of the TreeNodes with a selected CheckBox. This is a collection that manages the

actual collection of nodes with a CheckBox that have been selected, eliminating the need to do this programmatically.

There is no AutoPostBack feature in the TreeView that allows you to create an event handler when a node has been selected. Therefore, you typically add a Button or other control that initiates a post-back to the server to process the requested nodes in the TreeView control. This event handler needs to loop through the selected nodes and process the selections accordingly.

There is a TreeNodeCheckChanged event that fires when the checked status of a node changes between posts. This event only fires when the page is posted back to the server and not when the checkbox state actually changes. You will still have to loop through the selected nodes to determine what change you may be interested in processing.

Display Check Boxes in the TreeView Control

① Add a new Web page.

② Add a SiteMapDataSource to the page.

③ Add a TreeView control to the Page.

④ Set the DataSource to the SiteMapDataSource control.

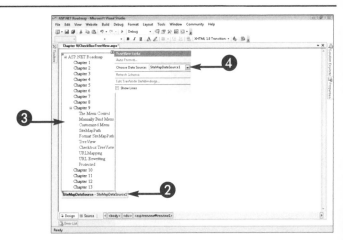

⑤ Set ShowCheckBoxes to All.

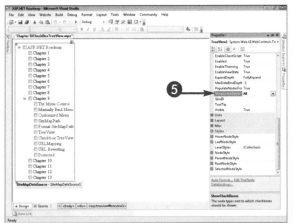

6 Add a `Button` control.

7 Double-click the button and add some code to echo the check box selections in the `TreeView` control.

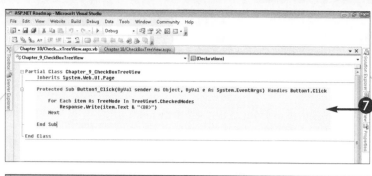

8 Open the page in a browser.

9 Select various check boxes in the TreeView.

10 Click Choose.

A list of checked nodes is listed above the TreeView.

Apply It

The `TreeView` control gives you the power to designate your own custom icons to display with each node. Following are seven `ImageURL` properties you can set to decorate the `TreeView` control:

`CollapseImageURL`	Image to indicate the node can be collapsed to hide child nodes
`ExpandImageURL`	Image to indicate the node can be expanded to show child nodes
`LeafImageURL`	Image to indicate a node has no child nodes
`NoExpandImageURL`	Image to indicate the node may not be expanded
`ParentNodeImageURL`	Image to indicate a parent node
`RootNodeImageURL`	Image to indicate the root nodes in the TreeView

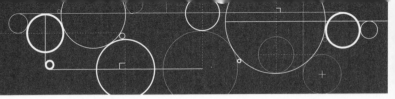

Use URL Mapping

URL mapping allows you to create a series of simple URLs that map to more complex URLs in your site. URLs are often rather complex with large `querystrings` or multiple subdirectories. URL mappings are configured in the `urlMappings` element of the web.config file of the Web site. The `urlMappings` element is located in the `system.web` element. The remapping actually occurs before any other processing of the request happens.

Mappings are added to the `urlMappings` section in an add element with two attributes: `url` and `mappedurl`. The `url` attribute represents the actual URL entered in the address bar of the browser. The `mappedurl` attribute is the actual URL it is mapped to. The `mappedurl` may contain `querystring` parameters but may not contain wildcard characters such as an asterisk (*). All mapping must be a page-to-page relationship or a one-to-one relationship.

By mapping a URL to another URL the mapped URL is never actually opened. You can map URLs with any extension to any other valid URL on the site. For example, you might want to map a legacy HTML file to a newer ASPX file.

Under the hood, the ASP.NET runtime checks to see if there are any URL mappings for the request URL. If so then it uses the `httpContext.RewritePath` method to update the request's URL to the mapped URL, including any `querystring` parameters.

URL mapping has several limitations: The first is a static mapping and requires someone to manually set up each mapping statement. The other is it does not support regular expressions or dynamic mapping. Dynamic mapping can be done by using URL rewriting.

Use URL Mapping

① Open the site's web.config file.

② Add a `urlMappings` element to the `system.web` section.

③ Add a mapped URL to the section to map `Treeview.aspx` to a page in the Web site.

④ Add a mapped URL to the section to map `Gridview.aspx` to another page in the site.

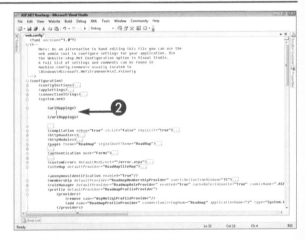

⑤ Open the Treeview.aspx URL.

● The buried page opens, but looks as though it is on the root of the site.

⑥ Open the Gridview.aspx URL.

● The buried page opens, but looks as though it is on the root of the site.

Note: *These two mappings are to pages on the book's companion Web site. You can map to any page on your site.*

Apply It

URL mapping should not be used in the place of a 301 redirect. A 301 redirect simply refers to telling the user agent, such as a browser or more importantly a search engine spider, that a resource is now in a new permanent location. When you implement URL mapping the URL is simply mapped to the new location and the Http Status sent to the client is 200, meaning this is a valid successful request. When you send a 301-status code to the client, you are saying this URL does not exist anymore, but refer to the new URL for future reference. To do this, create a custom `httpModule` and pass the new location and the status to the response header.

Perform a 301 Redirect with Code in a Custom httpModule:

```
Dim app As HttpApplication = CType(sender, HttpApplication)
Dim targetUrl As String = GetMappedURL(app.Request.RawUrl)
app.Response.StatusCode = 301 ' make a permanent redirect
app.Response.AddHeader("Location", targetUrl)
app.Response.End()
```

Use URL Rewriting

URL rewriting takes mapping to the next level by allowing dynamic URL mapping. Developers have created many ways to accomplish URL rewriting and most involve a combination of a custom `httpModule` and regular expressions to perform an efficient rewriting mechanism.

Typically the rules that govern the URL rewriting for a site are defined in the web.config file, XML file, database, or other custom data store. Regular expressions provide a concise language to define rules to parse public URLs to produce actual URLs with parameters used to produce the page.

Mapping needs to be done in the ASP.NET pipeline, so you must create a custom `HttpModule` to process the rewriting. Typically the module creates an event handler for the `AuthorizeRequest` event.

Most URL rewriting modules implement the regular expressions to parse the requested URL for parameters.

The common technique to use is a grouping syntax like (.*) and map that to the query string portion of the actual URL in the following syntax: mappedUrl="~/content.aspx?PageName=$1". The $1 represents the group collected from the regular expression. You can also maintain a table, such as a `Dictionary` object or `HashTable` to maintain a direct mapping of public URLs to actual URLs.

The big secret to rewriting URLs is the `HttpContext.Current.RewritePath` method. The `RewritePath` method has four overloads, which allows you to pass just the new URL `QueryString` parameters and indicate if the virtual path should be reset. The method assigns an internal rewrite path, which means the URL requested can differ from the actual URL that is being processed by the ASP.NET engine. Once the rewriting engine determines the actual URL for rendering, the actual URL is passed to the `RewritePath` method and is used by the remaining pipeline to complete processing of the request.

Use URL Rewriting

1 Add a new class file to the Web site.

2 Add a new custom `httpModule` that implements `IHttpModule`.

3 Add code to the custom `httpModule` to rewrite the request based on a regular expression.

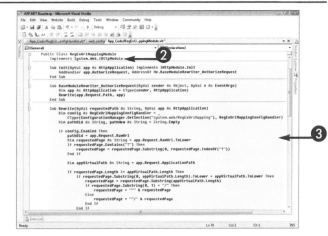

4 Add a new class file to the Web site.

5 Add a new class that implements `IConfigurationSectionHandler`.

6 Add code to the custom class to manage the regular expression rewriting rules in the web.config file.

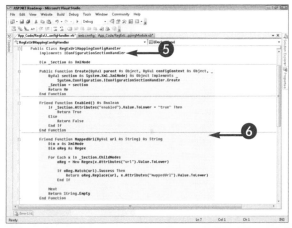

7 Open the site's web.config file.

8 Add sections to the config file to implement the custom regular expression rewriting rules.

9 Add a new section to the system.web element to define the regular expression rule.

10 Add code to the page to echo the QueryString parameter.

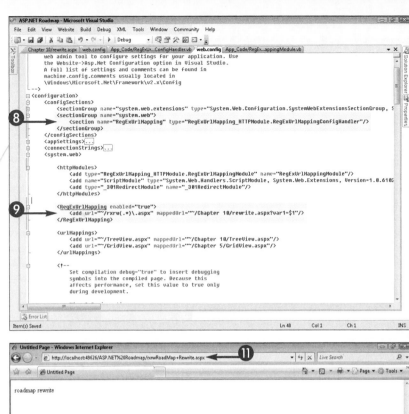

11 Open a URL in a browser that conforms to the regular expression rule.

The rewritten QueryString parameter is echoed on the page if the rewriting module is properly registered.

The `VirtualPathProvider` class allows you to abstract pages in a Web site from the files system or, really, any data store you want. This means you can store prebuilt content in a database, file system, and even cached in memory for fast loading. It also lends itself well to friendly URLs. There are some files that cannot be handled by the `VirtualPathProvider`, such as web.config, Global.asax, class files, and so on.

The `VirtualPathProvider` is an abstract or `MustInherit` class where you must define your own method overloads to manage the content. You must override the `FileExists` and `GetFile` methods to use the `VirtualPathProvider`.

You must register a `VirtualPathProvider` before you can use it. This is done by calling the `HostingEnvironment.RegisterVirtualPathProvider` method. This method is actually called in the `AppInitialize` method, which can be placed in any class in the App_Code folder. This method is automatically called by the framework.

Create a Master Page

Master pages are an easy way to manage a consistent layout to a group of pages or all the pages in an ASP.NET Web site. You add a Master page just like a normal page in Visual Studio. The simplest way to do this is to right-click the solution root of the application to add the Master page by selecting Add New Item from the context menu. In the New Item dialog box that appears, Master page is one of the choices. Type the name of your new Master page, click Add, and the page is added to the application.

A Master page contains the top-level HTML elements, including HTML, Head, Body, and Form. The layout itself is built with standard HTML elements, such as a table or StyleSheet positioning with DIV and SPAN HTML tags. It also contains any Web or HTML controls needed for the common layout.

In addition to basic layout code, a Master page contains at least one ContentPlaceHolder control. The child page that utilizes the Master page adds its local content, controls, and markup in a local Content control, which acts as a reference to the ContentPlaceHolder in the Master page. If the Master page contains multiple ContentPlaceHolder controls the child page may contain a Content control for each ContentPlaceHolder.

You can define the Master page for a specific page by setting the MasterPageFile directive to the path of the Master page file. You can also define this at runtime by setting the MasterPageFile property of your page in the PreInit event handler. This must be done in the PreInit event handler because of the way the ASP.NET pipeline executes the relationship between the Master and child pages. After this step, ASP.NET actually flips their relationship under the hood.

Create a Master Page

① Create a new Master page file.

② Add a simple Header and Side table layout for the page.

③ Move the ContentPlaceHolder control to a cell in the table.

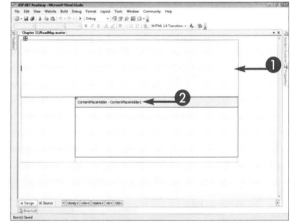

④ Add an H1 HTML TAG title to the top cell of the table.

⑤ Add a Menu control to the left cell of the second table row and set the StaticDisplayLevels to 2.

⑥ Add a SiteMapDataSource control to the page.

⑦ Assign the SiteMapDataSource to the Menu control.

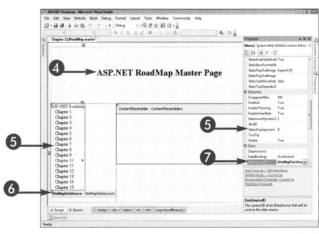

8 Add a new Web page to the site by selecting the Select Master page check box.

9 Select the Master page added in step **1**.

10 Add a simple message to the `Content` control.

11 Open the page in a browser.

● The layout for the page is inherited from the Master page, and the `menu` control provides navigation through the site.

Apply It

Another nice feature of Master pages is the ability to define your own base `MasterPage` class. You can create your own methods and properties that can then be inherited by any `MasterPage` you want. This is a great technique to manage common methods, properties, and control references you use on most pages.

The regular ASP.NET page can reference any of the public methods and properties of the Master page. The `MasterPage` property of the `System.Web.UI.Page` class provides direct access to the Master page. If you try to access public properties or methods defined in your Master page, then you must perform a cast to your `Master page` class.

A Custom Master Page Class Shell:

```
Public Class CustomMasterPage
 Inherits System.Web.UI.MasterPage

 Private Sub Page_Init(ByVal sender As Object, ByVal e As System.EventArgs) Handles Me.Init
  'Place core Initialization code here

 End Sub
End Class
```

Apply a Master Page

There are multiple ways a content page can have a Master page associated with it. After a Master page has been defined in an ASP.NET Web site, you can use it as a content page. It may be applied with the `MasterPageFile` directive or in the page's `PreInit` event handler. In addition, the Master page may be defined for the entire application in the web.config file. If you define the Master page at runtime, you must set the `MasterPageFile` property of the page in the `PreInit` event handler. After the page enters the initialization stage of the life cycle, it accesses information and applies the Master page layout and information.

```
<%@ Page Language="VB"
MasterPageFile="MySite.Master" %>
```

Applying the Master page in the web.config file causes the Master page to be rendered in any content page that contains a `ContentPlaceHolder` control. If the content page does not contain a `ContentPlaceHolder` control the Master page is not applied. Defining the Master page in the @page directive or at runtime overrides the Master page defined in the web.config.

```
<pages masterPageFile="MySite.Master" />
```

Apply a Master Page

1 Create a new Web page for a site with at least two Master pages defined.

2 Click the Source button to switch to Source view.

3 Set the `MasterPageFile` directive to the desired Master page.

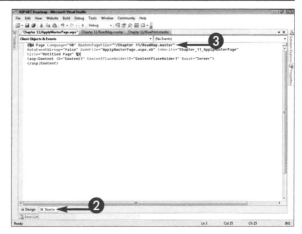

4 Click the Design button to switch to Design view.

5 Add a `Button` control to the `Content` control.

⑥ Double-click the button to create a `Click` event handler.

⑦ Add code to the `Click` event handler to set the `Session` variable to the `MasterPageFile`.

⑧ Add code to the `PreInit` event handler to toggle the `MasterPageFile`.

⑨ Open the page in a browser.

⑩ Click Switch to toggle between the Master pages.

The Master page changes between the two files available.

Apply It

The Master page for an individual page may be set at runtime. This can be commonly leveraged for multisite portals or sites where users can customize their layouts like a modern social networking site. Common ways to choose which Master page to apply are through the profile provider, `QueryString` parameters, form variables, session IDs, cookies, or custom application settings. Some applications display different Master pages based on user authentication, IP location (think a layout per country, state, and so on). To set the Master page at runtime, set the `MasterPageFile` property in the `PreInit` event handler based on any variable available.

Setting the MasterPageFile Property Based on a QueryString Variable:

```
Protected Sub Page_PreInit(ByVal sender As Object, _
 ByVal e As System.EventArgs) Handles Me.PreInit
 'Set the master page based on a QueryString variable.
 'If the variable does not exist, then default to the RoadMap.master
 If Not IsNothing(Request.QueryString("Master")) Then
  Page.MasterPageFile = "~/Chapter 11/" & Request.QueryString("Master") & ".master"
 Else
  Page.MasterPageFile = "~/Chapter 11/RoadMap.master"
 End If
End Sub
```

Access Master Page Properties and Events

Custom public properties, methods, and events can be created in a Master page's class file. These members may be accessed by creating a casted instance of the Master page class in the content page. You must know the type of class you are trying to cast because if the content page's Master page is not of the same type as you are casting you will cause exceptions to be thrown when you access these methods.

When using a Master page, you can set the page's title through the `Title` property of the Master page. The `Title` property as well as any other publicly accessible properties or methods are accessible through the `Page.Master` property. First, check to see if the `Master` property returns a reference to the `Master` page before accessing any property or method on the Master page.

Any custom members should be declared as public or else they will not be accessible in the content page's class. A property may be read-only or read-write. A method can return a value or just accept parameters. An event has a method signature that needs to be handled by the content page.

Any references to content created at runtime by the Master page that needs to be accessed by the content page should be done in the page's `LoadComplete` event handler. The `PageLoad` event fires in the content page before the `Load` event fires in the Master page. This is because the Master page actually becomes a child control of the page as the ASP.NET processes the request. The `LoadComplete` event is new to ASP.NET 2.0 and fires after the page's `Load` event has completed as well as any child controls on the page. See Chapter 2 for information on the event firing order.

Access Master Page Properties and Events

1. Create a Master page.

2. Add a simple layout to the Master page.

3. Click the Design button to switch to Design view.

4. Add an H1 tag, make it `runat server`, and assign an Id to it.

5. Open the code-behind file for the Master page.

6. Create a public property to get and set the `InnerText` of the H1 tag.

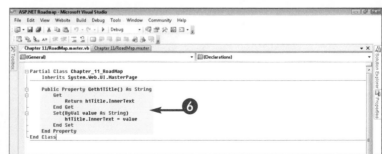

7. Create a new Web page that uses the Master page.

8. Switch to the page's code-behind.

9. Add an event handler for the LoadComplete event.

10. Add code to reference the Master page and echo the value of the public property.

11. Open the page in a browser.

The text content of the H1 tag of the Master page is echoed in the content page.

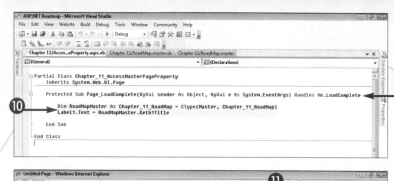

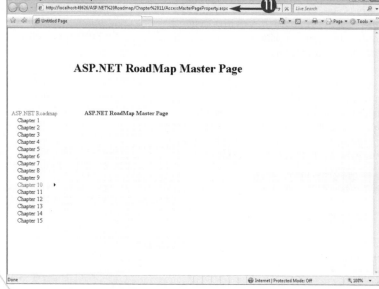

Apply It

To handle an event from a Master page class the content page must add an event handler manually and have a method to process the event that matches the signature of the event. The typical event handler signature has an object and a custom event handler argument class. The sender object is a reference to the object sending the event. The argument class contains a set of custom values that you can use to process the event.

Assign an Event Handler in the Content Page:
```
AddHandler myMasterPageRef.btnSubmit.Click AddressOf Submit_Click
```

An Event Handler Method Signature:
```
Protected Sub Submit_Click(ByVal sender as Object, ByVal e As System.EventArgs)
 'Do Some Work Here
End Sub
```

Access Controls on a Master Page

Programmatically, accessing controls on a page at runtime is a very common practice in ASP.NET, and it is often a common need when using Master pages, too. You can access controls through the content page by calling the `FindControl` method of a Master page class. The Master page class could also create a public property to access the control. This technique requires the content page to create a casted instance of the specific Master page class.

It is a good practice to type cast the reference to the control to ensure you are working with the correct control type. For example, if you try to access a `Label` control on the Master page you garner the reference like this, "CType(Master.FindControl("Label1"), Label). Now the properties of the `Label` control are accessible to the content page to read and change if necessary.

The content page can have a `MasterType` directive defined in its header. In the `MasterType` page directive the `VirtualPath` attribute set to the Master page's file is defined. For example, VirtualPath="~/MyMasterFile .master". This causes the Master page reference to be strongly typed, providing proper access to the members of the applied Master page. This includes any controls and properties contained in the Master page.

If you do not define the Master page in the page directive, you still need to strongly type any reference to the Master page. You can strongly type a reference to any object by casting it. You need to strongly type object references when the object is inherited from another class or interface, like `MasterPage`. An example would be dim mmp as MyMasterPage = CType(MasterPage, MyMasterPage). Any properties or controls you want to reference must be declared as public members of the Master page.

Access Controls on a Master Page

① Create a Master page file.

② Add a simple layout.

③ Add a button and set the text to Click Me.

④ Switch to code-behind.

⑤ Add a public `ReadOnly` property that returns a reference to the button.

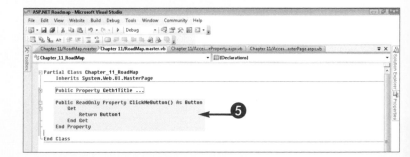

6 Create a Web page that uses the Master page.

7 Switch to code-behind.

8 Add a reference to the Master page in the `Page_Load` event handler.

9 Add an event handler for the button's `Click` event to echo the time of the event.

10 Open the page in a browser.

11 Click the button on the Master page.

The page updates each time the button is clicked.

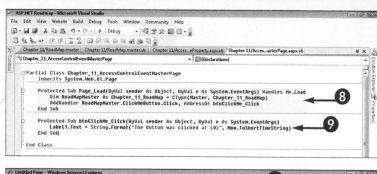

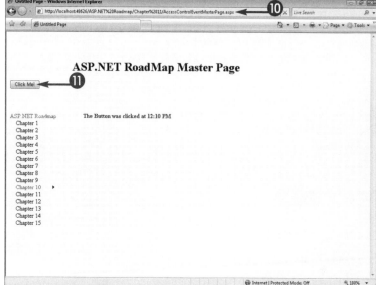

Apply It

Creating event handlers for controls on a Master page is a very useful trick. By creating a reference to the control in the Master page, an event handler for the control's events can be added as if it existed in the content page.

Declare an Event Handler for a Master Page Control:
```
Dim cmp As CustomMasterPage = CType(Master, CustomMasterPage)
AddHandler cmp.btnSearch.Click, AddressOf btnSearch_Click
```

Handle an Event for a Button on a Master Page:
```
Protected Sub btnSearch_Click(ByVal sender As Object, ByVal e As System.EventArgs)
 'Perform Search
End Sub
```

Use Nested Master Pages

Sometimes you may want to define a general layout for your application and still have common layout elements shared among groups of content pages. A Master page can declare its own Master page, in essence becoming a child Master page. The child Master page declares its own `MasterPageFile` just like a typical content page would and has a `Content` control for each `ContentPlaceHolder` of the parent Master page.

The parent Master page file would declare at one or more `ContentPlaceHolders` and a common layout. The child Master page declares corresponding `Content` controls where it defines the layout and controls what is passed to any content page or grandchild Master page that uses the child Master page. There are no limits how far Master pages may be nested.

Just like any Master page, the child Master page declares at least one `ContentPlaceHolder` control. The `ContentPlaceHolder` is carried to any content page that uses the child Master page.

The only problem with using nested Master pages is Visual Studio 2005 does not allow you to work with the pages in Design view. This can cause a problem when you need to use Design view to work with your child Master page or content pages. You can still work with the user interface code in Source view and all tags, tag attributes, and properties are available in Source view. It just takes away from the ease of development.

The ultimate hierarchy of the site from a Master page perspective can be a branching tree that resembles a pyramid. Each Master page can have an unlimited number of child Master pages and there is no limit to the number of child Master pages that can be nested.

Use Nested Master Pages

1 Create a new Master page.

2 Define a simple layout with a `ContentPlaceHolder` control.

3 Add some text or something else to indicate this Master page.

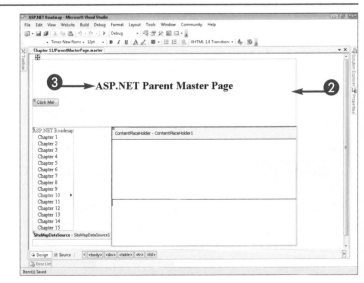

4 Create another Master page file.

5 Define a simple layout with a `ContentPlaceHolder`.

6 Add some text or something else to indicate this Master page.

7 Set the `MasterPageFile` to the first Master page created.

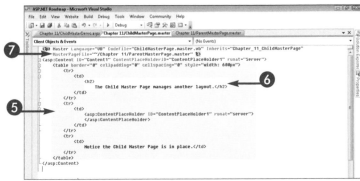

⑧ Add a Content page that uses the second Master page you created.

⑨ Add some text or something else to indicate this page.

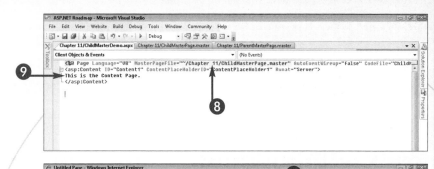

⑩ Open the page in a browser.

The layout reflects the nested Master pages and the Content page's content.

Apply It

Not every Web site is viewed by a specific browser such as Internet Explorer 7. Often, content needs to be specifically targeted to a particular browser such as Firefox or a Pocket PC. ASP.NET allows you to define multiple Master pages for a content page that corresponds to a different viewer.

This can be done in the page directive by adding multiple `MasterPageFiles` with a `Browser` attribute defined for it. The format is Opera:masterPageFile="~/OperaMaster.Master". A list of available browsers can be a system's browser file or added to your application specifically in a .browser file.

A Page Directive for Multiple Viewers:

```
<%@ Page Language="vb" AutoEventWireup="false" Inherits="MyPage" CodeFile="MyPage.aspx.vb"
MasterPageFile="~/MyMaster.master"

Opera:MasterPageFile="~/MyOperaMaster.master" Mozilla:MasterPageFile="~/MyMozillaMaster
.master" %>
```

Master Page
Caching Considerations

Developers often use output caching to increase the performance of their applications. Output caching places a copy of the page in memory for the specified period time and can be varied by a variety of directive parameters. If you place an Output `Cache` directive in a Master page, you will receive an error the second time the page loads because the ASP.NET engine cannot find the page.

You can cache Master pages, but they rely on the caching directive in the content page. The caching directive and the resulting caching also caches the Master page content as well as the content page. Caching a page with a Master page treats the combination just as if it were one file.

Output caching is a way to store dynamically generated pages in memory for a specified period of time. This drastically improves the performance of each cached page

in the Web site. Output caching is set using the `OutputCache` directive in the page header.

There are several attributes that can be set to define the caching mechanism. `Duration` specifies the time in seconds the page content is to be stored in memory. `VaryByParam` gives you the ability to specify different versions of the page to cache based on a comma-separated list of `POST` parameters. `VaryByHeader` specifies different versions of the page to cache based on a comma-separated list of `HTTP Header` names. The `VaryByControl` property is a semicolon list of control identifiers to vary the page's cached output. `VaryByCustom` is a list of custom properties that cause a variation of the cached page to be stored. When using a custom string you must override the `GetVaryByCustomString` method in the Global.asax file.

Master Page Caching Considerations

① Create a new Master page.

② Add a simple layout around the `ContentPlaceHolder` control.

③ Add some text and other elements needed on content pages.

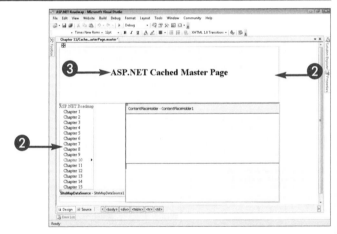

④ Add a new Web page.

⑤ Assign the Master page to the Master page created in step **1**.

⑥ Add a `Label` control to the `Content` control.

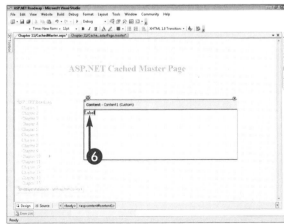

7 Click the Source View button to switch to Source view.

8 Add an `OutputCache` directive to cache the page for 10 seconds.

9 Add a declarative statement to display the current date and time.

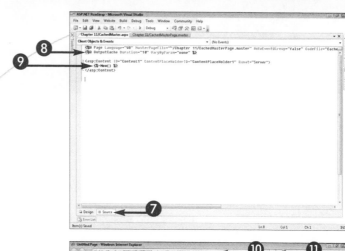

10 Open the page in a browser.

11 Reload by the page every few seconds by entering Ctrl+F5.

The value of the `Label` control updates every 10 seconds.

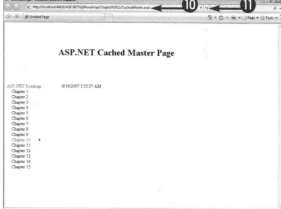

Apply It

One of the most common frustrations for developers new to using Master pages is declaring relative URLs to images and hyperlinks. The relative nature of the URLs can also vary based on if they are used in an HTML tag or a Web control. In the case of an ASP.NET Web control, all relative URLs are based on the location of the Master page. For HTML tags, the relative URL is interpreted from the content page's location.

While you could use absolute URLs, the drawback is they are hard-coded for a specific location that may change in the future, causing a maintenance nightmare. A common trick many ASP.NET developers use is creating a function in a base page class that dynamically creates URLs to images and other resources in the site.

A Common Function to Return a Dynamic Absolute URL:
```
Public Function RelativeURL(sResource as string) as string
  'CoreSourcePath is a property or configuration setting indicating
  'where to start the absolute path.
  Return String.Format("{0}/{1}", CoreSourcePath, sResource)
End Function
```

Applying the Dynamic Absolute URL
```
<img src=<%="RelativeURL("Logo.gif") %>/>
```

Create a Theme

ASP.NET themes empower the developer to create a series of custom design features that can be applied as needed to a Web site. Each Web site can have as many themes as desired. Themes are stored in the App_Themes folder with subfolder names representing each theme name.

The folder containing the theme can contain any of several files: images, skin files, style sheets, and text files. Skin files define uniform settings for a control's properties. There is no limit to the number of skin files you can include in a theme. A skin file can define anywhere from one to 100 controls settings before site performance begins to degrade.

Skins define property settings for controls. A style sheet defines style rules to be applied to any HTML element on the page. Style rules can be added to a theme by right-clicking the theme folder and selecting New Item. In the

New Item dialog box, select Style Sheet. You can hand code your style sheet rules or use the Style Builder dialog box, which is displayed by right-clicking in the definition of a style rule.

It is important to understand the order of precedence with themes. The Skin file always takes precedence over any conflicting style rule. For example, a style rule may be defined for an HTML INPUT element in a style sheet, but a skin definition for a TextBox might define different formatting. The skin's formatting is applied to the TextBox over the style rule.

When using images as part of a theme it is a good idea to create an images subfolder. Any control that uses an image and refers to this common location for the image is automatically resolved correctly by ASP.NET at runtime to match the URL to the image in the designated theme.

Create a Theme

① Add a new Skin file to a Web site.

Note: *If you do not have an App_Theme folder you are prompted to create the folder and the Skin file is placed there.*

② Add the Skin definition for a TextBox with a gray background and thin blue border.

③ Add a Label definition for Blue, Bold text.

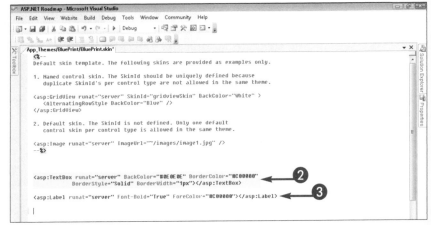

④ Add a Style Sheet to the theme.

⑤ Set the body rule to make the background color aliceblue.

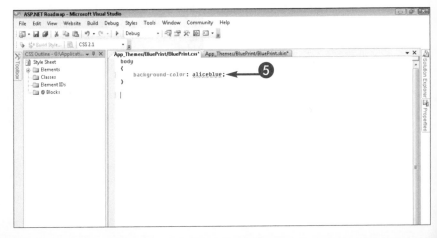

⑥ Add a new Web page to the site.

⑦ Set the Theme to your new Theme.

⑧ Add a `Label` control to the page.

⑨ Add a `TextBox` control to the page.

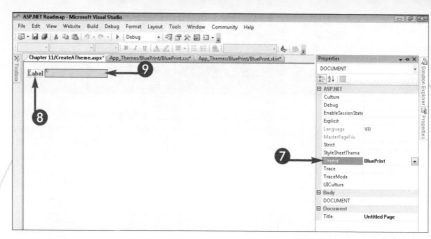

⑩ Open the page in a browser.

You can view the application of the various Theme settings.

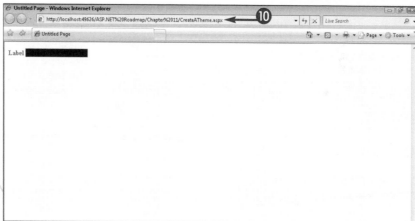

Extra

Using skins to define the visual appearance of controls is not a very efficient way to format the page. A skin creates much more code than defining the appearance in a style sheet. A style sheet is included in the page's header and downloaded the first time it is requested and cached on the client thereafter.

Formatting created in the skin file is done in-line for the control, thus creating much more code to be delivered to the client each time the page is requested. This leads to increased load times and extra bandwidth for each page request.

Similarly a style sheet may also reference images the same way and the path to the actual image is resolved correctly at runtime.

Apply a Theme

A SP.NET allows several ways to apply a theme to a Web site. You can apply themes to a page at several levels: the application, page, and control levels. The default theme for a Web site can be set in the web.config file. Each page can define its theme either through a page directive or at runtime. Each control can designate which theme it will use.

A theme can be defined for the entire site in the web.config file by setting the theme attribute of the pages element: <pages theme ="Roadmap">. You can also set the styleSheetTheme attribute to the name of the default theme.

Each page can define the theme to be used either through the Theme page directive or at runtime. Setting the theme at the page level overrides any theme setting in the web.config file. You can also set the styleSheetTheme

as a page directive. Setting the theme at runtime must be done in the PreInit event handler. Attempting to apply a theme at any later time causes an exception to be thrown. In the PreInit event handler the Theme property of the page can be set to the name of the designated theme. This is a popular method to use when users are allowed to customize the appearance of your site.

A skin can have multiple control definitions, designated by a differing SkinId. Each Web control can designate which SkinId is applied to it with the SkinId property. If there is no control definition matching the control with that designated SkinId in the theme, it is rendered as if no properties were set. If there are style rules or local properties for the control with no matching SkinId definition they are applied.

Apply a Theme

① Create a new Skin named BluePrint.

② Add the Skin definition for a TextBox with a black background and thin red border.

③ Add a Label definition for red, bold text.

④ Add duplicate entries with slightly differing settings and a SkinId of RoadMap.

⑤ Add a new Web page to the site.

⑥ Set the Theme to the BluePrint Theme.

⑦ Add a Label and TextBox control to the page.

⑧ Add another Label and TextBox control to the page.

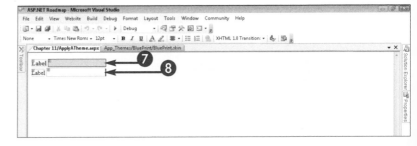

9 Set the `SkinID` of the second `Label` control to `RoadMap`.

10 Set the `SkinID` of the second `TextBox` control to `RoadMap`.

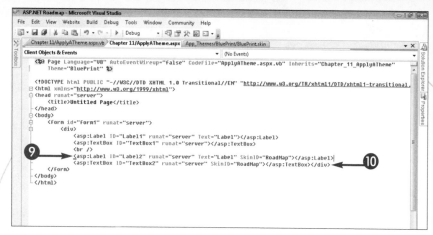

11 Open the page in a browser.

You will see the application of the different theme settings.

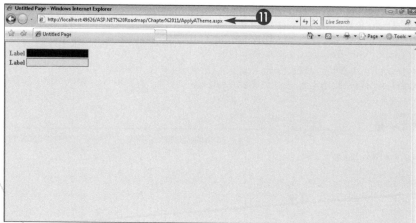

Extra

In some instances you will need to disable a theme for either an entire page or individual controls. To disable a theme for the entire page, set the `EnableTheming` attribute to `false` in the @page directive. Similarly, set the `EnableTheming` attribute to `false` for each control in which you do not want theme attributes to be implemented. Remember control attributes will be overridden by the settings defined in a theme, so if you have a control in which you do not want the themed settings implemented you must disable themes for the control.

Even if you disable theming at the page level individual controls may still have theming enabled by setting the `Enabletheming` property to `true`. The control can then specify the theme to apply by designating it through the `Theme` property of the control.

Create a Skin

You can add a `Skin` definition by adding a new item to a Web site just like any other file. It is added to the theme folder you designate. If a theme has not been created, the App_Theme folder is created. Multiple definitions for any control may be added to the theme as long as they are differentiated by a unique `SkinId`.

It is much easier to define the way a control should render in a normal Web Form first. This gives you the intellisense of Visual Studio and access to the control's properties. There is no intellisense or property window while editing a definition in a skin file, making it much harder to properly define the desired settings.

Creating the definition in a Web form first allows you to quickly see how the control is rendered and apply

changes until everything is satisfactory. Once the control definition is perfected the declaration can be copied to the skin file. The `Id` property must be removed and `SkinId`, if needed, applied.

The definition of a specific control can be done multiple times; each must have a unique `SkinId`, which means three versions of a `TextBox` layout could be defined in a skin and applied to a particular `TextBox` by designating the `SkinId` in the `TextBox` declaration. Placing a `Skin` in a Theme's folder adds it to that theme; it is leveraged by the controls on a page that uses that theme.

While `Skins` are an easy way to apply formatting to controls, their use tends to cause code bloat on pages sent to the browser. Skins cannot be applied to user controls, but controls in a user control may be skinned.

Create a Skin

① Add a new Skin file to a Web site.

Note: *If you do not have an App_Theme folder you will be prompted to create the folder and the Skin file will be placed there.*

② Add the Skin definition for a TextBox with a gray background and thin blue border.

③ Add a `Label` definition for Blue, Bold text.

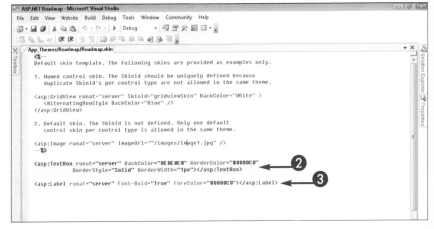

④ Add a Style Sheet to the Theme.

⑤ Set the Body rule to make the background color `aliceblue`.

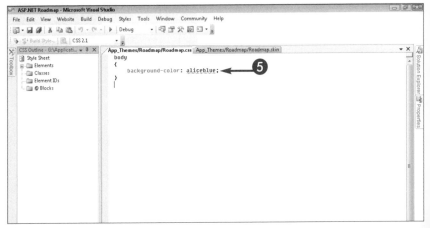

6 Add a new Web page to the site.

7 Set the `Theme` to your new theme.

8 Add a `Label` control to the page.

9 Add a `TextBox` control to the page.

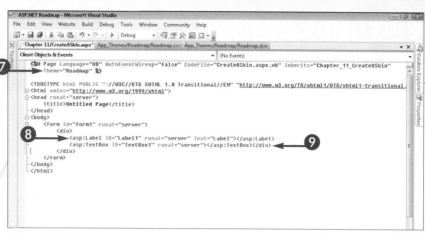

10 Open the page in a browser.

● You can view the application of the various Theme settings.

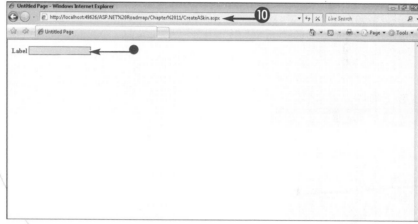

Apply It

You can name skins, which allows you to define when the skin is applied to a page. To do this when defining a control's attributes in the Skin file the `SkinID` property must be set. This means that a control may have multiple definitions in a single Skin file.

The Web control may then either inherit the default skin assigned in the page directive, the web.config file, or the specific skin defined in the control. The control declaration would set the `SkinId` to the specific `SkinId` to apply formatting for that specific instance of the control, say a `TextBox`.

Specifying the SkinId of a TextBox:
```
<asp:TextBox ID="txtQty" skinid="Skin2" runat="server"></asp:TextBox>
```

Set a Theme and Skin at Runtime

You can set the theme for a page at runtime by setting the `Theme` property of the page to the name of the theme that needs to be applied. This must be done in the `PreInit` event handler; any attempts to set the theme after the `PreInit` handler will result in an exception being thrown. The `PreInit` event is the first event raised when a page is requested. Setting the `Theme` at the page level, either in a page directive or at runtime overrides the Theme setting in the web.config file.

When multiple `Skins` have been assigned to a `Theme` this can also be set in the `PreInit` event handler. The `Page` class has a `SkinId` property that handles the name of the Skin to be applied to the controls on the page. Each control on the page can override this setting by specifying a specific `SkinId` to use.

`Theming` may also be disabled in the `PreInit` event handler; simply set the `EnableTeming` property to `false`. When using a Master page, any theme settings in the Master page take precedence over settings in the content page.

Similarly, you can set the `StyleSheetTheme` to the name of the theme you want to apply the style sheet to. You must also set the `StyleSheetTheme` in the `PreInit` handler as well.

You can set the skin for individual controls at runtime by setting the `SkinId` property of the control in the `Pre-Init` event handler.

Themes can be shared among applications on the same Web server. The theme must be added to the %Windows%\Microsoft.Net\Framework\{version}\ASP.NET ClientFiles\Themes folder. Any theme added to this folder can be immediately used on any Web site on the server.

Set a Theme and Skin at Runtime

1 Add a new Skin file to a Web site.

Note: *If you do not have an App_Theme folder you will be prompted to create the folder and the Skin file will be placed there.*

2 Add the Skin definition for a TextBox with a gray background and thin blue border.

3 Add a `Label` definition for Blue, Bold text.

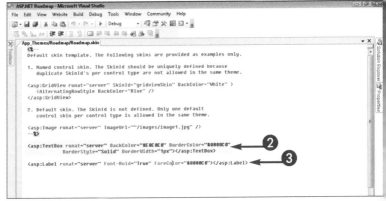

4 Create a new Skin named `BluePrint`.

5 Add the `Skin` definition for a TextBox with a black background and thin red border.

6 Add a `Label` definition for Red, Bold text.

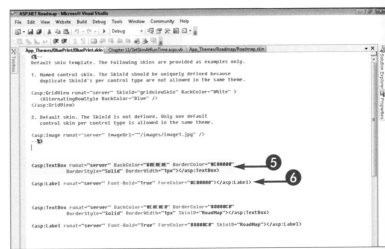

7 Add a new Web page.

8 Add a `Label` and `TextBox` control.

9 Switch to code-behind.

10 Add code to the `PreInit` event handler to toggle the theme.

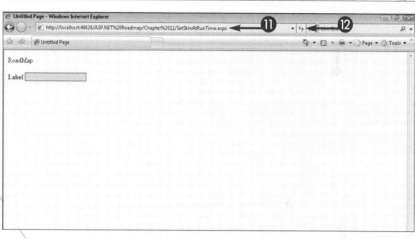

11 Open the page in a browser.

12 Reload the page to toggle the theme.

The colors and borders on the page change according to the applied theme.

Extra

Skins are a very inefficient way to apply formatting to Web controls because they create a lot of content bloat in the page being sent to the browser. This leads to slower load times and excessive bandwidth usage. Both symptoms should be avoided as much as possible to increase user satisfaction and reduce operational costs.

One of the best ways to avoid this code bloat is to use style sheets to define formatting for all elements in the site. This makes it easy not only to maintain, but helps increase site performance. Simply adding a Cascading Style Sheet to a Theme's folder causes it to be applied to every page that uses that Theme as an include file in the page header.

ASP.NET Web controls ultimately render HTML elements that can have style rules directly applied to them in element form. Each ASP.NET Web control has a `CssClass` property where a specific style rule can be applied.

Create a Cascading Style Sheet

Defining the formatting of a page or an entire Web site through Cascading Style Sheets (CSS) is a very efficient means to defining a consistent and manageable site appearance. Rules can be defined in many ways, such as specific HTML elements, element names, and style classes. Many modern sites are also using style sheets to define page layouts by using the positioning rules available in style sheets.

Visual Studio 2005 makes general editing of style sheets very easy. A style sheet can be added anywhere in a site's structure just like any other file. The easiest way is to right-click in the Solution Explorer and select Add New Item. Select Style Sheet from the New Item dialog box. The new style sheet file opens in the Visual Studio editor window.

Rules for a style sheet can be added by right-clicking the file and opening the Add Style Rule dialog box. This

dialog box can add a rule definition for an element, Class Name, or Element Id. Selecting an element displays a drop-down list of available HTML elements to create a rule. Selecting Class Name enables a `TextBox` to define the class's name and an optional element drop-down list. Selecting Element Id enables a `TextBox` to enter the name of the Element to create the style for. Any HTML element with the name attribute matching the name of this rule will have it applied.

After the rule definition is in place the actual rules need to be set. This can either be done by hand or through the Visual Studio Style Sheet Editor. Optionally, you can right-click inside the rule definition to see the Build Style choice, which displays the Style Builder dialog box. This dialog box provides an easy-to-use interface to define the most common elements of style rules, such as font and background rules.

Create a Cascading Style Sheet

① Add a new style sheet to the Web site.

② Right-click the Body element and select Build Style.

③ Set the font to Arial and Red.

④ Click OK to apply the settings.

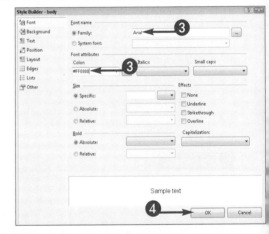

⑤ Right-click in the style sheet and select Add Style Rule.

⑥ Select P from the drop-down list.

⑦ Right-click the paragraph rule and open the Style Builder dialog box.

⑧ Set the font to Georgia, 11px, and Black.

Note: *You should set these two rules differently to see the differences.*

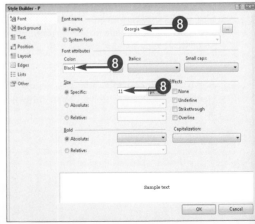

9 Add a new Web page to the site.

10 Add some sample text to the page.

11 Add a reference to the style sheet in the page's header.

12 Open the page in a browser.

The application of the style rules affect the text on the page.

Apply It

Style rules are applied in a specific order, where the last rule that is read wins. For example, there are several forms of an anchor (A) element that correspond to the differing states. The default rule should be defined first for the element. Any subsequent state rules are defined after the main rule for the TAG in the file. For example, `a:hover` defines how an anchor is rendered when a mouse is hovering over the link. `a:visited` defines how the link renders after a user has visited the target URL.

Style Sheet Rule Hierarchy:

```
a
{
 color: #000099;
}
a:hover
{
 font-weight: bold;
 color: #009933;
}
```

Create Personalized Properties

The ASP.NET personalization provider gives you the ability to store custom information about a user. Personalization properties are strongly typed items defined in the site's web.config file. Properties used in personalization are defined in the `properties` element of the `profile` element. The `Profile` object automatically makes the personalization properties that have been defined available at runtime. This happens automatically as soon as they are defined in the site's configuration.

The first step to adding personalization properties is to decide what properties are needed in the site. After these are defined they may be added to the profile `properties` element. Each property is added through an `add` element, which requires a `name` attribute be defined.

Optionally the type of the property may be defined with the fully qualified name of the type. A `defaultValue` for the property may also be defined. Another important

optional attribute is `allowAnonymous`, which defines if the property is available to unauthenticated users or not. A property can also be marked as `readOnly`, meaning the value can only be read by the application and not set. This can be useful for any property that might be calculated, such as a total or concatenated name.

`Personalzation` properties are accessed through the `Profile` property of the page. This property refers to the global `Profile` object that manages the personalized settings for the user. Each of the defined properties is available by calling the `Profile.PropertyName` property, where `PropertyName` refers to the name defined in the web.config file `Profile.FirstName`, for example.

Each of the strongly typed properties can be read or written to at runtime unless they have been marked as read-only. The default type setting of a property is a `String`, but if the type is indicated in the property definition it will be used. A property can be just about any type as long as it is serializable.

Create Personalized Properties

1 Open the Web site's web.config file.

2 Add a `profile` element.

3 Add a `properties` element.

4 Add several properties to collect personal information.

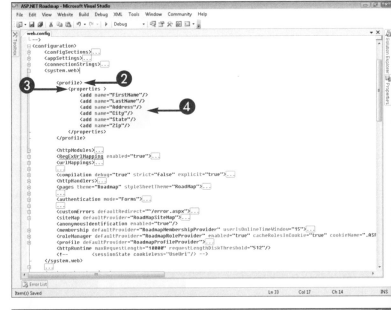

5 Add a new Web page.

Note: *For this example, the page should be protected and require authentication.*

6 Add a TextBox for each of the profile properties created in Step 3.

7 Add a button and set its text to Submit.

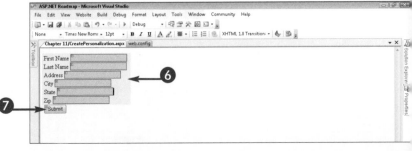

⑧ Double-Click the button to create a click event handler.

⑨ Add code to store the profile properties.

⑩ Add an event handler for the Page_Load event.

⑪ Add code to set the TextBox value for each Profile property.

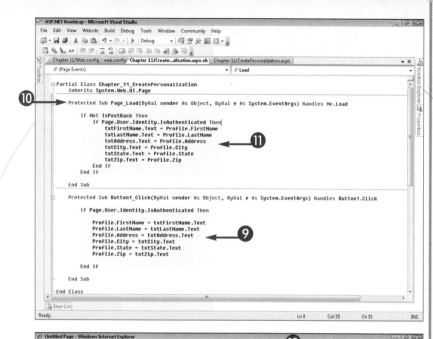

⑫ Open the page in a browser and type values for each property.

⑬ Click Submit.

The form stores the profile information.

Apply It

Personalization properties can be grouped, providing even more organization to the properties. Inside of the properties element in the configuration file an optional group child element may be defined. Inside of the group element, properties can be added exactly as they are to the properties element. The group element needs to have a name attribute defined.

Defining a Personalization Group:
```
<group name ="Shopping">
 <add name="CartId"/>
 <add name="LastOrderDate"/>
</group>
```

Accessing a Personalization Group:
```
If Not IsNothing(Profile.Shopping.CartId) Then
 Response.Write(Profile.Shopping.CartId & "<BR>")
End If
```

Use Anonymous Personalization

Personalization does not have to be limited to users who register with a site by using anonymous personalization. This can often lead to more use of the site by average users. Some sites may offer limited personalization capabilities for unregistered users, offering greater personalization as an enticement to register. This feature is turned off by default, but it can be activated by setting the appropriate settings in the web.config file.

The first step is to set the anonymousIdentification element's enabled attribute to true. This element is a child element of the system.web element. The unique identifier is stored in a cookie on the user's machine. All the personalization data is stored in the data store on the server. The cookie name may be defined by setting the cookieName attribute of the anonymousIdentification element.

The anonymous identifier is a GUID that can be accessed from the request object. The request object has a new property, AnonymouseId, that returns the GUID identifier.

There are two anonymous identification events that can be handled: OnCreate and OnRemove. The OnCreate event is fired when the anonymous account is first created. Similarly, when the account is removed the OnRemove event is fired. They both pass an AnonymousIdentificationEventArgs object, which has an AnonymousId property. This property can be set or read.

Each property can have the allowAnonymous attribute defined for it individually. This allows certain properties to only be available to authenticated users, while giving casual site users some personalization capabilities. The allowAnonymous attribute is a Boolean and can be set to either true or false.

Accessing a property that has not explicitly designated anonymous access causes a ProviderException to be thrown. Use caution when accessing properties that may not allow anonymous access.

Use Anonymous Personalization

1 Open the Web site's web.config file.

2 Add profile and properties elements.

3 Add several properties to collect personal information with allowAnonymous set to true.

4 Add an enabled anonymousIdentification element.

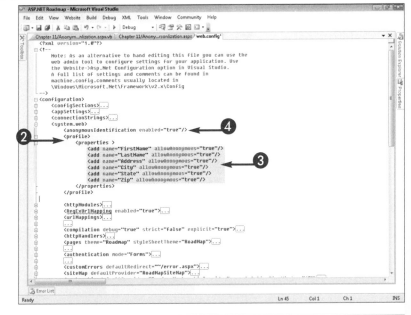

5 Add a new Web page.

6 Add a TextBox for each of the profile properties created in Step 3.

7 Add a button and set its text to Submit.

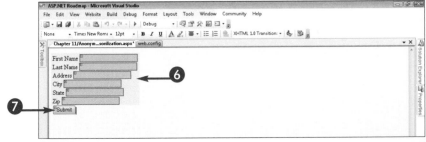

8 Double-click the button to create a `click` event handler.

9 Add code to store the `Profile` properties.

10 Add an event handler for the `Page_Load` event.

11 Add code to set the TextBox value for each `Profile` property.

12 Open the page in a browser and type values for each property.

13 Click Submit.

The form stores the profile information.

Apply It

Some properties may need to have default values defined, which may be done in the property configuration. The `defaultValue` attribute of the `add` element is used to define the initial value for any property the first time it is used, which is extremely useful for anonymous users who come to the site the first time.

Defining a Default Value for a Personalization Property:
```
<add name="State" allowAnonymous="true"
defaultValue="NC"/>
```

Anonymous personalization should be used with caution. A high-trafficked site can quickly build a large amount of anonymous personalization data for users. It is a good idea to define a purging mechanism to reduce the amount of data stored on the server.

Set Personalization at Runtime

T he Personalization provider provides access to the personalization system at runtime to manage properties and related events. Custom routines can also be written to migrate anonymous users to registered users, too. The `ProfileModule` class provides hooks to three events: `MigrateAnonymous`, `Personalize`, and `ProfileAutoSaving`.

When an anonymous user becomes a registered user the `MigrateAnonymous` event is executed. This event can be handled in the page or on the `Global.asax` file. The event delegate passes a `ProfileMigrateEventArg` object, which has an `AnonymousId` property. The `AnonymousId` property is used to access the user's personalization values. The `Profile` object has a `GetPropertyValue` method that accepts the user's identifier to access the value of the designated property. This identifier is assumed to be the current profile Id, but by providing the `AnonymousId`

value to the `GetPropertyValue` method, access can be made to any user's information on the site.

So setting the new profile properties to the previous version is pretty simple. Call the property directly from the `Profile` object and set it to the value from the previous profile's setting. `Group` properties can be migrated just as easily.

By default, the user's profile information is stored at the end of every page's execution. This feature may be turned off by setting the `automaticSaveEnabled` attribute to `false` in the profile element of the configuration file.

When the profile is automatically saved as a result of the page execution completing, the `ProfileModule.Profile AutoSaving` event is executed. A custom event handler for this event can also be defined to write custom code to determine if the profile needs to be saved. Each property has a `HasChanged` property that indicates if it has been changed.

Set Personalization at Runtime

1 Open the Web site's web.config file.

2 Add `profile` and `properties` elements.

3 Add several properties to collect personal information with `allowAnonymous` set to `true`.

4 Add an enabled `anonymousIdentification` element.

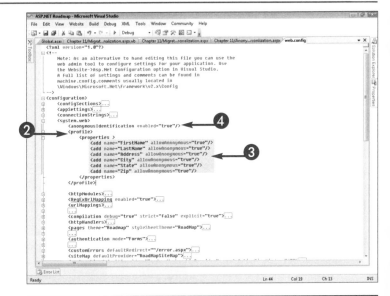

5 Add a new Web page.

6 Add a TextBox for each of the profile properties created in Step 3.

7 Add a Button and set its text to Submit.

8 Add a login control to the page.

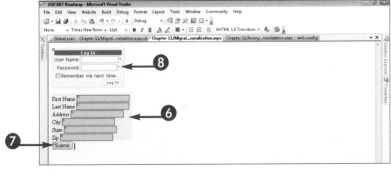

9 Add a `Profile_On` `MigrateAnonymous` event handler to the Global.asax file.

10 Add code to the event handler to migrate the profile.

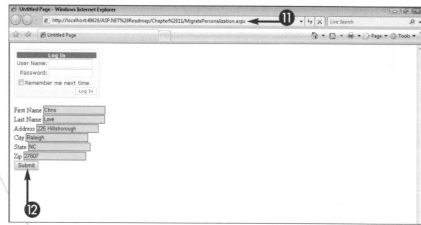

11 Open the page in a browser and type profile data.

12 Store the profile data by clicking the Submit button and then log in.

The anonymous profile migrates.

Apply It

Profiles can also be personalized at runtime by calling the `GetProfile` method and passing it an identifying key. This is done in the `Profile_Personalize` event, which passes a `ProfileEventArgs` parameter. The `ProfileEventArgs` has two properties: a read-only reference to the current `HttpContext` and the `Profile` being processed.

The `Personalize` event is raised just before the actual user profile is created. This gives you the flexibility to assign a particular profile to a user based on some setting or variable in the application. For example, a user might have a different profile for football and basketball season on a sports Web site.

Personlize a User's Profile:
```
Dim customProfile as ProfileCommon
customProfile = CType(ProfileBase.Create(User.Identity.Name), ProfileCommon)
If IsFootballSeason() then
 customProfile = customProfile.GetProfile("Football")
elseif IsBasketballSeason() then
 customProfile = customProfile.GetProfile("Basketball")
end if
```

Connect to an SQL Database with the SQLDataSource

The SQLDataSource control provides a way to declaratively connect to an ADO.NET SQL database, such as SQL Server, OLEDB, ODBC, or Oracle. It can be used to connect to an Access database, but the AccessdataSource control is more optimized for this purpose. The SQLDataSource control may be bound to any data control that supports the DataSourceId property. The SQLDataSource uses declarative binding, meaning the queries are maintained in the page code. Because of this, the SQLDataSource is not targeted to larger, high-performance sites with a full middle logic tier.

If you look at the declarative source code in the SQLDataSource, you will see several properties defined, one for each SQL statement: Select, Insert, Update, and Delete. The ConnectionString property is also defined; typically, this points to the ConnectionString defined in the web.config file. Additionally, there are a series of sections that define the parameters for each of the commands. Each parameter section contains one or more sections that define a parameter. Any of the command properties, such as the SelectCommand, can be either an SQL query or a stored procedure. Other commands are UpdateCommand, InsertCommand, and DeleteCommand. Each performs SQL tasks as implied by its name.

Each of the commands has an associated parameters collection: SelectParameters, UpdateParameters, InsertParameters, and DeleteParameters. Parameters can just be plain parameter values or obtained from a special source, such as a control on the page. The choices are ControlParameter, CookieParameter, FormParameter, ProfileParameter, QueryStringParameter, and SessionParameter. Each parameter type manages specialized features to work with a different source of a parameter value.

Connect to an SQL Database with the SQLDataSource

① Create a new Web page.

② Add an SQLDataSource from the Toolbox.

③ Open the Configure Data Source Wizard from the SQLDataSource's Smart Tag.

④ Click New Connection to configure a connection to your database.

⑤ Click Next.

⑥ Select a table or view from the database.

⑦ Select the columns to retrieve.

⑧ Click Finish.

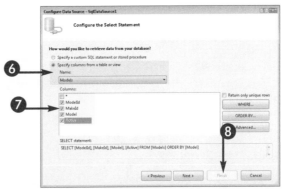

9 Create an update query from the Properties window.

10 Set the Parameters to match the columns to be updated.

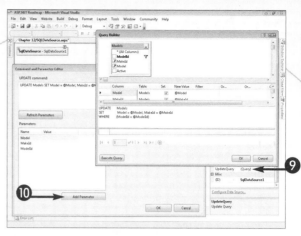

11 Create an InsertQuery from the Properties window.

12 Set the parameters to match the columns to be inserted and click Add Parameter.

The `SQLDataSource` may now be used to retrieve, update, and insert records from the selected table.

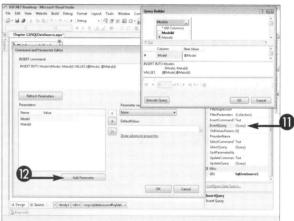

Apply It

The SQL strings for each command property defined by the wizard use string format syntax, where each parameter is represented by #. The # refers to the 0 index of the parameter in the corresponding collection.

The `SQLDataSource` control is no different than any other control from a fundamental aspect in that you can quickly add an instance of an `SQLDataSource` from the Visual Studio Toolbox to a Web page in Design view or create it by hand in Source view. After you add an `SQLDataSource` to a page, configure it to connect to the database. This can be done by hand in Source view, through the Properties window, or through the Configure Data Source Wizard.

The Configure Data Source Wizard walks you through the creation of a database connection if it is needed, creates SQL statements, and even allows you to test the Select statement. If you already have stored procedures defined in your database you can connect directly to them as well through the wizard.

Use the
Connection Object

The DataSource controls are great to quickly get a proof of concept application or get a low-demand application up and running. The .NET framework provides a series of classes to provide this type of access to SQL Server and ODBC-compliant databases. There are also many database vendors, such as Oracle, that offer their own connection objects modeled after the provided classes.

The DBConnection class is a foundation for more database-specific connection objects. It must be inherited from and cannot be directly used. There are five specific connection classes that ship with the .NET framework: SQLConnection, OdbcConnection, OleDbConnection, OracleConnection, and SQLCeConnection. The most commonly used Connection objects are for SQL Server and Access (OleDb). There is no limitation to other custom connectors that may be used or developed.

The connection classes manage a direct connection to the data store associated with the custom connection class. For example, the SQLConnection class is a highly optimized class for connections to SQL Server.

Each of the Connection classes must have a ConnectionString set before a connection can be made. The ConnectionString defines how to connect to the database. Each database requires a slightly different ConnectionString format, and each of the specific connectors is responsible for handling this string. The DataSource property is a read-only property that returns the name of the database used by the Connection object.

The Connection object must be opened before any communications take place. The Open method handles this operation. The connection must be explicitly closed as well by calling either Close or Dispose. If connection pooling is enabled, the connection is returned to the pool instead of being closed.

Use the Connection Object

① Create a MakesDB class.

② Create a function to return the desired ConnectionString.

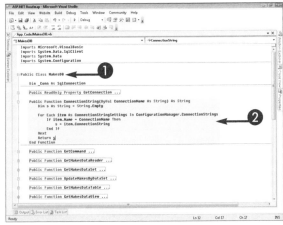

③ Define a class level variable of an SQLConnection object.

④ Create a ReadOnly property to return an open SQLConnection object.

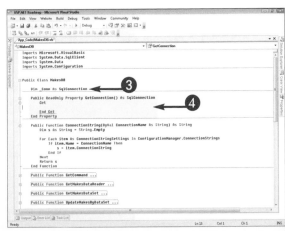

⑤ Add code to create a new `SQLConnection` object.

⑥ Return the new `Connection` object.

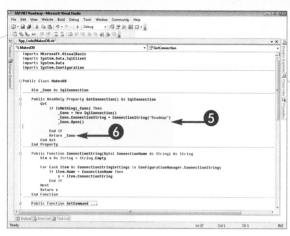

⑦ Add code to check to see if the existing `SQLConnection` object is closed.

⑧ If it is closed, open the connection.

The `SQLConnection` can now be used in conjunction with an `SQLCommand` or `SQLDataAdapter` object.

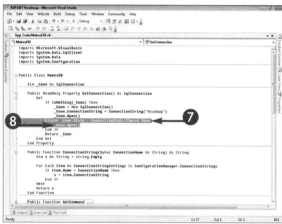

Apply It

It is a good idea to wrap up access to the `ConnectionString` in your application. A common way to do this is to create a property you can pass the name of the `ConnectionString` that returns the value from the `ConnectionString` element in the web.config file. It is a good idea to make this a read-only property.

A Read-Only Property to Return the Target ConnectionString:
```
Public ReadOnly Property ConnectionString(DB as string) As String
  Get
    Return System.Configuration.ConfigurationManager.ConnectionStrings(DB).ConnectionString()
  End Get
End Property
```

Use the Command Object

The Command object actually executes queries against the database designated in the Connection object. The Command object executes five commands: NonQuery, Reader, Row, Scalar, and XMLReader. It has four properties that must be configured before an execution is performed: CommandText, CommandTimeout, CommandType, and Connection.

The Connection property gets and sets the Connection object used to connect to the database. The CommandType gets and sets the type of statement that is being executed. The options are StoredProcedure, TableDirect, and Text. The StoredProcedure option designates an SQL stored procedure. The Text option indicates a standard SQL string, such as a Select or Update command to execute.

The CommandTimeout property gets and sets the number of seconds to wait for the command to execute before aborting. The default is 30 seconds. The CommandText gets or sets the SQL statement to execute.

The ExecuteNonQuery method executes the command and returns the number of rows affected. It is useful for Insert, Update, and Delete commands. The ExecuteReader method executes the command and returns a DataReader. The ExecuteRow method executes the command and returns a Record object, a single row.

The ExecuteScalar method executes the command and returns the value from the first column of the first row. The ExecuteScalar method is useful when a query returns an internal value, such as an Insert statement that returns the Identity of the new row. The ExecuteXMLReader method executes the command and returns an XMLReader. It should be noted there is not an ExecuteDataSet method. This is because of the complex nature of the DataSet object. Instead, the DataAdapter .Fill method is used to populate a DataSet object.

Use the Command Object

① Add a GetCommand function to the MakesDB class.

② Pass the Query text and the CommandType as parameters.

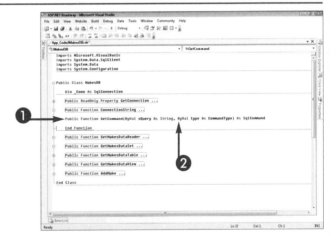

③ Create a new SQLCommand object.

④ Pass the Query text and get an SQLConnection object in the constructor.

⑤ Set the CommandType.

⑥ Return the SQLCommand object.

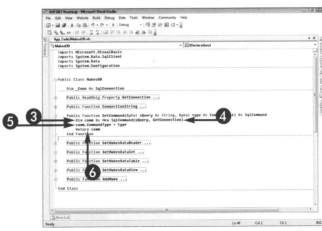

7 Add a `GetMakesDataReader` function to the `MakesDB` class.

8 Define a `Query` text.

9 Call the `GetCommand` method defined in step **1**.

10 Call `ExecuteReader` to return an `SQLDataReader`.

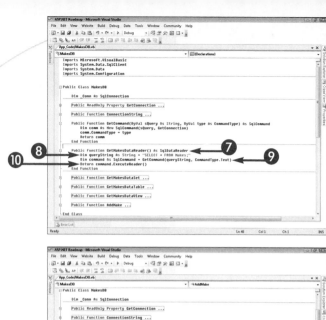

11 Add an `AddMake` function to the `MakesDB` class that calls a stored procedure.

12 Add any required parameters and call `ExecuteNonQuery` on the `SQLCommand` object.

The methods use the command object to execute the desired actions.

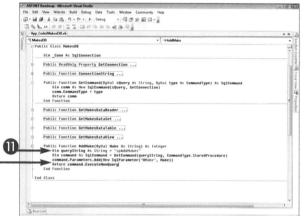

Extra

Asynchronous programming is a way to make an application perform better and provide a much richer user experience. When performing asynchronous database programming a call to the database is made that may take a few seconds or minutes to execute. Instead of the application waiting for the operation to complete and appearing to be hung to the end user, the application returns control back to the user interface and waits for the database operation to complete in the background. When the operation is complete, a `CallBack` function is executed and the results of the operation are handled at that point.

The `SQLCommand` object has several asynchronous methods that allow this type of programming, essentially all the normal methods prefixed with `Begin`. There is a corresponding `End` method that each call to a `Begin` method must be paired with. The `Begin` method returns an `IAsyncResult` object. The `IAsyncResult` represents the status of an asynchronous operation; when the `IsCompleted` property is `true` the operation has completed and the corresponding `End` method should be called. The asynchronous `End` method returns the number of rows affected by the query.

Retrieve a DataReader

The fastest way to retrieve data from a database is to retrieve a DataReader, which is a class that derives from IDataReader. The IDataReader interface allows the creation of a DataReader class that provides a means of reading a forward-only set of records. The IDataReader interface requires four methods and three properties be implemented in any class that implements the interface.

There are many available DataReader classes that are optimized for various data sources. The SQLDataReader and OLEDBDataReader are two of the most popular DataReaders. The SQLDataReader is optimized for SQL Server, while the OLEDataReader is optimized for OLE data sources. Other common options are for Oracle and ODBC data sources.

To read the data in a DataReader you loop through the records by calling the Read method. This method moves the reader to the next record in the result set. If it is successful it returns True. If it has reached the end of the results it returns False. Each DataReader is responsible for providing access to the data, but in general you access the fields in the current record by passing the name of the field or a zero-based index that references. Using the index method can prove problematic, so most developers use the field name.

After you read the records in the reader it must be closed. If the reader is not closed it hangs onto the connection, which leads to poor performance and memory leaks. The reader can be closed by calling the Close method. It takes no parameters. You do not want to call it once the reader is closed, so checking the IsClosed property before attempting to close the reader is a good practice.

Retrieve a DataReader

① Create a GetMakesDataReader function.

② Define a Query text.

③ Call the GetCommand method.

④ Call ExecuteReader to return an SQLDataReader.

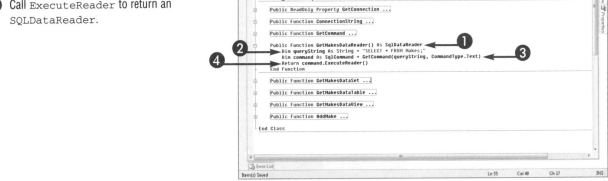

⑤ Create a new Web page.

⑥ Add a grid view and format it.

7 Open the code-behind file for the Web page.

8 Add a `BindData` method.

9 Call the `GetMakesDataReader` method defined in step **1**.

10 Bind the `SQLDataReader` to the `GridView`.

Note: *Make sure to close the* `SQLDataReader` *after the data is bound to the* `GridView`.

11 Open the page in a browser.

The `SQLDataReader` is bound to the `GridView`.

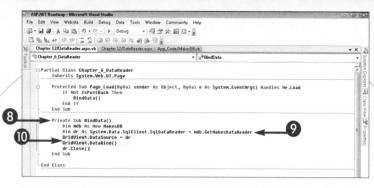

Extra

Calling fields in the data reader is not always easy, but most of the derived reader types provide specialized methods to retrieve values. The `SQLDataReader` class has several functions to access field values like `GetInt`, `GetString`, `GetDateTime`, and `GetBoolean`. The `GetDataTypeName` can be called to get the type of the field, but you must know the zero-based index of the field first. To work around this issue, because no one really knows the ordinal index of the field, the `GetOrdinal` method can be used to get the field's index.

SQLDataReader Get Methods:
```
Dim mHeight = dr.GetInt32(dr.GetOrdinal("Height"))
Dim mWidth = dr.GetInt32(dr.GetOrdinal("Width"))
Dim bVisible = dr.GetBoolean(dr.GetOrdinal("Visible"))
Dim dtStartDate = dr.GetDateTime(dr.GetOrdinal("StartDate"))
```

Create a DataSet

The DataSet is one of the most commonly used data objects in the .NET framework and is a key component of the ADO.NET architecture. It can contain multiple, related, and unrelated sets of records in memory. Each record set is contained in a DataTable and can have relations defined between each of the DataTables with DataRelation objects. UniqueConstraint and ForiegnKeyContstraint can also be used to enforce data integrity.

The DataTable objects contain the records from the data source, while the DataRelationCollection allows you to navigate though the table hierarchy. The Tables property manages interactions with the DataTables contained in DataTableCollection. The DataTables may be accessed by a numerical index or by their case-sensitive name.

The DataSet class can read and write data and schema as XML documents. The schema may be saved as an XML schema with the WriteXmlSchema method. Both schema and records can be saved using the WriteXml method. An XML document can be read using the ReadXml method.

The DataSet is filled by using a DataAdapter's Fill method, passing the DataSet object as its only parameter. The DataSet can be passed to multiple DataAdapters to have multiple named DataTables filled with data.

A DataRelation is used to relate two DataTable objects in the DataSet. Each DataRelation is made through DataColumn objects in the DataTables. For example, in a Customer/Orders relationship, the Customers DataTable is the parent and the Orders DataTable is the child of the relationship. A DataRelation can be thought of as a primary key/foreign key relationship in the database.

Create a DataSet

1. Create a GetMakesDataSet function.

2. Define a Query text, DataSet, and SQLDataAdapter.

3. Set the SQLDataAdapter's command object.

4. Call the Fill method to fill the DataSet.

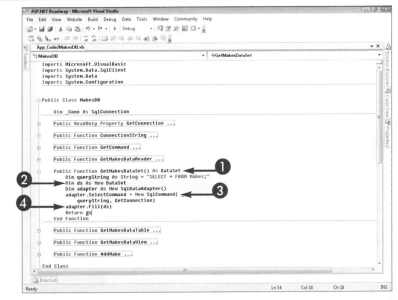

5. Create a new Web page.

6. Add a grid view and format it.

7. Open the code-behind for the Web page.

8. Add a `BindData` method.

9. Call the `GetMakesDataSet` method defined in step **1**.

10. Bind the `DataSet` to the `GridView`.

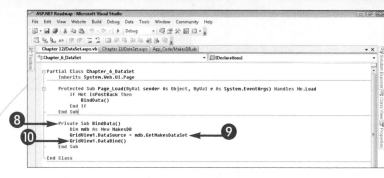

11. Open the page in a browser.

The `DataSet` is bound to the `GridView`.

Apply It

Creating a `DataSet` is a fairly routine process with code that is reused many times in most applications. Microsoft created the Enterprise Library, a collection of free and supported code, to manage many common programming tasks, including data access.

Retrieve a DataSet using the Data Access Application Block:

```
Public Function ExecuteDataSet(ByVal sProc As String, _
 ByVal ct As CommandType, ByVal arParam() As SqlParameter) As DataSet
 Dim db As Database = DatabaseFactory.CreateDatabase()
 Dim dbc As DbCommand = db.GetStoredProcCommand(sProc)
If Not IsNothing(arParam) Then
  For Each aParam As SqlParameter In arParam
    db.AddInParameter(dbc, aParam.ParameterName, aParam.DbType, aParam.Value)
  Next
 End If
 Return db.ExecuteDataSet(dbc)
End Function
```

Create a DataTable

Most developers like to use DataSets to hold records of data in memory, but they are nothing more than an organized collection of DataTables. The DataTable can directly be used by a .NET application to manage a table of data in memory. It has a DataView property that makes it easy to filter and sort the data at runtime. Each record is represented by a DataRow. There is a limitation to the number of rows that can be contained in a DataTable — 16,777,216. In most cases the computer will run out of memory first.

Records can be added to the DataTable at runtime by calling the NewRow method. This method returns a new DataRow object with the schema of the DataTable intact. The Schema of the DataTable is defined in the DataColumnCollection. The Schema of the DataTable must be defined before any records can be added.

The Schema of the DataTable is defined by creating DataColumn objects for each field in the record. These are added to the columns collection of the DataTable. If a column is the primary key it should be set to the PrimaryKey property of the DataTable.

For each new row being added to a DataTable, each column can be explicitly set. The NewRow method returns a new DataRow object based on the schema of the DataTable. Each column value needs to be set according to the rules of the columns (think fields that allow nulls or a date time that needs a valid date). When the row is set it can be added to the rows collection of the DataTable. When a DataSet is filled by a DataAdapter it automatically handles the creation of the schema and filling of the needed DataTables.

Create a DataTable

① Create a GetMakesDataSet function.

② Add code to return a DataSet with a list of car Makes.

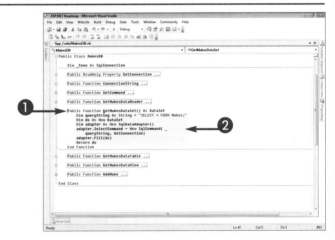

③ Create a GetMakesDataTable method.

④ Call the GetMakesDataSet method and return the first DataTable.

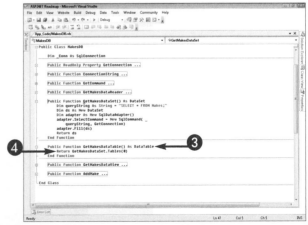

⑤ Create a new Web page with a `GridView`.

⑥ Add a `BindData` method to the code-behind.

⑦ Call the `GetMakesDataTable` method defined in step **3**.

⑧ Bind the `DataTable` to the `GridView`.

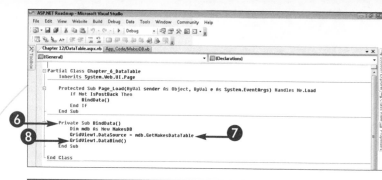

⑨ Open the page in a browser.

The `DataSet` is bound to the `GridView`.

Apply It

The `DataTable` fires events as data is manipulated. When data is updated the `RowChanging` and `RowChanged` events are fired. When a record is being deleted the `RowDeleting` and `RowDeleted` events are fired. Other events include `ColumnChanged` and `ColumnChanging`.

Handling a DataTable RowChanging Event:

```
AddHandler CarsTable.RowChanging, New _
  DataRowChangeEventHandler(AddressOf OnRowChanging)

Private Shared Sub OnRowChanging( _
  sender As Object, args As DataRowChangeEventargs)
  If args.Action <> DataRowAction.Nothing Then
    Dim actionStr As String
    actionStr = System.Enum.GetName(args.Action.GetType(), args.Action)

    Response.Write("   RowChanging: Action = " & actionStr & ", _
      CarID = " & args.Row("CarID").ToString())
  End If
End Sub
```

Use a DataView

The DataView class adds special functionality to the data contained in a DataTable object. The main features it is used for are sorting, editing, navigating, searching, and filtering data. A DataView can actually be bound to two different controls, but show different data. The DataTable's DataView is accessible through the DefaultView property.

The DataView can filter data much like an SQL Where clause through the RowFilter property. The RowFilter property manages the expression string to filter the data. The filter specifies a column name followed by the operator: FirstName = 'Chris', for example. In this example, a filter for the FirstName column is defined, and the value being filtered is encapsulated by single quotation marks because it is a string.

Date values must be escaped with the numbers symbol (#), such as StartDate < #7/1/2007#, when used in a filter expression.

If a column name contains a special character, such as a number (#) or caret (^), it must be wrapped in brackets: for example, [Phone#].

Filters can be combined with AND and OR operators, just like in an SQL Where clause. For example, (LastName = 'Farve' OR LastName = 'Rivers') AND (FirstName = 'Brett' OR FirstName = 'Phillip'). Like comparisons can also be performed, where both the percent (%) and asterisk (*) can be used for wildcard characters. Functions may also be used in the RowFilter expression. Standard SQL functions CONVERT, LEN, ISNULL, IIF, TRIM, and SUBSTRING can all be utilized to perform advanced data filters.

The Sort property manages the expression used to sort the rows in the DataView. Just like SQL, the sort expression can contain any of the column names and a directional indication of ASC or DESC. Column names are separated by a comma (,). The RowFilter and Sort can be used together to create a customized view of the data.

Use a DataView

① Add a GetMakesDataSet method to return a DataSet of car makes.

② Add a GetMakesDataTable method to return a DataTable of car makes.

③ Add a GetMakesDataView method to return the DefaultView.

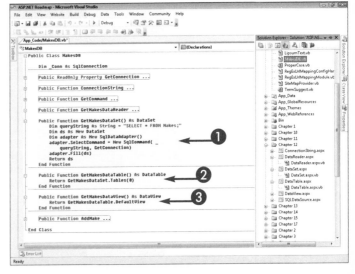

④ Create a new Web page with a GridView.

⑤ Add a BindData method to the code-behind.

⑥ Call the GetMakesDataView method defined in step 3.

⑦ Bind the DataView to the GridView.

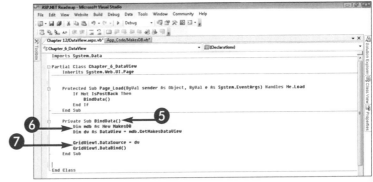

8 Add a `Sorting` event handler for the `GridView`.

9 Store the `SortExpression` and call the `BindDataMethod`.

10 Set the `Sort` property of the `DataView` before binding it to the `GridView`.

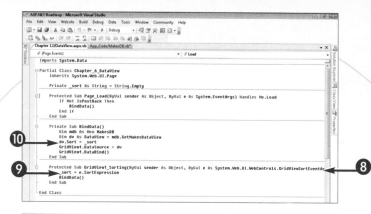

11 Open the page in a browser.

The `DataView` is bound to the `GridView`. The list can be sorted by clicking the column headings.

Use a DataAdapter

The primary purpose of the DataAdapter class is a bridge between data and a DataSet, performing data retrieval and updates. The Fill method sets the data in the DataSet object to match the data in the data source. The Update method does just the opposite by setting the data in the data source to match the data in the DataSet.

The SQLDataDataAdapter is specialized for working with SQL Server. For OLE data sources, there is the OleDbDataAdapter, while ODBC data sources use the ODBCDataAdapter.

The SQLDataAdapter has an overloaded constructor where the CommandText and SQLCommand objects can be set. If the Connection or CommandText is not set in the constructor they must be set before the Fill method is executed.

The Fill method has four overloads. The primary version accepts a DataSet object as its only parameter.

The Fill method returns the number of rows that were successfully added or updated, according to the SelectCommand of the associated Command object. Another Fill overload method accepts the DataSet, the Table name, an IDataReader (such as an SQLDataReader), a start record index, and the maximum number of records to bind.

The Fill method can also be used to set the data in a specific DataTable. One overload accepts a DataTable object and an IDataReader. The other accepts the same as well as the start record index and maximum number of records.

The Update method only accepts a DataSet object as its only parameter. Each record in the DataSet has an associated RowState property. This property is used to determine if the record should be Updated, Inserted, or Deleted from the data source. Each row is acted upon independently, not in a batch operation. Records are acted upon according to the indexes of the DataSet.

Use a DataAdapter

① Create a GetMakesDataSet function.

② Use an SQLDataAdapter to fill a DataSet.

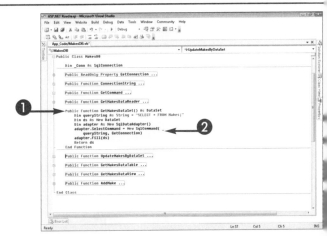

③ Create an UpdateMakesByDataSet method.

④ Pass a DataSet as its only parameter.

⑤ Call an SQLDataAdapter's Update method to update the records from the DataSet.

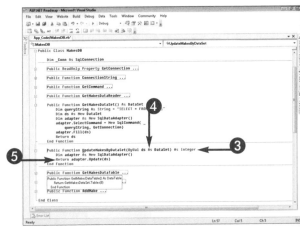

6 Create a new Web page with a `GridView`.

7 Add a `BindData` method to the code-behind.

8 Call the `GetMakesDataSet` method defined in step **1**.

9 Bind the `DataSet` to the `GridView`.

10 Open the page in a browser.

The `DataSet` is bound to the `GridView`.

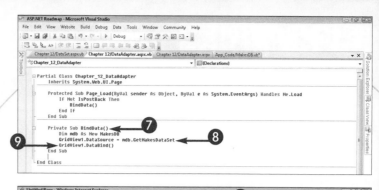

Extra

The Microsoft Enterprise Library Data Access Application Block has long been a favorite of many .NET developers to interact with SQL Server and Access databases. The Enterprise Library is a set of free code that is fully supported by Microsoft, and is tested and highly scalable. The Data Access Application Block provides several overloads of methods to retrieve datasets, including `DataReaders`, `ExecuteNonquery`, and `ExecuteScalar`.

The block is very trivial to configure and comes with an application that guides the developer through configuring any of the blocks for proper operation. In addition to the Data Access Application Block there are also blocks for custom exceptions, logging, caching, cryptography, and more. The entire library can be accessed at http://msdn2.microsoft.com/en-us/practices/default.aspx.

Pass Parameters to the Command Object

Most interactions with a database are not simple select statements. Passing straight SQL text is not an advisable practice because it could be highjacked by a malicious user trying an SQL injection attack. While stored procedures should always be used to interact with data, text commands and stored procedures alike can accept parameters. There are three parameter classes available, all targeted at specific data sources: SQLParameter, ODBCParameter, and OleDbParameter.

The SQLParameter class has seven overloads, accepting no parameters up to one that accepts 13 parameters. Typically, the overload that accepts the parameter name and the data type is used. Other parameters include the size of the data, value, parameter direction, parameter precision, the parameter scale, source column name, DataRowVersion, and a Boolean for source column mapping.

The SQLDataType object is an enumeration for all the various data types used by SQL Server. Common values are Int, Money, DateTime, Text, NVarChar, and XML. The ParameterDirection is an enumeration that specifies the direction of the parameter. The choices are Input, InputOutput, Output, and ReturnValue.

The SQLCommand and SQLDataAdapter classes both have a Parameters property. This manages an SQLParameterCollection that contains all the parameters used in the SQL statement being executed. Any of the commands can have a series of one or more parameters; the SQLParameterCollection can contain as little as one SQLParameter. The AddWithValue method supersedes the Add method overload that accepts a parameter name and value because of ambiguity issues. The OleDbCommand and ODBCCommand objects have similar parameter classes.

Pass Parameters to the Command Object

① Create a stored procedure to insert a new make.

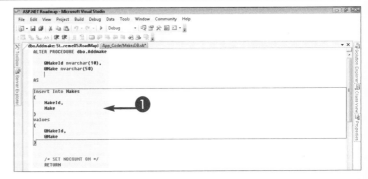

② Add an AddMake method, passing the MakeId and the Make as string parameters.

③ Create an SQLCommand calling the stored procedure in step **1**.

④ Add corresponding SQLparameters for the MakeId and Make.

⑤ Call ExecuteNonQuery to insert the record.

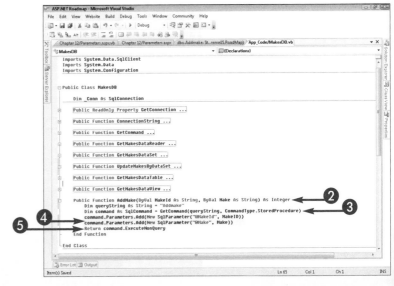

⑥ Create a Web page to collect input for a new `Make`.

⑦ Add a `Button` click event handler.

⑧ Call the `AddMake` function, passing the required values.

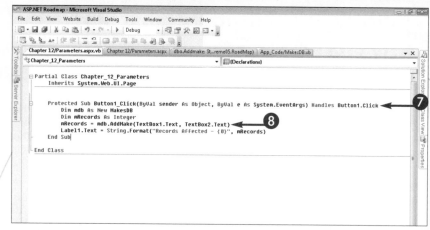

⑨ Open the page in a browser.

⑩ Type valid data and click Submit.

● The data is stored in the database and the number of records affected is returned.

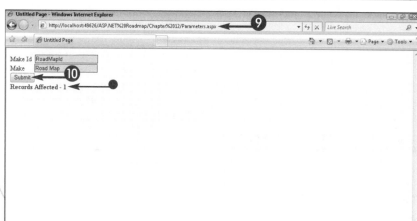

Apply It

The code provided in the example shows a very simple creation of an `SQLParameter`. Sometimes this is not sufficient and more detail must be provided. The `SQLParameter` constructor is overloaded. Also, many of the values available in the constructor overloads are also available as properties of the `SQLParameter` class. They can be set before they are added to the `SQLCommand`'s parameters collection.

Setting Details of an SQLParameter:

```
Dim parameter As New SqlParameter("@Model", _
        SqlDbType.VarChar, 50, ParameterDirection.Input, _
        False, 0, 0, "Model", DataRowVersion.Current, _
        "Accord")
    parameter.IsNullable = False

    command.Parameters.Add(parameter)
```

Setting Breakpoints and Break Conditions

Visual Studio offers a rich set of visual debugging tools to help developers find and diagnose problematic code. Debugging code is vital to the production of any quality application. To perform proper debugging, developers commonly employ breakpoints and tracing.

Breakpoints can be set by pressing the F9 key on the line where the developer wants to investigate the execution of the application. A breakpoint may also be set or added to an application by clicking the mouse in the left margin of a document window. Breakpoints can be set in any class file, SQL Stored procedure, and inline functions of a user interface page (.aspx, for example).

Not all lines can have an active breakpoint. If a line of code is not actually executed during runtime the breakpoint is not invoked. Typically, this occurs if a breakpoint is set on a line where a variable is declared

but not instantiated. The application must also have current object library files available for full debugging to occur. When an application is compiled in Debug mode these libraries are created.

After you set your breakpoint you can run your application and debug. The easiest way to accomplish this is to press F5 to start the application in Debug mode. When the application encounters the line you marked with a breakpoint it stops and moves to the line in Visual Studio. When the application breaks on the breakpoint it has access to all the currently used objects and their values. This enables you to see what is happening within the application and possibly correct any problems you may encounter.

A list of current breakpoints can be displayed by pressing Ctrl+Alt+B. Double-clicking an item in the list takes you to the line of code. The breakpoint may be disabled or even deleted from the list as well.

Setting Breakpoints and Break Conditions

1 Open a `Class` file with a method to set a breakpoint.

2 Add a breakpoint to the method by pressing F9 on a line of code.

3 Right-click on a page that calls the method in step **1**.

4 Click Set As Start Page.

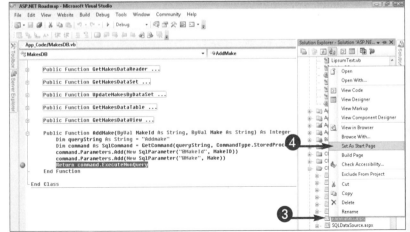

⑤ Start the application by pressing F5.

⑥ Click Submit to invoke the method in step **1**.

⑦ Examine the variable values in the application.

⑧ Step through the application by pressing F10 or F11.

The application stops on the breakpoint, allowing examination of variable values.

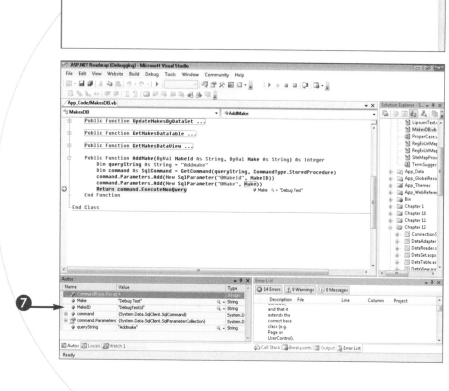

Extra

Just because you have set a breakpoint on a line of code does not mean a break must be executed each time the line is reached in the code. If you have a breakpoint set inside of a long-running loop you may only want to break if a certain condition is met or the line executes a certain number of times.

To set a breakpoint that breaks after a specific number of executions you can right-click on the line and select Breakpoint from the contextual menu. You will open a submenu with several choices. Click Hit Count. In the dialog box with options that appears, you can select from Always Execute to Execute when the count reaches a specified number, a multiple of a number, or greater than or equal to a specified count.

You can choose Condition from the same submenu. This displays a dialog box that enables you to set a condition to execute the breakpoint. You can set the condition to be when a variable reaches a certain value or changes in value. Other options are Filter, which allows you to define a more complex set of expressions, and When Hit, which either prints a message or executes a macro.

Debug a Web Site in Visual Studio 2005

O ne of the most important characteristics of a good development environment is the ability to easily debug the application. Visual Studio 2005 provides a rich set of easy-to-use debugging tools. It all starts by setting breakpoints on a relevant line of code. Next, the debugger needs to be initiated, which can be done by pressing F5 or manually attaching to a running process. As the application executes it will be interrupted when the line with the breakpoint set is executed. Visual Studio takes over, letting you step through the code examining the values of variables and methods.

Before debugging can be performed on an ASP.NET Web site, debugging must be turned on in the web.config file. You can do this by setting the debug attribute of the compilation element to true.

Initially Visual Studio sets the default page for execution to the Default.aspx, but this can be reset to any page in the Web site. Simply right-click on the initial page to start execution and choose Set as Default Page. The default page can also be set in the Properties dialog box for the Web site.

There are two types of build configurations: debug and release. The difference between the two is that a debug configuration includes object libraries for debugging. The compiler produces a PDB file that contains the object information for line-by-line debugging capabilities.

No other process can be running on port 80 if using IIS because only one application can communicate over port 80 without interfering with IIS. You may need to run a TCP/IP viewer, such as TCPView to see if any other applications are using port 80. The Cassini Web server, which is built into Visual Studio, executes the Web site on a random, available port.

Debug a Web Site in Visual Studio 2005

① Open a Class file with a method to set a breakpoint.

② Add a breakpoint to the top of a method by pressing F9 on a line of code.

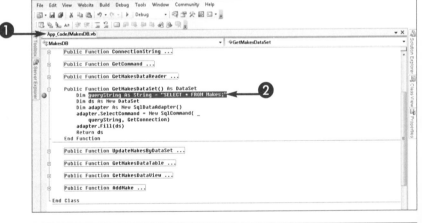

③ Right-click on a page that calls the method in step 1.

④ Click Set As Start Page.

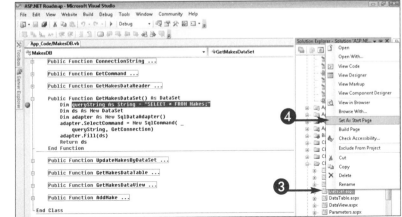

⑤ Press F5 to start the application.

⑥ Perform an action to invoke the method in step **1**.

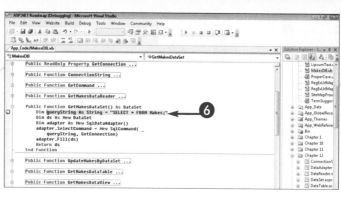

⑦ Examine the variable values in the application.

⑧ Step through the application by pressing F10 or F11.

As the application executes the variable values change as they are set on each line.

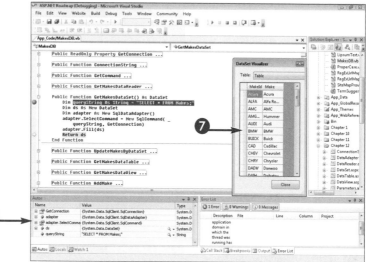

Extra

The Web site's Properties dialog box has a Start Options section. Here the Start action can be designated as the current page (meaning the page you are currently editing), a designated page, an external program, a specific URL, or nothing at all. The next setting specifies the actual server used to execute the Web site. This is important because the default Web server is the Cassini server included with Visual Studio.

A local instance of IIS may also be installed on the workstation and be used to execute the application. Finally, a remote server may also be used to execute the site. For this to work the user must have administrative permissions on the remote server.

The last section of the Start Options is Debuggers. Here a selection of ASP.NET Native Code and SQL Server can be made. To debug the Web site ASP.NET must be selected.

Debug JavaScript in Visual Studio 2005

JavaScript has long been a disturbing language for many developers to code with, mostly because of the limitations of debugging JavaScript (because it runs in the browser). Fortunately, Visual Studio 2005 makes debugging JavaScript much easier with Internet Explorer 5 and above. You can actually set a breakpoint inside of Visual Studio, but you must also reconfigure Internet Explorer to cooperate with the debug process.

In Internet Explorer, you need to open the Internet Options dialog box. Click Tools, then Internet Options. After displaying the dialog box, click the Advanced tab. Under the Browsing node make sure the Disable Script Debugging (Internet Explorer) option is deselected. Click OK to save this setting. To verify debugging is turned on, open the View menu in Internet Explorer. If Script Debugger is available as an option then debugging is enabled.

When debugging JavaScript is complete it is a good idea to reverse this setting or you may be prompted to debug JavaScript from many sites you visit. If you want to keep the debugging setting active you can also deselect the Display a notification about every script error option in the Advanced tab.

Open the page in Design view that contains the JavaScript you need to debug. Place a standard Visual Studio breakpoint on the line you want to break execution. If you find yourself not able to add a breakpoint, go back to Internet Explorer and open the Script Debugger.

To use debugging, press F5. When the application executes the line of code with your breakpoint you are taken to the normal Visual Studio debug experience. You can view the value of variables and step through code by pressing F10 (to step to the next line) and F11 (to step into a method) just like server-side code.

Debug JavaScript in Visual Studio 2005

1 Open Internet Explorer.

2 Click Tools ➔ Internet Options to open the Internet Options dialog box from the menu.

3 In the Internet Options dialog box, click the Advanced tab.

4 Deselect the Disable script debugging (Internet Explorer) option.

5 Click Apply.

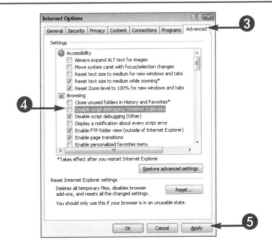

6 Open a Web page with JavaScript in a browser.

7 Click View ➔ Script Debugger ➔ Open to open the Script Debugger from Internet Explorer.

8 Open a Web page in Source view that contains a JavaScript function.

9 Press F5 to start the debugger.

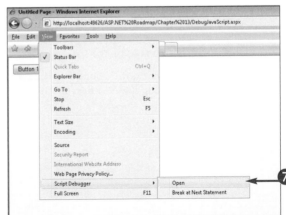

⑩ Set a breakpoint in the JavaScript function.

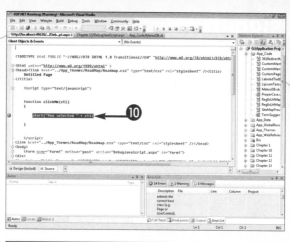

⑪ Perform the action to invoke the JavaScript function.

⑫ Examine the variables in the function.

⑬ Step through the function by pressing F10.

By debugging you can examine the value of client-side variables.

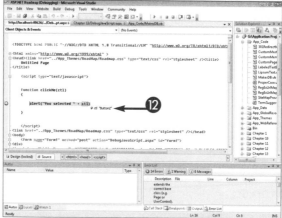

Extra

You are not limited to using Visual Studio alone to debug JavaScript. Because every browser platform has its own interpretation of JavaScript you often have to debug in those browsers to see how the code executes. FireFox has many add-ins that allow you to step through code running in FireFox. FireBug (www.getfirebug.com) is one of the most popular utilities.

FireBug is a FireFox add-in, which means you must be running FireFox to install FireBug. After you install FireBug you can open it from the Tools menu. FireBug opens in a window at the bottom of FireFox, and you can begin to work with JavaScript to track your bugs.

Another very popular FireFox add-in is the Venkman JavaScript debugger (www.mozilla.org/projects/venkman/). In Opera, you can use the JavaScript Console to review JavaScript errors. The downside to these tools is they do not work from inside Visual Studio, which means you cannot directly tie the operation of the application to the server-side code execution.

Design-Time Notifications

isual Studio provides many great visual indications to developers when there is a potential problem with the code they are writing. One of the most popular design-time notifications is the real-time debugger providing a visual indication of a syntactical error.

This causes a squiggly line to appear under the variable or logic statement that has a flaw in it; for example, if you try to pass a variable that is not of the proper type for a method's signature. The squiggly line notification is actually called a syntax notification and will also show a tooltip when the mouse if passed over it letting you know what the error is.

Visual Basic takes the notifications to the next level by providing a Smart Tag when you mouse over a notification. The Smart Tag notification may be selected to display a modeless dialog box that offers suggestions

for correcting the syntactical error. You can actually select a suggestion and it is automatically applied to your code.

The notifications extend to the design experience in Visual Studio. For example, if you write an invalid HTML tag or attribute, the same syntax notification mechanism is displayed. This is the case for both HTML and XML editing.

There are two types of tasks available in the Task List: User Tasks and Comments. The Task List window shows a list of user tasks that have manually been entered by the developer or maybe project management software that can talk to Visual Studio. A comment is a line of comments with a predefined prefix indicating the type of comment it is. For example, the line "TODO:Change the Connection String for Production" would be displayed in the list. You can define the Comment prefixes in the Visual Studio Options dialog box under Environment-Task List.

Design-Time Notifications

① Create a new Web page.

② Add a `GridView`.

③ Open the Smart Tag menu.

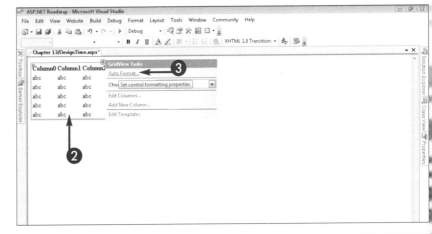

④ Switch to Source view of the ASPX page.

⑤ Remove the closing tag of the `GridView`.

A red underline Design-Time notification appears in the opening `GridView` tag indicating the closing tag does not exist.

6 Switch to code-behind view.

7 Add a `Page_Load` event handler.

8 Add code to call the `BindData` method.

A Design-Time notification appears indicating the `BindData` method does not exist.

9 Place a `TODO:` comment in the `BindData` method to remind you to add sorting capabilities.

10 Click View → Task List to open the Task List window.

● The task added in step **9** is listed under Comments.

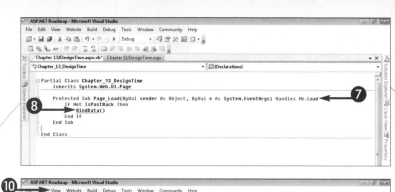

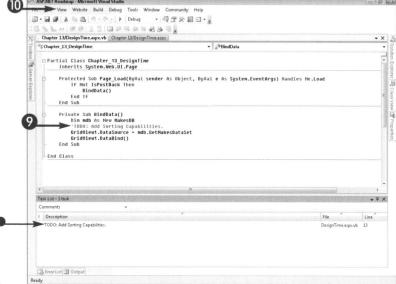

Extra

A nice feature of Visual Studio is the `Immediate` and `Command` Window. It allows you to execute a small piece of code while you are in Break mode. This is useful when you are on a problematic line of code and want to see how a modification of the code might work without having to retrace your steps. You can also assign variables to a value to see how that changes the execution of the code.

You can enter code in the `Immediate` window the same way you do in the Code editor to be executed. To view a variable or expression, prefix it with a question mark and press Enter.

You can change the `Immediate` window into a `Command` window by prefacing commands with a greater-than sign (>). This gives you access to the Visual Studio objects and macros so you can execute them without going to the menus. You can cycle through previous commands by using the up- and down-arrow keys. You may also have to preface certain parameters to methods with a forward slash (/), quotes (" "), or other delimiters in order for it to be interpreted correctly.

Use Tracing to Find Problems

Tracing can be one of the most important diagnostic tools a developer can use to track down errors or invalid states in Web applications. Tracing is simply the act of storing a message to be displayed to a developer as an application is being executed. In ASP.NET the Trace log is appended to the page's output.

You can enable tracing for an entire application by configuring the trace element in the web.config file. The element's enabled attribute and `pageOutput` attribute needs to be set to true. Optionally, the `requestLimit` can be set to a numerical value of the number of requests the Trace information has stored before it begins to purge them from the log.

You can also set tracing at the page level. The page settings take precedence over any application-specific settings. Page-level tracing is enabled by setting the Page directive's `Trace` attribute to `true`. Optionally the

`TraceMode` attribute can be set to `SortByCategory` or `SortByTime` (the default). Sorting trace entries by time is very useful because you can see which methods take up the most time. This information can prove invaluable when tracking down performance bottlenecks.

The trace output is positioned at the bottom of the actual page requested. It is a series of tables that includes Request Details, Trace Information, Control Tree, Session State, Application State, Request, and Response cookies, Headers, Form Collection, `QueryString` Collection, and Server Variables. The Trace Information section lists all `Trace.Write` methods called in the processing of the request. `Trace.Write` simply adds the text to the trace log and can associated it with a category. It is the most useful section when troubleshooting performance bottlenecks because it lists timing information. The other sections list values of various state and parameters processed by the page. These are very useful when tracking down errors due to invalid values.

Use Tracing to Find Problems

① Open the Web site's web.config file.

② Add a `trace` element to the system.web section.

③ Set the `enabled` attribute to `true`.

④ Set the `traceMode` to `SortByTime`.

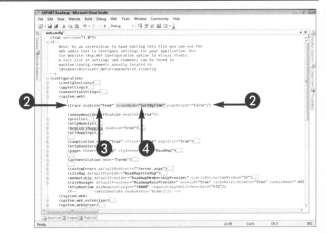

⑤ Add a new page to the Web site.

⑥ Click the Source button to switch to Source view.

⑦ Add a `TraceMode` attribute to the Page directive to `SortByTime`.

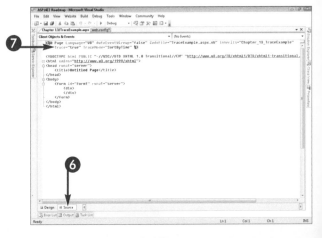

8 Switch to code-behind view.

9 Add `Trace.Write` statements to the `Page_Load` event handler.

10 Add a 5-second `Sleep` statement between the `Trace.Write` statements.

11 Open the page in a browser.

12 View the trace output in the page.

● The two Trace.Write messages are displayed in the Trace Information table.

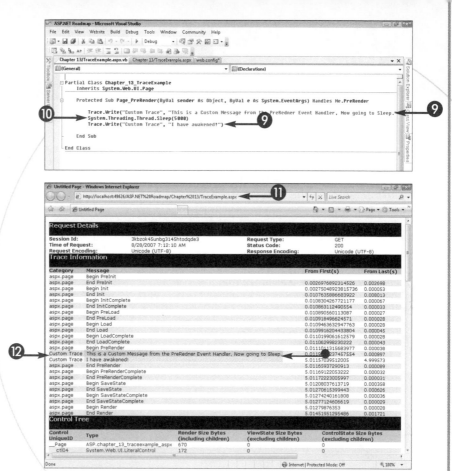

Extra

The `requestLimit` attribute specifies how many page requests trace logs are stored at any one time. These logs can be viewed through a nonexistent page, trace.axd. This page is actually a built-in handler to the ASP.NET engine. It can be opened by calling it directly from the root of the Web site as long as tracing is enabled.

The page lists all the current requests logged by the application up to the `requestLimit` setting. The list provides the time of the request, the file requested, the Http status code, the Http Verb used in the request, and a link to view the trace details of the request. The trace details will be a page with the identical trace information you see appended to the bottom of a page.

If tracing is enabled at the application level in the web.config file, but the `pageOutput` attribute is set to `false` all trace output will be only sent to the trace log. If tracing is enabled at the page level the output is appended to the page, overriding the `pageOutput="false"` setting. This can prove useful when tracking down issues on a live Web site.

Use the
Watch Windows

Knowing the state or value of variables is one of the most important parts of debugging errors in an application. Visual Studio gives you two ways to know the value of variables: in the editor and in watch windows. New to Visual Studio 2005 is the ability to mouse over a variable and the value or state of the variable appears in a `DataTip` window. The watch windows are typically displayed at the bottom left of Visual Studio while in Debug mode.

Watch windows have been a debugging staple for several years, and Visual Studio offers several watch windows: Autos, Locals, and Watch 1. A big advantage that a watch window has over the `DataTip` is it is not as varied as you move the mouse and it can be consistently displayed. As you step through the application, variables change values, which are displayed in the window.

While in Debug mode any variable can be added to the main watch window, Watch 1, by right-clicking the variable and selecting Add Watch. This places a reference to the variable anywhere in the application while in Debug mode.

The Autos Watch window creates automatic watch references to variables being immediately used by the application. As you step through the application the Autos Watch window automatically changes to variables being used on and around the line being executed.

The Locals Watch window displays all the variables local to a method. It displays all parameters passed to the method as well as any variable declared in the method.

One of the nice features of using a watch window to debug an application is the ability to change the value of a variable. This is extremely useful while stepping through an application to see how the application reacts if a variable has an altered value.

Use the Watch Windows

① Open a class file or code-behind of a Web page.

② Select a line of code to place a breakpoint.

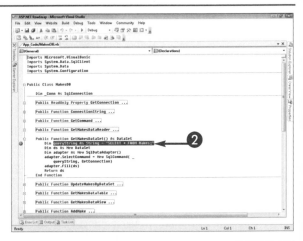

③ Right-click on a page that calls the method in step **1**.

④ Click Set As Start Page so the line chosen is executed.

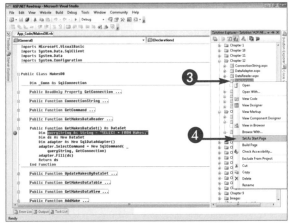

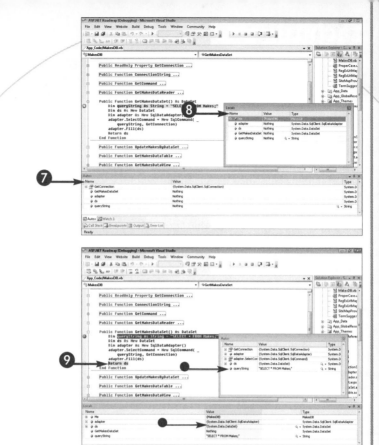

5 Press F5 to open the application.

6 Execute the application so the breakpoint is executed.

7 View the Autos Watch window.

8 View the Locals Watch window.

9 Step through the code by pressing F10.

● Changes in the variables appear in the watch windows.

Extra

Sometimes digging into a complex variable or a method cannot be satisfactorily done in a watch window. Visual Studio has a feature called a Quick Watch window. While an application is being debugged you can right-click a variable or method and select Quick Watch from the context menu. The Quick Watch dialog box appears with a list of properties and values for the object selected.

If an object is a class with child objects, they can be drilled into to examine the values of properties in the nested object. At the top of the dialog box the object being examined is displayed in a `TextBox` labeled `Expression`. This value can be changed to examine other objects or members of the initial object being examined. For example, a `DataSet` with multiple tables can be manipulated to display information only for one of the tables. The expression might look like this: ds.Tables(1).

If there is an error, such as a mistyped expression, the Quick Watch window will let you know and there will be no values to examine.

Attach to a Process

I n Visual Studio, you can attach to an existing process such as a Web site, an application running on the workstation, or if permissible, a remote machine. By attaching to a running process, you can debug an issue or application in one step, when it would normally take several steps to re-create the bug.

You can also choose Attach to Process from the Debug menu, or press Ctrl+Alt+P to display the Attach to Process dialog box. The Attach to Process dialog box displays and lists all the processes that are running on the workstation. The process grid lists the process name, ID, Title (if any), Type, UserName, and Session. Each of the columns can be sorted alphabetically in ascending and descending order.

For ASP.NET applications, there are two process names to select: aspnet_wp.exe and WebDev.WebServer.Exe. The first choice is for a Web site running under the local

instance of IIS. The WebDev.WebServer.Exe refers to the development Web server. When debugging against a virtual Web running in the local version of IIS, be aware that any other application actively running under IIS may also cause a breakpoint to execute. The other applications may also cause issues with your application if they process a request at the same time.

There can be multiple instances of the development Web server application in the list. When this is the case, use the Title column to differentiate the instances. The port number of the Web site is displayed, which can be compared to the site to be debugged.

After the process is attached to the Visual Studio debugger, normal debugging operations can proceed just as if the site was initiated by pressing F5. All object libraries are loaded and the debugger can properly step through the application and watch the variables.

Attach to a Process

① Press Ctrl+Alt+P to open the Attach to Process dialog box.

② Select the instance of a Web site by double-clicking it.

③ Execute the Web site.

④ Step through the application once a breakpoint is hit.

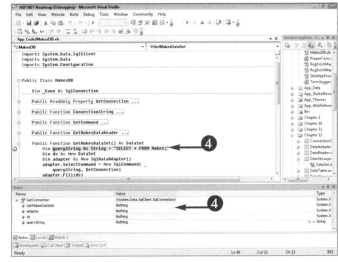

Use SQL Stored Procedure Debugging

A big part of building modern Web sites is building back-end databases with stored procedures to interact with application data. Stored procedures are essentially functions written in SQL that interact with tables, views, database function, and even other stored procedures to either retrieve, insert, update, or delete values.

Visual Studio 2005 enables the application developer to take advantage of the debugger by stepping inside a database's stored procedures as they are executed. You must have the Professional or Team System version of Visual Studio to perform SQL stored procedure debugging. You must also have the remote debugger installed. If you are running SQL Server 2000 you need to configure DCOM for SQL debugging. Unlike debugging a Web or desktop application, you cannot use F11 to step into a stored procedure from the

application. You can set a breakpoint and reach that line in the stored procedure through a normal F5 debug operation.

You should also be aware of any firewall blocks between the developer's workstation and the SQL database if they are not on the same machine. You may have to allow this traffic, but should check with your network administrator about helping with this. This can be a problem on Windows XP Service Pack 2 or Windows Vista's firewall, and you must configure the firewall to allow this traffic.

You will also need to be running Visual Studio with a user account that has administrative access to the remote SQL Server machine. Accounts may be added to the SQL Server's sysadmin using the sp_addsvrrolemember stored procedure. You will also need to make sure the account has permissions to run the sp_enable_sql_debug stored procedure.

Use SQL Stored Procedure Debugging

① Define a breakpoint in a stored procedure.

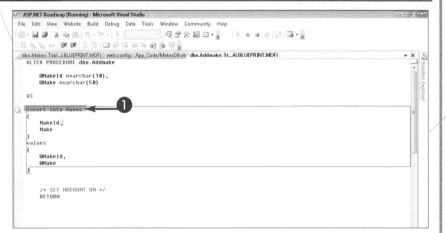

② Press F5 to execute the Web site in Debug mode.

③ Call the stored procedure in step **1**.

④ Step through the stored procedure.

You can evaluate the values of variables in the stored procedure.

Use Page-Level Exception Handling

Each Web form in ASP.NET inherits from the Page class, which has an Error event that is raised when an unhandled exception is not handled before processing leaves the page. You can create your own Error event handler to process any exceptions that may be unhandled. It is also a good idea to handle common expected exceptions in a base Page class where you can process specific exceptions in a routine manner.

The Error event is raised whenever an unhandled exception occurs during the execution of the page. If an exception occurs, but is handled in the page's Error event, it will not be passed to the application level. Exceptions can be managed by using a Try...Catch...Finally block, where a block of code is wrapped by the Try statement. If an exception occurs in the block of code, it is caught by the Catch statement, where it can be gracefully handled. The Finally

statement is not required, but is typically where any finalization code is executed, regardless of the exception state. The closing of database connections are an example of typical code contained in a Finally block.

When the page's Error event is raised the exception can be accessed by calling the Server.GetLastError method. This method returns an instance of the exception that was thrown, and now the information about the exception can be processed. The rendering of the page will not complete, but the Response object is available so a simple error message may be relayed to the user through a Response.Write.

In addition to just handling the error in the page's error event handler, a custom page redirection can also be made on a page-by-page basis. In the Page Directive the ErrorPage attribute points to a destination page to send to the browser when an Exception occurs on the page.

Use Page-Level Exception Handling

① Create a new Web page to collect user input.

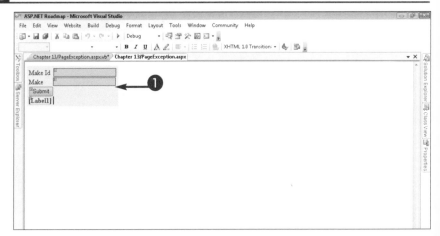

② Create an event handler for the Submit button.

③ Add code to store the user input to the database.

④ Instead of declaring a new instance of the data class, just declare it.

By not instantiating (using the new operator) the data class will not exist, causing an exception.

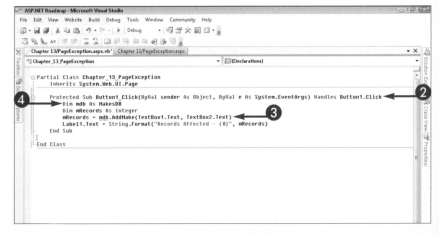

⑤ Add an `Error` event handler to the page.

⑥ Add code to log the error.

⑦ Add code to display a friendly error message to the user.

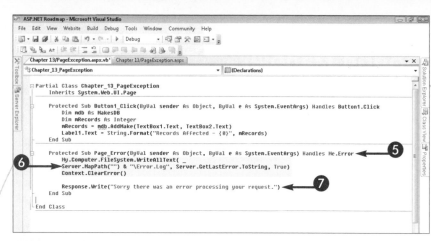

⑧ Open the page in a browser.

⑨ Type data and submit the form.

● The friendly error message is displayed and the error is logged to be corrected.

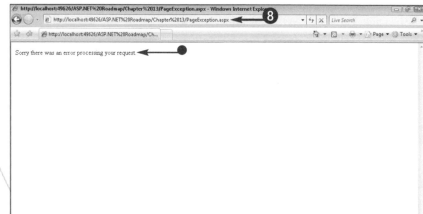

Extra

Throwing and catching exceptions adds extra overhead to your applications. You should try to manage any exceptions within your code and instead display informative error messages to your users. For example, instead of bubbling up an exception for an invalid value you might validate the values format and display a more subtle message to the user to correct the value to the proper format. Often this can be accomplished by using the `Validation` controls, custom server-side validation routines, and regular expressions.

In the walkthrough, you created a situation where the class did not exist yet and threw a `NullReferenceException`. Some classes contain shared (VB) or static (C#) methods. Shared methods are available from a class without it being instantiated. The `String.IsNullOrEmpty` is a common shared method use to check for empty strings. To declare a shared method, add shared before function or sub in the method definition.

Define a Global Exception Handler

Each ASP.NET Web site can have one Global.asax file, which is actually an HttpModule definition. This file allows you to create event handlers for each of the events in the ASP.NET pipeline. One event that can be handled is the Error event. This event is the last step any unhandled exceptions are passed as they bubble up from the cause.

This event can be leveraged to perform several functions, such as logging the error to an error log or error alerting system and possibly performing a custom redirect to an error message page. The Error event signature has two parameters: a sender and an EventArgs. Because of the nature of the Global.asax page you may not need to reference these two parameters to process the error. You can call Server.GetLastError to get the exception object and its information to process. The exception

object will have at least a Message, Source, and StackTrace properties that you can examine. The Message property is the error message that would normally be displayed in the browser. The Source gives you the line number of the error, but only if the debug object files are available. The StackTrace can be extremely useful because it walks you through the steps of methods taken to create the error. This information can be extremely valuable in re-creating and ultimately correcting any error-prone code.

It is also a good idea to log as much information about the request as possible. The Request object is available in the Global Error event, and can be used to gather information about the request, such as the user's IP address, username, and so on. Knowing as much about the state of the user's request and session as possible goes a long way to troubleshooting the bug.

Define a Global Exception Handler

① Open the Global.asax file. If the site does not have one, then add it.

② Add code to log any error to a log file.

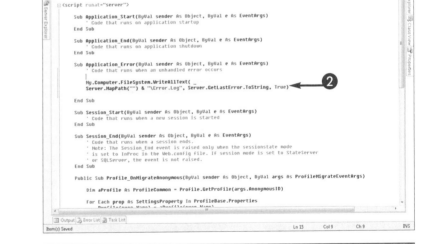

③ Add a standard page to display when an unhandled exception occurs.

④ Add a friendly message to let the user know there was an error.

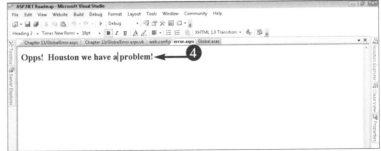

5 Open the site's web.config file.

6 Configure the `customErrors` section to redirect any unhandled errors to the page added in step **3**.

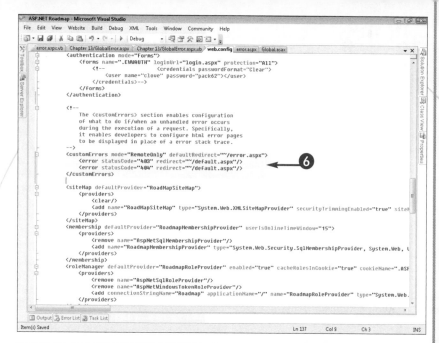

7 Open a Web page that will cause an error.

8 Perform any action on the page to cause the error.

When the exception occurs the global error handler is invoked and the user is routed to the standard error page.

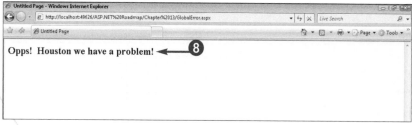

Extra

A common technique for logging errors is using the Logging Application Block that is part of the free Enterprise Library from Microsoft. This block is a set of tested and scalable code available for free from Microsoft to manage the logging of information in a Web site. The Logging Application Block is configured in the web.config file and can be called from anywhere inside of the application.

The Logging Application Block allows developers to incorporate standard logging and instrumentation functionality in their applications. Applications can use the Logging Block to log events to a variety of locations, such as the event log, e-mail messages, a database, a message queue, a file, and WMI.

The Logging Application Block helps with application development in a number of ways. It helps maintain consistent logging practices. It also eases the learning curve for many developers by using a consistent architectural model.

Send an E-Mail

Sending an e-mail from a Web site is a very common task for most applications. Many times they are automated messages to let the user know an action occurred, such as a password reset, placement of an order, or reporting of an error. The .NET framework offers a rich set of classes to manage the sending of e-mail that include the capabilities of including binary attachments, HTML formatting, priorities, and multiple recipients. These are available in the System.Net.Mail namespace.

To send an e-mail, you must have access to a Simple Mail Transport Protocol (SMTP) server. If you do not know the address of your SMTP server, check with your system administrator to find the correct address and any authentication you may need from your Web server. SMTP is a protocol defined in RFC 2821 to send e-mail. You can configure the SMTP server in the system.web element of the web.config file.

The SmtpClient class manages the sending of e-mail over SMTP and can either use an explicitly set mail server or one configured in the site's web.config file. You must either set the server or have one defined in the site's configuration or the e-mail cannot be sent. The SmtpMail class has one public shared method, Send, which can accept either a MailMessage object or series of parameters that define a message. Because it is a shared method you can call the method without creating an instance of the SmtpMail class.

The MailMessage class contains properties that define a mail message. The Sender property contains the message's From address. The Recipient property contains a collection of target addresses. The Subject property contains the text for the subject line of the message. The Body property contains the content of the mail.

Send an E-Mail

1 Create a new Web page.

2 Add TextBoxes for the To Address, the From Address, and the Subject.

3 Add a message body TextBox.

4 Set the message body TextMode to Multiline.

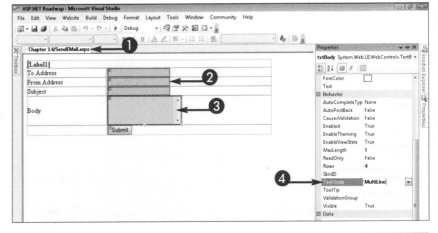

5 Add a button and double-click it to add a Click event handler.

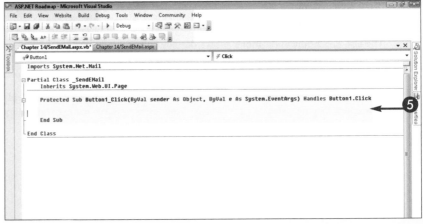

6. Create a new `SmtpClient` object.

7. Call the `Send` method of the `SmtpClient` object.

8. Pass a new `MailMessage` object to the `Send` method.

9. Set a confirmation message after the message is sent.

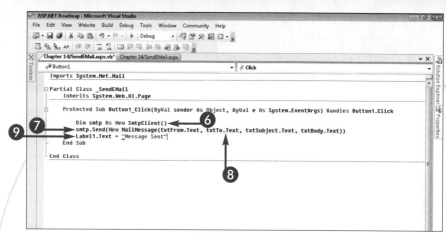

10. Open the page in a browser.

11. Complete the fields.

12. Click Submit.

   The e-mail is sent to the recipient and the confirmation message is displayed.

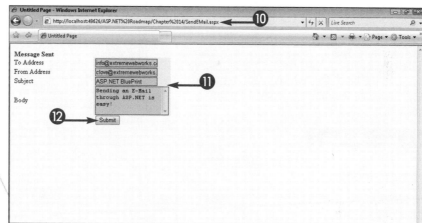

Apply It

Most modern e-mail clients read messages in HTML format, but there are still many clients that cannot read formatted text, such as a BlackBerry. The `MailMessage` has an `AlternateViews` property collection. An `AlternateView` is a class that manages the format of an e-mail message. You can specify a message body as either text or HTML formats.

The `AlternateView` class accepts a parameter for the body of the message and a mime type, `MediaTypeNames`. This is an enumeration that can indicate `HTML`, `Plain` text, `XML`, or `RichText` formats.

Configure Alternating Views:

```
message.AlternateViews.Add( _
 new AlternateView(body, MediaTypeNames.Text.Html))
message.AlternateViews.Add( _
 new AlternateView(body, MediaTypeNames.Text.Plain))
```

Send an E-Mail Attachment

Sending attachments such as PDFs or Word documents is common in many business applications. The .NET mail `MailMessage` class's `Attachments` collection manages the binary files attached to a message, such as images or documents. An `Attachment` is a class that contains either a `String`, `Stream`, or file name and can be set through any of the six constructors.

The `Attachment` class has a `ContentType` property to specify the mime type of the file. The `ContentType` property is a `ContentType` class. This class represents the MIME protocol Content-Type header and has several important properties. The `Boundary` property manages the boundary parameter in the header. The boundary is used to indicate the boundary between different parts of the message, such as the message body from an attachment.

The `CharSet` property represents the `CharSet` value of the header that indicates the character set to be used in the e-mail; for example, `us-ascii`. The `MediaType` property is a `MediaTypeNames` enumerator and can be either `Plain` text, `HTML`, `RichText`, or `XML`. The `Name` property gives the attachment a unique name to be referenced in the message. The `Parameters` property of the header specifies a key-value pair of parameters that may be needed for various media types.

Sending attachments can sometimes be a delicate process. Many e-mail accounts have limits to the amount of storage they have, so e-mails with large attachments may not be delivered. Other networks may have size limitations set up as to how large an e-mail can be before it is rejected. Finally, make sure your attachments do not contain a virus. Many systems will not only block your message but may also block your IP address from further communications.

Send an E-Mail Attachment

1. Create a new Web page.

2. Add To Address, From Address, and Subject TextBoxes.

3. Add a multiline TextBox for the message body.

4. Add a `FileUpload` control for the file attachment.

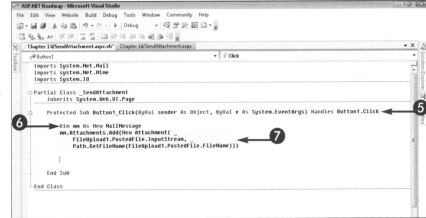

5. Double-click the Submit button to create a `click` event handler.

6. Create a new `MailMessage` object.

7. Add an attachment using the `InputStream` of the `FileUpload` control.

⑧ Set the remaining
`MailMessage` values.

⑨ Create a new
`SmtpClient` and send
the `MailMessage`.

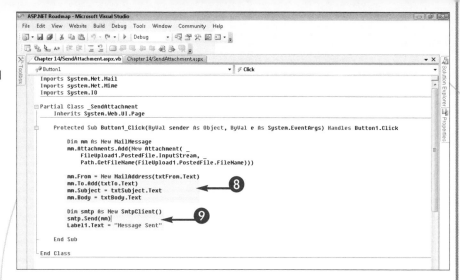

⑩ Open the page in a
browser.

⑪ Type values in the fields,
including the
attachment.

⑫ Click Submit.

The e-mail and
attachment are sent to
the recipient.

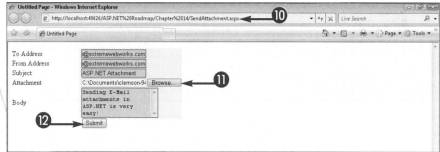

Apply It

An attachment may be created with a file name or a stream, and you may also specify either the
`ContentType` or name the MIME type in the constructor. It is a good idea to specify the `ContentType` or
MIME type when creating an attachment.

You can also use a stream to create the attachment, which can be useful if you are not attaching a file on the
file system, but maybe a file from memory or directly off the network.

Send a File Directly from the FileUpload Control:
```
Dim mm As New MailMessage
 mm.Attachments.Add(New Attachment( _
 FileUpload1.PostedFile.InputStream, _
 ddlMimeType.SelectedValue))
```

Create a Custom Page Class

By default, all page classes inherit from the `System.Web.UI.Page` class, which contains many methods and properties that are useful to just about all pages in an ASP.NET Web site. But there are many times a developer reuses common methods and properties that are specialized to a particular site or might be common across all applications in the enterprise. For example, a common method may be useful to validate customer or employee identification in the site. Another example might be adding references to common utility classes that offer methods to perform common routines such as sending e-mail or formatting user input.

Because .NET is an object-oriented framework, you can create your own custom page class that inherits from the `System.Web.UI.Page` class. This class can also be used as a base class to derive other page classes with more

specific members, such as site administration or shopping cart.

The custom page class must inherit from the base page class for it to be a valid class to inherit pages from. The code-behind file contains the class definition for the class used by the page. By default, it inherits the `System.Web.UI.Page` class. This can be replaced by a reference to the custom page class. Once this is done, the class for the Web page has access to the members of the custom page class.

Any method or property declared in the custom page class that is a public or protected member may be accessed by the child classes. This includes methods, properties, events, and variables. To call members from the parent class or any page class it inherits from, they can be called directly or by using the mybase (VB) or this (C#) object, `mybase.myCustomMethod()`. These objects are simply references back to the current class.

Create a Custom Page Class

① Add a new class to a Web site.

② Inherit the class from `System.Web.UI.Page`.

③ Add a `Function` to return the current time.

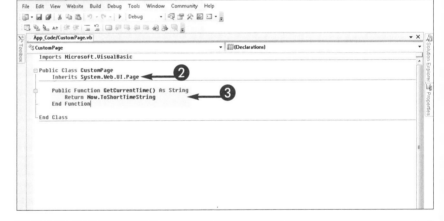

④ Add a new Web page to the site.

⑤ Add a `Label` control.

⑥ Add a `Button` control and then double-click it.

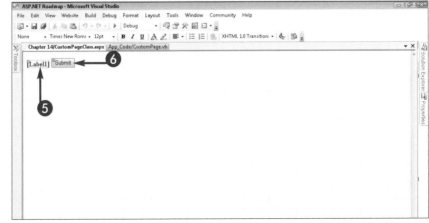

7 Add a `click` event handler to the button.

8 Change the class to inherit from the class created in step **1**.

9 Add code to set the label's text to the `GetCurrentTime` method.

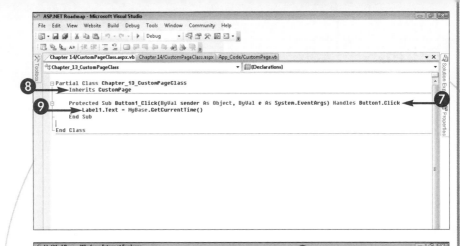

10 Open the page in a browser.

11 Click the button to update the time in the label from the base class function.

The `GetCurrentTime` method of the base class sets the time in the label control.

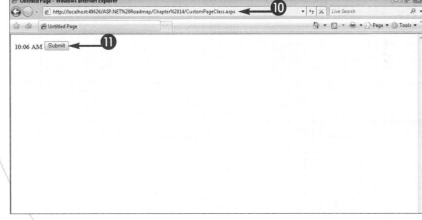

Apply It

Events may be handled in a custom `page` class, just like a code-behind `page` class. The exact same method signature and accompanying Handles clause can be used to handle the page event. This can be useful to ensure an event in the ASP.NET page pipeline is handled consistently by the application. A common example is to create a custom handler for the `Page Error` event. The error may be processed and logged, and proper notification sent to site administrators. Adding this functionality to a base `page` class is very efficient because it abstracts it to a commonly accessible location that can easily be maintained.

Create a Common Page Error EventHandler:

```
Private Sub Page_Error(ByVal sender As Object, ByVal e As System.EventArgs) Handles Me.Error

  Dim ex As Exception = Server.GetLastError()

  LogException(ex)
  SendAdminNotifications(ex)
End Sub
```

Create a Custom HttpHandler

Every request in ASP.NET is processed by an httpHandler. A request for a page is processed by the page request handler and so on. You can create your own httpHandlers to render content based on the request. For example, many sites use a handler to manage retrieving images from a database or rendering dynamic JavaScript to the browser. There are two types of handlers you can program: Generic handler and a custom class that implements the IHttpHandler interface.

The Generic handler is the easiest to create. You can add this to the site the same way you do any other resource, through an Add New Item operation. This adds a new file to the Web site with the .ashx extension. You can call it directly through the browser or even map it with URL Mapping or Rewriting to pass its parameters via a friendly URL.

A handler must implement the ProcessRequest method. This method has a single parameter, an HttpContext object that references to the current page context. Within this method you can access any QueryString parameters and other properties directly from the context object. You can process the request based on the parameters passed to the handler to create the content or pass a file stream back to the browser.

To save a file or other stream source directly to the browser you can save the object to the Response.OutputStream. The Response object also has two other methods useful for streaming content to the browser. For textual content you can simply use the Response.Write method, just like you do when programming a normal page. To pass a file on the file system, you can call the Response.WriteFile method, passing it to the path to the file. You should also set the MIME type of the content being sent to the browser through the Response.ContentType property — for example, 'text/plain'.

Create a Custom HttpHandler

① Add a new generic handler to the Web application.

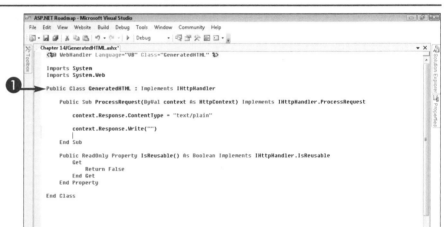

② Replace the provided Response.Write with a statement to generate a basic HTML header.

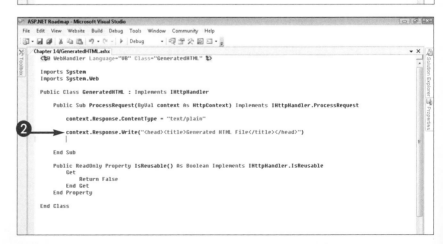

③ Add a `Response.Write` to produce a Body and H1 elements.

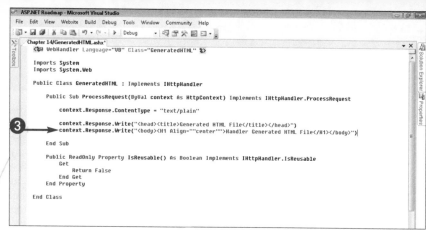

④ Open the handler in a browser.

● The generated page is rendered to the browser. You can view the page's source to see the header tag.

Apply It

You can create a custom class that implements `IHttpHandler`, but you cannot directly access the class through a URL. You would need to register the custom class in the Web configuration file in the `httpHandlers` section. You need to associate the request type, which is the full name of the handler class, the path or the file extension to be associated with the request, and the verb, or method the request is made such as a POST. Finally, you can specify if the request should be validated.

When you do this, you will also need to register or map the file extension to be processed by the handler in IIS to be processed by the ASP.NET engine. For example if you want to process all GIF files through a handler then you will want to change the mapping in IIS to pass all GIF files through the ASP.NET engine.

Custom Handler Declaration:

```
<httpHandlers>

 <add verb="GET,HEAD" path="ScriptResource.axd" type="System.Web.Handlers
.ScriptResourceHandler, System.Web.Extensions, Version=1.0.61025.0, Culture=neutral,
PublicKeyToken=31bf3856ad364e35" validate="false"/>

</httpHandlers>
```

Create a Custom HttpModule

There are many times when you may need to create a custom routine to perform processing somewhere in the ASP.NET pipeline. HttpModules allow you to create custom modules to intercept events in the pipeline to perform specialized logic. For example, you may want to perform some special logging of each request made to all the image files on a site or have a custom authentication routine. All registered modules are executed each time a resource is requested through the ASP.NET pipeline.

A good example for when to use a custom HttpModule is to perform a 301 redirect when a resource gets moved. A 301 status redirect tells requesting clients the URL they are requesting no longer exists, but passes the new location. Search engine spiders use this information to update their references to sites so they do not pass visitors to dead pages.

An HttpModule must implement the IHttpModule interface, which means it must implement the Init and Dispose methods. In the Init method, you need to add an event handler for the pipeline event that needs to be intercepted. To do this you must create an event handler method with a standard signature that accepts a sender object and event arguments parameters. The sender object is a reference to the Application context or HttpApplication object.

You can use the Dispose method to clean up any resources used by your HttpModule. Typically, this is not needed but is provided just in case and is required to be implemented by the IHttpModule interface.

All HttpModules must also be registered in the Web configuration file in the httpModules section of the system.web element. In the add element, the module type and name attributes are specified.

Create a Custom HttpModule

① Add a new class file to the App_Code folder named 301RedirectModule.vb.

② Add `Implements IHttpModule` to the class declaration and press Enter.

The Dispose and Init methods appear.

③ Add a method called Process301 with the argument signature of a sender object and e as EventArgs.

④ Add a function called Get301Mappings that returns a Hashtable.

⑤ Create a simple Hashtable routine to add some mappings for nonexistant URLs to their new URLs.

⑥ Add code to the Process301 method to check the incoming request against the 301 mappings that returns a header with the 301 information included.

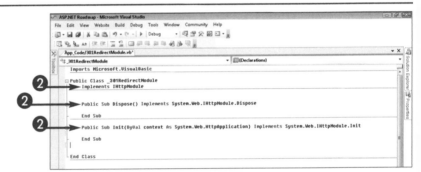

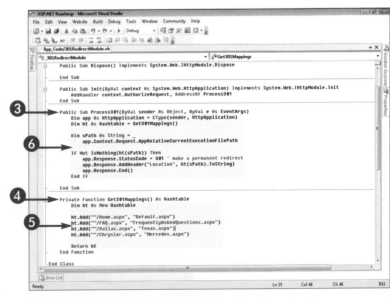

7 Open the web.config file.

8 Add a reference to the `301RedirectModule` to the `httpModules` section.

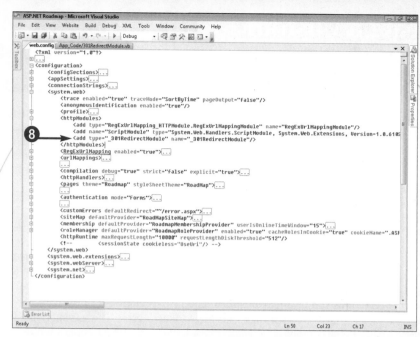

9 Open your Web browser.

10 Request one of the URLs that has been mapped to a new location.

● You are redirected to the new location. If you examine the request with an HTTP sniffer like Fiddler you would be able to see the 301 status code in the response headers.

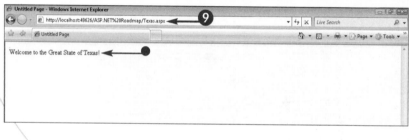

Apply It

In order for an `HttpModule` to properly operate you must add at least one event handler for an event in the ASP.NET pipeline. This requires you to call `AddHandler` in VB or add an event handler in C#, plus the corresponding method to process the event.

In VB, you use the `AddHandler` statement that takes two arguments: the event to be handled and the `AddressOf` the method to handle the event. In C# it is a little different. You can declare the event and use the `+=` syntax to add the actual event handler to the event. The signature of the event that handles the event must have a signature that matches what the event calls; for example, an object and event argument as parameters.

Manually Add an Event Handler:
```
AddHandler context.AuthorizeRequest, AddressOf Process301

Public Sub Process301(ByVal sender As Object, ByVal e As EventArgs)
'Process the event here
End Sub
```

Create a Custom ConfigurationSection

A SP.NET configuration settings may be extended with XML configuration elements of your own. You must create your own configuration section handler that derives from `System.Configuration.ConfigurationSection` class. The custom class handles any programmatic access to your custom configuration data. A custom section must register itself in the `configSections` element of the web.config file before it is recognized by ASP.NET when the site is executed.

The custom handler interprets and processes the settings defined in the custom section of the web.config file and returns a configuration value based on the settings through custom properties. The configuration object that the handler class returns can be any data structure; it is not limited to any base configuration class or configuration format. ASP.NET uses the configuration object to read and write to your custom configuration element.

Each property in the custom section class must be prefixed with at least a `Configuration` property attribute. The `Configuration` attribute takes the name of the property and can be followed by a series of named parameters or XML attribute names. There are also property attributes that can be declared to enforce validation rules, such as the `StringValidator`.

You can add the section handler declaration in a different configuration file than the one where you add your custom configuration elements providing that the configuration file where the section handler is declared is higher in the configuration file hierarchy.

The type attribute of the section element must match the manifest of the assembly or there will be a configuration error. The assembly file itself must be in the same ASP.NET application directory as the Web.config file that defines it.

Create a Custom ConfigurationSection

1. Add a new `RegExURLMappingConfigHandler` class to the App_Code folder.

2. Inherit the class from the `IConfigurationSectionHandler` interface.

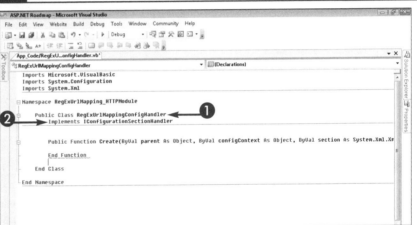

3. Add an `XmlNode` named `_Section`.

4. Add a method to implement the interface's `Create` method.

5. Set the `_Section` to the section variable of the `Create` method.

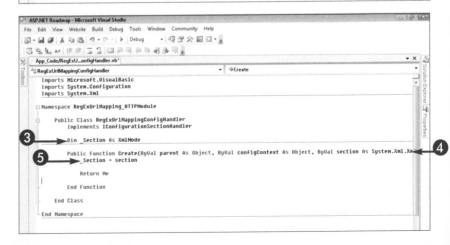

6 Add an `Enabled` function that returns `true` or `false`.

7 Add code to the `Enabled` function to read the enabled attribute.

8 If the attribute is equal to true then return `True`; otherwise return `False`.

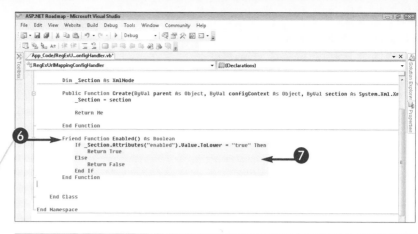

9 Add a `MappedURL` function that returns a string.

10 Add code to loop through the `ChildNodes` of the `_Section` node.

11 Add a check to see if the URL matches the `url` attribute of each child node.

12 If there is a match, return the value of the `url` attribute.

This class can now be used to read the custom configuration section for a URL rewriter.

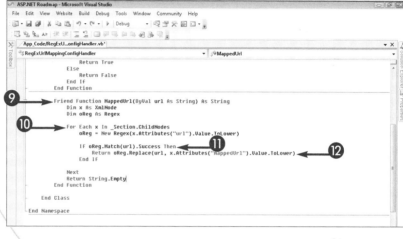

Apply It

To programmatically access your custom configuration data you need to obtain an instance of your custom configuration object and use the `System.Configuration.ConfigurationManager.GetSection (System.String)` method or the `System.Web.Configuration.WebConfigurationManager .GetSection(System.String)` method to populate it. Because the custom section handler uses a `Hashtable` as the configuration object, the `GetSection` method returns a `Hashtable`.

Programmatically Access the Custom Configuration Data:
```
Dim config As RegExUrlMappingConfigHandler = _
 CType(ConfigurationManager.GetSection("system.web/RegExUrlMapping"), _
 RegExUrlMappingConfigHandler)

Dim pathOld As String, pathNew As String = String.Empty

If config.Enabled Then
 pathNew = config.MappedUrl(requestedPage)
End If
```

Localize Content

ocalizing an application means making the application readable and runable in multiple locations, where a location is a country and a language combination. A location is represented by a language and a country code: en-US for U.S. English and en-UK for British English.

Besides obvious language differences there are also formatting rules specific to each location; dates vary across the different locales, for example. Other differences may be a language like English that is read left to right, while Arabic is right to left.

The .NET framework supports end-to-end Unicode. The `CultureInfo` class and, in particular, the `CultureInfo.Culture` and `CultureInfo.UICulture` properties, determine how things are formatted. A nice feature in .NET localization is the culture is assigned on a per-thread basis.

.NET uses resource files that are XML files with an .resx extension to store primarily strings and images. These files are compiled and embedded in .NET assemblies. Each resource is indexed by a resource id and locale and can be retrieved by calling the `HttpContext.GetLocal resouceObject` or `GetGlobalResourceObject` methods.

You can also use the locale info to cause locale-specific formatting. A date, for example, will render in differing formats based on the locale and you can ensure it is properly rendered by passing a culture object to the `ToString` method; `Now.ToString(new CultureInfo("fr-CA")`.

You will have to set the user's locale explicitly because the Web site is running on your server and your locale. This can be done by creating an event handler for the `BeginRequest` event in the `Global.asax` file. In this method, you assign the current thread's `CurrentCulture` property. You may also want to ensure the currency symbol is consistent with the symbols for your site's locale.

Localize Content

1. Add a `DropDownList` control to a Web page.

2. Add a `Literal` control for Culture and a `Literal` control for Date.

3. Add a `Label` to the Web page.

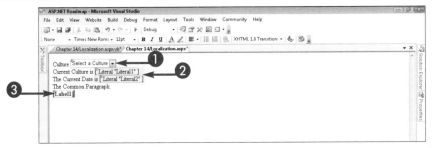

4. Add a list of cultures and their names to the `DropDownList` control.

5. Click OK.

6. Set the `DropDownList` control to AutoPostBack.

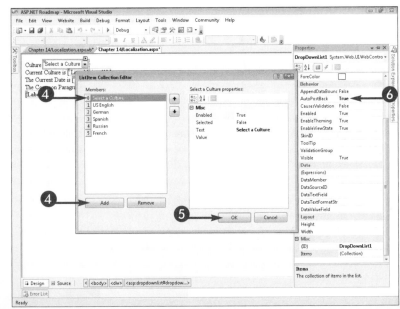

7 Create a `SelectedIndex Changed` event handler for the `DropDownList` control.

8 Add code to set the `Literal` and `Label` controls to culturally targeted content.

9 Create a `GetLocalized Text` function to return a translated string to the `Label` control.

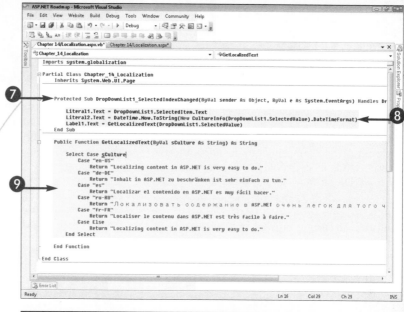

10 Open the page in a browser.

11 Select different cultures.

● The content changes.

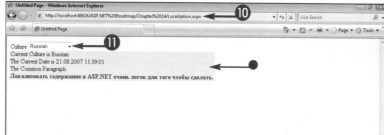

Apply It

The `Localize` control makes it very easy to localize large chunks of data and works very similarly as the `Literal` control. The main difference between the `Literal` control and the `Localize` control is the ability to edit content in Design view.

To define the resource string to display, use the `meta:ResourceKey` syntax, passing the name of the resource string to display.

Example Localize Control Tag Declaration:

```
<asp:Localize ID="Localize1" runat="server" meta:resourceKey="LocalizeTest"></asp:Localize>
```

Use the Cache API

Each ASP.NET application has one unique instance of the Cache object. It can be used for storing any data while making it available to every request and every page, control, and component in the application. This is a very useful object that allows you to store commonly used, but rarely changing variables in memory.

The application Cache object has two properties: Count and EffectivePrivateBytesLimit. The Count property returns the current number of items held in the Cache object. The EffectivePrivateBytesLimit returns the number of kilobytes the Cache object is using to store the values.

The Cache object supports several methods: Add, Get, GetEnumerator, Insert, and Remove. Add and Insert add items to the cache. The difference is if an item already exists the Add method fails but the Insert method replaces the existing value. The Get method

returns a specified value. The GetEnumerator allows you to iterate through all the Cache objects. Remove deletes an item from cache.

The Insert method has four overloads that accept up to seven parameters; key, value, dependencies, absoluteExpiration, slidingExpiration, priority, and onRemoveCallback. The key and value parameters are the minimal combination and provide the variable name and value of the cached item. The absoluteExpiration and slidingExpiration values enable you to specify an absolute expiration time and sliding expiration interval. The priority value specifies how important the item is. The onRemoveCallback is a method name that is called as soon as the item is removed from cache. This is useful to reload it when it expires.

You should always check to see if a value is in cache before using it. The Cache object supports scavenging, which means it purges values when memory resources become low.

Use the Cache API

① Add two Button controls to a Web page.

② Label one button Update.

③ Label the other button Get Cached.

④ Add a GridView control.

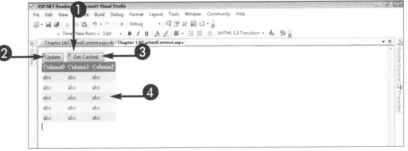

⑤ Double-click each button to create Click event handlers.

⑥ Add code to the Update button to add a new time to a list and cache it.

⑦ Bind the list to the GridView.

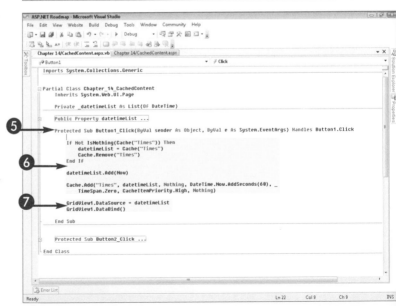

8 Add code to the Get Cached button to bind the cached data to the `GridView` control.

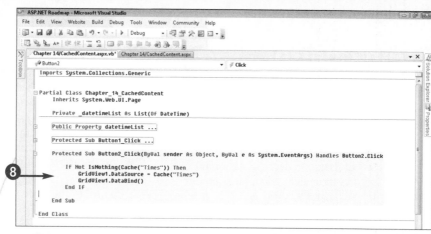

```
Chapter 14/CachedContent.aspx.vb    Chapter 14/CachedContent.aspx
Button2                                              Click

    Imports System.Collections.Generic


  Partial Class Chapter_14_CachedContent
        Inherits System.Web.UI.Page

        Private _datetimeList As List(Of DateTime)

        Public Property datetimeList ...

        Protected Sub Button1_Click ...

        Protected Sub Button2_Click(ByVal sender As Object, ByVal e As System.EventArgs) Handles Button2.Click

            If Not IsNothing(Cache("Times")) Then
                GridView1.DataSource = Cache("Times")
                GridView1.DataBind()
            End If

        End Sub

  End Class
```

9 Open the page in a browser.

10 Click Update a few times to build a list.

11 Wait a few seconds and click Update to bind the cached data.

Note: *If you wait until after the Cache has timed out there will be nothing bound to the* `GridView`*.*

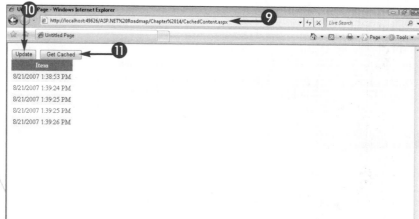

```
http://localhost:49626/ASP.NET%20Roadmap/Chapter%2014/CachedContent.aspx

Update   Get Cached
            Item
8/21/2007 1:38:53 PM
8/21/2007 1:39:24 PM
8/21/2007 1:39:25 PM
8/21/2007 1:39:25 PM
8/21/2007 1:39:26 PM
```

Apply It

If you want an item to stay in memory for a specified period of time you should set the `absoluteExpiration` time. This removes the item from cache and forces you to reload the data the first time it is used after the expiration. This helps keep the memory usage lower and the data relatively fresh. The following shows how to load a list of makes in the cache object for 30 minutes.

Cache a DataTable:

```
Dim dtMakes as DataTable = CType(Cache("Makes"), DataTable)
If isNothing(dtMakes) then
 dtMakes = GetMakesasDataTable() 'Method that handles retrieving the list.
 Cache.Insert("Makes", dtMakes, Nothing, DateTime.Now.AddMinutes(30), Cache.NoLidingExpiration)
End if
```

Encapsulating functionality and user interface in a reusable component enables ASP.NET developers to more rapidly and consistently develop applications. Web controls are designed to manage this task by providing a foundation to derive user interface controls. A Web control can be derived either from the `Control` class or the `WebControl` class.

Controls that have little or no visual aspect to them should be derived from the `Control` class. The `Control` class has also been traditionally used to build composite controls, but in ASP.NET 2.0 the `CompositeControl` class should be used. The `Control` class is used to derive other control classes, such as `WebControl`, `UserControl`, and even the `Page` class.

To create a user interface in a control the `Render` method must be overridden. This method passes an `HtmlTextWriter` object used by the control to render the HTML content to the browser. The `HtmlTextWriter`

class has several methods that can be used to control the layout of the control. The `RenderBeginTag` method writes the opening tag for the specified HTML element. The `RenderEndTag` writes the corresponding closing HTML tag for the specified element.

Child controls are added by adding an instance of the child control to the `Controls` property. The `Controls` property is a `ControlCollection` object. The controls are rendered in the order they are added to the collection.

The `WebControl` class derives from the `Control` class and adds many methods and properties that modify how a control is rendered. Common properties managed by the `WebControl` class control the foreground and background colors, the font used, and its attributes such as color and size. Dimensions, such `Height` and `Width`, of the control are also provided properties. Not every control inherited from `WebControl` implements every property, so you should check the control's documentation before assuming a property is supported.

Create a Custom Control

① Add a new class to a Web site.

② Inherit the class from the `System.Web.UI.Control` class.

③ Override the `Render` method.

④ Add a property to manage the number of paragraphs to display property.

⑤ Add a function to return the `Lipsum` paragraphs as a `StringCollection`.

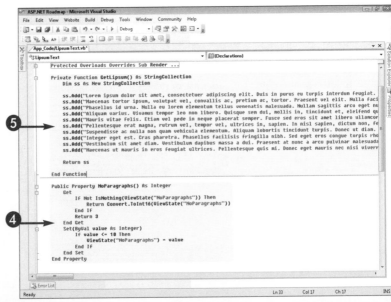

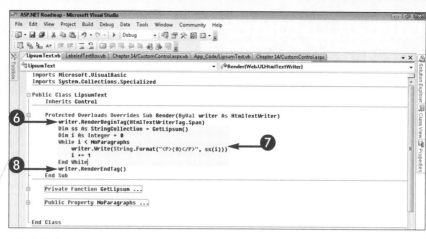

6 Call the `Render BeginTag` method of the render's `HtmlText Writer` parameter.

7 Add code to write the number of paragraphs specified in the `NoParagraphs` property.

8 Call the `RenderEndTag` method of the render's `HtmlTextWriter` parameter.

9 Add a reference to the `Lipsum` control to a Web page.

10 Set the `NoParagraphs` property of the control property.

11 Open the page in a browser.

The control is now rendered in the browser.

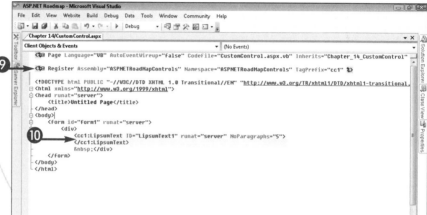

Apply It

The `ViewState` property comes with inheriting from the `Control` class. The `ViewState` allows a control to maintain state across post-backs, but comes with a potential performance penalty. As more values are stored in the `ViewState` the page becomes larger, thus causing a performance hit.

The `ViewState` is stored in a hidden field in the web page called `__VIEWESTATE` as a 64-bit encoded value. Access to the `ViewState` is available by simply calling the `ViewState` property and passing the name of the parameter to be set or retrieved. Often a control developer uses the `ViewState` to manage the values of properties set of the control.

A Typical Control Property Using ViewState:
```
Public Property Text() As String
    Get
        Dim s As String = TryCast(ViewState("Text"), String)
        Return IIf((s Is Nothing),String.Empty,s)
    End Get
    Set
        ViewState("Text") = value
    End Set
End Property
```

Create a Custom Composite Control

U sing existing controls to create a useful control can be easily done with the `CompositeControl` class. The `CompositeControl` class inherits from the `WebControl` class, thus inheriting all of the base members available to all controls. The `CompositeControl` class is an abstract class, meaning it cannot be used directly and it must be inherited.

The `CompositeControl` class provides containers for both naming and control designer functionality for your custom controls that encompass child controls. The `CompositeControl` class inherits from `WebControl`, so all the members of `WebControl` are available.

The `INamingContainer` interface is implemented by the `CompositeControl` class, which is required to ensure that all child control ID attributes are unique and can be located on post-back for data binding.

Each custom control built using other Web controls should derive from the `CompositeControl` class. This class provides base functionality such as built-in verification that child controls have been created prior to being accessed. It also enables the design-time environment to re-create the collection of child controls naturally.

A composite control must override the `CreateChild Controls` method to create the child controls. The first action is to call the `Controls.Clear` method to remove any existing controls from the `ControlCollection`. Each control must be instantiated and added to the `Controls` collection once all its properties are properly created.

The custom composite control can expose a series of properties to manage properties on each child control. The value of these properties is available in the `CreateChildControls` method. An example might be a `TextBoxWidth` to manage the width of `TextBox` control in the composite control. This would be a normal public integer property.

Create a Custom Composite Control

① Add a new class to a Web site.

② Inherit the class from the `System.Web.UI.Composite Control` class.

③ Add a `TextBox` variable to the class.

④ Add a `Literal` variable to the class.

⑤ Add a property to manage the label's `Text` property.

⑥ Add a property to manage the `TextBox`'s `Text` property.

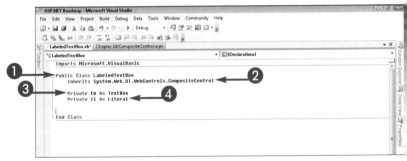

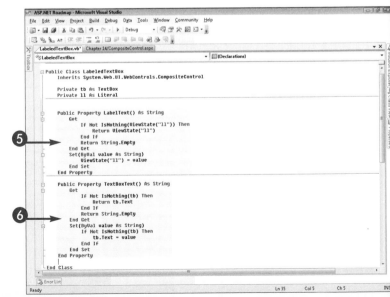

7 Create a method that overrides the `CreateChildControls` method.

8 Add code to the method to create a new instance of the `TextBox` and `Literal` controls.

9 Set the `Literal`'s text from the `LabelText` property.

10 Set the `TextBox`'s `Text` property to the `TextBoxText` property.

11 Open the page in a browser.

12 Type a value in the `TextBox` control.

13 Click Submit.

● The control is ready to be added to a Web page.

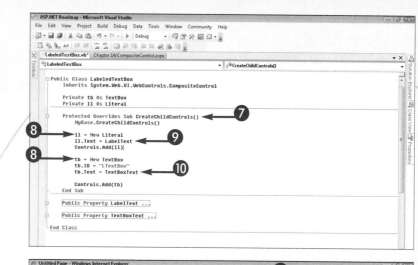

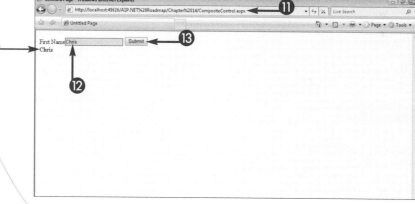

Extra

The `ControlDesigner` and `CompositeControlDesigner` classes are the base classes to use to extend a Web control in Design mode. A designer is used to define how a control's properties can be defined while a page is in Design mode.

A control designer can be used to define automatic formatting selections; typically, these are accessible to the programmer through the Smart Tag. To implement automatic formatting, the `AutoFormats` property, `OnAutoFormatApplied` method, and `DesignerAutoFormat` and `DesignerAutoFormatStyle` classes need to be used.

Action lists define the options available in the control's Smart Tag. `Control Designer Regions` manage editable regions of the control at design time.

Many controls implement Templates, such as the `Repeater`. Templates require the use of the `TemplateGroups` and `InTemplateMode` properties as well as the `TemplateGroup` class.

There are also several methods available to manage the design-time rendering of the control. The `GetDesignTimeHTML`, `GetEmptyDesignTimeHTML`, `GetErrorDesignTimeHTML`, `UpdateDesignTimeHTML`, and `CreatePlaceHolderDesignTimeHTML` methods all provide the HTML to render at different stages of the control's design-time life cycle.

Create a Web Service

Web services were created to help share structured data over the Internet. Exposing methods remotely is nothing new to programming, but directly exposing structured return values from a URL was not easy in the early days of the Internet. Web services allow a cross-platform methodology to call methods on a remote Web server by passing data serialized as XML. A simple example would be calling a word processing Web service that exposed methods to check spelling or proper casing of words. Each method would accept a word or string of words and appropriately process them and return the corrected versions.

ASP.NET makes building a Web service a very intuitive process because it automatically takes care of all the Web service serialization and standards compliance. An ASP.NET Web service is a class with a series of publicly exposed methods that have special attributes designating

methods as a Web method. The class itself has a set of special attributes that designate it as a Web service.

When a new Web service is added to a Web site or a project adds a reference to an external Web service a code file is placed in the App_Code folder that contains a proxy class. The .asmx file has a WebService directive, which is similar to the Page directive for a normal Web Form. The WebService directive has four attributes: `Class`, `Code-Behind`, `Debug`, and `Language`.

The actual class file added to the site for the Web service has several attributes added to the class. They designate the class as a Web service and the standards the service implements. The base attribute is `WebService`, which specifies the namespace for the Web service. The default is http://tempuri.org. The `WebServiceBinding` attribute defines what standards the service implements, the default being WSI 1.1. You can think of the `WebServiceBinding` as a class interface that defines the minimum signature and serialization the service implements.

Create a Web Service

① Right-click the root of the Web site in Solution Explorer.

② Click Add a New Item.

③ Click Web Service from the list.

④ Click Add.

⑤ Create a Web method named `ProperCase` that accepts a string parameter.

⑥ Add localization code to the `ToTitleCase` string.

⑦ Return the modified string from the Web method.

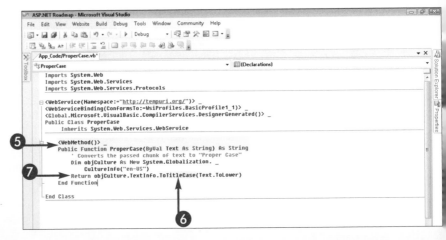
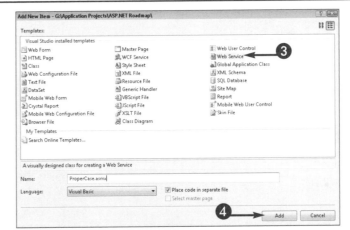

8 Open the Web service directly in a browser.

9 Type a phrase with random capital letters.

10 Click Invoke to submit the Web service.

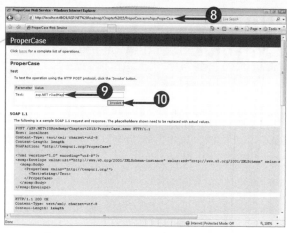

11 View the result returned in a new browser.

● The string submitted is now properly cased.

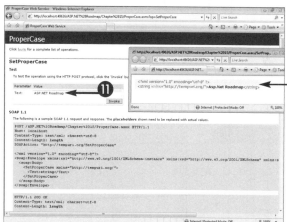

Apply It

Often code is written with overloaded methods, which are not allowed by default as defined by the WSI 1.0 standard. To remove confirmation to this WSI standard change the `WebServiceBinding` attribute to `WsiProfiles.None`.

Additionally, each signature of the overloaded method must have its own `MessageName` set in the `WebMethod` attribute.

Overloaded Web Service Class:

```
<WebServiceBinding(ConformsTo:=WsiProfiles.None)> _
Public Class ProperCase
  Inherits System.Web.Services.WebService
 Public Function SetProperCase(ByVal Text As String, ByVal bHTMLEncode As Boolean) As String
  'Perform Actions here.....
End Function
```

Consume a
Web Service

U tilizing remote Web services with the .NET platform and Visual Studio is very easy. Similar to adding a reference to a class library, a Web reference is added to the Web site. Visual Studio takes care of adding all proxy code and classes to the site to manage serializing the data to and from the Web service. You are not limited to calling remote or third-party web services; Web services that are part of the Web site can actually be added to the site as a Web reference.

To add a reference to a Web service right-click the top node of the Web site in the Solution Explorer window. Choose Add Web Reference from the context menu. When the Add Web Reference dialog box appears you can add the URL to the remote Web service or you can choose to list services available in the solution or on your workstation. Clicking Go retrieves any Web services that reside at the specified URL. A list of methods appears in

the main window, while a list of available services appears on the right.

There is another field on the right side of the dialog box for the Web reference name. This field defines the class namespace used to reference this Web service in your application. After the name is defined, click Add Reference to create the code to call the Web service.

After adding the reference to the application it can be called like any other class from a class library. Many Web services offer sophisticated data structures to manage the data being produced. Adding a Web reference to the Web site automatically creates proxy classes to manage this data, both in terms of values being passed to the service as well as what is received. There is no need to worry about the messy nature of properly serializing and de-serializing data.

Consume a Web Service

① Right-click the root of a Web site.

② Select Add Web Reference from the context menu.

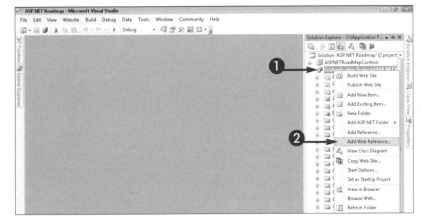

③ Select Web Services in this Solution.

④ Select a Web service in the list.

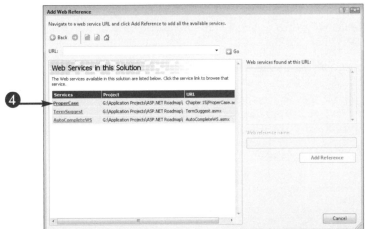

Note: *If you have not added a Web service to the site, you will not have this option.*

5 Add a name to the Web reference.

6 Click Add Reference.

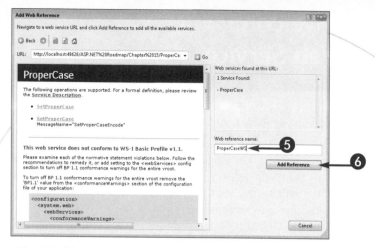

7 Create a new Web page and open the code-behind file.

8 Create a new instance of the Web service in the Load event handler.

9 Call the SetProperCase method, passing a poorly cased string.

10 Wrap the call to SetProperCase in a Response.Write.

Opening the page will display a properly cased version of the string.

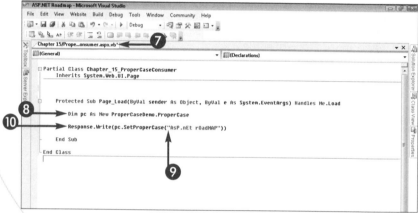

Apply It

Calling a remote Web service can prove to be problematic at times because of network latency or a busy server. Fortunately, the .NET framework automatically provides asynchronous methods for each Web service consumed by an application. This means a Web method may be called on a remote Web service and the Web site can continue processing normally, without pausing to wait for a return from the remote service. A callback method is automatically called when the Web service call returns a response for processing.

Calling a Web Service Asynchronously:

```
Protected Sub Button1_Click(ByVal sender As Object, ByVal e As System.EventArgs) Handles
Button1.Click
  Dim pc As New ProperCaseDemo.ProperCase
  Dim iar As IAsyncResult
  iar = pc.BeginSetProperCase(TextBox1.Text, Nothing, Nothing)

  Do Until iar.IsCompleted
  TextBox1.Text = pc.EndSetProperCase(iar)
  Loop
End Sub
```

Use the Live.com Search Web Service

Microsoft has many public Web service APIs available and utilizing these services can enhance the usability of your Web site. Among the most popular is Live.com Search. Live.com Search exposes methods and classes to give approved applications and Web sites the ability to perform search engine queries and use the data as they see fit.

The first step to using Live.com is to obtain an application ID from Microsoft to identify your queries. Navigate to http://search.msn.com/developer and click Create and Manage Application IDs. After you sign in with your Windows Live ID, click Get a new App ID to create a new application ID for your application. This ID will be used in the `AppId` property of the `SearchRequest` object passed to the service.

To integrate Live.com Search into an application, add the Web reference http://soap.search.msn.com/webservices .asmx?wsdl to the service's WSDL. To use Live.com

Search, a reference to the namespace you gave the Web reference needs to be added to the page's class file or to a class created to wrap all the calls to the service. In the class method used to perform the actual query a new `MSNSearchService` object needs to be instantiated. A `SearchRequest` object that this will be passed as a parameter to the `Search` method of the `MSNSearchService` object must also be instantiated. It contains several properties that define the search and the `AppId` property.

The `Query` property contains the search phrase. The `Requests` property contains an array of `SourceRequest` objects. A `SourceRequest` contains properties that define the type of search to be performed and optionally the way the results are filtered and sorted. Once these objects are set, the `Search` method of the `MSNSearchService` is called. It returns a `SearchResponse` object that contains all the results of each search type requested.

Use the Live.com Search Web Service

① Add a new Web reference to a Web site.

② Type the URL for Live.com WSDL, http://soap.search.msn.com/ webservices.asmx?wsdl.

③ Add a reference name.

④ Click Add Reference.

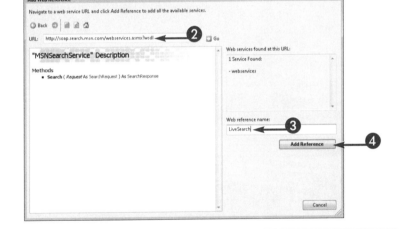

⑤ Add a new Web page to the Web site.

⑥ Add a TextBox to collect the search query.

⑦ Add a Go button to submit the query.

⑧ Add a `GridView` to display the results.

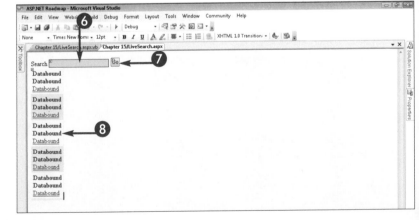

9 Double-click the Submit button to create a `click` event handler.

10 Add code to query Live.com Search.

11 Add code to bind the results to the `GridView`.

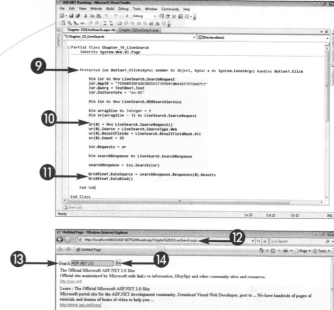

12 Open the page in a browser.

13 Type a phrase to search.

14 Click Go.

● The results from Live.com appear in the `GridView` control.

Apply It

Live.com Search is not limited to just search results; other resources are also available. The service can be set to return images, phone book listings, news, spelling, weather, stock quotes, and movies. Searches can also be pared down to local areas by providing a U.S. Zip code or latitude, longitude, and radius information.

The service can perform multiple search types with one query, returning an array of search result sets. The `SourceRequest` object should have its `Source` set to one of the `SourceType` enumeration options. Each `SearchRequest` can have one `SourceRequest` for each search type.

Perform an Image Search through Live.com
```
Dim srImages as New SourceRequest
srImages.Source = SourceType.Image
'Perform Search

For each r as Result in sResults
  Response.write(r.Image.ImageURL)
next
```

Introduction to ASP.NET AJAX

Microsoft wants developers to be able to easily develop Rich Interactive Applications (RIAs) using the ASP.NET framework. The use of AJAX is a very important aspect of creating these rich user interfaces. AJAX is simply the use of JavaScript and the `xmlHttpRequest` object to make asynchronous partial page updates.

Microsoft released the early alpha and beta versions of the ASP.NET AJAX framework, at the time known as Atlas, in 2006. This framework is a set of prebuilt and tested AJAX classes that can be leveraged by ASP.NET developers to quickly add AJAX features to their Web applications.

Microsoft made the use of the framework very easy by creating several controls to help developers create AJAX applications without having to actually write any confusing JavaScript code. The primary control needed on

every page is the `ScriptManager`, which encapsulates the core JavaScript methods needed by the ASP.NET controls and subsequently the ASP.NET AJAX ToolKit. When using Master pages the `ScriptManager` can either reside on the content page or the Master page. When it resides on the Master page the content page must have a `ScriptManagerProxy` control.

The ASP.NET AJAX framework also features the `UpdatePanel` control. This control wraps up a section of controls and content on a page to enable partial page updates without any special coding. The `UpdatePanel` can specify triggers to initiate an asynchronous partial-page update from a control outside of the panel.

The `Progress` control displays a visual indicator on the page to let the user know there is a background process running. The `Timer` control periodically executes a `Tick` event on the server. This event handler can be used to perform some server-side processing.

Introduction to ASP.NET AJAX

① Add a `ScriptManager` and an `UpdatePanel` to a new Web page.

② Add a `TextBox` and `Button` control to the `UpdatePanel`.

③ Add a `DropDownList` control to the `UpdatePanel`.

④ Add a series of colors to the `DrowDownList` by opening the `ListItem` Collection Editor by clicking the Edit Items option in the `DropDownList` SmartTag menu.

⑤ Click OK.

⑥ Double-click the button to create an event handler.

⑦ Add the value of the `TextBox` to the list of `DrowDownList` items.

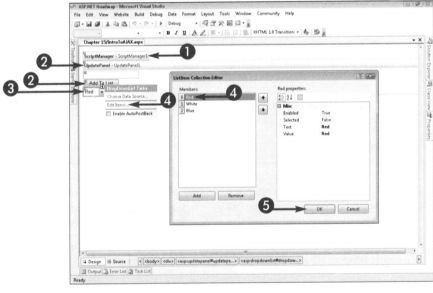

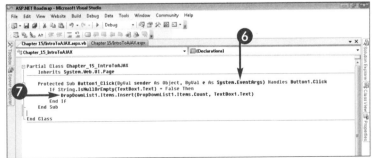

8 Open the page in a browser.

9 Enter a new color in the TextBox.

10 Submit the page by clicking the Add To List button.

● The page performs a partial page update, and the TextBox's color is added to the DropDownList.

Extra

Almost simultaneous to the release of ASP.NET AJAX, Microsoft released a set of controls to the ASP.NET community based on the framework — the ASP.NET AJAX Control Toolkit. It is available for download from CodePlex.com. It is a completely open source and free library of AJAX controls to add to ASP.NET Web sites.

The toolkit features many controls that provide very popular and useful functionality right out of the box. This project has been released to the community and continues to grow as users create more controls and add them to the toolkit. It can be downloaded with and without the source code and includes a sample Web site to see how to apply each control.

The Rating control gives users the ability to provide valuable feedback as to how they perceive an item. The AutoCompleteExtender gives the ability to offer suggestions to the user when entering textual data in a TextBox control. The MaskedEditExtender preformats data as the user enters it in a TextBox. This can be extremely useful when collecting phone numbers, currency, social security numbers, and so on.

Use the
Update Panel

The ASP.NET `UpdatePanel` is a quick way to AJAX-enable any Web page. You can perform content refreshing on specific parts of the page without causing the page to perform a full post-back to the server.

To use the `UpdatePanel` control, first add a `ScriptManager` control to the page. If the `ScriptManager` has been added to a Master page you would then add a `ScriptManagerProxy` control to the content page. If the Master page does not have a `ScriptManager` control present you can add the `ScriptManager` directly to the content page. Now you can add an `UpdatePanel` to the page. You can have more than one `UpdatePanel` on a page.

The `UpdatePanel` specifies a region of the page that can be updated without refreshing the entire page through a server round trip. The difference between a normal post-back and an asynchronous post-back is that the only HTML elements that are updated are contained within the specified region of the `UpdatePanel`.

Content is added to the `UpdatePanel` declaratively by using a `ContentTemplate` element. To add content programmatically, use the `ContentTemplateContainer` property of the `UpdatePanel`.

You are not limited to causing an asynchronous update with a control contained in the `ContentTemplate`. You can specify a post-back control by defining an `AsyncPostbackTrigger`. An `AsyncPostbackTrigger` is added to the `triggers` element, where you can specify each and every control that triggers a post-back of the `UpdatePanel`'s content.

`UpdatePanels` may be nested or placed inside of another `UpdatePanel`. When the parent `UpdatePanel` is updated all of the nested `UpdatePanels` are also updated. By default, when a nested `UpdatePanel` causes a post-back, only its content is updated.

Use the Update Panel

1 Add a new Web page to a site.

2 Add a `ScriptManager` control.

3 Add an `UpdatePanel` control.

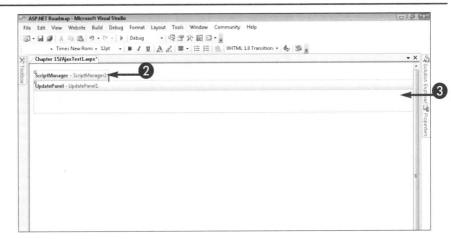

4 Add a TextBox to the update panel.

5 Add a label to the update panel.

6 Add a button to the update panel.

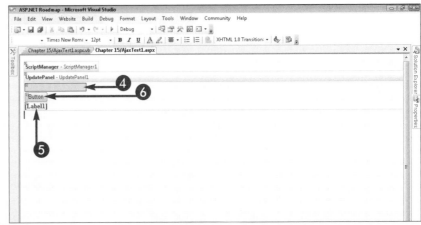

⑦ Double-click the button to create a `click` event handler.

⑧ Add code to set the label's text to the `TextBox`'s text value.

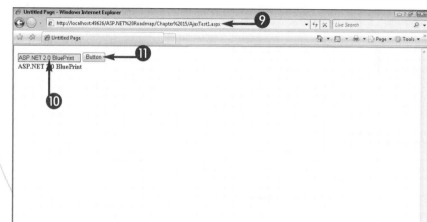

⑨ Open the page in a browser.

⑩ Type some text in the TextBox.

⑪ Click the button.

The page performs a partial page update, and the label's text is set.

Extra

UpdateMode can be either Conditional or Always. If the UpdateMode is set to Always the UpdatePanel's content is updated on each and every post-back made by the page. This includes posts caused by other UpdatePanels. If the UpdateMode is set to Conditional it is updated only when the post-back is caused by the UpdatePanel's trigger, the Update method is explicitly called for the UpdatePanel, when a parent UpdatePanel is updated, or when ChildrenAsTriggers is set to true and any child UpdatePanel is posted back. Controls contained in any child UpdatePanels do not cause the parent or outer UpdatePanel's content to be updated unless the ChildrenAsTriggers is true. If the ChildrenAsTriggers is set to false and the UpdateMode is set to Always an exception will be thrown. The ChildrenAsTriggers should only be used when the UpdateMode is set to Conditional. Setting the UpdateMode to Conditional reduces the overall load on the server because only a small amount of data is transported across the wire when a post-back is invoked.

Use the Timer Control

There are many common scenarios where content on a page may need to be updated without the user explicitly causing a post-back to the server to update the content. You can use the AJAX `Timer` control to cause post-backs to occur at designated intervals. You can use an `UpdatePanel` with the `Timer` control; partial-page updates are processed at the time interval. In fact, you can use a `Timer` control with multiple `UpdatePanels`. You are not limited to partial-page updates, however; the `Timer` control can cause the entire page to post back to the server.

To use the `Timer` control, you must have an instance of the `ScriptManager` control or `ScriptManagerProxy` control present on the page. The control actually embeds from JavaScript that initiates the post-back to the server. This JavaScript is dependent on the methods included with the `ScriptManager`.

If you want to handle the post-back event from the `Timer` control you can create an event handler for the `Tick` event. The event handler has a basic signature, and `Object` and `EventArgs` parameters. You use this event handler to fire off any server-side processing needed.

The post-back interval is defined by setting the `Interval` property of the `Timer` control. The `Interval` property is an integer that specifies the number of milliseconds between post-backs. The default interval is 60,000 milliseconds, but may be set to any time frame needed. Be careful, because a short interval generates a lot of network traffic and server load.

When you place a `Timer` control inside of an `UpdatePanel` you do not have to do anything extra to cause the panel's content to refresh. The `Timer` automatically causes the update at the interval's duration.

Use the Timer Control

① Add a new Web page to a site.

② Add a `ScriptManager` control.

③ Add an `UpdatePanel` control.

④ Add a `Timer` control outside of the update panel.

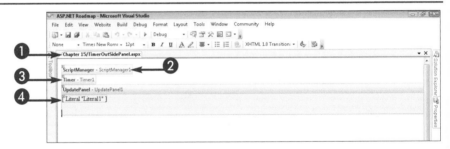

⑤ Click the Source button to switch to Source view.

⑥ Add a `Triggers` section to the update panel.

⑦ Add an `AsyncPostBack Trigger` to the timer's `Tick` event.

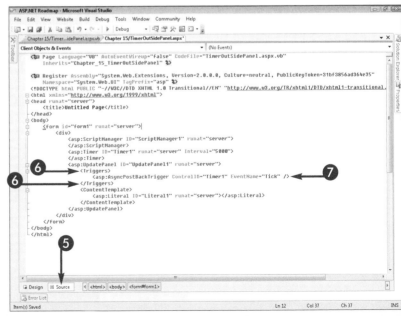

8 Switch to code-behind view.

9 Add an event handler for the timer's `Tick` event.

10 Set the `Literal` control's `Text` property to the current time.

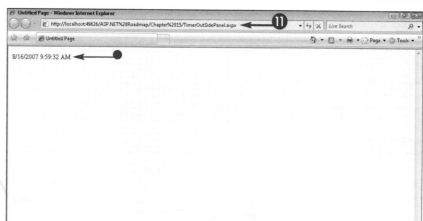

11 Open the page in a browser and let it sit.

● The `Timer` control executes its `Tick` events.

Apply It

The `Timer` control can be used from outside an `UpdatePanel` to cause a post-back. A `Trigger` needs to be configured in the `UpdatePanel` to trigger the post-back on the `Timer`'s `Tick` event.

Setting a Trigger to an External Timer Control:
```
<asp:ScriptManager ID="ScriptManager1" runat="server">
</asp:ScriptManager>
<asp:Timer ID="Timer1" runat="server" Interval="5000">
</asp:Timer>
<asp:UpdatePanel ID="UpdatePanel1" runat="server">
 <Triggers>
 <asp:AsyncPostBackTrigger ControlID="Timer1" EventName="Tick" />
 </Triggers>
 <ContentTemplate>
 <asp:Literal ID="Literal1" runat="server"></asp:Literal>
 </ContentTemplate>
</asp:UpdatePanel>
```

Use the Progress Control

One of the most common needs for many Web sites is the ability to visually indicate to users that their requests are being processed; the `UpdateProgess` control provides this functionality. This can be in the form of an animated GIF file, updating text. The `UpdateProgress` control works with the ASP.NET AJAX framework to provide this type of feedback mechanism.

`UpdateProgress` controls can be placed inside or outside an `UpdatePanel`. When the `UpdatePanel` is updated by an asynchronous post-back, the `UpdateProgress` control is displayed. This is true even if the `UpdateProgress` control is inside another `UpdatePanel` control. In the case of a nested `UpdatePanel`, a post-back that originates inside the child panel causes any `UpdateProgress` controls associated with the child panel to display. Any `UpdateProgress` controls associated with the parent panel are also displayed. `UpdateProgress` controls

associated with the parent panel are displayed when a post-back originates from an immediate child control of the parent panel.

If there are multiple `UpdatePanels` on the page, you can specify which `UpdatePanel` will cause the `UpdateProgress` control to render its feedback through the `AssociatedUpdatePanelID` property. The `DisplayAfter` property gets or sets the delay in milliseconds before the `ProgressTemplate`'s contents are displayed. The `DynamicLayout` gets or sets if the `ProgressTemplate` is rendered dynamically or only when it is needed. If `DynamicLayout` is set to false then the template is only hidden causing the space to be unused when not being rendered. The `UpdateProgress` control renders a `<div>` element to surround the content in the `ProgressTemplate`. It is displayed or hidden depending on whether the associated `UpdatePanel` control has caused an asynchronous post-back. The `UpdateProgress` control is not displayed in initial page rendering and for synchronous post-backs.

Use the Progress Control

① Add a new Web page to a site.

② Add a `ScriptManager` control.

③ Add an `UpdatePanel` control.

④ Add a `Progess` control outside of the `UpdatePanel`.

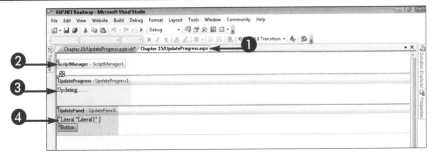

⑤ Click the Source button to switch to Source view.

⑥ Enter an indicator to the `ProgressTemplate`.

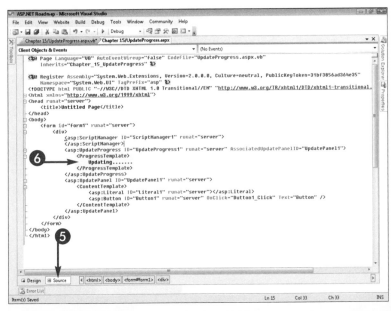

7 Double-click the button to create a `click` event handler.

8 Add a `Thread.Sleep` statement to pause execution for 5 seconds.

9 Add code to set the `Literal` control's text to the current time.

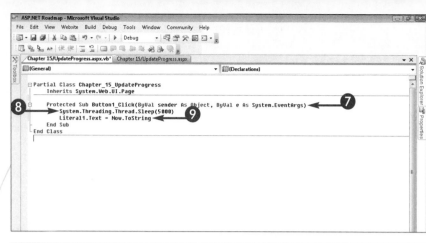

10 Open the page in a browser.

11 Click the button to display the time.

The progress template appears.

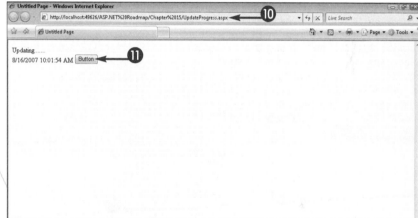

Apply It

Canceling a long-running operation can be a desired function, but is not easily accomplished without AJAX. The ASP.NET library includes a `PageRequestManager` class that aides this task. It can be invoked via JavaScript on the client. The easiest way to test this is to add a Cancel button to the `ProgressTemplate`.

Cancel a Long-Running Request:
```
<script language="javascript" type="text/javascript">
<!--
var prm = Sys.WebForms.PageRequestManager.getInstance();
function CancelAsyncPostBack() {
  if (prm.get_isInAsyncPostBack()) {
   prm.abortPostBack();
  }
}
// -->
</script>
```

Calling the Cancel Function from the Cancel Button:
```
<input id="Button2" type="button"
 value="cancel" onclick="CancelAsyncPostBack()" />
```

G iving users the ability to provide instant feedback on products, ideas, or services is an important feature offered by many Web sites, The Rating control provides a great interface for this. It is part of the ASP.NET AJAX Toolkit. Many modern sites provide an AJAX interface to allow users to submit ratings on the item by selecting a graphical representation without a full post-back.

The control enables you to designate custom images, initial rating value, how the images are aligned, and their direction. There are four image style properties that are used to define the images displayed in the control. Each one uses a style sheet rule instead of a URL because it is more efficient. The StarCssClass sets the style for a visible star. The WaitingStarCssClass sets the style for a star being hovered over. The FilledStarCssClass sets the style for a star in filled mode. The EmptyStarCss Class sets the style for a star in empty mode.

The RatingAlign property sets the alignment of the stars in the control. It represents an Orientation enumeration with the two choices being Horizontal and Vertical. The RatingDirection sets the direction the stars display the rating. The choices are LeftToRightTopToBottom and RightToLeftBottomToTop.

The MaxRating property sets the highest value that may be chosen. The CurrentRating property is used to set an initial value of the control. If the ReadOnly property control is set to true, the user cannot submit any choices.

When a user selects a value or image in the rating control the Changed event fires. It passes a RatingEventArgs parameter, which carries the selected value in its Value property. If the Rating control is part of an UpdatePanel you can easily use this value to update any textual content representing the value.

Use the Rating Control

① Create a new Web page.

② Add a ScriptManager control and an UpdatePanel to the page.

③ Add a Rating control to the page.

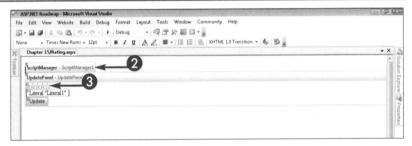

④ Click the Source button to switch to Source view.

⑤ Set the Star StyleSheet classes.

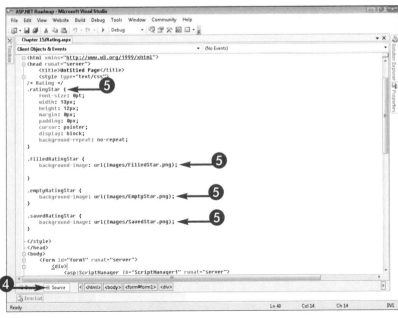

6 Double-click the button to create a `click` event handler.

7 Add code to set the `Literal` control's text property to the `Rating`'s selection.

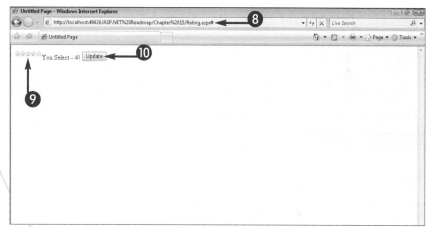

8 Open the page in a browser.

9 Select a rating in the `Rating` control.

The page does not flicker and the `Rating` control updates.

10 Click Update.

The selected value of the `Rating` control is displayed in the `Literal` control.

Apply It

The `Rating` control `Changed` event does not cause other controls to update when a selection is made. So if you have a `Label` or `Literal` control that needs to be updated to reflect the selection made by the user it will not occur, even if all the controls are contained in an `UpdatePanel`. To overcome this feature you must add a `Button` control or other means to force a `postback` to the server to cause the indicator to update. The `CurrentRating` property returns the current selection in the `Rating` control

Updating Controls to Indicate the Rating Control Selection:
```
Protected Sub Button1_Click(ByVal sender As Object, ByVal e As System.EventArgs)
  Literal1.Text = String.Format("You Select - {0}!", Rating1.CurrentRating)
End Sub
```

Use the AutoComplete Extender

The `AutoComplete Extender` control makes adding suggestion functionality trivial for the ASP.NET developer. One of AJAX's first useful applications was Google's search suggestion feature. This works by analyzing what you are typing and offering a list of potential search phrases in a list below the Search box. This is now a standard feature on many sites.

The `AutoComplete Extender` works by attaching to a `TextBox` control and associating with a Web service to provide suggestions. Suggestions appear in a panel below the `TextBox` control. Suggestions are supplied by the designated Web service and can be any list of strings. There are no rules to define what types of results are required to be returned.

The Web service method is defined by setting the `ServiceMethod` property: simply supply the name of the method. The method's signature must return an array of strings and accept a string and integer. The string property is the `prefixText` or the current value entered in the `TextBox`. The integer property is the number or count of results to return. The `ServicePath` sets the URL of the Web service that contains the `ServiceMethod`.

The `TargetControlId` property sets the Id of the `TextBox` being extended. The `MinimumPrefixLength` property defines the minimum number of characters that must be entered before the `ServiceMethod` is called. The `CompleteInterval` is a delay in milliseconds before the Web service is called. `CompletetionSetCount` is the number of results expected from the Web service.

The Web Service called by the `AutoCompleteExtender` must have the `System.Web.Script.Services` `.ScriptService` attribute applied at the class level. It must also have the `System.Web.Script.Services` `.ScriptMethod` attribute applied to the `WebMethod` called.

Use the AutoComplete Extender

① Create a new Web page.

② Add a `ScriptManager` control to the page.

③ Add a `TextBox` and `Button` controls to the page.

④ Add an `AutoCompleteExtender` control to the page.

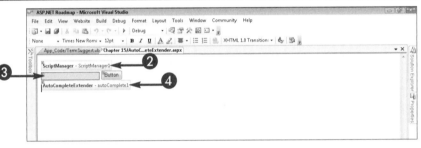

⑤ Add a Web Service to the Web site.

⑥ Create a method named `GetCompletionList` that accepts a string and integer.

⑦ Add code to the Web service method to return a list of search suggestions.

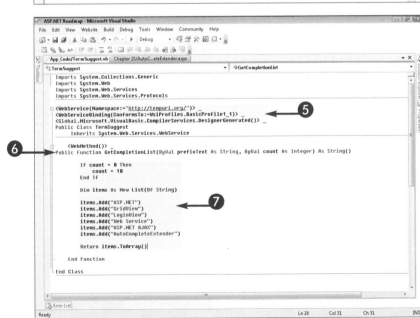

8 Open the Web page in Source view.

9 Set the `Auto CompleteExtender` properties to call the Web service method.

10 Set the `Auto CompleteExtender` properties to extend the `TextBox` control.

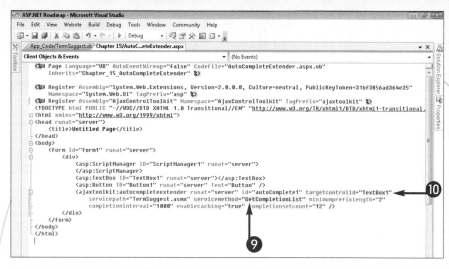

11 Open the page in a browser.

12 Type a value in the TextBox.

13 Click Submit.

● The suggestions appear below the text box.

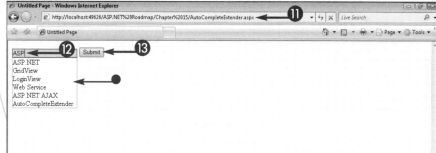

Apply It

The use of the `AutoCompleteExtender` control should be thought of as a live index of the Web site's content. In the case of a search engine or a documentation library, seeding the suggestions is a good idea, but they should be added as users search for varied phrases.

Tracking these search phrases can be useful to determine how a search is being used by users and what is actually being sought. For an e-commerce site, this information can help to better target content or to set up cross references to specific products. These competitive advantages can be the difference between a profitable site and one that does not meet expectations.

Store a User's Search Phrase:
```
Protected Sub Button1_Click(ByVal sender As Object, ByVal e As System.EventArgs) Handles Button1.Click
 Dim CustomSearches As New SiteSearches
 CustomSearches.AddSearch(TextBox1.Text)
End Sub
```

Use the Masked Edit Extender

When designing a user interface, assume the user will not enter the data in the correct format in a `TextBox`; the `MaskedEdit` extender provides a way to guide users. You can easily reformat supplied data, but it is often helpful to the user to see what you expect and be guided a little. The `MaskedEdit` control extends a regular `TextBox` by applying a client-side format to the data as it is entered by the user.

`MaskedEdit` is an ASP.NET AJAX extender that attaches to a `TextBox` control to restrict the kind of text that can be entered. The `MaskedEdit` extender applies a "mask" to the input that permits only certain types of characters/text to be entered and in a predefined format. The supported data formats are `Number`, `Date`, `Time`, and `DateTime`. `MaskedEdit` uses the culture settings specified by the browser to apply specific formats, such as dates and currencies.

There are several `MaskTypes` available to further define the type of data to be entered. The choices are `None` for no validation; `Number`, which allows only numerical text; `Date`, which forces a known date format; `Time`, to format hours, minutes, and seconds, and `DateTime`, to format a combination of the two.

The `Mask` property defines the actual format allowed by the `TextBox`; (999) 999-9999 would be a typical U.S. phone number `Mask`. For a `Time` or `DateTime` mask the `AcceptAMPM` property indicates if AM or PM is displayed for the time. The `AcceptNegative` property indicates if a negative number is allowed for numeric input. If the `AutoComplete` property is set to `true` the extender will automatically fill in any missing content from the mask; `AutoCompleteValue` specifies the character used. If the `ClipBoardEnabled` property is `true` the user may paste values from the clipboard.

Use the Masked Edit Extender

① Create a new Web page.

② Add a `ScriptManager` control to the page.

③ Add `TextBox` and `Button` controls to the page.

④ Add a `MaskedEditExtender` control to the page.

⑤ Add a Label to the page.

⑥ Click the Source button to switch to Source view.

⑦ Set the `MaskedEdit Extender` to a `Date` mask.

⑧ Set the `MaskType` to `Date`.

⑨ Set the `TargetControlId` to the `TextBox`.

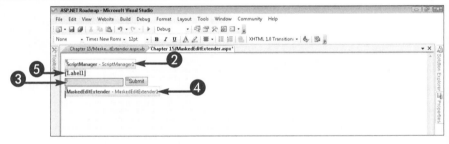

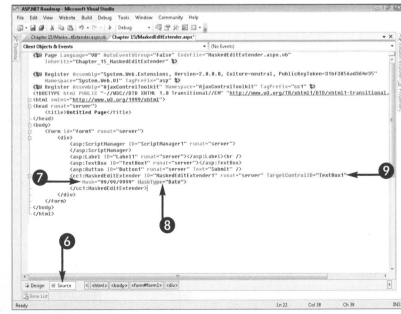

⑩ Double-click the button to create a `click` event handler.

⑪ Set the text of the label to the date in the `TextBox`.

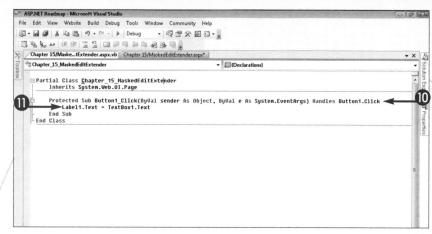

⑫ Open the page in a browser.

⑬ Type a date in the text box.

⑭ Click Submit.

The `MaskedEdit Extender` enforces the date format in the text box.

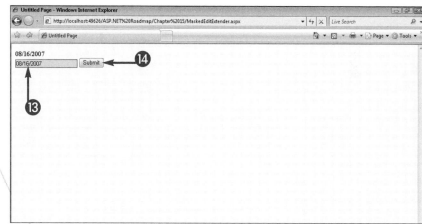

Apply It

Validating user input is very important to ensure the Web applications function properly. Providing useful visual information as to what type of data and the format of that data goes a long way to a pleasant user experience.

The `MaskedEditValidator` is a custom validator control that attaches to the `MaskedEdit` extender and its associated `TextBox`. It verifies that the input text matches the pattern specified in the `MaskedEdit` extender. The `MaskedEditValidator` works like a regular validator control, except it is optimized for the AJAX Control Toolkit.

MaskerEditValidator Declaration:

```
<ajaxToolkit:MaskedEditValidator
  ControlExtender="MaskedPhoneExtender"
  ControlToValidate="txtPhoneNumber"
  IsValidEmpty="False"
  EmptyValueMessage="Phone Number is required"
  InvalidValueMessage="Phone Number is invalid"
  Display="Dynamic"
  TooltipMessage="Input a phone number"/>
```

INDEX

Numbers

301 redirect
custom `HttpModule`, 296–297
URL mapping, 221

A

abstracting methods, 171
access control. *See also* authenticating users; passwords
Web page content, 194–195
Web sites, 49
Add New Item dialog box, 6–7
Add Reference dialog box, 14–15
adding. *See also* creating
buttons to pages, 54–55
Code Snippets, 20–21
DLL references, 14–15
event handlers, 16–17
files to Web sites, 7
links to bulleted lists, 82–83
projects to Web sites, 4–5
roles, 168–169
text boxes to pages, 54–55
users to. *See also* `CreateUserWizard`; membership providers
roles, 176–177
sites, 150–151
Web controls to Web pages, 12–13
Web pages to Web sites, 6–7
AJAX
cancelling operations, 321
Control Toolkit, 315
enabling, 316–317
input validation, 326–327
overview, 314–315
post-back interval, 318
progress indicator, 320–321
suggestion box, 324–325
timer, 318–319
user feedback, 315, 322–325
aligning images, 56–57, 60–61
.ascx file extension, 13

ASP.NET. *See also specific elements*
application life cycle, 29
platform description, 28–29
Web page life cycle, 30–31
ASP.NET membership providers. *See also* membership providers
configuring, 146–147
Forms authentication, 147
redirecting failed authentication, 147
session timeout, 147
verifying user credentials, 146–147
ASP.NET ViewState Helper, 41
.aspx file extension, 8, 28
assemblies, linking to Web pages, 46
`Assembly` directive, 46
asynchronous programming, 257
attachments, e-mail, 290–291
authenticating users. *See also* access control; membership providers; passwords
method, specifying, 49
redirecting failed logins, 147
sitemaps, 209
authorizing users. *See* authenticating users; membership providers; passwords
Autos Watch window, 280

B

binding
data list, 128–129
data to sitemap controls, 202–203, 206–207
details view, 134–135
forms view, 140–141
grid view, 112–113
menu items, 208–209
templates, 124–125
books and publications
ASP.NET ViewState Helper, 41
ViewState Decoder, 41
break conditions, 270–271
breakpoints, 270–271
browser compatibility
debugging, 275
Master Pages, 233
verifying Web pages, 18–19

INDEX

Copy Web Site utility, 24–25

CreateUserWizard
  collecting user information, 186–187
  content access control, 194–195
  content customization, 194–195
  creating site members, 184–185
  custom membership systems, 187
  customizing, 186–187
  formatting, 186–187
  login interface, adding, 188–189
  login status, displaying, 190–191
  passwords
    changing, 198–199
    creating, 184–185
    retrieving, 196–197
  styles, defining, 186–187
  templates, 186–187, 194–195
  user name, displaying, 192–193
creating. *See also* adding
  CSS (Cascading Style Sheets), 244–245
  Master pages, 224–225
  menus, 206–207
  navigation strip, 212–213
  page elements. *See specific elements*
  passwords, 184–185
  site members, 184–185
  sitemaps, 200–201
  skins, 240–241
  themes, 236–237
  Web services, 308–309
cross-page post, 47, 98–99
cross-site scripting, protecting against, 53
.cs file extension, 8
CSS (Cascading Style Sheets)
  creating, 244–245
  formatting database data, 131
  formatting tables, 131
  themes, 243
customizing. *See also* personalization
  buttons, 56–57
  configuration, 298–299
  configuration settings, with XML, 298–299
  controls, 47, 304–307
  CreateUserWizard, 186–187

httpHandler, 294–295
HttpModule, 296–297
input validation, 106–109
login, 189
membership providers, 144
membership systems, 187
menus, 210–211
page content, 194–195
programming logic. *See* httpHandler; httpModule
templates, 7
Web controls, 13, 47
web.config file configuration, 48

D

data views, 264–265
databases
  binding data
    data list, 128–129
    details view, 134–135
    forms view, 140–141
    grid view, 112–113
    templates, 124–125
  buttons, 138–139
  deleting records
    details view, 134–135, 138–139
    forms view, 143
    grid view, 122–123
  displaying data
    data list, 128–129
    details view, 134–135
    forms view, 140–141
    grid view, 112–113
    templates, 124–125
  editing data
    details view, 134–135, 138–139
    forms view, 142–143
    grid view, 120–121
  formatting
    CSS (Cascading Style Sheets), 131
    data list, 128–131
    details view, 136–137
    grid view, 114–115
    templates, 126–127

INDEX

INDEX

menus
  binding, 208–209
  creating, 206–207
  customizing, 210–211
multiple per site, 200–201
navigation strip
  creating, 212–213
  formatting, 214–215
navigational hierarchy
  check boxes, 218–219
  setting, 208–209
  tree view, 216–217
performance, 204
security trimming, 204–205, 209
URL mapping, 220–221
URL rewriting, 222–223
skin files, 236
skins
  See also Master pages
  See also styles
  See also templates
  See also themes
  applying to controls, 237–238, 243
  creating, 240–241
  setting at runtime, 242–243
  versus style sheets, 243
  themes, 242
SmartTags, 9, 276. *See also* properties
SMTP (Simple Mail Transport Protocol), 288–289
.snippet file extension, 21
Solution Explorer window, 10
sorting databases, 118–119, 264–265
Source view, 8
SQL databases
  connecting to
    asynchronous programming, 257
    Command object, 256–257
    Connection object, 254–255
    performance, 257
    SQLDataSource, 252–253
    timeout, setting, 256–257
  data views, 264–265
  datasets, creating, 260–261
  datatables, creating, 262–263

editing records, 264–265
filtering, 264–265
inserting records, 266–267
navigating, 264–265
passing parameters to, 268–269
retrieving data, 258–259, 266–267
searching, 264–265
sorting, 264–265
updating, 266–267
SQL injection, protecting against, 53
SQL server membership providers, 145, 148–149.
  See also membership providers
SQL stored procedures, 283
squiggly lines, 276
Starter Kits, 5
state, maintaining
  across post-backs, 305
  hidden data, 84–85
stepping through processes, 90–91
storing cookies, 42–43
style sheets
  CSS (Cascading Style Sheets), 244–245
  definition, 236
  editing, 244–245
  rule order, 245
  versus skins, 243
styles
  See also Master pages
  See also skins
  See also templates
  See also themes
  calendars, 71
  controls, 214–215
  `CreateUserWizard`, 186–187
subkeys, cookies, 43
submitting
  to another page, 98–99
  forms, 56–57
suggestion box, 324–325
summarizing error messages, 110–111
surveys, 90–91
synchronizing locations, 24–25
syntax notification, 3

336

X

3m

For more professional instruction in a visual format, try these.

All designed for visual learners—just like you!

Read Less–Learn More®

Visual®

Excel® Data Analysis
2nd Edition

Data analysis tools on CD-ROM!
• FinOptions XL, Analyse-It®, SigmaXL, and other trial software
• Macro codes, an e-version of the book, and more

Your visual blueprint™ for analyzing data, charts, and PivotTables

ISBN-10: 0-7645-9780-9
ISBN-13: 978-0-7645-9780-0

Ajax

Bonus!
Companion Web site includes all code used in the book

Your visual blueprint™ for creating rich Internet applications

ISBN-10: 0-470-04306-7
ISBN-13: 978-0-470-04306-6

Excel® PivotTables and PivotCharts

• Step-by-step, visual instructions show you how to take command of these Excel tools.
• Companion Web site includes all data files and code used in the book.

Your visual blueprint™ for creating dynamic spreadsheets

ISBN-10: 0-471-78489-3
ISBN-13: 978-0-471-78489-0

For a complete listing of *Visual Blueprint*™ titles and other Visual books, go to wiley.com/go/visual

Visual®
An Imprint of WILEY
Now you know.